SCIENCE *for* LIFE

SCIENCE *for* LIFE

The Teaching of Science in Canadian

Primary and Elementary Schools

Ruby L. Gough
Alan K. Griffiths

Memorial University of Newfoundland

HARCOURT
BRACE
CANADA

Harcourt Brace & Company, Canada

Toronto Montreal Fort Worth New York Orlando
Philadelphia San Diego London Sydney Tokyo

Canadian Cataloguing in Publication Data

Gough, Ruby L. (Ruby Louise), 1923-
    Science for life: the teaching of science in
Canadian primary and elementary schools

Includes bibliographical references.
ISBN 0-03-922868-1

1. Science – Study and teaching (Primary).
2. Science – Study and teaching (Elementary).
I. Griffiths, Alan K. (Alan Keith), 1936-
II. Title.

LB1585.G68 1994   372.3'5   C93-094651-0

Publisher: Heather McWhinney
Editor and Marketing Manager: Joanna Cotton
Developmental Editor: Lisa Collins
Editorial Assistant: Laura Paterson Pratt
Director of Publishing Services: Jean Davies
Editorial Manager: Marcel Chiera
Supervising Editor: Carol Tong
Production Manager: Sue-Ann Becker
Manufacturing Co-ordinator: Denise Wake
Copy Editor: James Leahy
Cover Photos: Brett Lamb
Cover Design: Avril Orloff
Interior Design: Avril Orloff
Typesetting and Assembly: McGraphics Desktop Publishing
Printing and Binding: Edwards Brothers Incorporated

∞ This book was printed in the United States of America on acid-free paper.

1 2 3 4 5   98 97 96 95 94

◆ ◆ ◆ ◆ ◆

This book is dedicated
to my grandchildren
Jennifer, Natalee, Jim, Sarah, and Rachel

Ruby L. Gough

and to my grandchildren
David, Alan, Andrew, and Susan

Alan K. Griffiths

who will live their lives in the
twenty-first century.

PREFACE

Welcome to the world of children's science, and to the world of the teacher dedicated to its encouragement. There are few more exciting or challenging places to be. This book is dedicated to helping you to make the most of your opportunities to enhance children's explorations in science, to promote their understanding, and to cultivate their interest.

Although the "voice" used will be that of student-teacher educator, the content is also of direct interest and usefulness to practising teachers. The book is reflective in nature, and you will be asked frequently to work through activities deliberately designed to evoke reflection, so that you may draw from them to develop your personal theory about the teaching of science.

The book builds progressively from a consideration of the goals and directions of the science curriculum and their basis in the nature of science and the nature of children; to the creation of positive environments for learning; to developing strategies for the implementation and evaluation of teaching and learning; to beginning science early and ensuring that science is for all children; to emphasizing science, technology, and society relationships and the need for school science to prepare today's children for their role as citizens in the world of tomorrow. The four sections successively present these elements.

Part 1 focusses immediately on the reflective teacher, on the aims of the science curriculum, and on the concept of what it means to be scientifically literate. Children's thinking and scientists' thinking are explored and brought together through analogy with a "black box" whose contents may be probed and explored but remain uncertain and subject to change. The chapters that follow get to the heart of the content of the science curriculum, namely, approaches to the development of scientific process skills and the concurrent development of scientific concepts.

Part 2 draws from the first section to translate theory into practice. The beginning chapter emphasizes the importance of creating an encouraging climate for learning science, and monitoring and maintaining such an environment, including day-to-day management of the science program. Unit planning and lesson planning are developed in the context of three orientations to curriculum, which are translated into a continuum of teaching strategies, ranging from teacher-centred to child-centred in approach, and illustrated by activities drawn from a variety of current and recent school programs. The preparation and delivery of lessons are represented through a wide range of teaching models, and specific approaches such as the use of discrepant events, brainstorming, role playing, and play are introduced. Specific attention is paid to the importance of motivational techniques in stimulating and maintaining interest at this level, and to the development of appropriate questioning techniques both by teachers and their students. The chapters on teaching methods are followed by an elementary treatment of evaluation theory, and a wide variety of evaluation techniques ranging from conventional free-response test questions to the use of checklists and portfolios. The final chapter in this section compares goals of science education globally, nationally, and provincially, and offers a comprehensive examination of available curriculum resources.

Part 3 follows the theme that science is for all children and suggests that this goal can be realized if science begins in the early years and if attention is paid to individual differences among students. The section begins with the very special world of the young child in the first year of school and in the primary years that follow, and uses this as an opportunity to focus on the usefulness of play as a vehicle for learning, not only for beginners, but for all children. It suggests that the child-centred ways of teaching and learning characteristic of the beginning years should permeate the years that follow. Providing for individual differences in interests and abilities, learning styles, and cultural backgrounds sets the tone for provision for the intellectually, physically, and emotionally challenged as well as the gifted and talented, both within and outside regular classrooms.

Part 4 focusses on the relationships between science, society, and the world in which we live, and on the need to prepare children to understand these relationships and to live effectively in the world of tomorrow. It underscores the importance of developing concern for the environment in the early years of school and gradually developing the ability to make informed judgements on issues related to science, technology, and society. The content of this concluding section reflects the title of the book: *Science for Life*. We live in a changing world, and this is nowhere more evident than in science and technology. Futurizing is fun. When futurists have their fun with their projections for the future, especially when they look forward 70 years or more into the future of today's children, they produce a range of possible worlds quite different from the world of today. The last chapter invites you reflect on what you have learned, to recapitulate the main ideas you have gleaned and the conceptual structure you have begun to develop about the teaching of science in the primary and elementary grades. The aim is to set you off on a voyage of personal discovery. We warn you, it is a voyage that may have no end ...

Throughout the book a number of important emphases have been included. First of all, it is a book intended for a Canadian audience. We have attempted to give it a Canadian flavour in several ways. Each chapter profiles the work of a scientist who lives or has lived in Canada. These profiles are featured in chronological order to show the progress of Canadian achievements in science. Each chapter also contains excerpts "From a Teacher's Journal," representing the views of Canadian teachers about aspects of the content of the specific chapter. Throughout the book Canadian references have been cited frequently and Canadian achievements have been highlighted. Chapter 9 includes a comparison of provincial goals for elementary science and the resources available provincially for implementation of programs at this level. In Chapter 13, which deals with the interactions of science, technology, and society, many of the topics presented are Canadian in emphasis.

The potential of science teaching/learning for enhancement of other areas of the primary and elementary school curriculum is an important emphasis in this book, with a special focus on the role of language in science. Interwoven through interdisciplinary units, such as "The Bay" (Chapter 4), "Snails and Trails" (Chapter 5), "Bouncing Balls" and "Wanted — Dead or Alive" (Chapter 6), and other science experiences, such as the Earth Day ceremony (Chapter 6), "Mealworms" (Chapter 7), "Rainy Day Things," and "Growing, Growing" (Chapter 10), are many opportunities to take advantage of the natural partnership between language arts and science. Children can be motivated and encouraged to talk and write about their experiences, and to use poetry and prose to initiate further explorations.

Throughout the book there are a number of suggestions for semester-long projects in which student teachers may wish to become involved. These projects are useful as preparation for similar activities that will be part of science curriculum and instruction. For example, an extremely practical component of the book is a collection of life science units (Appendix A) that have been tested many times as semester projects for student-teachers and subsequently used successfully with the children in their classrooms. Another suggestion that has tremendous potential for learning and also for later use in the classroom is an activity in Chapter 11 that invites student-teachers to develop a learning centre based on a specific unit in science.

Activities are interspersed with the content of each chapter, many times using an inductive approach, so that ideas evolve from the activity. Each activity is followed by a conversational "Reflecting and Sharing," which invites the reader to share what has been discovered, to reflect on its implications for teaching and learning, and to pursue the topic in greater depth through additional readings or further investigations. In many cases, student-teachers are invited to become learners again, as they participate in children's activities they will later use in their classrooms.

In addition to its Canadian focus, *Science for Life* is also unusual in the depth of its treatment of a number of other issues. The chapters on the beginning years, and on teaching exceptional children, as well as the chapters relating to evaluation and to science, technology, and society, are unusually comprehensive for a book of this kind. It is probably true that we have erred on the side of generous detail; if this is so, it is left to the reader, or the professor, to be selective. Although there are some threads connecting chapters, it is possible to be selective and to choose to emphasize or leave for another day some chapters or parts of chapters. We hope you will enjoy the book and find it to be a worthwhile contribution to your life as a teacher.

Acknowledgements

To Heather McWhinney, for the encouragement to begin, and to make this a truly Canadian methods text for student-teachers preparing to teach science in Canadian primary and elementary schools.

To Lisa Collins, for insightful editing, coupled with the knack of reading the manuscript from the point of view of the student as well as the professor, and the art of listening to ideas and offering valuable suggestions for improvement and organization.

To the Faculty of Education, Memorial University of Newfoundland, for support and encouragement.

To Bruce Burton, for sharing his notes (Appendix A) on a selection of very successful life science projects through which he has guided many preservice teachers.

To the teachers throughout Canada who contributed advice and wisdom through the medium of the "From a Teacher's Journal" inserts in each chapter.

To Laura Walsh, for her skill and unfailing patience as she painstakingly produced figures and tables and numerous drafts of the manuscript.

To the staff and students of Orde Street Public School, Queenston Drive Public School, Ossington/Old Orchard Public School, and Island Public/Natural Science School for sharing through photographs their experiences in science.

To Bonnie Shapiro, Richard Williams, David Jardine, Murray Smith, Paul Hart, Kate LeMaistre, and Lila Woolfe, who reviewed the manuscript and offered their suggestions.

And, finally, to our families, for letting this project take priority over everything; and to our friends, who put friendships on hold until the book was completed.

A NOTE FROM THE PUBLISHER

Thank you for selecting *Science for Life: The Teaching of Science in Canadian Primary and Elementary Schools,* by Ruby L. Gough and Alan K. Griffiths. The authors and publisher have devoted considerable time to the careful development of this book. We appreciate your recognition of this effort and accomplishment.

We want to hear what you think about *Science for Life: The Teaching of Science in Canadian Primary and Elementary Schools*. Please take a few minutes to fill in the stamped reply card at the back of the book. Your comments and suggestions will be valuable to us as we prepare new editions and other books.

◆ ◆ ◆ ◆ ◆

BRIEF CONTENTS

PART 1   CHILDREN AND SCIENCE: DESIRED LEARNING OUTCOMES

CHAPTER 1	Directions: The Goals of the Science Curriculum	3
CHAPTER 2	The Nature of the Child and the Nature of Science	27
CHAPTER 3	The Processes of Science	59
CHAPTER 4	Building Concepts in Science	83

PART 2   FROM THEORY TO PRACTICE

CHAPTER 5	Creating a Positive Climate for Learning Science	135
CHAPTER 6	Planning for Instruction: Teaching Strategies	183
CHAPTER 7	Developing Science Teaching Skills	233
CHAPTER 8	Evaluation of Sciencing	293
CHAPTER 9	Selecting Curriculum Resources	325

PART 3   SCIENCE FOR ALL CHILDREN

CHAPTER 10	The Beginning Years	381
CHAPTER 11	Meeting Individual Needs	423
CHAPTER 12	Teaching Exceptional Children	461

PART 4   SCIENCE FOR LIFE

CHAPTER 13	Science, Technology, and Society	511
CHAPTER 14	Science for a Changing World	543
Appendix A:	*Life Science Projects for the Primary and Elementary Grades*	569
Appendix B:	*Playing Different Roles*	589

◆ ◆ ◆ ◆ ◆
CONTENTS

PART 1 **CHILDREN AND SCIENCE: DESIRED LEARNING OUTCOMES**

CHAPTER 1	**DIRECTIONS: THE GOALS OF THE SCIENCE CURRICULUM**	**3**
	Becoming a Teacher	5
	Concerns of Student-Teachers	8
	Domains of Learning	11
	Creative Thinking	14
	Aims: Desired Outcomes	16
	Scientific Literacy	19
	Orientations to Curriculum	22
	Looking Back and Looking Forward	23
CHAPTER 2	**THE NATURE OF THE CHILD AND THE NATURE OF SCIENCE**	**27**
	The Child as Learner	28
	Jean Piaget	30
	Jerome Bruner	37
	Lev Vygotsky	39
	Robert Gagné	41
	Robbie Case	45
	The Nature of Science	48
	What Is Science?	48
	The Status of Scientific Knowledge	49
	Does Science Have a Method?	50
	A Constructivist View of Science	51
	The Scientific Attitude	53
	Looking Back and Looking Forward	54
CHAPTER 3	**THE PROCESSES OF SCIENCE**	**59**
	Teaching the Science Processes	67
	Observing	67
	Inferring	67

Classifying	69
Quantifying	70
Communicating	70
Predicting	70
Hypothesizing	71
Defining Operationally	71
Controlling Variables	72
Interpreting Data	73
Experimenting	73
Formulating Models	73
Integration into the Curriculum ... and Beyond	75
Talking Science	78
Looking Back and Looking Forward	80

CHAPTER 4	**BUILDING CONCEPTS IN SCIENCE**	**83**
	The Importance of Concept Development in Science	84
	What Is a Concept?	85
	Types of Concepts	86
	Types of Concepts: Approaches to Instruction	90
	How Concepts Are Formed	94
	"Stepping Stone" Ideas	95
	Selection of Content	96
	Selection of Concept Areas	99
	Approaches to Concept Development	101
	A Conceptual Themes Approach	102
	Constructivist Approaches	103
	Other Approaches to Concept Development	114
	A Learning Hierarchy Approach	114
	A Meaningful Learning Approach	115
	Children's Alternative Conceptions	116
	Change of State in Water	118
	Living and Nonliving	119
	Earth as a Cosmic Body	119
	Changing Children's Conceptions	121
	Looking Back and Looking Forward	125

PART 2	**FROM THEORY TO PRACTICE**	
CHAPTER 5	**CREATING A POSITIVE CLIMATE FOR LEARNING SCIENCE**	**135**

Characteristics of a Positive Learning Environment 137

Classroom Climate 140

    Studying Classroom Interactions 142

Searching for Excellence 146

Exemplary Practice in Science and Mathematics
Education 148

Classroom Environment: The Early Years 153

Characteristics of a Child-Centred Environment 154

    A Nuturing Environment 154

    A Climate for Growth 155

    A Climate for Self-Direction 156

Exemplary Practice: Reviewing the Data 156

The Role of Management in Classroom Climate 157

    A Common Factor: Orderliness 158

Components of Effective Management 159

    Physical Setup of the Classroom 161

    Equipment and Materials 164

    Storage of Equipment and Materials 166

Safety in the Elementary Classroom 168

    Orderliness and Cleanliness 168

    Care with Open Flames 168

    Electrical Safety 169

    Plastic versus Glassware 169

    Lenses and Light Beams 169

    Water Play and Spills 169

    Plastic Bags and Balloons 169

    Using the Senses 170

    Eye Protection 170

    A First-Aid Kit 170

    A Positive Approach to Safety 170

Procedures and Routines 170

    Preparing and Organizing Learning Centres 171

    Group Activities 172

Minimizing Misbehaviour 174

    Discipline with Dignity 174

Beyond the Classroom 175

    Field Trips 175

    Planning for Project Work 176

Involving Parents in School Science 177

Looking Back and Looking Forward 177

CHAPTER 6	**PLANNING FOR INSTRUCTION: TEACHING STRATEGIES**	**183**
	Beginning the Adventure	185
	Scientists as Children	185
	Children as Scientists	185
	Planning Instruction	187
	The Transmission Orientation	189
	The Transaction Orientation	191
	The Transformation Orientation	192
	Planning Units and Lessons	194
	Unit Planning	195
	Lesson Planning	198
	Teaching Strategies: The Transmission Orientation	199
	Expository Methods	199
	Teaching Strategies: The Transaction Orientation	204
	Learning through Inquiry/Discovery	206
	Science across the Curriculum	209
	Science and Language Development	211
	Language Arts and Science	213
	Teaching Strategies: The Transformation Orientation	218
	Looking Back and Looking Forward	228
CHAPTER 7	**DEVELOPING SCIENCE TEACHING SKILLS**	**233**
	Creating Encouraging Environments	235
	Developing Concepts	236
	Concept Teaching Models	237
	Developing Thinking Skills	243
	Learning through Discovery	243
	Problem Solving Using Process Skills	246
	Developing Inquiry Skills	250
	Using Motivational Techniques	256
	Discrepant Events	256
	Co-operative Learning	257
	Open-Ended Problems	257
	Brainstorming	259
	Buzz Groups	260
	Dilemma Analysis Cards	261
	Role Playing	261
	Play as a Motivational Technique	262

Developing Questioning Skills 272
Research on Teacher Questioning 272
Improving Teacher Questioning Patterns 275
Improving the Quality of Teacher Questions 275
Encouraging and Refining Pupils' Questions 283
Problem Solving in Action 283
Science Days 284
Poster Sessions 284
Science Challenges and Science Olympics 284
Looking Back and Looking Forward 287

CHAPTER 8   EVALUATION OF SCIENCING   293

Aspects of Evaluation 295
Domains of Learning 297
Cognitive Domain 297
Affective Domain 300
Psychomotor Domain 301
Planning for Evaluation 303
Evaluation Techniques 306
Observing 306
Portfolios 313
Testing Instruments and Formal Reports 313
Validity and Reliability 319
Looking Back and Looking Forward 321

CHAPTER 9   SELECTING CURRICULUM RESOURCES   325

Getting Started 326
Evolving Criteria for Selecting Resources 327
Conceptual Analysis 327
Curriculum Guides: Some Influences 329
Worldwide Trends in Science Education 329
National and Regional Influences 330
Curriculum Guides and Policy Statements 334
Intent of the Curriculum 335
Content of the Curriculum 346
Curriculum Resources: A Historical Overview 348
National Science Foundation Programs 348
Textbook-based Programs 350

Programs of the 1970s and 1980s	353
Programs under Development in the 1990s	356
Other Resources	365
Government Publications	365
Science Trade Books and Magazines	366
Nonprint Resources	367
Looking Back and Looking Forward	368

PART 3   SCIENCE FOR ALL CHILDREN

CHAPTER 10	**THE BEGINNING YEARS**	**381**
	Children as Preschool Scientists	383
	A Brief History of the Kindergarten	385
	Froebel's Kindergarten	385
	Maria Montessori	387
	Setting the Tone: The Beginning Years	388
	Kindergarten: A Special Experience	389
	Child-Centred Instruction	390
	NAEYC Guidelines	391
	Developing Basic Learning Skills	393
	Developing Other Basic Learning Skills	399
	Learning through Play	402
	Materials for Children's Play	404
	An Integrative Approach	406
	Looking Back and Looking Forward	415

CHAPTER 11	**MEETING INDIVIDUAL NEEDS**	**423**
	Recognizing Uniqueness	425
	Differences in Interests and Abilities	426
	Differences in Interests and Abilities: Possible Strategies	427
	Differences in Learning Styles	430
	Differences in Learning Styles: Possible Strategies	430
	Cultural Differences	431
	Regional Concerns and Recommendations	433
	Cultural Differences: Possible Strategies	435
	Overcoming Gender Bias in Science Education	438
	Gender Equity: Possible Strategies	442

Science for All: Some Practical Suggestions 443
    Co-operative Learning in Science 443
    Learning Centres 448
The Role of Computers 451
    Computers and the Personalization of
        Teaching/Learning 451
Looking Back and Looking Forward 456

CHAPTER 12   TEACHING EXCEPTIONAL CHILDREN   461

Exceptional Children in Canada 463
    Mainstreaming 464
Science for the Intellectually Challenged Child 468
    Adapting Materials and Pacing Instruction 471
    Computers in Special Education 472
    Activity Sheets 474
    Choosing Content 474
Science for the Physically Challenged Child 477
    Meeting the Needs of the Orthopedically
        Challenged Child 478
    Meeting the Needs of the Visually Challenged Child 480
    Meeting the Needs of the Hearing Challenged Child 483
Science for the Emotionally Challenged Child 486
The Gifted and Talented: Meeting the Challenge 487
    Recognizing and Fostering Creativity 488
    Provisions for the Gifted in Canada 488
Teaching the Gifted Child 491
    Early Intervention and an Open Environment 491
    Messing About in Science 492
    Fostering Synchronicity 492
Models for Teaching the Gifted 493
    The Open Classroom and the SOI Model 493
    The Enrichment Triad/Revolving Door Model 495
    The Mentor-Directed Enrichment Project 497
    The Purdue Three-Stage Model 497
    Individual Science Packets 499
Teaching the Gifted in the Regular Classroom 499
Thinking Back 500
Looking Back and Looking Forward 501

PART 4   **SCIENCE FOR LIFE**

CHAPTER 13	**SCIENCE, TECHNOLOGY, AND SOCIETY**	**511**

STS in Education … 512
Comparing Science and Technology … 513
    The Genetic Code … 513
    Plate Tectonics … 514
    Metals … 514
STS: Two Faces of the Coin … 516
    Toward a Balanced Position … 518
Interweaving STS with Science … 522
    Science and Health … 523
    From Technology to Science … 523
    From Societal Needs to Science … 523
    A Thematic Approach: STS Units … 523
Sources of STS Information … 524
Canadian Science and Technology … 525
The Faces of Technology … 526
    Technology as Problem Solving … 526
    Technology as Construction … 528
    Technology: Ethical Issues … 528
Attitudes about Science and Technology … 529
The Environment: A Special Case … 530
    Resources for Environmental Education … 531
    Field Trips … 536
Looking Back and Looking Forward … 537

CHAPTER 14	**SCIENCE FOR A CHANGING WORLD**	**543**

Signs of Change: Focus on Space … 545
Signs of Change: A National Vision … 547
    The Canada-Wide Science Fair … 547
    National Science and Technology Week … 549
    The Science Culture Canada Program … 549
    The Canada Scholarships Program … 549
    The Scientists in the Schools Program … 550
    Provincial Guidelines … 551
Futuristics … 552
    What Futurists Are Saying … 553

Recommendations for Change 556
Review and Reflection 559
Looking Back and Looking Forward 563
A Final Word 563

Appendix A: *Life Science Projects for the Primary and Elementary Grades* 569
Appendix B: *Playing Different Roles* 589

Credits and Permissions 595
Index 597

◆ ◆ ◆ ◆ ◆
LIST OF ACTIVITIES SUITABLE
FOR CLASSROOM USE

ACTIVITY 1.2	Sinkers and Floaters	10
ACTIVITY 1.3	Filling a Foilboat	12
ACTIVITY 2.2	A Very Black Box	29
FIGURE 2.1	Life in a Hay Infusion	47
ACTIVITY 2.10	Picturing a Scientist	49
ACTIVITY 2.11	Different Perceptions	52
ACTIVITY 3.2	Coloured Solutions	64
FIGURE 3.1	A Unit on Snow*	77
ACTIVITY 4.2	Going Fishing	90
ACTIVITY 4.3	Paths of Light	91
ACTIVITY 4.4	Mapping Magnetic Fields	92
ACTIVITY 4.7	Isopods' Response to Light	106
FIGURE 4.7	An Interest Map: The Bay*	113
FIGURE 4.8	A Specimen Hierarchy: Separation of Objects	115
ACTIVITY 5.1	Snails and Trails*	138
ACTIVITY 6.6	Bouncing Balls: A *Science 5/13* Discovery Lesson	207
FIGURE 6.3	Topics That Have Arisen from Bouncing Balls*	208
ACTIVITY 6.7	Wanted — Dead or Alive: An *Innovations in Science* Lesson	214
FIGURE 6.5	A Tree for All Seasons*	216
ACTIVITY 6.8	An *Insights* Lesson (Grade 1)	221
ACTIVITY 6.9	Earth Day, 1990: The Ceremony of the Rock	225
FIGURE 6.8	The Ceremony of the Rock*	225
ACTIVITY 7.3	Water Drops: A Discovery Lesson	243
ACTIVITY 7.4	Further Practice with Process Skills	249
ACTIVITY 7.5	An Inquiry Session	253
ACTIVITY 7.6	Open-Ended Problems	258
ACTIVITY 7.8	Dilemma Analysis: Role Playing	261
ACTIVITY 7.9	"Messing About" with Mealworms	265

ACTIVITY 7.10	Bubbles	270
ACTIVITY 7.12	In How Many Different Ways?	281
FIGURE 7.12	How Does the Number of Coils Affect the Strength of an Electromagnet?	285
ACTIVITY 10.3	Observing: Fun with the Five Senses	394
ACTIVITY 10.4	A Multisensory Activity	398
ACTIVITY 10.5	Developing Basic Skills	399
FIGURE 10.1	Rainy Day Things*	409
FIGURE 11.1	Building Bridges: From "Challenge" to "More to Explore"	428
ACTIVITY 12.3	Creating Roots: A Linear Exploration	482
FIGURE 12.1	A Large Charge	473
FIGURE 12.2	Moving Around	475
FIGURE 12.3	What Can Your Magnet Pull?	476
FIGURE 12.5	A Sample Science and Art Lesson	484
FIGURE 12.6	soi-based Activities	494
ACTIVITY 13.7	Awareness of Nature	533
ACTIVITY 13.8	A Scavenger Hunt	534
ACTIVITY 13.9	The Concept of Environment	534
ACTIVITY 13.10	Environmental Dilemmas	535
APPENDIX A:1	Plant Propagation	570
APPENDIX A:2	Seed Germination	573
APPENDIX A:3	Hay Infusion	575
APPENDIX A:4	Growing Moulds	576
APPENDIX A:5	Hydroponics	578
APPENDIX A:6	Local Insects	580
APPENDIX A:7	Mealworms	581
APPENDIX A:8	Brine Shrimp	583
APPENDIX A:9	Plant Growth	585
APPENDIX B	Energizer: Different Points of View	590

Note: Titles marked* have potential for development into units.

PART 1

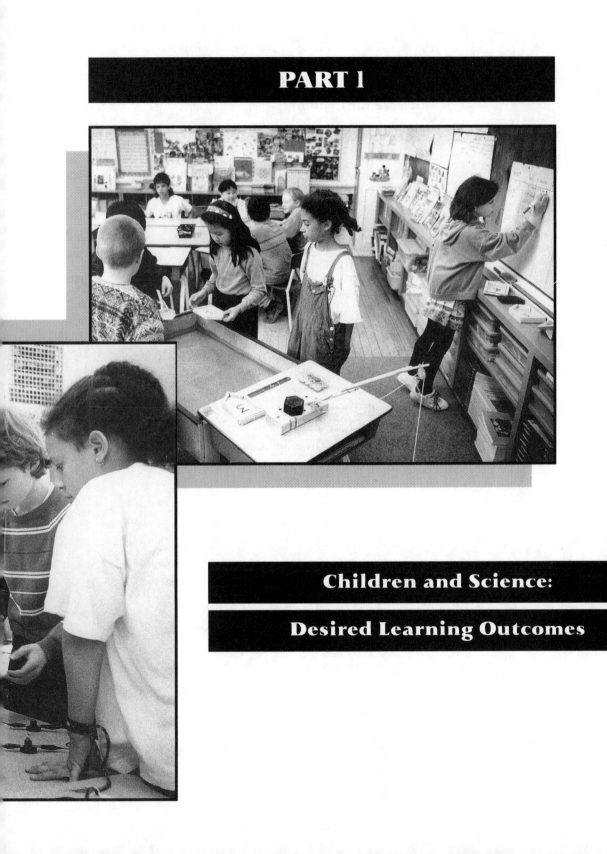

Children and Science:

Desired Learning Outcomes

■ ■ ■ ■ ■ ■

CHAPTER 1 *Directions: The Goals of the Science Curriculum*

CHAPTER 2 *The Nature of the Child and the Nature of Science*

CHAPTER 3 *The Processes of Science*

CHAPTER 4 *Building Concepts in Science*

The focus is on the reflective teacher, considering potential cognitive, affective, psychomotor, and social outcomes of science curriculum and instruction, and thinking of elementary science in the context of how children learn and the nature of science. Cognitive outcomes — science process skills and science concepts — are discussed in separate chapters, but their concurrent development and interdependence are emphasized. These outcomes, together with affective and social outcomes, contribute to the overall, long-range goal of scientific literacy. The importance of building from children's existing conceptions is highlighted.

CHAPTER 1

Directions: The Goals of the Science Curriculum

SCIENCE IN THE SCHOOL CURRICULUM

has a number of

DIFFERENT GOALS

that lead to

COGNITIVE OUTCOMES	AFFECTIVE OUTCOMES	PSYCHO-MOTOR OUTCOMES	SOCIAL OUTCOMES	OTHER OUTCOMES

still integration

including the learning and development of

FACTS, CONCEPTS, AND PROCESSES	GENERAL SCIENTIFIC LITERACY AND CREATIVITY	ATTITUDES, INTERESTS, AND VALUES	SKILLS SUCH AS USING A MICROSCOPE, ETC.	CO-OPERATION AND RESPONSIBILITY

all enhanced by

THE REFLECTIVE TEACHER

◆ ◆ ◆ ◆ ◆

Let us make [education] an encounter where

one generation helps the next generation

to meet the past and to understand the present

in order to journey into the future.

PAUL J. BLACK (1986)

There will probably be no more exciting day in your career as a teacher than the day on which you meet your first class for the first time. You will be excited and perhaps a little scared. The butterflies in your stomach may seem like a flock of birds. All eyes will be upon you. What will you do? What will you say? What adventures will you and your children share in the year to come? What might the children get out of their time with you? In this chapter you are asked to think about this, particularly with respect to children's learnings relating to science. Activity 1.1 invites you to think about your role as a beginning teacher.

activity 1.1 — LOOKING AHEAD

What are your hopes and aspirations as a prospective teacher? What kinds of challenges and rewards lie ahead for you? Try to think of ten specific problems you might face, and what kinds of solutions may be available to you. Write down your thoughts, so that you will have them to share in the discussion that follows, and to compare with later.

❑ Reflecting and Sharing

What you were asked to do in Activity 1.1 was to reflect upon the teaching and learning situation. Especially in recent years, writers such as Donald Schon (1983), in his book *The Reflective Practitioner,* and George Posner (1985), in his book *Field Experience: A Guide to Reflective Teaching,* have influenced teacher educators to encourage student teachers and practising teachers to reflect upon their teaching and upon other aspects of teaching and learning. Douglas Barnes (1991), a prominent British educator, also emphasizes the need for reflection, but cautions that it is difficult to implement. Barnes draws from Schon (1983) and others to refer to the concept of *frame,* which represents the clustered set of expectations through which individuals organize not only their knowledge of the world but also their behaviour in it. "The frame that experienced teachers take to a lesson enables them not only to recognize what is happening but also to consider the action that they would take if they were playing the teacher's role" (16). Teachers' frames determine what they will attend to, ignore, emphasize, change, and so on. Teachers who can frame only in one way are limited in their responses to situations. In contrast, effective teachers appear to have multiple frames, which allow them to see more alternative courses for action in different situations. It is likely that teachers-in-training and beginning teachers are limited in their available frames, especially if they have not yet learned to reflect upon their actions and the consequences of these actions. What might typical frames include? Wood (1981) suggests the following:

1. Preconceptions, often implicit, about the nature of what they are teaching, and, for secondary specialists, about the subject they teach and how to interpret it;
2. Preconceptions about learning and how it takes place, though modified by a view of what can be achieved in the classroom;
3. Preconceptions about students (in general, and about the particular group being taught) that place limits upon what is thought to be useful or possible;
4. Beliefs about priorities and constraints inherent in the professional and institutional context;
5. The nature of his or her overall commitment to teaching — vocational, professional, career-continuance (291–92).

A reflective teacher is more likely to be an effective teacher, and from time to time throughout this book you will be presented with opportunities for reflection. You will frequently be asked to consider situations and to focus your thoughts on these situations, sometimes alone, sometimes as a member of a group. After each activity there will be an opportunity for reflecting and sharing — a time for you to reiterate and extend your own ideas and share the thoughts of others. Before moving on to Reflecting and Sharing, it is important that you think through the activities because your thoughts, which mirror your developing perspective on teaching and learning, are valuable and important in the whole process of becoming a teacher.

◆ ◆ ◆ ◆

BECOMING A TEACHER

Posner (1985) suggests that all teaching situations have four features in common: *context,* representing all that constrains, facilitates, or otherwise influences what teachers and learners do with subject matter; the *subject matter* itself; *learners;* and *teachers*. Think about these as you imagine yourself in the earliest days of your teaching, your internship. The descriptions that follow are from the logs of students who have recently completed their internship. Only the names have been changed. Nora's description is a graphic example of a perceptual change that occurred within her first week at the school where she did her internship:

> When we drove up to the school for the first time I was appalled. The school looked to be in a state of disrepair; graffiti seemed to cover the walls, and some windows were boarded up. Yet when I left at the end of the day I had realized that the teachers were caring, that the children's work was displayed everywhere. I was surprised to find that classes were widely mixed with respect to ability and age. After a few days I came to a grave realization. Many of the children came from broken homes, many from poverty and neglect. Many need special attention. It is nothing unusual for a teacher to hug and cuddle a child who has been hurt or just simply needs it. I have come to realize that this school is what a school should be. Children learn there. Not just about academics; they also learn about giving, sharing, and caring about life. The school is completely geared to the children. Nothing is avoided because it is inconvenient for the teacher; rather, everything is given because it is essential to the children. My first impression wasn't what I thought it would be. I expected a perfect school full of perfect children coming from perfect families. What I got was reality.

Jean, interning with Grade 1 children, wrote, after a day when she experienced discipline problems:

> I became very frustrated in this lesson and I was very anxious to finish before the children did anything else bad. I learned that no matter how long it takes it is important to have the children's attention so that maximum learning will take place rather than rush it through to get it over with and have very little learning take place.

Mary, a third intern, commented on her inability to get across new concepts:

> I found managing the group more difficult than usual. Some of the methods I had used previously failed to show similar results. I felt I lost the children's attention. At the same time I began to panic and felt extremely nervous ... I learned a number of things. First, have all of the materials ready to go. I also learned that it is valuable to present exam-

ples of things that aren't quite the same as the concept you are teaching. I learned that it is important to have a number of classroom methods. To rely on one or two strategies doesn't always work.

The situations described above are real and typical, but of course represent only a minute fraction of the experiences of any teacher. It is possible to find in the above vignettes all four of the parameters suggested by Posner, namely, concerns relating to learners, teachers, subject matter, and context.

From a Teacher's Journal

My hopes on my first day as a teacher were that everything would go smoothly and that children would perceive me right away as "their teacher." Some fears were that I would not have enough planned to fill the day, that children might get bored, that they might ask questions, especially in science, to which I did not know the answer.

If I were to relive that day I would relax, and encourage the children to talk to me and tell me about themselves and their interests. I know now that much of what they would tell me would be related to their fascination with the world, and that the science program can begin right there. The best advice I would give to an inexperienced teacher is: "Do not expect too much of yourself, but do your best. Do not be afraid to learn with your students and from your students."

Linda Nadeau

Grand Falls, NF

Concerns of Student-Teachers

Posner extends the list of possible teaching concerns slightly by drawing from Schwebel (1979, 12–13). In each case, the percentage at the end of a state-ment represents the proportion of a group of 139 elementary student-teachers who expressed that concern.

CONCERNS ABOUT LEARNERS

1. Discovering and developing the potential talents of each child (76.3%).
2. Presenting the work in ways that engage the students' interest (74.0%).
3. Adapting assignments to the needs of the individual student (69.8%).
4. Working with students who don't seem to care if they learn or not (81.3%).

CONCERNS ABOUT SUBJECT MATTER

1. Teaching students to think through problems on their own (71.2%).
2. Finding sufficient time to cover the required material effectively (61.2%).
3. Getting students to apply what they have learned to new problems (63.3%).
4. Presenting material in ways that foster understanding (64.0%).

CONCERNS ABOUT CONTEXT

1. Finding ways to control the students effectively (72.6%).
2. Dealing with students who interfere with others' work (70.4%).
3. Providing all the pupils with opportunities for class participation (55.4%).
4. Dealing with classroom troublemakers (68.4%).

CONCERNS ABOUT TEACHERS

1. Not falling into routine methods of presenting material (69.1%).
2. Finding ways of keeping up with new ideas in education (57.5%).
3. Achieving a good understanding of personal strengths and weaknesses with respect to teaching (56.8%).

To some extent these concerns will be addressed in various parts of this book. You too will learn by reflecting on your thoughts and experiences, not only as you read this book but also as you progress through your career. Given the focus of the book, what follows will be directed toward science teaching and learning, but you are reminded that this is often just one part of the complex web of interactions going on in any school at any time. However, among your responsibilities as a primary or elementary teacher will be the teaching of science,

*Many elementary student-teachers are concerned about presenting new concepts in
ways that engage the students' interest. This teacher has captivated her students by encouraging
them to use many of their senses.*

and you probably have many questions in your mind as you accept this challenge
along with others you will face as a beginning teacher.

How will you begin? What topics will you teach? How will you approach
them? What kinds of problems will you face? What possible solutions will there
be? Most important, what will the children get out of the activities? You will
consider these kinds of questions and others as you progress through this book.
Keep in mind your role as a teacher of science by considering one main question
when doing the activities that follow. The question is: If children in the primary
and elementary grades were doing these activities, what might they learn?

The responses to this question represent the *potential outcomes* of these activities.
Collectively, they represent a strong selection of the possible kinds of outcomes
of implementing a science curriculum. As you carry out the next activity, make a
list of the possible outcomes for children's learning that might be realized. If
possible, discuss your list with others before proceeding to Activity 1.2.

activity 1.2 — SINKERS AND FLOATERS

Everyone knows that some things sink in water while others float. You may also know that sometimes objects that we expect to float don't. For example, under some circumstances even a boat may not float, as in Farley Mowat's book *The Boat That Wouldn't Float*. But what kinds of things usually float and what kinds of things don't?

Begin with a collection of objects, some of which you think will float and some you think won't. If you have some objects about which you are doubtful, include them also. Place the objects in turn in a bowl of water or in a sink partially full of water. Try them one at a time. Here are some possible objects: pieces of wood, soft plastic, hard plastic, polystyrene (for example, insulation), buttons of different shapes and sizes, cotton thread, wool, a ball of modeling clay, a stone, aluminum foil, a piece of soap, a small plastic cup, a marble, a peanut, a potato chip, a potato, a leaf ... Feel free to add others.

You probably didn't have many surprises. You may have found a different answer for a few objects depending on how you placed them on the water. However, for you, this was a simple activity with few, if any, surprises. As such, the activity may not have been very exciting either. But what about the children you will teach? What would they make of this activity? What would be the *potential outcomes* for them? Without reading on, try to list as many potential outcomes as you can.

❏ Reflecting and Sharing

How did you make out with your list of possible outcomes for children's learning in science that might stem from this activity? Compare the ideas on your list with those that follow, and try to think of ways to classify the different kinds of outcomes that were identified.

Facts. There were some obvious *facts* that might be learned. For example, some objects float while others sink, and some hover between floating and sinking. Therefore, factual knowledge is one kind of outcome.

Concepts. Underlying this factual knowledge are the *concepts* of floating and sinking, and, looking ahead, somewhere in these children's future, the concepts of buoyancy and density.

Scientific Processes. A third kind of outcome relates to the *processes of science*. Represented here are operations such as observing and coming up with operational questions that lead into experimenting, and so on. In a later chapter you will become familiar with a larger list of commonly accepted scientific processes. With respect to Activity 1.2, some *observing and classifying* were involved, and there may have been some *experimenting*. Did you make a table of your results? If so, you were *communicating*. Science educators commonly refer to about a dozen such processes as important skills that may be developed from science curricula.

Other Outcomes. There are many more kinds of potential outcomes. For children, just manipulating the objects would require some *psychomotor skills*. And, in addition to the exploring and discovering aspects, but directly related to these, the development of *attitudes*, both positive and negative, would be a potential outcome. There is the possibility of extension to *other curriculum areas*, such as literature — perhaps a story or poem about sinkers and floaters — or to art, through representation of sinkers and floaters in drawings. Perhaps you had other ideas. The combined lists at least serve to illustrate the wide range of possible outcomes that may emerge from a seemingly simple activity. Selection from such outcomes is related to what educators consider to be significant aims of education. As a teacher, you will either have to make such selections or understand and react to similar decisions made by others. You may find it useful to think in terms of three major kinds of learning, often referred to as the *domains of learning*.

◆ ◆ ◆ ◆ ◆

DOMAINS OF LEARNING

Educators have found it useful to categorize learning into three domains, called the *cognitive domain,* the *affective domain,* and the *psychomotor domain*.

Cognitive. The cognitive domain includes knowledge and its use. The most comprehensive description of the learning outcomes that fit within this domain is provided by Bloom's *Taxonomy* (Bloom et al. 1956), which categorizes cognitive learning into six major categories. These categories are knowledge, for example, that rocks typically sink in water; comprehension, for example, understanding that the weight of the rock plays a part in this; application, for example, predicting whether an untried object will float or sink; analysis, for example, identifying criteria for separation of sinkers and floaters; synthesis, for example, suggesting a way in which to combine the results obtained by different children in the class; and, finally, evaluation, for example, determining whose attempt is best.

Affective. The affective domain relates not to possession and use of knowledge, but to an individual's feelings, attitudes, and values with respect to an event, a situation, a course, and so on. Learning in this domain is also divided into a number of categories ranging from being prepared to attend to a stimulus of some kind, for example, listening to the teacher's instructions; to being receptive, for example, following the teacher's instructions; to being committed, for example, working hard at the activity; to valuing, for example, looking forward to such activities; and, finally, to developing an integrated personal belief system, for example, that science offers a good way to make sense of the world.

Psychomotor. The psychomotor domain is different again, and involves the use of manipulative skills such as using a dropping pipette, a pair of scissors, a microscope, and so on. It too has a number of levels, ranging from simple motor activity to the exhibition of complex manipulations to the creation of a motor action that is novel to the child.

Each of these domains is described in greater detail in a later chapter dealing with evaluation of learning. They have been introduced at this time to aid you as you consider the aims and outcomes of science instruction. In addition to considering outcomes within these formalized domains, it is also worth considering other outcomes such as the development of social skills and links with other areas of the curriculum. Think about each of the above kinds of outcomes as you consider the next activity.

activity 1.3 FILLING A FOILBOAT

Here is another interesting activity. Try it, perhaps with some children, and once again think of possible learning outcomes for the children you may teach.

One of the objects you investigated in Activity 1.2 was a piece of aluminum foil. If the foil was flat when you placed it on the surface of the water, it probably floated. In any case take a piece of foil, flatten it, and try again. Now take a larger piece of foil about 15 × 15 cm and make it into a boat, but try to make the boat in such a way that it will carry as heavy a load as possible.

Put your design to the test by seeing how many coins or washers or buttons or marbles or some other small objects the boat will hold before sinking in a container of water such as a large bowl or a baby bath or a sink. Repeat the process three times, changing the design of your boat each time. Compare your results with those of your classmates to see who is the champion.

What was the best kind of design? Long and lean like a battleship? Flat and fat like a barge? Smooth and spherical like half a globe? Some combination of these? Or perhaps something totally different?

Did you add the objects carefully; or did you drop them roughly; or did you place them strategically? Did you use a mixture of objects for your load, or did you choose the lightest objects? Do you think children would think of the same things that you did? Most important, how do you think children would behave in doing the same activity? What would be the important outcomes for them? Make a list. When your list is complete, examine it and decide how many different kinds of outcomes are represented.

❏ Reflecting and Sharing

How many different possible outcomes did you find? Here are some suggestions. You may have others.

Cognitive Outcomes. Once more there was the potential to gain *factual information* and understanding about objects that float, this time in terms of the shape of the object. Potentially all levels of the cognitive domain might be observed. Again there were potential *conceptual gains,* such as greater understanding of floating and sinking. Again there were potential gains in the application of *scientific processes.* Many processes might be observed, especially perhaps experimenting and quantifying.

Affective Outcomes. Did you find the activity interesting? More important, would children find it interesting? Would activities like this affect their attitudes to science? Might they be influenced in their judgement of the value of scientific activities in the general curriculum of the school? In a sense, this activity is an extension of children's earlier experiences such as water-play, a popular event in preschool and kindergarten classrooms. Typically, children enjoy "messing about" with water. Enjoyment is central to effective affective development.

Psychomotor Outcomes. Activity 1.3 provides good opportunities to develop children's skills in the psychomotor domain. Placement of the objects in the boat would need to be carefully done, and good construction of the boat would be vital. These are psychomotor outcomes.

Social Outcomes. Social outcomes would also be readily apparent as children co-operate with partners. Also, healthy competition would be evident. However, it should also be possible to show that competing scientists and their teams may also learn from their competitors and may openly provide information to others. Remembering that you are dealing with the development of young children, you would be interested in looking for some incremental gain in learning to work and share with others, as well as concentrating on cognitive, affective, and psychomotor outcomes.

These students are filling their foilboats to determine how heavy the boats must be to sink, and which is the best-designed boat. Experiments like this help students to develop their cognitive, affective, psychomotor, and social skills.

Other Curriculum Outcomes. Finally, as in so many situations encountered in the science curriculum, there are golden opportunities to *extend the learning to other curriculum areas*. There would be language development through the communication of results, and perhaps a story about building a superboat; artwork through the design of the foilboats; and mathematics through estimating, counting, and using arbitrary units for the cargo. There would be much potential for the development of children's creativity. This is the focus of the next section.

◆ ◆ ◆ ◆ ◆

CREATIVE THINKING

Many curriculum guides refer to the need to foster children's creative thinking. Unfortunately, there is no commonly agreed-upon definition of creativity, partly because creativity seems to be considered differently in different content areas, and in different cultures.

Creativity is often associated with divergent thinking, in which multiple approaches to solving a particular problem may be considered. For example, how many uses can you think of for a pencil? Five, ten, fifty? Try it with a group of children. You may be surprised.

But creativity is much more than divergent thinking. Sometimes it is the very opposite, when it is found in convergent thinking. Sometimes a problem has only one solution, but finding that solution may require a great deal of creativity. Whether divergent or convergent, sometimes a flash of inspiration, seemingly out of the blue, but more likely the product of a period of incubation, yields a significant insight by a scientist ... or a child.

One thing is certain. Creativity follows from intellectual challenge, and the teacher who offers challenge, who encourages "different" ideas, and who resists premature closure will be more likely to develop creative thinkers. A variety of

From a Teacher's Journal

My advice to a new teacher is to be prepared. Spend time during the summer organizing and setting up your classroom. Get to know where everything is kept in your new school. Plan as much as possible of your curriculum in advance, and start collecting your materials. I put everything into theme boxes, which keeps it all together so that I can locate it quickly when I'm ready to start. Take the time to read the teachers' guides, identify the skills you will need to teach, and block them out in a preview for the year. Do as much as possible ahead of time so that you will know where you are headed. Concentrate on the daily planning of the lessons, while keeping the long-term goals for the year in mind. Observe and keep careful records of children's growth in intellectual, emotional, social, and physical areas.

Cynthia Clarke

Richmond, BC

potentially helpful techniques exist, including the use of open-ended problems and brainstorming. In the science curriculum, there is no shortage of novel problems from which the teacher may draw appropriate examples to enhance creative thinking. Some of these are dealt with in a later chapter. Useful sources include Liem (1981) and De Vito and Krockover (1976).

◆ ◆ ◆ ◆ ◆

AIMS: DESIRED OUTCOMES

Expected outcomes are found in provincial curriculum guides as statements of aims for science education. Aims are desired general outcomes selected from a range of possibilities, and these vary from culture to culture, community to community, time to time, teacher to teacher, and child to child. To gain some appreciation of how aims change over time, compare the current aims of science education in your province with earlier versions. For example, today's aims may include reference to the effects of science and technology in today's society. Earlier aims might have focussed on the scientific or technological details of the processes involved.

Another useful source of information about what Canadians consider to be important aims of science education is Report 36 of the Science Council of Canada (1984) entitled *Science for Every Student: Educating Canadians for Tomorrow's World*. The report indicates four broad aims for science education in Canada, namely:

1. Science for the informed citizen.
2. Science for further education.
3. Science for the world of work.
4. Science for personal development.

These are very broad aims, indeed, and without further articulation would be of very little use to the classroom teacher. However, they are worthwhile in indicating the general direction of science education in this country. They are also consistent with our focus on "science for life." Briefly, the report focusses upon:

◆ the development of informed citizens who are able to deal with the inter-actions between science, technology, and society in their everyday lives;
◆ the development of autonomous citizens who are able to evaluate and use science most effectively in their everyday lives, whether or not they work directly in science-related careers; and
◆ the development of abilities relating to rational and critical thinking.

Still at the level of global aims, but slightly more specific, Report 36 proposes three initiatives that are represented in the following eight statements of intent:

1. Guaranteeing science education in every elementary school.
2. Increasing the participation of young women in science education.
3. Challenging high achievers and science enthusiasts.
4. Presenting a more authentic view of science.
5. Emphasizing the science–technology–society connection.
6. Setting science education in a Canadian context.
7. Introducing technology education.
8. Ensuring quality in science education (33).

The first item includes the suggestion that ministries of education require at least 45 minutes a day to be set aside for science teaching in elementary schools. All eight statements are significant to educators as they attempt to provide high-quality science education in the primary and elementary grades, even though they are only slightly less general than the aims referred to above. In themselves the statements provide no direct guidance to the teacher in his or her daily role, but knowledge of them and the role they play in determining the curriculum is useful to the teacher in interpreting the intended curriculum.

You may be wondering whether the kinds of statements listed above are of much significance to science education in the primary and elementary grades. You may be wondering whether they appear to be aimed more at students in the later years of schooling. The answer is a resounding no! The place to begin working toward the accomplishment of these aims is at the beginning of schooling. The content and quality of curriculum and its delivery in the early years of schooling sets the scene very forcibly for what is to follow. The high-school teacher, and the university professor for that matter, is much more dependent on the foundation laid in the early years of schooling than is often recognized. Think about it: a house built without a solid foundation will surely not last. The early years *are* vital to the developing structure of science education. What kind of science curriculum in the early years will provide this foundation? The next activity invites you to consider this further.

- - - - - - - - - - - - - - -

activity 1.4   DOMAINS OF LEARNING AND AIMS

In this activity, you are asked to examine a list of statements, each of which refers to an activity performed by children in Grades 1 to 6. The list illustrates not only the idea of different domains of learning but also a range of typical activities that occur in primary and elementary classrooms. In fact, these are all activities you may wish to try with children. Read each statement and identify it with the appropriate domain. For this purpose treat concepts and processes as separate domains, and again treat "social outcomes" and "other curriculum areas" as if they were domains:

1. A Grade 3 class investigates objects that produce sound and finds that sound is produced by objects that vibrate. *C Pn*

2. After collecting rocks, children in a Grade 2 class sort them into groups according to observable differences such as colour, heaviness, and texture.

3. Grade 3 students learn to manipulate a microscope correctly so that the lens won't be damaged.

4. Grade 6 students do an assignment in which they research the life of a famous scientist and then write about what attracted the scientist to science.

5. A Grade 5 class, entrusted with looking after a small mammal such as a hamster or a rabbit, is concerned about what will become of it during the school vacation.

6. Following an activity in which drops of food colouring are added to containers of water at different temperatures, Grade 4 students make multicoloured paintings to illustrate what they saw.

7. As an analogy to illustrate how sensory inputs are transmitted through the human nervous system, a group of children are instructed to stand in line and hold hands. Starting at one end, each person squeezes the right hand of the next person as soon as his or her own right hand has been squeezed.

8. In an investigation of differences between body parts in different individuals, the feet of all children in the class are measured and a histogram is produced of foot length versus number of children.

9. A Grade 4 class makes a model of a conglomerate rock by gluing together lots of small rocks.

10. After finishing an ecology unit, a child seeks out a book on environmental pollution.

11. Grade 6 students pay a visit to a fish hatchery and are concerned to find that overfishing is depleting fish stocks in the ocean.

12. During a visit to the seashore, Grade 3 children collect small aquatic organisms. Afterward they write a story about a day in the life of a chosen organism.

13. In a unit relating to air and its properties, Grade 4 children carry out a number of activities designed to illustrate the existence of air pressure.

14. Members of a Grade 6 class experiment to find the best way to keep an ice cube from melting.

15. A Grade 5 class constructs a wormery from pieces of wood and Plexiglas.

16. Some children are so enthused about science that they can't wait for a chil-

dren's science program on television every Saturday.

17. A Grade 3 class volunteers to go on a bottle drive to raise money to help clean up a polluted river running through their community.

18. After a unit on the science of sound, a Grade 3 class gives a rendition of "ten green bottles" performed on ten bottles containing different amounts of green-coloured water.

❑ Reflecting and Sharing

Now that you have finished categorizing, compare your answers with the following interpretations. Some activities may reasonably have more than one focus, and consequently your answer may sometimes differ from the suggested responses. Try to understand the rationale for the arrangement of the numbered statements. To check the arrangement of the suggested responses, draw a line below activities 6 and 12. What you then have are three blocks of activities. In each block the first item represents *concept development;* the second item represents *a process outcome;* the third item represents a *motor skill outcome;* the fourth item represents *affective domain outcomes,* including both attitudes taken by scientists in their work and interest in science by students; the fifth item represents a *social outcome;* and the sixth item represents an *outcome that extends science to other curriculum areas*.

These six kinds of outcomes do not exhaust all possibilities by any means, but they represent a range of possibilities. You will realize that no items relating to the learning of verbal information were included. This does not suggest that such an outcome is not of some importance but rather that it has often been overemphasized in primary and elementary science. The learning of verbal information should not form a major part of science curriculum and instruction at this level.

None of these outcomes, of course, will be developed in isolation. There will always be a parallel development of cognitive, affective, psychomotor, social, and interdisciplinary outcomes as children are involved, with your guidance, in investigations in science. Through their own active involvement in their own learning, they will build a conceptual structure that will lead toward some degree of *scientific literacy* in their adult lives and the incentive to keep on learning and to refine this broad goal, which, in many ways, encompasses all the rest.

◆ ◆ ◆ ◆ ◆

SCIENTIFIC LITERACY

What is the ultimate aim of science education in Canadian schools? Perhaps to produce a citizenry that is as scientifically literate as possible? This goal does not necessarily mean the same to all who are concerned with implementing it.

The difficulty of defining scientific literacy is pointed out by Champagne and Lovitts (1989) in the 1989 yearbook of the American Association for the Advancement of Science (AAAS), *This Year in School Science 1989,* which focusses entirely on scientific literacy. The contributed papers by various science educators indicate the vagueness with which this term has been surrounded in position statements and curriculum guides, although the chapter by Collins brings the concept down to the level of the elementary school curriculum. Champagne and Lovitts note that, for Collins, scientific literacy is a "desired level of depth and breadth of scientific understanding appropriate to the interests and needs of the students being taught, set within the context of the needs of the community in which the student lives" (12). Collins's definition is based on a dynamic three-part conception of scientific understanding:

♦ *A structural component:* the knowledge products of scientific inquiry, namely, facts, concepts, relationships, events, theories, and models.
♦ *A procedural component:* a repertoire of skills necessary to manipulate the elements of scientific knowledge, including posing problems, the use of process/inquiry skills, creative and critical thinking.
♦ *A human component:* emphasizing the interrelatedness of the natural sciences to each other, to other disciplines, and to the daily life of persons in a scientific and technological society, and the fact that what scientists choose to explore is influenced by the concerns of society.

Figure 1.1 illustrates the three components of scientific understanding on which this conception of scientific literacy is based. To teach for scientific understanding at any level, all three components must be included. Similarly, in your lessons it will be important to recognize the concurrent development of cognitive, affective, psychomotor, and social outcomes, rather than focus on any of these in isolation. Consider the following working definition of a scientifically literate person:

A scientifically literate person is one who understands the nature of science and its products and processes sufficiently well to function effectively with the level of science and its technological applications in the daily life of the society of the day.

Such a definition is consistent with a separation of aims into the cognitive, affective, psychomotor, and social domains, and with the theme *science for life.* However, it is worth noting that there is no one level of scientific literacy that is appropriate for all, or indeed attainable by all. The prospective scientist, for example, will need to attain higher levels of scientific literacy than will the consumer of science, but this is not different from the distinction between the professional writer and most of the reading public. Although they may be encouraged to write creatively, children are not educated in primary and ele-

FIGURE 1.1

Scientific Literacy: Components of Scientific Understanding

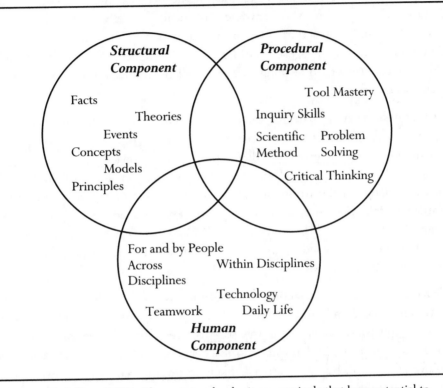

Source: A. Collins (1989). Elementary school science curricula that have potential to promote scientific literacy (and how to recognize one when you see one). In A.B. Champagne, B.E. Lovitts, and B.J. Calinger, eds., *This year in school science 1989: Scientific literacy,* 135. Washington, DC: American Association for the Advancement of Science. Copyright © 1989 by the American Association for the Advancement of Science, Washington, DC.

mentary schools with careers as writers in mind. They are educated to be functionally literate. Those who wish to become writers will train to do so much later. Nor do educators need to treat schoolchildren as if they will become scientists. Such concerns may also be addressed later. In the case of literature and science, it is possible to create interest and excitement that will lead to a desire for further study, among some of the population at least. But, as a teacher, your attention will be focussed primarily on the early development of the scientifically literate citizen rather than on the literate scientist. This direction will be pursued in subsequent chapters.

◆ ◆ ◆ ◆

ORIENTATIONS TO CURRICULUM

In this chapter, you have considered some ideas about the goals of the science curriculum and the role of the teacher in the primary and elementary grades. Before moving on, it is worthwhile to consider briefly the organization of curriculum and instruction. One useful approach is provided by Miller and Seller (1985), who suggest consideration of different curriculum organizations under three broad headings, which they label transmission, transaction, and transformation.

Transmission. As is true for each of the other two orientations, a variety of instructional approaches fit within the transmission orientation. However, this orientation is characterized by direct transfer of knowledge, values, and skills from teacher to student. Underlying the transmission approach is the belief that knowledge of the world can be broken down into small units that are best learned by following an appropriate sequence. Programmed learning is an extreme example of this, but wherever the teacher or text is acting as the source of information to be passed on as directly as possible to the learner, the transmission orientation is in evidence.

Transaction. The transaction orientation involves much more interaction between teacher and student than is found in transmission-oriented curricula. The student is no longer a relatively passive receiver of information, and is more likely to be involved in dialogue with teacher, text, or others. The teacher is still in overall control, but the learner is likely to be involved in the construction of meaning rather than just receiving it. In this orientation, a problem-solving approach is evident. This orientation is consistent with inquiry learning.

Transformation. The transformation orientation is concerned with the development of social, environmental, and spiritual consciousness, and aims to help the individual develop personal fulfilment in some or all of these respects. In some applications, it is ecological and in others political in its emphasis. In each case, the overall aim is to improve the life of the individual and people in general. Schools are intended to be on the cutting edge of social and political change. Education is intended to go well beyond the transmission of knowledge or its transaction, and is likely to lead to radically different kinds of interactions between teachers, students, and community. The curriculum is likely to be holistic rather than compartmentalized into specific subjects or smaller components.

◆ ◆ ◆ ◆ ◆

LOOKING BACK AND LOOKING FORWARD

In this beginning chapter, you have been introduced to some ideas about the potential outcomes of science curriculum and instruction in the primary and elementary grades. These outcomes were related to domains of learning — cognitive, affective, and psychomotor — and encompassed as well social outcomes and outcomes related to other areas of the curriculum. By thinking about outcomes that may be realized when children are involved in school science, you have begun to define goals for science education in the primary and elementary grades.

Although goals are broad statements of intent, they become attainable if they are broken down into specific outcomes that a teacher has in mind as a unit is planned, activities and investigations selected, materials gathered, and children involved. The greater the emphasis on holistic learning, the more likely that outcomes in all domains will be realized, and the greater the likelihood that the experiences provided will bring children a little closer to the broad goal of scientific literacy.

You will find later that each of the kinds of outcomes you have identified is represented in the statements of goals in the curriculum guides and policy statements for your province or territory. About midway in this text, you will be given the opportunity to review these guides as preparation for your teaching. In keeping with the way this chapter began, and with the need for you to continue to construct your own meaning about the teaching of science in the primary and elementary grades, the chapters that follow will continue to allow you to experience and reflect on your experiences as you build that conceptual structure.

In this chapter, you considered three orientations to curriculum and instruction. You will later set these in the context of the nature of science and the nature of the child. Each of the groups of outcomes that you have evolved in Chapter 1 will be explored in depth in later chapters. As you progress through the book, think of yourself as a teacher-learner, learning in much the same way that your students will learn as you explore science together and they, too, are encouraged to reflect on their experiences and their own thinking about them.

CANADIAN ACHIEVEMENTS IN SCIENCE

ALEXANDER GRAHAM BELL (1847–1922)

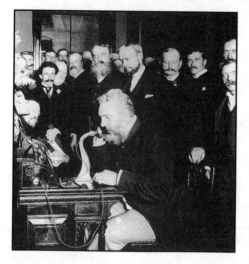

Alexander Graham Bell was born in Edinburgh, Scotland, on March 3, 1847. From his father he learned to teach the deaf to speak through "visible speech" — a phonetic alphabet in which the tongue and lips are used to make sounds. After his family moved to Brantford, Ontario, in 1870, he began experimenting with the harmonic multiple telegraph. Later, when he obtained teaching positions at the Boston School for the Deaf and Boston University, he spent nights working on the multiple telegraph. He built his own equipment at first, and later hired Thomas Watson to construct the apparatus. Within a year of his patent of the harmonic multiple telegraph, his experiments with the telephone progressed to the moment on March 10, 1876, when Watson heard on the receiver in the bedroom of the Exeter Place boarding house in Boston the now famous words that Bell uttered in his laboratory — "Mr. Watson. Come here. I want to see you."

In 1880, his award of the Volta Prize for scientific achievement enabled him to open a research laboratory in Washington, D.C., where he developed the gramophone. Other inventions were the photophone, for sending messages on a focussed beam of light, and the telephone probe, used by surgeons to locate bullets embedded in the body. Later, Bell's summer home near Baddeck, Nova Scotia, became a gathering place for scientists and engineers who worked along with Bell as his interests turned to aeronautical research. His wife Mabel, deaf since childhood and keenly interested in his work, supported with her own money the formation of the Aerial Experiment Association (ASA). The combined talents of the ASA were responsible for translating Bell's models into the design of huge kites made of tetrahedral cells, and for the invention of a succession of flying machines, and, finally, during World War I, the hydrofoil.

Bell's meticulous records of ideas and events, together with artifacts from his experimental work, are preserved at the Alexander Graham Bell National Historic Park near Baddeck. The underlying theme of the park is that as a teacher, scientist, and inventor, Alexander Graham Bell dedicated his life, with unusual success, to the benefit of humanity.

REFERENCES

Barnes, D. (1991). The significance of teachers' frames for teaching. In T. Russell and H. Munby, eds., *Teachers and teaching: From classrooms to reflection,* 9–32. London: Falmer Press.

Black, P.J. (1986). The school science curriculum: Principles for a framework. In A.B. Champagne and L.E. Hornig, eds., *This year in school science 1986: The science curriculum,* 13–33. Washington, DC: American Association for the Advancement of Science.

Bloom, B.S., et al. (1956). *Taxonomy of educational objectives: Cognitive domain.* New York: McKay.

Champagne, A.B., and B.E. Lovitts (1989). Scientific literacy: A concept in search of definition. In A.B. Champagne, B.E. Lovitts, and B.J. Calinger, eds., *This year in school science 1989: Scientific literacy,* 1–14. Washington, DC: AAAS.

Collins, A. (1989). Elementary school science curricula that have potential to promote scientific literacy (And how to recognize one when you see one). In A.B. Champagne, B.E. Lovitts, and B.J. Calinger, eds., *This year in school science 1989: Scientific literacy,* 139–55. Washington, DC: AAAS.

De Vito, A., and G.H. Krockover (1976). *Creative sciencing: Ideas and activities for teachers and children.* Toronto: Little, Brown.

Liem, T.L. (1981). *Invitations to science inquiry.* Lexington, MA: Ginn.

Miller, J.P., and W. Seller (1985). *Curriculum perspectives and practice.* Toronto: Holt, Rinehart & Winston.

Mowat, F. (1974). *The boat that wouldn't float.* Toronto: McClelland & Stewart.

Posner, G.J. (1985). *Field experience: Methods of reflective teaching.* New York: Longman.

Schon, D.A. (1983). *The reflective practitioner.* New York: Basic Books.

Schwebel, A. (1979). *The student teacher handbook.* New York: Barnes and Noble.

Science Council of Canada (1984). *Science for every student: Educating Canadians for tomorrow's world.* Report 36. Ottawa: Science Council of Canada.

Wood, P.E. (1981). Strategies, commitment and identity: Making and breaking the teacher. In L. Barton and S. Walker, eds., *Schools, teachers and teaching,* 283–302. London: Falmer Press.

CHAPTER 2

The Nature of the Child and the Nature of Science

THE INFORMED SCIENCE TEACHER

considers

**THE NATURE OF CHILDREN
AS LEARNERS**

as interpreted

by psychologists

such as

PIAGET

BRUNER

GAGNÉ

CASE

VYGOTSKY

and also considers

THE NATURE OF SCIENCE

including ideas

about

THE CONSTRUCTIVIST NATURE OF SCIENCE	THE TENTATIVE STATUS OF SCIENTIFIC KNOWLEDGE	THE ATTITUDES THAT SCIENTISTS BRING TO THEIR WORK

as influences

on

SCIENCE CURRICULUM AND INSTRUCTION

◆ ◆ ◆ ◆ ◆

Science is the belief in the

ignorance of experts.

Richard Feynman (1968)

In Chapter 1, you considered four different kinds of learning outcomes that can be achieved as children progress through primary and elementary school science. In this chapter, children's thinking is approached through the eyes of several psychologists who have influenced science curriculum and instruction. Selected aspects of the nature of science itself are also introduced. In the context of this book a comprehensive treatment of these topics is not possible, but you'll see that both are speculative and intriguing. You will be fascinated by the link between the worlds of the scientist, the psychologist, the teacher, and the child, as each internalizes *science for life*.

◆ ◆ ◆ ◆ ◆

THE CHILD AS LEARNER

As a child, and even as a university student, you probably had difficulty understanding new content at times. You may have wondered why. As a teacher, you will sometimes be puzzled about why, even on occasions when you feel you are at your best, your students fail to understand. Why do people encounter learning problems? What are some of the barriers to learning that our students encounter? How can teachers reduce these barriers? Educational psychologists are concerned with such questions and have some possible answers to them. Before turning to some of these, try the following activity.

activity **2.1** **LEARNING PROBLEMS**

Think back to when you were a child in school, and try to remember ten or more types of learning problems you encountered. Afterward, compare your list with the one that follows.

❑ Reflecting and Sharing

Perhaps you remember having difficulty with:

◆ mathematical reasoning;
◆ learning content that seemed to have too many words;
◆ imagining situations you hadn't met before;
◆ linking different ideas together;
◆ understanding analogies;
◆ following the teacher's language;
◆ breaking complex problems into simple parts;
◆ combining a number of simple ideas into an integrated whole;
◆ holding a number of ideas or instructions together;
◆ "seeing the woods for the trees"; or
◆ maintaining interest in the subject matter.

If your students have such difficulties what could you do, as their teacher? Answers to such problems can be found by considering suggestions rooted in educational psychology. In this chapter, you will focus on the work of several educational psychologists whose suggestions have been influential in science education. But first, a cautionary activity.

activity 2.2 A VERY BLACK BOX

A common activity in many science curricula is to have learners describe all they can about the contents of a closed box without opening the box. The activity may be used in various ways, among which is an intention to say something about scientific inquiry. To begin, ask a colleague to place one or more objects in a box and to seal the box. Don't look while this is being done. Now try to find out all you can about the contents of the box without opening it. Keep notes to help you if you wish. Do not continue reading until you have finished your investigation.

❑ Reflecting and Sharing

Perhaps you tilted the box, shook it, listened to it, even smelled it. As a result, you may think you know a lot about its contents. Perhaps there is one object inside. Perhaps there are more. Perhaps the box contains a flat object, or a ball, or a cylinder. Perhaps it contains objects that interact in some way. Now ask your colleague to take away the box, and to agree never to tell you what it contains.

Were you right or wrong about its contents? You will never know. This is the point of the activity. You may be absolutely right or you may be very wrong, but you will never know for sure. This is the position in which scientists find themselves in their work. They think they know the answers to their problems, but they can't be sure. This is where psychologists find themselves as they try to imagine how learning takes place. They can manipulate their special kind of black box, the mind, in various ways as they test their hypotheses, but they cannot open the box. They obtain evidence that supports or doesn't support their hypotheses, but they cannot be sure, and, making matters worse for them, it is often possible to explain the same evidence in different ways. Think about the implications of this activity as you read through this chapter, which begins with a discussion of the work of Jean Piaget.

Jean Piaget (1896–1980)

Especially since the early 1960s, Piaget has had a major impact on science curriculum and instruction. He not only published extensively himself, but his work's appeal to others has resulted in an immense literature. How can educators make sense of this literature and draw from it that which is most important to the teaching of science and other subjects? First, it is necessary to distinguish theory from the observations made as that theory developed.

The best-known aspects of Piagetian theory are:

◆ *Intellectual development,* in the form of changes in existing intellectual structures, occurs in *stages* that are distinct rather than continuous in nature.
◆ *Personal activity* is essential to the intellectual development of the child.
◆ Intellectual development within and between stages occurs through a process of *self-regulation,* also referred to as *equilibration.*
◆ The process of self-regulation may be explained as involving *assimilation* of ideas new to the learner, followed by *accommodation* of these new ideas, as existing intellectual structures change into new ones.

For Piaget, each of the above features is common across different disciplines. Let's examine each in a little more detail.

STAGES OF DEVELOPMENT

Probably the most familiar aspect of Piagetian theory is the suggestion that intellectual development is represented in stages. Piaget suggested that four stages exist, namely, the *sensorimotor, preoperational, concrete operational,* and *formal operational* stages. It is common for educators and others to associate specific ages with each stage. However, we won't concern ourselves with this as there is ample evidence that such distinctions are quite arbitrary. Consider the following as a rough guide:

◆ Except for those who are severely developmentally delayed, no school-age children will exhibit behaviours associated with the sensorimotor stage, and we will not dwell on it here.

◆ Children in the first few years of school are likely to exhibit behaviours representative of Piaget's stage of preoperational thought, and some aspects of this will continue throughout the primary and elementary years.

◆ By the time they leave elementary school, most children will exhibit behaviours typical of Piaget's stage of concrete operations, and some will have advanced to behaviours associated with formal operational thinking.

This is not the place to consider an extensive treatment of the work of Piaget and his many supporters, but what follows will give you a sense of it.

Preoperational Thought. According to Piaget, the preoperational child is perception-bound and is limited to immediate events. Typically, this child is egocentric, in that objects and events are seen from the child's perspective. The child will not be able to reason reversibly. For example, the child may agree that she has a sister but will not realize that the sister has a sister, namely herself. According to Piaget, the preoperational child will not be able to imagine the steps in a sequence, will have difficulty classifying things according to more than one dimension, and will often explain natural phenomena in ways that are nonsensical to older children. This child may believe that a cloud is alive because it moves. Finally, according to Piaget, the preoperational child will fail to conserve physical properties of substances in the face of a perception of change. For example, the child will believe that the weight of an object changes if its shape changes. Such limitations clearly have implications for instruction, and are likely to pose severe limitations on children's understanding of scientific phenomena. Consequently, it is usual for preschool and early school programs to provide a variety of opportunities for children to handle and sort a variety of objects and materials, in order to help them overcome these limitations.

Concrete Operational Thought. According to Piaget, the child develops a different view of the world between about 7 and 11 years of age. Classification becomes more comprehensive; the perspectives of others are considered; events are explained more logically; and conservation reasoning develops. Activity 2.3 illustrates some aspects of this.

activity 2.3 PIAGETAN TASKS: CONCRETE OPERATIONS

Try the activities that follow with some children between 5 and 11 years of age. Use a range of ages. All of the activities are derived from Piaget:

1. Place five pennies so that they are arranged in a square with one penny in the centre. Ask the child to count them. Rearrange the pennies and ask the child to tell you, without counting, if the number of pennies is now more, less, or the same. Then ask for a reason. The child who says that the number of pennies is still the same shows conservation of number and is exhibiting concrete operational thought. The child who says that the number of pennies is different does not yet conserve number and is not behaving in a concrete operational manner.

2. Pour some liquid into a large, tall glass. Pour the same amount of liquid into a second identical glass. Ask if the amount is the same. Adjust if necessary. Then pour all of the liquid from the second glass into half a dozen smaller containers. Ask: "Is the amount of liquid in all of the containers together the same as in the first glass?" If the answer is yes, ask "Why?" If the answer is no, ask "Why not?" A concrete operational child will answer that they are the same because no liquid was taken away or added since the first pouring. A child who does not yet conserve liquid amount will say that the amount of liquid is different.

3. Make two balls of Plasticine. Weigh each on a simple balance. In front of the child, adjust each ball of Plasticine so that both weights are the same. Then break one ball into a number of smaller pieces. Ask the child whether the weight of all of these pieces together is the same as the weight of the ball that was left untouched, or whether its weight is more or less. The child who has not yet learned conservation of weight will say that they are not the same weight.

❏ Reflecting and Sharing

The tasks represented in Activity 2.3 illustrate three aspects of conservation, namely, conservation of number, conservation of liquid amount, and conservation of weight, respectively. According to Piaget, other conservations that typically develop between ages 7 and 11 include conservation of length and conservation of area. However, there is ample evidence that some children will exhibit some conservations before they are 7 years of age, and that some adolescents and adults will fail to make some conservations.

The five-penny problem tests a child's ability to conserve numbers, indicating the development of concrete operational thought.

Think about such limitations in terms of children's ability to deal effectively with ideas that are typically encountered in science curriculum and in everyday life. Most important, think about what you might do as a teacher to help children overcome these limitations.

Formal Operational Thought. Just as the preoperational child is limited when compared with the concrete operational child, the concrete operational child is limited in other ways when compared with the formal operational person. Piaget and others have developed many tasks through which they have inferred the structure of formal operational reasoning. Two such tasks are illustrated in Activity 2.4. Try them with the same children whom you involved in Activity 2.3.

activity 2.4 PIAGETAN TASKS: FORMAL OPERATIONS

1. Make a drawing of a simple object. The drawing should be 4 inches high. First, ask the child to measure the height of the drawing. Second, tell the child that there is a similar drawing elsewhere, but that it is 6 inches in height.

Third, ask the child to measure the height of the original drawing in centimetres, to the nearest whole centimeter. The answer should be 10 cm. Now ask what is the height of the unseen drawing in centimetres. The child who is capable of formal operational thinking will use a ratio strategy, and will answer correctly that the height of the unseen drawing is 15 cm. The child who is concrete operational will probably say that the height is 12 cm, having applied an inappropriate additive strategy.

2. Place five differently coloured objects — red, blue, green, yellow, and white — in front of the child. Ask the child to suggest in how many ways it is possible to group one, two, three, four, and five objects, respectively, and to indicate each grouping by writing down the appropriate letter(s). Give a few examples; for instance, RBGY as one, YW as another, and B as another. Tell the child that order doesn't matter, so that YW is the same as WY, for example. The formal operational child will work systematically, perhaps starting with all five, then all possible combinations of four, all possible combinations of three, then two, and finally the five single colours. The nonformal operational child will be largely unsystematic, will quickly become confused, and will probably fail to suggest all possibilities. Even if all possibilities are identified, the child would not be considered formal operational if a systematic strategy has not been adopted.

❏ Reflecting and Sharing

You will find such tasks, as well as many others, in any treatment of the work of Piaget and his followers. It is very interesting and instructive to try them with children.

The two tasks that were used in Activity 2.4 illustrate proportional reasoning and combinatorial reasoning, respectively. According to Piaget, some other aspects of formal operational thinking include recognition of the need to control variables; the exclusion of irrelevant variables; the ability to form hypotheses; the ability to use analogies; and the ability to reason with abstract ideas. Research suggests that few 13-year-olds exhibit such behaviours to any marked degree, but it also shows that some younger children do exhibit them.

Whether or not you accept Piaget's explanations of the limitations in performance that his tasks expose, these kinds of limitations pose potential problems for the teaching and learning of science. With this in mind it is useful for the teacher to examine the textbook in use, as well as other curriculum materials and the teacher's own instructional practices, in terms of the thinking processes involved. Activity 2.5 invites you to try this.

PIAGETIAN ANALYSIS

2.5 Obtain the science text for any grade of your choice. Identify three examples of content that, when considered from a Piagetian perspective, will be likely to give difficulty to children at that grade level. Discuss your analysis with a colleague. Now ask your colleague to find three more examples, which will then be discussed with you. In each case, discuss whether the two of you can find a way around the potential difficulties.

PERSONAL ACTIVITY

Personal activity is central to most science curricula for a variety of reasons. Such reasons include the need to provide concrete examples to students, to develop particular practical skills, to develop specific science process skills, and to encourage motivation. Direct personal contact with materials and events is central to Piaget's theory of how children develop intellectually. Piaget consistently argued that individuals develop intellectually through interacting with their environment, and that this is even more essential for children in the primary and elementary age group and younger. According to Piaget, the thought processes of these children are usually bound to consideration of concrete or familiar experiences.

SELF-REGULATION OR EQUILIBRATION

For Piaget, in an appropriately designed curriculum situations should be contrived in which an explanation is almost within the grasp of the learner, but the learner has to stretch a little, intellectually, to reach it. In this way, according to Piaget, the learner actively constructs new mental structures. If the stretch is too great, the learner fails to make the necessary construction and development is stifled. If no stretch is necessary, or if the teacher comes forward with an explanation too soon, specific knowledge may be attained but no gain in intellectual capability occurs. Piaget names the overall process, when successful, *equilibration* or *self-regulation*. He refers to what happens as *assimilation* of a new idea followed by its *accommodation* into the learner's intellectual structure.

Clearly, some learning occurs inside and outside school, whether or not the learning environment is designed to provide opportunities for self-regulation. However, educators who favour the Piagetian approach design science curriculum and instruction as a series of events that consistently produce an appropriate level of disequilibrium.

As an illustrative example of the process of self-regulation, try writing your name backwards. You probably can't do it on your first attempt, but after several

This student has been given the materials necessary to develop understanding of a problem. Piaget referred to this process as equilibration or self-regulation.

trials, you probably can. If so, you have accommodated to the disequilibrium that this task caused you. Note, however, that any gain is potentially twofold. On the one hand, you learned some content in the form of a new skill. On the other hand, in wrestling with the problem you extended your intellect, however minutely. The best-known example of a science curriculum that deliberately provides a series of disequilibria while also teaching science content is the Science Curriculum Improvement Study (scis).

CURRENT PERSPECTIVES

Recall the earlier black box activity, Activity 2.2. When you finished the activity, you could not be certain about the contents of the box. You will never know what was contained in it. Similarly, Piaget could not be certain of what is contained in the human mind. Nor can his followers. The theoretical aspects of Piaget's work remain controversial. There is dispute about the notion of stages, for example, in that there is evidence that individuals sometimes exhibit competencies that are representative of a higher stage, while failing to exhibit others from a lower stage. There is good evidence that it is possible to train individuals to exhibit representative competencies earlier than Piagetian theory suggests. The principle of equilibration is difficult to support with empirical evidence. Where does this leave you, as you consider your role as teacher? Many educators remain convinced of the usefulness of Piagetian principles. At the very least, difficulties experienced by children as they try to understand physical and natural phenomena have been exposed.

Jerome Bruner (b. 1915)

About every ten years, a major review of research on teaching is published under the title *Handbook of Research on Teaching*. In the second of these (Travers 1973), two prominent science educators, Lee Shulman and Pinchas Tamir, suggest that every so often a field is influenced by the publication of a "great book." They cite Jerome Bruner's *The Process of Education* (1960) as such a book. Bruner's book and other publications by him in the 1960s and 1970s were highly influential on the development of education, and science education in particular. This influence is still in evidence today.

Like Piaget, Bruner believes that the learner should be active in constructing meaning. However, for Bruner, the responsibility for children's learning should be shared more between teacher and learner through a process of guided discovery. The learner's "act of discovery" is vital, but what is discovered is shaped and contained by the culture.

In *The Process of Education,* Bruner makes four claims with respect to structure, and four claims with respect to discovery learning. Regarding structure, Bruner states:

- ◆ Understanding the fundamental structure of a discipline makes it more comprehensible.
- ◆ Understanding of fundamental principles is important to transfer of learning.
- ◆ Unless new content is placed into a structured pattern, it is rapidly forgotten.
- ◆ Structure allows a narrowing of the gap between advanced and elementary knowledge and understanding. It enables the learner to relate new learning to old, and provides a framework and direction for further advancement.

An emphasis upon the structure of the discipline implies a sense of purpose, an attitude that supports learning the grand scheme of the discipline rather than discrete pieces of information, and the gaining of intellectual strength from seeing that the specific focus of the moment is a link in a larger scheme. For example, within the broad theme of "Living Things," a consideration of "communities" can be linked back in time to children's prior understanding of the classification of living things into plants and animals, and linked forward to the concept of populations and then to the impact of environmental effects on the size of a population. Within the same theme, observed characteristics of living things can be related to inherited characteristics and further to genetic explanations of these. This can lead, in turn, to a link with environmental effects on populations, and so on.

Later, in his article "The Process of Education Revisited" (1971), Bruner retracted some of his earlier claims about the importance of structure, but consider for yourself whether you personally find it easier to learn when you attempt to learn new content in isolation or, conversely, whether it is easier when you are able to place new content into the context of a larger picture.

DISCOVERY LEARNING

Bruner makes these claims regarding discovery learning:

◆ Discovery learning promotes intellectual potency through its focus on what would today be called "empowering the learner to construct meaning from events."

◆ Discovery learning encourages a shift from extrinsic to intrinsic rewards. That is, the reward for learning is the pleasure of personal involvement rather than some kind of artificial reward.

◆ Discovery learning enables the learner to learn the heuristics of discovery or, in other words, how to develop techniques that lead to discovery.

◆ Discovery learning facilitates conservation of memory. What the learner personally creates is less likely to disappear from memory.

Consider how appealing Bruner's suggestions are to you personally. Note, however, that just as his emphasis on structure was modified, Bruner also later de-emphasized the importance of discovery learning. In *The Relevance of Education* (Bruner 1974), he becomes more concerned with the passing on of culture, and less with the idea of individual discovery. Concerned with the need to ensure the relevance of children's school experiences to their future lives, Bruner (1974) becomes more concerned with training and brings "into serious question whether discovery is a principal way in which the individual finds out about his environment" (84).

There are distinct similarities in the views of Piaget and Bruner. Both believe in enabling the learner to construct meaning, a view that has become fashionable again in the science education literature. However, for Bruner, construction of meaning is more in the control of the teacher, the school, and the general milieu than it is for Piaget. A further difference between Bruner and Piaget lies in the

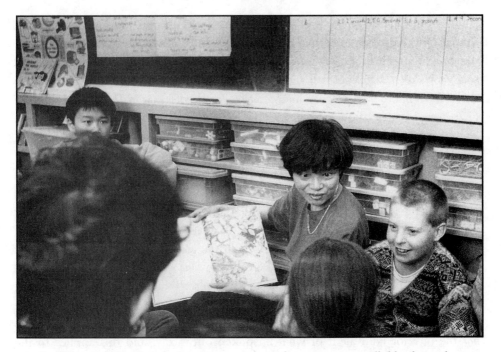

For Bruner more so than for Piaget, construction of meaning is controlled by the teacher, the school, and the general environment. The teacher leads the discussions but encourages students to come to their own conclusions.

role of language. For Bruner, language is more important to intellectual development than it is for Piaget. For Piaget, the formation of appropriate intellectual structures is necessary to the development of language, while for Bruner the existence of appropriate language skills is a prerequisite for intellectual development. Support for Bruner is also found in the work of the late Russian psychologist, Lev Vygotsky.

Lev Vygotsky (1896–1934)

Vygotsky was a contemporary of Piaget in the early part of Piaget's career. Vygotsky died in 1934, but his ideas have been resurrected in recent years. Bruner (1986), for instance, writes about "The Inspiration of Vygotsky." Vygotsky differs significantly from Piaget in his greater emphasis on the role of language in cognitive development, and in his emphasis on the importance of egocentric thought to the development of reflective thinking.

Piaget, in *The Growth of Logical Thinking* (Inhelder and Piaget 1958) and elsewhere, documents the widespread existence of egocentric thought, in which children up to about 7 years of age see events from an individual perspective not shared by others. For example, such a child would not understand why another person looking through the same window as the child may not see what the child sees. For Piaget, egocentric thought has no useful function and the child needs to overcome it in order to progress intellectually. For Vygotsky, as in *Thought and Language* (1962), egocentric thought is important in leading to *inner speech,* which in turn leads to reflective thinking, an important component of intellectual development.

Vygotsky's view of development takes on added importance in the context of the strong movement toward constructivism in science education today, an approach that will be described more fully later. Briefly, constructivism involves identifying the learner's initial understanding of a concept and enabling the learner to continue personal development of it. Vygotsky also emphasizes the need for this, and considers the teacher's task to be to help the learner navigate the gap between awareness and understanding, a gap he calls the *zone of proximal development.*

Two points are important to the teacher here. First, according to Vygotsky, the role of the teacher is to help the child navigate the gap, not to chart the course for the child. Second, the role of inner speech is critical. Inner speech is *not* the interior equivalent of what is spoken outwardly, and this applies to the teacher's speech as well as that of the child. Inner speech directs reflective thinking, which in turn directs external speech, but the contents of inner speech are different from what emerges as the spoken word. An important corollary is that the teacher's conceptual understanding can never be perfectly absorbed by the student. After instruction, each student's concept is at least a little different from that of the other students, and also different from the teacher's concept.

---

activity 2.6 THE ZONE OF PROXIMAL DEVELOPMENT

Choose a partner in your class, or better still, select a child as partner. Choose a topic that you know well but that your partner doesn't. Write down, in point form if possible, your understanding of the topic. Do not show it to your partner. Explain the topic to your partner, and then ask your partner to explain the topic to you in his or her own words.

☐ Reflecting and Sharing

Were you completely successful in your role as teacher? Probably not, but you are almost certainly thinking now about how you could have explained your topic

From a Teacher's Journal

Educational psychology has been useful to me as a teacher because of the insights it provides into children's intellectual, emotional, and social development, and the importance of growth in all these areas. I base much of what I do in science on Piaget's theory that learning is an active process in which concepts are derived through concrete experiences and through social interaction with other children.

I believe that children are innately curious about the world around them, and that they initiate activities to explore it and to learn about it. As educators, we must guide children's learning through integrated, enriched, hands-on activities that are related to real-life experiences. Learning experiences should be encouraged that extend children's thinking and encourage them to question and explore their thoughts through communication with both adults and peers.

Sharron Cooke

Richmond, BC

better. Did you try to find out your partner's initial understanding before helping her or him across the gap? However hard you try, your partner's understanding may never be exactly the same as yours.

Robert Gagné (b. 1916)

Robert Gagné takes an opposite view of the relationship between learning and development to that held by Piaget, Bruner, and Vygotsky. For the latter group, specific learning depends upon the learner's general level of intellectual development. For Gagné, the accumulation of specific learning is the mechanism through which intellectual development takes place. The difference may be illustrated by reference to Activity 2.7, which has been used by both sides to support their position. The activity is commonly found in elementary and middle-school science programs.

activity 2.7 THE DENSITY OF A ROCK

While a science student in school, you probably carried out an activity in which you determined the density of an irregularly shaped object. If you have access to a graduated cylinder and a simple balance, do the following: Weigh a small, uneven rock of about 1 cm in diameter. Immerse the rock in about 50 mL of water in a graduated cylinder, noting the water level before and after you do this. The difference in water level is equal to the volume of the rock. Given that density is defined as the mass per unit volume of a substance, determine this by dividing the mass of the rock by its volume.

❑ Reflecting and Sharing

You probably had little difficulty determining the density of the rock, or in understanding the concept of density. You probably found the concept to be more difficult if you encountered it when you were in school. Why would you have had difficulty then? More important, why would your students have difficulty now? Note, by the way, that we are distinguishing between getting the right answer and understanding density.

Many researchers have shown that few individuals below the age of 13 understand that the volume of water displaced by an object immersed in water is equal to the volume of the object. The Piagetian explanation for this is that these individuals have not yet developed the mental structures that are necessary to enable them to imagine the object physically occupying the same amount of space as the water displaced.

For Gagné, the explanation is quite different. Gagné suggests that failure to conserve displaced volume is caused by the absence of specific, related prior learning, rather than by the absence of generalized mental structures. The curriculum developer's task is, therefore, to identify an appropriate sequence of content, and the teacher's task is to place the learner at an appropriate point in the sequence. According to Gagné, the sequence should be derived by starting at the desired end product and asking the question, "In order to be able to do this, what should the learner already be able to do?" The same question is then asked of the answer, and so on until the complete sequence is identified. Such a sequence is called a *learning hierarchy*. The best example of a curriculum based upon this kind of analysis is *Science: A Process Approach II*, a K–6 curriculum. In general, the learning-hierarchy approach has not been particularly popular in curriculum development, but Gagné's insistence on the need to consider what the learner is already able to do is useful advice to teachers.

DOMAINS OF LEARNING

Although Gagné is probably best known for his work on learning hierarchies, his commentary on *domains of learning* may be more directly useful to teachers. Gagné identifies five kinds of learning, namely, *intellectual skills, cognitive strategies, verbal information, motor skills,* and *attitudes*. He suggests that each domain is different, not only in terms of the kind of learning involved but also in terms of appropriate teaching strategies.

The meaning of each of Gagné's five domains is illustrated in the following concrete example. Consider a Grade 5 science activity concerned with reflection of light. Children are experimenting to find out if there is a relationship between the angle of incidence and the angle of reflection when a beam of light strikes a flat mirror. Setting up the apparatus and manipulating it during the activity involves learning in the domain of motor skills. As a result of the activity, the physical law that the angle of incidence equals the angle of reflection should be obtained. The ability to apply this law to other similar situations represents learning in the domain of intellectual skills. This domain includes the learning of concepts and their application in routine problem solving. The ability to apply the law to new and different situations, for example the design of a periscope, is representative of learning in the domain of cognitive strategies. The ability to state the law obtained is an example of the use of verbal information, which is a fourth domain. Finally, the learner's feelings while doing the activity would be representative of the attitude domain of learning. Clearly, there is overlap between Gagné's domains and the three domains described in Chapter 1. What Gagné adds is specificity about appropriate conditions for learning and evaluation. His recommendations concerning this are summarized in Table 2.1.

Gagné's suggestion that each of the five domains requires different conditions of learning, as well as different approaches to determining whether learning has taken place, is important to you as a teacher.

TABLE 2.1

Instructional Planning: Gagné's Recommendations

Type of Expected Outcome	Instructional Features	Outcome Question
Verbal information	Meaningful context; suggested coding schemes, including tables and diagrams	Will the student be able to state the desired information?
Intellectual skill	Prior learning and recall of prerequisite skills	Will the student be able to demonstrate the application of the skill?
Cognitive strategy	Occasions for novel problem solving	Will the student be able to originate new problems and their solutions?
Attitude	Experience of success following the choice of a personal action: or observation of these events in a human model	Will the student choose the intended personal action?
Motor skill	Learning of executive routine; practice with informative feedback	Will the student be able to execute the motor performance?

Source: R.M. Gagné (1974). *Essentials of learning for instruction,* 102. Hinsdale, IL: Dryden Press. Reprinted with permission from Allyn and Bacon.

activity 2.8   IDENTIFYING DOMAIN EXAMPLES

Obtain a text for a grade of your choice. Identify at least one example each of content representative of Gagné's five domains of learning. Try to decide whether the approach taken in the text is consistent with Gagné's suggestions for effective learning. If it is not, try to suggest better alternatives. If possible, discuss your analysis and suggestions with a colleague.

The view of instruction suggested by Gagné is much more consistent with a transmission orientation model than that presented by Piaget and Bruner. Like Bruner, Gagné is concerned with emphasizing the development of the structure of the subject. However, for Gagné, the structure is likely to be more fixed, and discovery learning in Bruner's sense is not likely to be encouraged.

Can there be a combination of the theoretical positions we have considered, or of other positions? The work of prominent Canadian researcher Robbie Case suggests the possibility of such a combination.

Robbie Case (b. 1944)

At present, it does not seem to be possible to explain all observations of learning and development by any one extensive theory. For example, Piaget's theory of intellectual development fails to explain adequately how an individual has difficulty with a task that is similar in structure to another task that poses no difficulty, or why it is possible to train individuals to exhibit behaviours well beyond what appears to be their existing stage of development. Similarly, Gagné's representation of human learning fails to explain why individuals may seem to have all of the necessary prerequisites to learn a new task, yet fail to do so. Suggestions by Canadian researcher Robbie Case provide possible answers to these questions.

Case draws upon the work of another Canadian, Juan Pascual-Leone, who developed a construct that he called *mental power* or *M-power*. M-power represents the number of things that an individual can hold in mind simultaneously. According to Pascual-Leone, this number increases with age, but Case suggests that the number does not increase after an individual is about 2 years old. According to Case, what changes with age is the development of more and more powerful routines that enable the individual to combine mental operations in ways that decrease the total number of things that need to held in mind simultaneously.

Whether or not it is related to age, the concept of M-power is worthy of consideration. It explains some of the anomalies in the positions held by Piaget and Gagné. For example, Case explains the finding that some children cannot cope with a particular Piagetian task, even though they can cope with an apparently similar task, by suggesting that the M-power demand is greater in the former task. Similarly, with respect to Gagné's hierarchical model of learning, Case suggests that when an individual fails to learn a new concept, even though the necessary prerequisites have been learned, failure is again explainable on the basis of M-power. In each case, it is important to realize that what must be held in mind includes not only the demands of the task itself but also other factors such as the number of instructions in the text, additional teacher comments, and any other influences that demand simultaneous attention.

Case documents a number of research studies to support his contention that it is possible to arrange instruction to deliberately match the M-power required by the learning task to the M-power of the learner, and thereby to enable successful performance in situations that would otherwise result in failure. For example, Case (1974) successfully trained a group of 8-year-olds to control variables in a problem involving a number of bending rods, and then showed that this success transferred to different problems requiring control of variables. According to Piagetian theory, this result should not have been possible, even with individuals many years older. How can such results be achieved? Case (1980) suggests the following procedure:

1. Identify the learner's own strategies.
2. If the strategies are incorrect, demonstrate their inadequacy.
3. Explain why the strategies are inadequate.
4. Demonstrate a correct strategy.
5. Elaborate and explain this strategy further.
6. Provide situations for further practice, coaching, and guidance.

Case is consistent with Piaget in recommending the need to identify the learner's initial level of functioning; to select learning tasks that require a moderate increase in intellectual function; and to provide opportunities for consolidation. In this sense, he is consistent with the SCIS application of Piagetian principles. Case differs from Piaget in his emphasis upon the need to focus on the child's learning strategy; to demonstrate the limitations of that strategy; and to introduce a new strategy that is consistent with the capacity of the learner's working memory.

Case is also consistent with Gagné in his focus on logical analysis of the particular learning task; in his emphasis upon the need to establish the learner's initial understanding; and in his emphasis on the need to combine these two considerations when arranging instruction. He differs from Gagné in his focus on minimizing demands on the learner's short-term memory; in his direct focus on the overall problem rather than on individual components; and in his focus on the shortcomings of the individual's own approach.

Case provides a bridge between Piaget and Gagné, while also providing additional suggestions of his own. He is also consistent with Bruner and Vygotsky, in that he recognizes the importance of the culture and language in assisting the child's intellectual development. At the very least, consideration of the relationship between the M-demand of the learning situation and the M-power of the learner is likely to be useful when you are considering the arrangement and organization of instruction. Activity 2.9 illustrates how you can approach this.

activity 2.9 IDENTIFYING M-DEMAND

Consider the information represented in Figure 2.1. Determine how many different inputs you think the children must attend to as they pursue this activity in a normal fourth-grade classroom setting. Consider whether these collective inputs are likely to overload these children's working memory. If so, what will you do about it as their teacher?

☐ Reflecting and Sharing

Perhaps you listed the following:

◆ Written instructions.
◆ Teacher instructions, for example, repeating the warning about taking care in the proper use of the microscope, reporting results, etc.

FIGURE 2.1

Life in a Hay Infusion

Your teacher will boil some hay in water and leave it to sit for a few days. When your teacher tells you, do the following:

1. Pick up some of the water using a medicine dropper.
2. Place a few drops of the water on a microscope slide.
3. Carefully place a cover slide on top.
4. Mount the slide on a microscope.
5. Carefully adjust the eyepiece until you have a clear picture of what is on the slide. Be careful not to push the objective lens (the lens at the bottom end of the microscope tube) into the slide.
6. Make drawings of what you see.

Note: Handle the microscope and slides carefully. If anything breaks, tell your teacher at once.

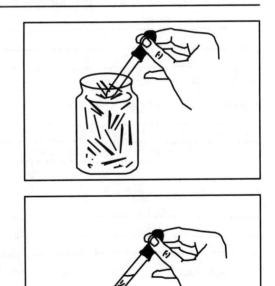

- ◆ Skills to be recalled, such as making a slide, using a medicine dropper, etc.
- ◆ Technical terms, for example, eyepiece and objective lens.
- ◆ Linkage with previous activities, for example, how to use a microscope.
- ◆ Extraneous influences from other children, other parts of the school, or the community.

Clearly, there are a number of things to consider, and of course you may have thought of more. The text itself helps by breaking the instructions into parts and by providing two diagrams. You may begin by ensuring that the children recall necessary skills and information. You may have the children progress at the same rate by providing instructions one step at a time, thereby diminishing the load on working memory. You may demonstrate each step just before they do it. You may provide a diagram to illustrate each step. You can probably think of other possibilities.

Clearly, you can approach any content in this way. To conclude this activity, examine a text for a grade of your choice. Identify several activities that appear to involve an excessive load on the memory of the children involved, and consider what steps you would take to reduce this.

When you have completed Activity 2.9, turn next to the second focus of this chapter — selected aspects of the nature of science itself.

◆ ◆ ◆ ◆ ◆

THE NATURE OF SCIENCE

What is science? Is there such a thing as *the* scientific method? What is the status of scientific knowledge? These questions are the focus of this section.

What Is Science?

The question "What is science?" seems simple enough. Yet, a simple, commonly accepted, useful definition is both elusive and potentially constricting. Given the range and complexity of modern science, perhaps this is not surprising. It is not really possible, for example, to place the work of an organic chemist, a theoretical physicist, an ornithologist, a paleontologist, and a radio astronomer within one overall framework, in terms of what they do and how they function. Yet, we recognize all as scientists. What binds them together as scientists, and what makes their work recognizable as science?

Whatever their precise focus of interest, scientists are individuals who are attempting to explain the workings of the natural and artificial world, in contrast to technologists, for example, who are concerned with the manipulation of that world for the good of humankind. But how would you know a scientist if you saw one? What is your image of a scientist? This subject is pursued in Activity 2.10.

---

activity 2.10 PICTURING A SCIENTIST

Write a paragraph describing your image of a typical scientist. Make a drawing to illustrate your description. Ask several other people, including some typical primary and elementary children of different ages, to do the same thing.

☐ Reflecting and Sharing

How did you represent the typical scientist? How did the people who helped you? Research carried out in a number of countries suggests that the most common image is that the typical scientist is male, old, eccentric, wears glasses, has wild hair, and is more than a bit peculiar. He works in a laboratory, probably surrounded by strange-looking technical apparatus. By extension, science is also typically conducted in a laboratory and is strange and a bit beyond ordinary mortals.

In reality, this is a caricature of science and scientists. There is no such person as a typical scientist, nor is there a typical scientific problem. Scientific problems, scientists, and the methods they employ vary widely. Typically, the only commonality is that the ultimate aim is to explain the working of the natural and artificial world in ways that are open to testing by other people. But what is the status of the knowledge obtained? The answer to that question is important to you as you consider the teaching of science.

The Status of Scientific Knowledge

Step back in time for a moment to think about some questions of interest to science in the past:

◆ Is the sky a big, blue dome? Yes, in the minds of the ancients ... but not today!
◆ Are some living things generated spontaneously from mud and muck? Yes, in the minds of scientists before Pasteur ... but not today!
◆ Are chemicals from living organisms held together by a vital force, while those from nonliving organisms are not? Yes, before Wohler... but not today!

> ✍ **From a Teacher's Journal**
>
> An explanation of science and scientists that young children would understand is: "A scientist is a person who watches and learns about our world — the Earth, other planets, the sky, plants, animals, and people. Scientists do experiments to discover information about the world and pass it on to us. A new word for the world around us, and for what science is all about, is 'environment.' We can do many activities in our classroom to help us learn about our environment."
>
> *Doreen Collins*
>
> *Toronto, ON*

◆ Are atoms the smallest units of matter, indivisible into smaller units? Yes, before Becquerel... but not today!

◆ Do the continents move? No, at least before Wegener... but today they do!

What of today? Today, we believe in particles that have charm; in black holes in extraterrestrial space; in an oscillating universe; in agelessness if we could only move fast enough; in "chaos." Will tomorrow's world believe these ideas? We don't know, but consider the following statement from a UNESCO (1980) handbook for science teachers: "The twentieth century scientist should be certain of only one thing, that in the end everything he knows may turn out to be wrong." This statement was followed by the comment that "Children must know that no one really knows." Why is this? Why can't scientists be sure? What is wrong with the scientific method? Does science have a method?

Does Science Have a Method?

It is usual in school textbooks, and in books written with future teachers in mind, to say something about *the* scientific method. Typically, it is represented as a series of steps that successively involve identifying a problem, stating a hypothesis, creating a plan to test the hypothesis, carrying out the plan as an experiment, presenting the data, and drawing conclusions. Traditionally, this is the format of scientific papers, through which scientists communicate their findings to other scientists. However, eminent scientist Sir Peter Medawar (1974) had this to say about the scientific paper: "The scientific paper is a fraud." He did not mean that scientists cheat, although some may, but rather that while the scientific paper presents the technical details of an experiment and its results, it does not convey the personal, human story involved.

In a sense, the scientific paper is analogous to a newspaper report of a sports event. Usually, if you read the report of a sports event, you learn the names of some of the players, the final score, and selected interesting aspects of the game, but most of what really happens is not, indeed could not be, reported. The same is true for the scientific paper. The final score, together with a few essential details, is presented for all to see, but the internal processes, mental and emotional, that preceded it are never apparent. Usually, only the "plays" that turned out to be particularly significant are reported. In this way, the scientific paper tells little about the real process of "sciencing." It should not be held up as a model of the practice of real science, or for the practice of school science. Real science does not follow a routine, stylized procedure. Nor does good school science. In each case, the ability to *construct* successful solutions to problems is involved. This constructivist view of science is popular today. It is considered next.

A Constructivist View of Science

The fundamental basis of constructivism is summed up well by Johnson-Laird (1983):

> Human beings ... do not apprehend the world directly; they possess only internal representations of it, because perception is the construction of a model of the world. They are unable to compare this perceptual representation directly with the world ... it *is* their world (156).

The models to which Johnson-Laird refers are not only those in the minds of scientists at the frontiers of science; more important for education, they are the constructions that all of us, including the youngest child, make in trying to make sense of our world. A vitally important corollary for the constructivist position is that none of us, child or adult or scientist, can be sure that what is represented is all that is really there. Therefore, all of our ideas about the world are subject to modification or even outright rejection in the light of more convincing ideas. Just as surely, these newly constructed ideas are also uncertain.

Does this mean that scientific knowledge is worthless? Not at all. It is to be tested against experience, and it will be found to be more or less useful, but for the constructivist there is no *final* objective reality to be found. Karl Popper (1959), an eminent philosopher of science, captures this idea when he says the following about science:

> Science does not rest on solid bedrock. The bold structure of its theories rises as if it were above a swamp. It is like a building erected on piles. The piles are driven down from above into the swamp, but not down to any natural base and if we stop driving the piles deeper it is not because we have reached firm ground. We simply stop when we are satisfied that they are firm enough to carry the structure, at least for the time being (111).

A prominent science educator, Rosalind Driver (1988), describes science as "not so much a discovery but a carefully checked 'construction' ... scientists construct theoretical entities (magnetic fields, genes, electron orbitals ...) which in turn take on 'a reality'" (136–37).

In an influential publication, constructivist thinker Erich Von Glaserfeld (1989) presents science as subjectively dependent on the knower; as a mapping of what, in the light of human experience, turns out to be feasible; as knowledge that can never be acquired passively; and as knowledge that is enhanced by interaction with others, but that ultimately is in the mind of the individual as a product of self-organization. In other words, all individuals have constructs that are different in some degree from the constructs of other individuals. Activity 2.11 illustrates this idea.

- - - - - - - - - - - - - - -

activity 2.11 DIFFERENT PERCEPTIONS

Ask some friends to observe an event with you and to write down everything that occurs. Better still, try this with a group of children. The event may be something as simple as watching a group of students come into class, or a group of children at play. Compare each person's perceptions and interpretations of the event.

❑ Reflecting and Sharing

How did observers differ in their perceptions and interpretations, in their constructions of reality? Probably quite a lot. What, then, of scientists faced with an unexplored aspect of the world? They will surely make different constructions. What of children facing new challenges in their everyday world and in their science classes? They, too, make individual constructions. Educational researchers refer to such constructions by children as *naive conceptions, alternative conceptions, alternative frameworks, children's science,* and so on. Whatever these constructions are called, the significant factor is that individuals differ in their understandings. The extent of these differences has become apparent only in recent years. Examples are presented in Chapter 4, where children's ideas of scientific phenomena are examined more closely.

Constructivism is largely consistent with the writings of Piaget, Vygotsky, and, to a lesser extent, Bruner. It fits readily with the transaction and transformation orientations to curriculum. It also presents a particular view of scientific knowledge. If you accept this view, you cannot teach science as a body of knowledge to be communicated to your students. You must encourage your students to develop and test their own ideas; to become constructors rather than receivers of knowledge.

◆ ◆ ◆ ◆ ◆

THE SCIENTIFIC ATTITUDE

Just as scientists have been described as sharing a common scientific method, they have also often been described as sharing a common scientific attitude. With relatively minor variations, the "scientific attitude" includes the following: objectivity in data collection and in the processing of data; willingness to suspend judgement until enough information upon which to make a decision is available; scepticism and critical-mindedness about new information and theoretical claims, regardless of who the claimant may be; willingness to change opinions in the face of new evidence that contradicts existing ideas; and humility. One persuasive analyst, Michael Mahoney (1979), strongly disputes such traditional views. According to Mahoney, scientists are often illogical, especially when defending what they believe and when attacking what they do not; they are often closed-minded rather than open-minded, and hold on tenaciously to their views even against substantial contrary evidence; they tend to select data that support their case and to ignore data that do not; they are often secretive, failing to share vital knowledge until it is to their benefit to do so; and they tend to rush to hypotheses and theories long before their data warrant.

Generally, suggests Mahoney, the typical scientist behaves differently according to the context of the moment. The scientist may be objective or emotional, open-minded or closed-minded, a suspender of judgement or an impetuous spinner of the truth. According to Mahoney and others, it is the most successful scientists who tend to depart most from the typical stereotypes. According to this view, the stereotypical scientist is a caricature of real scientists, and the image of science usually presented in science texts and in teaching methods texts is a caricature of real science. In light of this, should teachers continue to present an image that may be, to some extent at least, false? You have to answer this question for yourself. Perhaps it is reasonable to develop attitudes such as objectivity, critical-mindedness, and suspension of judgement as part of children's general education, provided that not too much is made of these as characteristics of all science and that the essentially human aspects of scientific creativity are not ignored. Where better to present science as a human endeavour than in the primary and elementary grades? Where better to present science as being related to many aspects of people's lives today? Where better to consider *science for life*?

◆ ◆ ◆ ◆ ◆

LOOKING BACK AND LOOKING FORWARD

Theories about how children learn and the need to make science programs true to the nature of science have been recurring themes in curriculum development since the 1960s. The Piagetian influence in particular is reflected in the science education literature, underscoring the importance of providing children with ample opportunity for direct experiences with their natural world, so that knowledge can be constructed through their own active involvement in learning. These tenets find their expression in science curricula that emphasize involvement in hands-on science as a way of developing concepts from raw experience, and in the placement of science content at appropriate levels to match the children's level of development.

A second developmental psychologist, Jerome Bruner, has also been influential in shaping science curriculum and instruction. Bruner's emphasis on making explicit the "big ideas" of a subject through a process of discovery learning is still evident in many curriculums in use today.

A third developmental psychologist, Vygotsky, died long before the science curriculum reform of the 1960s. His emphasis on the role of language, especially "inner speech" and the need to consider the child's existing understandings, is influential in the current constructivist movement in science education. Later chapters in this book show that elementary science curricula developed from the 1960s to the 1990s have been heavily influenced by developmental psychology.

Despite the widespread popularity of the developmental view of learning, some psychologists such as Robert Gagné operate from a much more direct perspective. They believe that the teacher's task is to transmit the subject as directly as possible. Gagné's approach tends to be tightly structured, as he attempts to build directly upon earlier learning.

Finally, Robbie Case focusses on the complexity of the learning task. He believes that it is important to prevent the number of components relating to the overall learning situation from exceeding the number of components that the learner can hold in mind at one time.

Just as psychologists construct models of how the mind works, scientists construct models to explain how the world around us works. Both are combined in the currently popular constructivist approach to science education. According to this approach, teachers should identify children's existing understandings and provide opportunities for personal modification and development.

As they strive for understanding, children, like scientists, adopt personal attitudes to the task of "sciencing." It has often been suggested that school science should strive to encourage the "scientific attitude." There are convincing arguments that this may be a false image.

In this chapter, some philosophical aspects of the process of sciencing have been considered. In the next chapter, attention shifts to consideration of some practical processes that are involved when scientists — and children — practise their science.

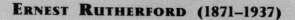

CANADIAN ACHIEVEMENTS IN SCIENCE

ERNEST RUTHERFORD (1871–1937)

E rnest Rutherford was born and received his undergraduate education in New Zealand. He spent most of his research career in England. Yet it was work carried out at McGill University in Montreal, where he was a professor of physics from 1897 to 1907, that earned him the Nobel Prize for Chemistry in 1908. Rutherford left England for Canada in 1897, one year after the phenomenon of radioactivity was discovered in France by Becquerel. By the time he returned to England ten years later, Rutherford was the major figure in a field that has revolutionized our understanding of matter.

Rutherford received his Nobel Prize largely for his work with Frederick Soddy, his colleague at McGill. Their work showed that natural radioactivity could be explained by the spontaneous breakdown of atoms to form new atoms while at the same time emitting energy as radiation. This idea is accepted today but at that time was strongly resisted by many scientists.

For almost 30 years after receiving his Nobel Prize, Rutherford continued to be a major force. His greatest contribution was probably in 1911 when he solved a problem arising from the work of two colleagues, Hans Geiger and Ernest Marsden. His results showed that alpha particles generally passed through finely beaten, solid-gold foil, but puzzlingly, about one in 2000 were deflected back more or less in the direction from which they had come. How could this be? The answer is simple, provided you have a genius like Rutherford to suggest it. Most of the alpha particles, themselves positively charged, must pass through empty space, but the occasional one must strike a small, relatively heavy, positively charged part of atoms of which the metal is composed. Thus was born Rutherford's nuclear model atom.

One of the greatest experimental scientists of all time, Rutherford was also known as an outgoing, compassionate man. He was president of a group dedicated to helping refugees flee Germany at the height of Nazi influence in the 1930s.

❏ REFERENCES

Bruner, J.S. (1960). *The process of education*. Cambridge, MA: Harvard University Press.

————. (1971). The process of education revisited. *Phi Delta Kappan* (September): 18–21.

————. (1974). *The relevance of education*. Markham, ON: Penguin.

————. (1986). The inspiration of Vygotsky. In *Actual minds, possible worlds*. Cambridge, MA: Harvard University Press.

Case, R. (1974). Structures and strictures: Some functional limitations on the course of cognitive growth. *Cognitive Psychology* 6:544–73.

————. (1978). A developmentally based theory and technology of instruction. *Review of Educational Research* 48:439–69.

————. (1980). Intellectual development and instruction: A Neo-Piagetian view. In A.E. Lawson, ed., *1980 AETS Yearbook: The Psychology of Teaching for Thinking and Creativity*. Columbus, OH: ERIC.

Driver, R. (1988). A constructivist approach to curriculum development. In P. Fensham, ed., *Development and dilemmas in science education*, 133–49. New York: Falmer Press.

Feynman, R. (1968). What is science? *The Physics Teacher* 7(6):313–20.

Gagné, R.M. (1974). *Essentials of learning for instruction*. Hinsdale, IL: Dryden Press.

Glaserfeld, E. von (1989). Cognition, construction of knowledge, and teaching. *Synthese* 80:121–40.

Inhelder, B., and J. Piaget (1958). *The growth of logical thinking*. New York: Basic Books.

Johnson-Laird, P.N. (1983). *Mental models*. Cambridge: Cambridge University Press.

Mahoney, M.J. (1979). Psychology of the scientist. *Social Studies of Science* 9:349–75.

Medawar, P. (1974). Is the scientific paper a fraud? In C. Sutton and J. Haysom, eds., *Readings in science education*, 14–16. London: McGraw-Hill.

Popper, K.R. (1959). *The logic of scientific discovery*. London: Hutchinson.

Science: A Process Approach II (1974). Lexington, MA: Ginn.

Science Curriculum Improvement Study Teacher's Guides (1970). Chicago: Rand McNally.

Travers, R.M., ed. (1973). *Second handbook of research on teaching.* Chicago: Rand McNally.

UNESCO (1980). *Handbook for science teachers.* Paris: UNESCO Press.

Vygotsky, L. (1962). *Thought and language.* Cambridge, MA: MIT Press.

CHAPTER 3

The Processes of Science

EXPERIMENTAL SCIENCE
involves the
use of
SCIENTIFIC PROCESSES
which include
SIMPLE PROCESSES
such as

Observing	Classifying	Quantifying	Communicating
Inferring		Predicting	

and

COMPLEX PROCESSES
such as

Defining Operation- ally	Interpreting Data	Formulating Models	Hypothesizing
Controlling Variables		Experimenting	

all of which can be developed
effectively in
AN ACTIVITY-BASED SCIENCE PROGRAM

◆ ◆ ◆ ◆ ◆

Science as I know it is getting excited over

the crazy idea ... trying to figure out how to

do it, playing around with equipment

and stocks, and then spending all that time

doing the experiments.

DAVID SUZUKI (1987)

In Chapter 2, you considered some aspects of the nature of science. The focus of that discussion was the process of sciencing, as viewed from a philosophical perspective. In this chapter, the process of sciencing is considered again, but this time in terms of the operational processes that are involved. This chapter is designed to help you understand the nature of these processes.

Although some science educators dispute the wisdom of adopting a strong process-oriented approach to the teaching and learning of science, most agree that it is worthwhile to pay direct attention to children's development of these processes.

At one extreme, whole curricula have been built around the development of children's learning of scientific processes. The most notable example of this is *Science: A Process Approach* (1967) and its 1974 revision *Science: A Process Approach II*, a K–6 curriculum first developed in the 1960s, following a conference of American scientists. Twelve operational science processes believed to be fundamental to the practice of science were identified at this conference. Although SAPA is little used today, perhaps because of its very structured transmission orientation, many other curriculum developers have drawn from it their inspiration for the development of scientific processes.

At the other extreme, some educators have argued strongly against a process emphasis, and programs have been developed that make no direct reference to processes.

Many science educators accept Kirkham's (1989) position that a balanced education in science entails a dynamic equilibrium involving the processes, content, and context of science. Process skills are worth developing, even when they are not the central focus of the curriculum. It is important to strike a balance between content development and process development. Process and content can be considered separately, like two sides of the same coin, but we see them as alloyed into one coherent whole. It is possible to take most science curriculum activities and use them to develop processes or content, but it is also possible to develop both processes and content through the same activity. As children develop their understanding of science content, and their ability to use science processes, these two aspects come together through children's active involvement in the context of realistic science, perhaps contrived by the curriculum developer or perhaps arising naturally as children's interests are stimulated and developed.

This chapter has three main parts: first, an activity to introduce you to the meaning of each process; second, an illustration of an activity that you can conduct with children; and third, some concrete suggestions about how to deal with challenges you may encounter as you teach these processes to children.

The following activity is designed to introduce you to twelve science processes. Before you begin, please note that although each process is identified separately in this activity, and is discussed separately later in the chapter, in any realistic science activity a number of processes are interwoven.

activity 3.1 THE EFFECT OF EXERCISE ON PULSE RATE

Begin this activity by taking your pulse. Count the number of times your pulse throbs in fifteen seconds. A pulse rate of 18 beats per 15 seconds is about average, although individuals vary quite widely.

The problem that is being investigated is: What is the relationship between amount of exercise and pulse rate? First, a form of exercise must be selected. Suppose that stepping up and down on a kitchen chair is chosen as the form of exercise for this investigation. This choice represents the first process in the activity, *defining operationally*. For the purpose of this activity, exercise is defined as the operation of "stepping up onto the seat of a kitchen chair, then stepping down again."

Suppose you decide to step up and down ten times, and further suppose that you find that your pulse rate increases. You have carried out a second process, *observing*. If quantities are involved in your observation — for example, that your pulse rate increases by, say, fifteen beats per minute — you are also using a third process, *quantifying*.

Suppose you decide, after a little thought, that the result you obtained was quite possibly part of a pattern in which pulse rate gradually increases with amount of exercise. As long as your idea is testable, your thinking represents a fourth process, *hypothesizing*.

To test your hypothesis, you need a plan. Suppose that your plan is to take your pulse before exercising; that you will then step up and down first 10, then 20, then 30, then 40, and, finally, 50 times; that you will take your pulse each time after you climb a new number of steps; and that you will allow your pulse to come back to the original rate before each new trial. As you carry out your plan, you are systematically varying a particular factor, the number of steps, to determine its effect on something else, pulse rate. In doing this, you are performing a fifth process, *experimenting*.

Suppose that you decide to organize your results, so that they will be as clear as possible, by putting them in a graph or table. When you do this, you are performing a sixth process, *communicating*.

After you have collected and organized your data, you are in a position to say something about the success of your hypothesis. Do the results support your hypothesis? Whatever you find, on the basis of your results you are able to make a statement that indicates whether or not the data support your hypothesis. When you do this, you are *interpreting data*, a seventh process.

Suppose you find from your experiment that the increase in pulse rate is directly proportional to the amount of exercise. You might wonder, "What if I stepped up and down 60 times? What would my pulse rate be then?" By extending your graph, you can make a reasoned response to this question. When you do this, you are *predicting*, an eighth process.

In collecting your data, you would probably use the same chair for each trial. What if you sometimes used a high chair and sometimes a low one? Would the results be the same? Probably not. Your results would be confused, because you would have failed to consider an additional factor that could cause a change in the results. Holding constant all factors other than the one under investigation is called *controlling variables*, a ninth process.

Your experiment can be repeated by having other people step up and down on the chair. Without testing anyone, you may expect the results to differ for different people. For example, you may expect an overweight person to show a faster rise in pulse rate. This expectation is not based on your data, because your data were obtained by testing only one person, yourself. Your expectation is based on a prior belief that overweight people often have more difficulty exercising, that they may exert a greater strain on their hearts, and that this affects their pulse rate. Such a chain of reasoning, based on prior belief, is called *inferring*. This is a tenth process.

To investigate your inference further, you must separate your subjects into at least two categories, "average weight" and "overweight." When you divide into categories, you are employing an eleventh process, *classifying.*

Pulse rate is related to heart rate; you probably have a mental model of the human circulatory system, in which your pulse represents the frequency with which the heart pumps blood through veins and arteries in a regular repeating motion. This was not always understood, but it is the accepted model today. The invention of this model represents a twelfth process, *formulating models.*

❏ Reflecting and Sharing

You have just encountered twelve commonly used science processes. As you have seen, they are not difficult to identify and they arise naturally in a typical science activity.

How available are these processes to the children you will teach? Can you jump right in, no matter how young the children in your care? Anyone who has worked with young children, and with older children or adolescents, can tell you that what children appear to be able to learn changes with age and experience. Experts with different psychological persuasions explain this differently. A Piagetian does not expect a typical 8-year-old to recognize the need to control variables when designing an experiment, because the necessary formal operational thought processes are not yet acquired. A Gagnéan also expects difficulty, but explains this difficulty in terms of the time it takes to build up the necessary subordinate competencies that come together in successfully applying the control of variables. Some disagreement with each of these positions is observed from Robbie Case, who has successfully demonstrated that 8-year-olds can exhibit the need to hold constant all variables except one, the manipulated variable, provided the children are taught how to break down the task into a sufficiently small number of components (Case 1974).

In practice, in normal settings, some science processes are more difficult for younger children than are others. This was recognized by Gagné when the SAPA curriculum was initially developed. In SAPA, six processes, namely, observing, classifying, inferring, predicting, communicating, and quantifying, are characterized as *simple processes,* while defining operationally, hypothesizing, interpreting data, formulating models, controlling variables, and experimenting are thought to be more difficult because they are *integrated processes* that involve combinations of simpler processes. Whatever *your* perspective, it is important to keep an open mind and to develop these processes as well as you can in the children you teach. The next activity will give you additional practice. It will be particularly meaningful if you have some children do it.

activity **3.2** **COLOURED SOLUTIONS**

The idea for this activity is drawn from an *Elementary Science Study* unit of the same name, although the activity is used here for a different purpose. Our purpose is to show how a simple, commonly used elementary science activity can yield a wide range of scientific processes.

You will need: four medium-sized jars; a package of salt; four transparent vials or small bottles; a medicine dropper; and four different food colours.

Half-fill one jar with water. Add a tablespoon of salt to this and stir. Repeat until no more salt will dissolve. Count the number of spoonfuls of salt that dissolve. Label this solution A. Prepare a second solution by dissolving half as much salt in the same amount of water. Label this solution B. Prepare a third solution containing half as much salt as solution B. Label this solution C. Finally, half-fill the fourth jar with water, but add no salt. Label this D. Add several drops of food colouring to solutions A, B, C, and D so that each is a different colour.

About half-fill a clear vial with liquid A. Repeat for liquids B, C, and D in three similar vials. Place the four vials on a piece of white paper. Using the medicine dropper, carefully drop one drop of each liquid from each jar into each of the liquids in the vials. In each case, your eyes should be more or less level with the vial. Determine whether each added drop sinks or floats. If a drop sinks first and then floats, call that floating.

Is there a pattern in your results? If you had some children do it, did they find a pattern? What processes are involved as children do this activity?

Source: *The ESS reader* (1970). Newton, MA: Education Development Center.

❑ Reflecting and Sharing

The following processes are involved: observing, controlling variables, communicating, and defining operationally.

First, in order to obtain accurate results it is necessary to watch carefully what happens to the drops. Thus, the process of *observing* is involved.

Second, if not controlled, a number of factors can affect the results. Some children may have difficulty because they are careless. This introduces a second process, *controlling variables*. If the height of drop varies significantly, it is difficult to get consistent results. Similarly, if several drops are squirted out in quick succession, or if the angle of dropping varies considerably, then several factors that can affect the result are not controlled. Holding these factors constant, so that a fair test is conducted, represents controlling variables. It is quite possible to arrive at the notion of a "fair test" in a situation like this without having to lead children too much. The idea of a fair test is the essence of the process of controlling variables.

A third process that is very much in evidence is *communicating*. Did you think to put your results in a table? Did the children? It is usually easier to see a pattern in results when you do. Young children, and older ones if they have not been taught to do so, will not think of setting out results in the form of a table. Yet, once they have observed that tabled results often seem to speak up for themselves as if saying, "Here I am, this is what you found out," the usefulness of the table becomes evident to children, and readily becomes second nature.

A fourth process that is also important in this activity is *defining operationally*. The critical aspect of the activity is deciding whether each particular drop of liquid sinks or floats. This judgement is sometimes difficult because some drops sink first and then rise again to the surface. Also, drops lose their identity as they rise within the larger volume of liquid and diffuse into it. Definitions for "sink" and "float" must be developed. It is appropriate to define sinking as when a drop falls to the bottom and remains there. Conversely, a drop floats either when it never falls to the bottom or when it falls but rises again. These definitions are operational definitions of floating and sinking. Note that defining operationally is often related to classifying. In this activity, application of an operational definition enables separation into two groups: sinkers and floaters. Such separation is an example of classification.

As you have seen, the four processes (observing, controlling variables, communicating, and defining operationally) occurred quite naturally in the "coloured solutions" activity. This may be as far as the activity can be extended before about Grade 5 or 6. However, it is possible eventually to get much more out of it. Up to this point your attention has been focussed on the "what?" question. You have been concerned with what happens, not *why*. When you turn your attention to "why?" a whole new world opens up. Why does one coloured liquid sink in each of the others? Why does one float on each of the others? Why did you get the particular pattern of results that you observed?

The answer is fairly obvious to young children. Heavier things sink, lighter things float. Which, of course, is not quite true! A large battleship floats in water while a small stone doesn't. But first, pursue the line of reasoning that says that the pattern of sinking and floating in the activity is directly related to the weights of the drops of liquid. This is an *inference*, because it is based directly on past experience. Assume that the red liquid sank in each of the others, that the blue liquid sank in the yellow and the green, that the yellow sank in the green only, and that the green floated in each of the others. An appropriate inference is that red is the heaviest liquid, followed in order by blue, yellow, and green. Note that this statement represents an inference, not an observation. It offers an explanation for the observations that were made. It is also important to note that the explanation follows directly from past experience. As long as you confine your thoughts to what happens when just one equal-sized drop of each liquid is dropped into each of the others, this explanation holds up perfectly well. What if the drops are different in size? Would the result be different? That would be relatively easy to check by using droppers with different-sized openings. You would find that the order of sinking and floating remains the same, whatever the sizes of the drops.

You probably realize that the key factor here is that each liquid has a different density, where density is defined as mass per unit volume. But note that "density" is a much more complicated concept than mass as it involves a relationship between two factors, mass and volume. It is easy to compare masses directly, but it is not easy to compare densities directly. It may be possible to extract from children the idea that density rather than mass is the key factor, or it may be possible to lead them to it. Either way, the suggestion of density rather than mass as the key factor is testable. As a *testable* explanation that is not derived directly from past experience, a statement such as "liquids sink in other liquids that have a lesser density and float in other liquids which have a greater density" is an example of a *hypothesis*. Note that a hypothesis must be testable. In the present case, it is readily testable, either by weighing equal volumes of the different liquids or by determining the volume of equal weights. Testing the hypothesis in either of these ways is an example of *experimenting*. Determining volumes and/or masses involves *quantifying* statements *about the variables involved*. Finally, when the results of mixing liquids of different densities have been collected, a summarizing statement is obtained. This is called *interpreting data*.

As a further check, you may want to ask the children who have got this far to forecast the results of mixing some liquids of different densities from those already considered. Such a forecast involves a further process, *predicting*. Predicting involves forecasting some future event from information about one or more related past events.

A final process that can be drawn from this activity is *formulating models*. In the discussion we moved from the simple but limited explanation that mass is the key factor to the much more useful explanation that density is what is involved. However, density is much more difficult to comprehend than mass, as it involves a relationship between two factors and can be determined only indirectly. It is possible to get around this difficulty to some extent by formulating a mental model, which in this case can be understood most easily by making a physical model, as follows:

Consider a very light container completely filled with solution A, and another identical container completely filled with solution D. Each container is closed and then weighed. Now each container is placed in a beaker of the other liquid and held so that it is fully immersed in the other liquid and is about half-way down.

Clearly, you now have a situation in which each container is displacing exactly the same volume of the other liquid. The density of liquid A is greater than the density of liquid D. You know that you have equal volumes, but A weighs more than D. What will happen if each container is now released?

Container A will sink because it is now clearly replacing an equal volume of liquid D, but it is heavier than an equal volume of liquid D. Container D will float because it is lighter than the volume of liquid A that it is replacing. This is exactly the situation when one drop of each liquid takes the place of one drop of the other. This is your mental model.

In Activities 3.1 and 3.2, you looked closely at the meaning of twelve scientific processes. Although they are potentially generalizable, content plays a role in their use. Most people apply process skills better when the content concerned is familiar to them. Some processes are more difficult for children to develop than others. You will need to help children develop what they can, without forcing those processes that give difficulty to individual children. Suggestions to help you do this are presented next.

◆ ◆ ◆ ◆ ◆

TEACHING THE SCIENCE PROCESSES
Observing

Observing involves the perception of an object or event by way of any one or more of the senses. The act of observation is not theory free, but what individuals choose to pay attention to is governed by what they believe to be important. However, children need to be taught to use the maximum number of senses possible in any observation, to be quantitative, and, where possible, to note negative evidence. If you can develop the first two aspects of observation in children by the time they leave elementary school, you will have done well. If you can just encourage the use of all of the senses, you are doing well.

Inferring

Inferring is linked very closely to observing. Inferring allows us to give meaning to observation statements by relating them to past experiences or information. You should not be surprised, then, that the ability to make appropriate inferences often depends upon prior training. For example, an experienced medical practitioner reacts quite differently to an elderly person's chest pains than might a worried spouse. The doctor infers indigestion, perhaps, while the spouse infers a heart attack. Of course, the spouse may be correct, but the more experienced physician is more likely to be correct. Children need to realize that there are

From a Teacher's Journal

In setting up scientific activities for children in the elementary classroom, it is very important to give them clear, step-by-step directions with the routines and procedures for investigations. If children are to become adept at using science processes, it is important that they understand what they are expected to do. My advice to beginning teachers is to illustrate explanations with concrete examples and give lots of guidance and practice.

In teaching the process of observing, it is good to begin by using experience charts to note children's descriptions of physical characteristics of things. Later they can do the same thing in their groups, pooling and making notes of their observations.

Asking "What if ..." questions encourages children to make hypotheses and to think of ways of setting up tests and to identify the factors they will need to keep the same (controlling variables) when they test their hypotheses. A flowchart helps them with the sequencing of the steps to follow as they work through an investigation. Recording their observations in their groups helps children to consolidate their learning experience.

Sandra Shepherd

St. John's, NF

good and bad inferences, but, most important, they should be led to understand the dangers of making "observation" statements that are really inference statements. There is a simple way to distinguish between these two kinds of statements. If a statement does not rely directly on one or more of the senses, it is not an observation statement. On the other hand, a statement that relies on past experiences rather than on one or more senses is more likely to be an inference statement.

Children need to be taught to use as many senses as possible in any observation.
This child can learn a lot about starfish by looking, touching, and smelling.

Classifying

Like observing, classifying is a process that is typically a focus of attention in the early grades, whether or not it is part of a science course. When young children are taught to identify characteristics such as colour, shape, or size, they are inevitably being taught to classify. They cannot learn "red" without learning "not red"; they cannot learn "square" without learning "not square"; they cannot learn "larger" without learning "smaller"; and so on. Such example/nonexample distinctions are not only vital in themselves but form the basis for development of classification "keys," which soon begin to be useful in elementary science and beyond. In fact, as you will see in Chapter 4, classifying is fundamental to concept formation.

Despite its apparent simplicity, classifying as a skill can become complex. Even the examples above have their difficulties. Square versus circle is an easy distinction, but square versus rectangle and circle versus eclipse are less easy. Colours have many hues. Where do the intermediate colours belong? Large and small are clearly relative terms. What is large to a young child may be small to an adult.

Classification can become even more complex. Some classifications that are introduced in the primary and elementary grades, such as living/nonliving, plants/animals, and solids/liquids/gases, depend on the identification of observable attributes. Children at this level can usually learn to make such classifications. However, other classifications, such as element/compound/mixture and physical/chemical change are not made on the basis of attributes that are directly observable. Such classifications are not likely to be understood readily by children at this level.

Quantifying

Quantifying is defined as the use of an agreed-upon unit to represent the amount of a variable involved in an activity. The unit can be conventional, such as the use of grams to represent mass. It can also be unconventional, as exemplified by the investigator who decides to measure length in terms of an arbitrary unit such as the length of a pencil. Clearly, quantifying involves the use of numbers, but it must be understood that those numbers must represent the amounts of the variables directly involved in an activity. We are quantifying when we want to know not just what happens, but also how much it happens.

Communicating

In a general sense, one important way in which humans communicate is through speech. This is just as true in science as in any other area of human endeavour. However, with the intention of emphasizing other useful means of communication, oral communication is often ignored as an example of the process "communicating." In its role as a scientific process, communicating usually means the use of tables, different kinds of graphs, and illustrations such as drawings to illustrate methods and results. Such representations soon become natural to children when they are shown how to use them. As a teacher, you need to be alert to good opportunities to demonstrate the usefulness of these means of communication. The well-known adage "one picture is worth a thousand words" is not necessarily true, but there is no doubt that tables, graphs, diagrams, and photographs can often express experimental methods and findings more clearly and succinctly than a written description.

Predicting

Predicting is the forecasting of a future event on the basis of observed regularities in past or present events. Note that predicting is not guessing. Predicting involves extending what we already know to suggest something that we can reasonably expect. One of the most important things to stress about predicting is that it is not only potentially useful but also potentially risky. The advertising media and politicians, for example, sometimes extrapolate (go well beyond their data) in persuading us to buy their products or policies. Extrapolation is necessary to predicting, but it is always potentially risky. We can never know for sure that past and present events will necessarily extend into the future. For example, the fact that inflation has not increased in the first half of a year does not mean that it will not increase in the second half. Or, consider the beginning teacher who extrapolates the teachers' salary scale for the first ten years of service and expects his or her salary to rise at the same rate for the rest of a 40-year career. Such an extrapolation will result in acute disappointment!

Hypothesizing

The word hypothesis is frequently misused. It is often represented as a guess or an educated guess. However, a hypothesis is not a guess, educated or not. A hypothesis is a tentative, testable explanation of an observed event. To be considered a hypothesis, a statement must be testable. It should always be possible to enclose a hypothesis within an "if ... then" statement. It should be possible to say "*If* [statement of hypothesis] is to be considered acceptable, *then* [test implication statement] should be observable." The use of "if ... then" statements is a good way to encourage children to write hypotheses.

Defining Operationally

There are good philosophical arguments against the use of operational definitions in science. However, it is often useful to ensure that we mean the same thing by the same terms. A trivial example of this is to ask what is "old" or "young." You can be sure you would get different answers from a 7-year-old and a septuagenarian. Or what about "driving too fast"? That depends, legally, on where you are. In some areas, you would not be able to protest against a 30 km/h limit, while in others 90 km/h is not driving too fast. A good operational definition enables ready and consistent distinction between examples and nonexamples. An operational definition is distinguishable from a theoretical definition by its ability to allow us to focus on concrete properties as the means of distinction. Clearly, this is particularly useful in the primary and elementary grades. For example, the operational definition "An acid is a substance that turns litmus red" is comprehensible to children in the elementary grades because they can perform a direct test. In contrast, the theoretical definition "an acid is a proton donor" is not comprehensible to them because no direct test is available.

Controlling Variables

In a typical report of a scientific investigation, it is common to consider three types of factors that are important to the investigation. These are referred to as *dependent, independent,* and *controlled variables.* The first two are also sometimes referred to as *responding* and *manipulated.* Terminology like this is often confusing in itself, and there is ample evidence that young children have difficulty in understanding the underlying concept of controlling variables. It is useful to encourage children to talk of controlling variables as an attempt to conduct a "fair test," perhaps avoiding substantial reference to the other terms referred to above. If you must use these other terms, be aware that there are potential problems.

Most scientific investigations involve determination of the effect of one factor, which we call the independent or manipulated variable, on another factor, which we call the dependent or responding variable. A number of possible factors may have an effect on the same dependent or responding variable. In order to determine whether any one of these possible factors really does have an effect, all of the other possible factors must be eliminated or held constant. This is what is meant by "controlling variables." The dependent variable is never "controlled," although there is a popular misconception that it is because it is the variable that potentially changes as the independent variable is changed. In this sense, the dependent variable *appears* to be under the control of the independent variable. But, *by definition,* this is not what we mean by controlling variables.

To give an example, consider a pendulum. What affects how long it takes for the pendulum to swing to and fro once? It is possible to think of several factors that may possibly affect the result, for example, the length of the pendulum; the weight of the "bob"; the amplitude (that is, how far the bob is drawn from centre before it is let go); whether the "bob" is released or is pushed. Each of these factors can be investigated singly, holding the others constant. In this investigation, the time taken for the pendulum to swing to and fro once is the dependent variable. Each of the four possible factors that *might* affect this is, in turn, the independent variable, while the three held constant are, in turn, the controlled variables. For example, when the weight of the bob is the variable that is deliberately changed it is the independent variable. Length, amplitude, and push are kept constant and are the controlled variables. When length is varied, it is the independent variable, and the weight, amplitude, and push are the controlled variables, and so on, for the other two possibilities. In each case, the dependent variable is always the time taken for the pendulum to swing to and fro once.

Interpreting Data

When scientists (and children) carry out investigations, they conclude by trying to identify patterns and relationships in their data. This is what is meant by "interpreting data." As an illustrative example, consider the pendulum activity again. If you carried out this activity, you would find that only one factor, the length of the pendulum, affects the time that it takes for the pendulum to swing to and fro. When you make this statement, on the basis of consideration of your data, you are interpreting the data.

In some instances, examination of the results of an activity may suggest that there is no relationship between the variables of interest. Such a statement is also an interpretation of the data.

Perhaps the most important aspect of teaching children to interpret data is to teach them to be careful not to make wild extrapolations beyond their data, and to be on their guard against others who do.

Experimenting

Experimenting is a compound process that typically involves many of the other processes. When you are considering the extent to which your teaching involves your students in experimenting, it is important to realize that involving children in activities does not necessarily mean that they are experimenting.

Experimenting involves selection of hypotheses, controls, and designs to illuminate the problem in question. It involves skills in planning, implementation, and interpretation. Good experimenting is a purposeful activity that is best fostered by practice and by good guidance from an insightful teacher. In helping your students plan experiments, do not tie them to the popular, yet mythical, traditional scientific method recipe. Experimenting is more dynamic than this. Teach them to consider the quality of their hypotheses. Ask for clear-cut testable hypotheses, and teach them to plan for how they will process and interpret their data before they start to collect it. Finally, when students exhibit planning difficulties, don't be too alarmed. There is evidence that they perform experiments better than they design them.

Formulating Models

Scientists often make sense of the world by explaining the unfamiliar in terms of the familiar. A scientific model is often an analogy, a line of thought that says, "Let us think about this as if it were like that. Now, it follows ..." What follows is a conceptual invention, a model. For example, the kinetic molecular theory is a

Good experimenting should involve skills in planning, implementation, and interpretation. These students record their data and collaborate on their results.

model that allows us to think about, understand, and predict observable properties of matter. It is often useful in teaching to encourage children to think in terms of such models. However, we must be careful to distinguish model building as a conceptual activity from model building as the construction of replicas. As an example, consider a balloon slowly deflating. A child might suggest this happens because little particles of gas pass through little holes in the wall of the balloon. That would be formulating a model. On the other hand, if the child had already been taught this explanation and was subsequently asked to make a physical model of this, following the teacher's directions, this would not be formulating a model.

There is more that can be said about each of these science processes, but this discussion offers a good introduction. Develop these processes with patience. Be aware that it is necessary to revisit them frequently as good opportunities arise.

◆ ◆ ◆ ◆ ◆

INTEGRATION INTO THE CURRICULUM ...
AND BEYOND

It is quite possible to teach scientific processes for their own sake, but it is more meaningful to set them in the context of real-life situations. This is often easier to arrange within the primary and elementary curriculum than in the later years of schooling, especially if a topic or project approach is adopted. Excellent examples of this are found in the British curriculum *Science 5/13* (1972) and its forerunner *Nuffield Junior Science* (1963). As well as providing many good ideas for

From a Teacher's Journal

Children have difficulty with abstractions, and sometimes flounder without set procedures to follow. Most students need to be led through the steps of an activity at first, but as they have repeated experiences throughout the year they gain in confidence.

The process that seems to present the most difficulty is controlling variables. This is taught at the start of an activity by having all the children sit in a central place, such as on a carpeted area around the teacher. The next step is to have a whole-class brainstorming session, and to list on a chart the factors they think will make a difference to the outcome of the experiment, for example, the brightness of a bulb. These factors are listed on the chart, and children decide which factor they would like to test. The main objective or purpose of the activity is then written at the top of the chart and left there to guide children in working through the investigation. Once they know what factor they are going to test, they check the list of variables on

(continued)

From a Teacher's Journal (continued)

the chart for the other things that have to be kept the same. For example, if they are testing the effect of length of wire on the brightness of the bulb, the kind of bulb and battery in the circuit must be the same, as do the type of wire, thickness of wire, and so on.

Next, working in pairs or in groups no larger than four, children carry out the procedure, recording observations and findings and drawing conclusions from their results (interpreting data). Students also individually write up an account of the activity, including the pur-pose or objective of the investigation, hypothesis, observations, and what they found out. This helps to focus the discussion when the class comes back to the carpet to discuss the results and to think of reasons for any discrepancies between the findings of the various groups.

Sandra Shepherd

St. John's, NF

a wide range of science topics, these curriculum materials frequently provide good examples of how science can develop from an introductory question that may initially seem to have little to do with science. Typical topics include: "Looking At a Snail," "Bendability," "Change," "Sunflower Plant," "Rats," "Time," and "Rainbow Reflections." The number and range of topics is restricted only by the limits of your imagination, or, more important, the imaginations of the children with whom you are working. Any such development inevitably provides many opportunities to develop science processes. This is illustrated next by reference to a typically Canadian topic, "Snow." A possible development is represented in Figure 3.1. How far you take this topic depends in part on you, but mostly on your students.

FIGURE 3.1

A Unit on Snow

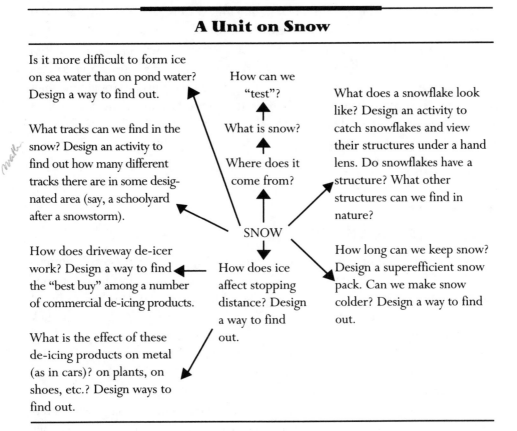

Is it more difficult to form ice on sea water than on pond water? Design a way to find out.

What tracks can we find in the snow? Design an activity to find out how many different tracks there are in some designated area (say, a schoolyard after a snowstorm).

How does driveway de-icer work? Design a way to find the "best buy" among a number of commercial de-icing products.

What is the effect of these de-icing products on metal (as in cars)? on plants, on shoes, etc.? Design ways to find out.

How can we "test"?

What is snow?

Where does it come from?

SNOW

How does ice affect stopping distance? Design a way to find out.

What does a snowflake look like? Design an activity to catch snowflakes and view their structures under a hand lens. Do snowflakes have a structure? What other structures can we find in nature?

How long can we keep snow? Design a superefficient snow pack. Can we make snow colder? Design a way to find out.

Figure 3.1 indicates a number of possible directions that can be taken. Any of these can potentially lead to further possible directions. Many lead naturally to investigations. The phrase "design a way to find out" occurs repeatedly in Figure 3.1. When there is a question relating to events in the natural and artificial world, an experiment is seldom far away.

As students begin to think about designing an experiment, they will inevitably begin to invoke several scientific processes. As they conduct the experiment, more processes are involved, and as they reflect on and process their results and communicate their findings, further scientific processes follow. It is not only easy to involve most of the processes described in this chapter in such an activity, it is difficult to avoid them. Make use of such opportunities to involve your students in real-life activities designed to investigate real problems of interest to the students themselves. That is sciencing!

Much more can be made of the unit on snow than just the application of scientific processes. It is easy to integrate the unit with other curriculum areas. It can be related to social studies, for example, through a consideration of the effect of snow clearing on city planning, or by considering the way of life of children who live in snow-free climates. It can be related to language through children's poems or stories about snow. It can be related to art and music through drawings and songs. The point being made here is that there is more to sciencing than science! Science is integrally related to other aspects of life. Further, "science for life" is illustrated particularly well by the application of the processes of science, not only within science but also in everyday life.

◆ ◆ ◆ ◆ ◆

TALKING SCIENCE

One of the scientific processes discussed in this chapter is the process "communicating." In that discussion, emphasis was placed on nonoral forms of communication. The purpose of this was to emphasize the usefulness of other means of communication, not to suggest that pupil talk is unimportant. In fact, pupil talk is considered vital as children develop their scientific understanding.

In Chapter 1, you were introduced to the concept of the teacher as reflective practitioner. The child, in the role of learner, can also be considered as a reflective practitioner.

Children who are encouraged to talk about their understandings and developing ideas are more likely to become reflective thinkers. As a teacher, you have a vital role in this process. Children must be encouraged to help each other explore personal understandings, and the teacher must be prepared to stand aside as they do this. Douglas Barnes (1976) emphasizes the need to allow children to talk without interference from the teacher:

> The teacher's absence removes from their work the usual source of authority; they cannot turn to him to solve dilemmas. Thus ... the children not only formulate hypotheses, but are compelled to evaluate them for themselves (29).

Barnes suggests that they can do this in only two ways: by testing their hypotheses against their existing view of "how things go in the world," and by going back to "the evidence."

The teacher has a dual role to play: as facilitator when needed and as interested spectator at other times. The effective teacher will encourage discussion

These students compare notes and share ideas about their experimenting.
Children who are encouraged to talk about their developing ideas together are more likely to
develop effective practices for reflective thought.

but not dominate it; will encourage children to express their ideas freely; will help them probe their own ideas and those of others; will illustrate that it is better to be wrong than silent; and will make use of their ideas whenever possible.

As a teacher, you need to be aware that science has a technical language that begins to develop even in the early years of schooling. As Richard Feynman (1968) suggests, technical language should be minimized and technical words introduced only when necessary. Some words have a different meaning in science than in their everyday use. For example, in everyday use the word "incident" refers to an event of some kind. In science, the same word may refer to a ray of light. Some technical words sound similar to common words, causing children to "hear" the wrong word. Sutton (1974), for example, cites 11-year-olds who refer to a conical flask variously as a "comical" flask, a "chronicle" flask, and a "coracle" flask. It is important to realize that language can be both a facilitator and a barrier to understanding.

◆ ◆ ◆ ◆ ◆

LOOKING BACK AND LOOKING FORWARD

Although there is no such thing as "the" scientific method, it is possible to identify a number of operational processes that occur frequently in the practice of science.

In this chapter, twelve scientific processes, namely, observing, inferring, classifying, quantifying, communicating, predicting, hypothesizing, defining operationally, controlling variables, interpreting data, experimenting, and formulating models are described. Each process is illustrated in detail, and suggestions are given both to help you teach the processes effectively and to identify and counter typical difficulties that children have as they learn to apply them.

There is more to practical and project work than performing individual process skills, but unless these skills are developed the results of children's practical work may be inadequate and misleading. Yet, doing science well is not simply a matter of performing a number of processes. It is important to involve children in whole investigations that make the need for use of the processes explicit. It is also important to realize that these processes extend beyond science to many other aspects of life and hence enable better integration of science with other components of the school curriculum.

Processes and concepts provide a dual thrust to the science curriculum. Practical science inevitably involves the application of a number of scientific processes. Scientific investigations are guided by existing concepts and yield new concepts. Processes and concepts are inextricably intertwined. The next chapter focusses on the nature and learning of scientific concepts.

CANADIAN ACHIEVEMENTS IN SCIENCE

HARRIET BROOKS (1876–1933)

Born in Exeter, Ontario, and later moving with her family to Quebec, Harriet Brooks was the first woman to be awarded a Master of Physics at McGill University and one of the leading experimental physicists of her day. In 1899, she was appointed tutor of mathematics at Victoria College in Toronto, and was also invited to join Ernest Rutherford's research group. At McGill, her experimental results were acknowledged by Rutherford as crucial to the progress of research in radioactivity. She identified the emanation from radium (the gas now called radon) as a radioactive gas of molecular weight in the 40–100 range. Her subsequent research led to the idea of the successive changes of elements, with each new element producing its own radiation.

Advanced studies during a year at Bryn Mawr College in the United States earned her a fellowship to Cambridge University, where she worked with J.J. Thomson at the Cavendish Laboratory. Back at McGill in 1903, she continued comparisons of the radioactive decay of thorium, radium, and actinium. In 1904, she showed that when a radioactive substance breaks down and radiation is released, the atom recoils in the opposite direction. Her discovery of the recoil phenomenon, later an important technique in separating the elements, was largely overlooked by the scientists of the day.

From 1904 to 1906, she taught physics at Barnard College in New York City. There she had her first encounter with what being a woman meant to her career; she broke her engagement to be married when she was told she would have to choose between career and family. After an unsettled period, she joined Marie Curie's research group in 1907 and, while there, was considered at Manchester as a candidate for the John Harling Fellowship. In a letter of recommendation for the fellowship, Rutherford referred to her as "next to Mme. Curie ... the most prominent woman physicist in the department of radioactivity." Harriet Brooks was faced again with a choice dictated by the attitudes of the day. She did not accept the fellowship; instead, she married Frank Henry Pitcher and settled down to family and social life in Montreal. She died at the early age of 56, after a long illness attributed to her exposure to radiation at a time when protection was not considered necessary.

☐ REFERENCES

Barnes D. (1976). *From communication to curriculum*. Harmondsworth: Penguin.

Case, R. (1974). Structures and strictures: Some functional limitations on the course of cognitive growth. *Cognitive Psychology* 6:544–73.

Elementary Science Study (1968). *Colored solutions*. San Francisco: McGraw-Hill.

Feynman, R. (1968). What is science? *The Physics Teacher* 7(6):313–20.

Griffiths, A.K. (1987). *The evaluation of science processes*. Toronto: Holt, Rinehart and Winston.

Kirkham, J. (1989). Balanced science: Equilibrium between context, process and content. In J. Wellington, ed., *Skills and processes in science education,* 135–50. London: Routledge.

Nuffield Junior Science: Teachers' guides, 1, 2 (1963). London: Collins.

Science 5/13 (1972). London: Macdonald Educational.

Science: A Process Approach (1967). New York: Xerox.

Sutton, C.R. (1974). Language and communication in science lessons. In C.R. Sutton & J.R. Haysom, eds., *The art of the science teacher,* 41–53. London: McGraw-Hill.

Suzuki, D. (1987). *Metamorphosis*. Toronto: Stoddart.

CHAPTER 4

Building Concepts in Science

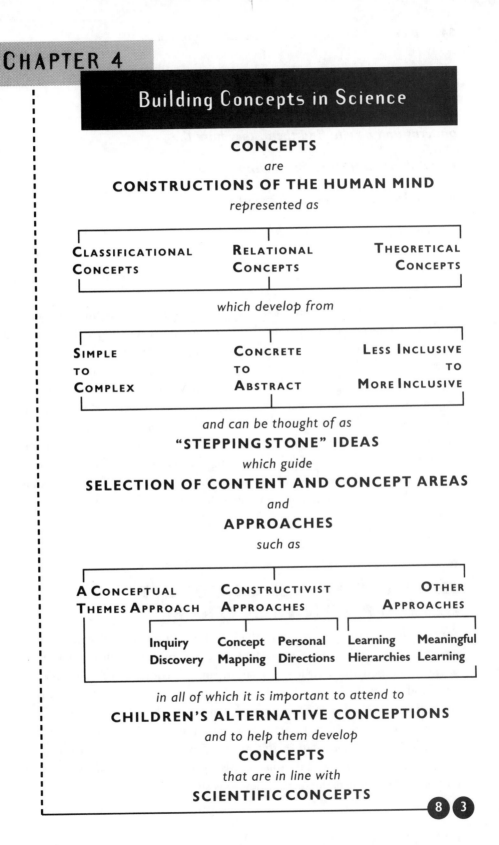

CONCEPTS

are

CONSTRUCTIONS OF THE HUMAN MIND

represented as

CLASSIFICATIONAL CONCEPTS	RELATIONAL CONCEPTS	THEORETICAL CONCEPTS

which develop from

SIMPLE TO COMPLEX	CONCRETE TO ABSTRACT	LESS INCLUSIVE TO MORE INCLUSIVE

and can be thought of as

"STEPPING STONE" IDEAS

which guide

SELECTION OF CONTENT AND CONCEPT AREAS

and

APPROACHES

such as

A CONCEPTUAL THEMES APPROACH	CONSTRUCTIVIST APPROACHES			OTHER APPROACHES	
	Inquiry Discovery	Concept Mapping	Personal Directions	Learning Hierarchies	Meaningful Learning

in all of which it is important to attend to

CHILDREN'S ALTERNATIVE CONCEPTIONS

and to help them develop

CONCEPTS

that are in line with

SCIENTIFIC CONCEPTS

◆ ◆ ◆ ◆ ◆

When children learn the importance of

patterns and how to find them, they have the

knowledge and tools to begin simplifying

and understanding a complex world.

SUSAN LOUCKS-HORSLEY ET AL. (1990)

Although the development of science process skills and the building of science concepts are explored in separate chapters, they are really inseparable both in the practice of science and in children's learning in science. As you read this chapter, continue to keep in mind the interdependence of these two kinds of outcomes. There is an intermingling of processes and concepts as children observe, classify, communicate, and set up "fair tests." Children come to their science experiences with ideas already formed and forming, and are involved in concept building as they try to make sense of their observations of natural and physical phenomena. In turn, they become more adept at using science process skills as they pursue new questions and plan ways of testing and refining ideas. Concept building and process skill development together form the framework for organizing the curriculum and planning instruction.

◆ ◆ ◆ ◆ ◆

THE IMPORTANCE OF CONCEPT DEVELOPMENT IN SCIENCE

Concept development is central to the learning and practice of science, and, in a very real sense, is the most important outcome of curriculum and instruction. Science, as a body of knowledge, is an organized, connected framework of concepts and conceptual themes that have been abstracted over the centuries as a result of humankind's struggle to explain, understand, and learn from the natural and physical world. If children are to function effectively in the world, they should become familiar with a selection of concepts from the major scientific disciplines. The challenge for educators is to find ways of organizing curriculum and instruction so that the learner develops such concepts.

The organization of science into concepts and conceptual themes makes manageable the fantastic growth of knowledge in all areas of science. In each science discipline there are recognizable patterns of organization, with a limited number of major scientific concepts giving structure to each discipline. New facts and concepts are linked to the central ideas of the major disciplines and to broad themes such as energy, systems and interactions, and patterns of change, which transcend disciplinary boundaries. Children engage in a similar kind of abstracting process as they, too, try to order their experiences and learn from them. They construct ideas in much the same way that scientists construct theoretical entities, and for the same purpose — to seek explanations and understanding of the world around them. Through the experiences provided in the primary and elementary grades, and the opportunities given to think about what they observe and experience, children can begin to build a foundation of ideas. These ideas lead to a functional understanding of scientific concepts and to scientific literacy in adult life.

Unfortunately, traditional ways of teaching science, and science curriculum materials in which highly complex and abstract concepts are introduced at increasingly earlier years of schooling, have often prevented adequate concept development. Children are left with little choice but to try to "learn" concepts at a superficial level by memorizing definitions rather than developing understanding inductively through experience. Central to concept building in the early school years are real, concrete experiences in science with real, concrete materials. These experiences should be tied to the lives of children, involving them from the start with a desire to know more and allowing them to see relationships between objects and events that they have had no reason to believe are connected. With repeated and varied experiences, they begin to see patterns in these common occurrences and acquire a better understanding of natural and physical phenomena.

◆ ◆ ◆ ◆ ◆

WHAT IS A CONCEPT?

Why is it important for you to plan science lessons that stress the development of concepts rather than the learning of discrete facts? One reason already mentioned is the value of concepts in reducing to manageable size the many diverse stimuli that impinge upon our consciousness. New information and new observations and experiences are more meaningful and are retained longer when they are linked to growing concepts rather than learned in isolation. The best way to begin thinking about scientific concepts, or any concepts for that matter, is to focus on their categorizing and integrating functions.

Attempts to define a concept suggest that:

1. A concept is an idea or generalization based on perceived regularities or essentially common features of a class of objects, events, or other concepts. These regularities or patterns help us to bring order to experience and explain the world around us.

2. Identifying and categorizing these names or symbols help us think about the concepts and talk to one another about them. Such communication is an important aspect of learning. Since concepts are the tools of thought, communication, and understanding and are the basic units of learning (Pines 1980), they are extremely important to the teacher and the student.

3. Concepts — gradually constructed through many related experiences, with new learning linked to what the learner knows and facts related to growing concepts — are flexible, subject to change, and never really complete. Concepts are in a continual state of refinement or progressive differentiation. This is true of the major concepts that make up the structure of science, as well as the concepts that form in the mind of a student.

4. There are different levels of concepts. Low-level or concrete concepts are at the base of the hierarchy, and high-level or abstract concepts are at the top. There is a progression from simple to complex and also from less inclusive to more inclusive as new understandings are added to growing concepts. Small children's concepts are limited to a few objects or events and to what is directly observable through the senses. As children grow older, their concepts become more inclusive and encompass a wider range of instances. As they progress through life, children also attain different levels of understanding. Their growing concepts enable them to use past experience to deal with new experiences.

Types of Concepts

In addition to thinking of concepts as arranged in a hierarchy from concrete to abstract, simple to complex, and less inclusive to more inclusive, it is useful to think of three types of concepts — *classificational, relational,* and *theoretical.* Each type of concept has implications for the level of schooling where it is most appropriate. Their names hint at their meanings.

Classificational Concepts

Classificational concepts are defined by the presence or absence of certain qualities. Classificational concepts are important in the primary grades as children make sense of the world by grouping similar objects and events into categories. Examples of classificational concepts are: circle, square, rock, mineral, insect, mammal. The ability to classify objects develops in the primary years. Classifying on the basis of one attribute occurs in the first year of school, whereas the development of classification schemes based on two or more variables occurs with most children in the second or third year of school. Children's understandings are enhanced as they progress through the grades and grow in the ability to form more sophisticated concepts. For example, after placing a number of materials in the pathway of an electric circuit and noting whether the bulb lights or does not light, Grade 4 children classify the materials as either conductors or nonconductors of electricity. With repeated experiences, they come to a tentative generalization: Metals conduct electricity; most nonmetals do not.

RELATIONAL CONCEPTS

Relational concepts express relationships between other concepts. Relational concepts are of different levels of difficulty for children. A concept showing a relationship between concrete concepts, such as the concept that living things need food for growth, is relatively easy for children to develop. More difficult for them

These students sort buttons into categories according to shape, and progress from classification on the basis of one attribute to classification schemes based on a number of attributes.

is the concept of the pitch of a sound as a function of frequency or speed of vibrations. More difficult still is the concept of density defined as the mass of a substance per unit volume.

Although for young children the concept of "living things" takes time to develop, the needs of living things can be identified readily with food and growth because of the relevance of these ideas to their everyday lives. The concept of a relationship between pitch and frequency of vibrations evolves through many new and related experiences; the development of the concept is helped by the fact that pitch and vibrations are both observable through the senses. Density is an abstraction expressed as a mathematical relationship in terms of observable concepts — mass and volume. According to Piagetian theory, relational concepts involving mathematical and proportional reasoning require formal operational thought. These concepts present difficulty for most elementary students. Similarly, relationships between abstractions may also be beyond the realm of most elementary students because of their need for concrete referents at this stage of development.

THEORETICAL CONCEPTS

Theoretical concepts are abstractions explained in terms of underlying theories. Curriculum should be organized so that the experiences children have in the primary and elementary grades will lead to an understanding of these more abstract ideas when they are needed later in life.

Like all concepts, theoretical concepts are constructions of the human mind and are always undergoing refinement. For example, each individual holds a personal concept of an atom, and it is likely that it is different now from the concept that person held earlier in life. The theoretical concept of the atom has progressed from the Greek concept of an atom as the smallest observable piece of a substance to Dalton's conception of atoms as small, invisible, indivisible balls; to the Bohr concept of an atom as being like a miniature solar system containing two kinds of smaller particles; to a wave-mechanical concept; and to a concept of atom as containing many smaller particles, some of which have strange properties such as "charm." It is unlikely that you hold a modern physicist's concept of an atom. Nor is it likely that tomorrow's physicists will entirely accept today's conceptions.

activity 4.1 **CONCEPT TYPES**

The following statements include examples of each of the three types of concepts. Identify the type of concept represented in each statement.

A. A kindergarten class is learning how the months of the year can be grouped as different seasons. *C*

B. A Grade 1 class is learning to separate objects according to colour, shape, and size. *C*

C. A Grade 2 class is learning that living things are distinguished from nonliving things according to properties such as independent movement, reproduction, and the need for food. *C*

D. A Grade 3 class is learning how solids, liquids, and gases differ in their physical characteristics. *C*

E. A Grade 4 class is learning how to measure the speed of a moving object. *R*

F. A Grade 5 class is learning about predator–prey relationships and how a change in the size of one population in a food web affects the size of each population in the web. *R*

G. A Grade 6 class is learning how scientists use fossil records to reconstruct changes in the earth's environment dating back millions of years. *T*

H. A Grade 7 class is using a kinetic molecular model to explain expansion and contraction of gases. *T*

❑ Reflecting and Sharing

The first four statements represent classificational concepts. Each statement represents separation into groups according to observable characteristics. Most concepts in the primary grades are classificational in nature.

Statement E involves the concept of speed. This concept can be understood only by relating the distance travelled by an object to the time taken for the object to move that distance. As such, it is a relational concept.

Statement F is another relational concept. It can be formed only by combining two simpler concepts. Without a prey there can be no predator, and without a predator there can be no prey. The kind of argument involved in predicting the effect of changing one population in a food web on other populations in the web is also relational, involving argument of the kind, "If I do this, then this follows." In a typical food web problem, this argument would be repeated a number of times, as each change has implications for other populations. In effect, a food web is a network of relational propositions.

The last two statements involve more than sorting into groups or combining two or more other concepts. They involve understanding that scientists weigh possibilities to arrive at plausible explanations that cannot always be verified directly, and that may or may not be correct. Theoretical concepts aren't likely to be taught in the primary grades and are not commonly taught in the elementary grades. However, terms such as atom, gene, gravity, energy, and so on are frequently encountered in curriculum materials for these levels. The task is to engage children in many related physical experiences so that understanding of these theoretical concepts increases as children progress through the grades into the middle school years.

Types of Concepts: Approaches to Instruction

The three kinds of concepts described here require different approaches to teaching. For this reason, it is useful for teachers to consider the *type* of concept when planning instruction.

CLASSIFICATIONAL CONCEPTS

Classificational concepts require that a number of examples and nonexamples of the concepts be given to students. For example, a child won't learn the concept "blue" without being exposed to several blue objects of different shapes and sizes and a corresponding number of objects that are not blue. Similarly, children need concrete experiences with a variety of objects in order to be able to separate those that are attracted by a magnet from those that are not attracted by a magnet. Do the following first-grade activity with a group of children.

---

activity 4.2 GOING FISHING

1. Arrange children at tables in groups of three or four. Place a plastic bowl or "fishpond" containing an assortment of small objects — buttons, coins, popsicle sticks, paper clips, washers, pieces of chalk, etc. — in the centre of each table.
2. Supply each child with a "fishing pole" made from a wooden dowel to which is attached a piece of string with a magnet at the other end.
3. Have ready for each group a YES tray and a NO tray, and have the children sort the objects on the appropriate tray.
4. After the first exploratory play, add things to the pond and have children predict which will be attracted to the magnet and which will not.
5. Record class results on an experience chart, and encourage children to choose other objects to test so that these results can be added to the YES and NO columns on the chart. To make the chart meaningful to children, include on the chart a sketch of each object, together with its printed name.
6. Encourage children to generalize about what they have learned.

RELATIONAL CONCEPTS

Relational concepts require students' prior understanding of the component concepts that combine to form the new concept. For example, understanding that "the angle of incidence equals the angle of reflection when light is reflected in a mirror" requires understanding of the component concepts angle, angle of incidence, angle of reflection, and normal.

activity
4.3

PATHS OF LIGHT

Follow the steps in the *Addison-Wesley Science, Level 5* activity reproduced in Figure 4.1 to see how this fairly sophisticated relational concept can be derived from simple experiences with light beams, mirrors, and folded paper.

FIGURE 4.1

Paths of Light

Something to Try

Compare the path of light before it hits a mirror with the path after it hits. How is it the same? How is it different?

To find out you will need a mirror, paper, crayons, scissors, and a flashlight. Tape black paper over the end of the flashlight. Cut a slit from the centre to the edge of this paper. When the light shines through the slit onto the paper, it will make a narrow path.

Next, fold a sheet of paper in half. Open it out flat. Lay it in front of an upright mirror. The edge should be even with the mirror. And the fold should be in line with the centre of the mirror. A small mirror will stand upright if you tape it to a book or block of wood.

Shine a beam of light across the surface of the paper. Aim it where the fold and mirror meet. Can you see a second path of light leaving the mirror? Using a crayon or pencil, trace both paths. Then cut the paper along the paths you have drawn. What is the shape of the cutout paper? Fold the cutout piece along the same fold line. Do the pieces on both sides of the fold match?

Do this again several times. Put a new piece of folded paper in position next to the mirror each time. And hold the flashlight in a different position. But be sure the light is always hitting the mirror at the fold line. Are the angles on each side of the fold always the same?

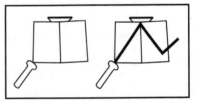

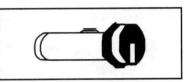

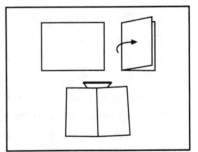

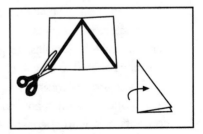

Source: V.N. Rockcastle et al. (1984). *Addison-Wesley Science, Teacher's Guide, Level 5,* 200. Menlo Park, CA: Addison-Wesley.

THEORETICAL CONCEPTS

When teaching theoretical concepts, it isn't possible to provide concrete examples and directly observable attributes. For this reason, models are often used to illustrate theoretical concepts. Think back to the Grade 1 activity on magnets. In subsequent years, the concept of magnetic attraction is revisited and expanded as children discover that magnets attract objects through materials and that magnets attract objects from a distance. At some point in their schooling, children may be given the name "magnetic field" to designate the space in which a magnetic force exists. The following demonstration is used traditionally to add concreteness to this theoretical concept.

activity 4.4   MAPPING MAGNETIC FIELDS

◆ Place a bar magnet on the stage of an overhead projector.
◆ Place a sheet of transparency film over the magnet.
◆ Sprinkle iron filings slowly onto the film, and note the patterns and direction in which the iron filings line up around the magnet.
◆ Make a drawing to record what you see.
◆ Use pairs of bar magnets and more iron filings to show the patterns near pairs of magnets, as like poles repel and unlike poles attract each other.

❑ Reflecting and Sharing

As you look back on Activities 4.2, 4.3, and 4.4, you are aware of differences in complexity of the types of concepts and corresponding differences in the levels of difficulty that they might pose for learners. You may judge the "fishing pond" activity as appropriate for introducing the concept of magnetism to first graders. You may have some questions about whether the "paths of light" activity is appropriate for most children in Grade 5, or whether it should be placed at a higher grade level in a curriculum plan for elementary science. What about the concept of magnetic field? And at what point in their schooling could the domain theory of the structure of magnets (the theory that a magnet may consist of many sets of particles, called "domains," aligned in the same direction) be used to explain observations related to magnets?

These are all concerns you will have, as teachers, when you plan your lessons. Your concern with many concepts that show relationships between other concepts and with theoretical concepts such as field, atom, molecule, gene, energy, gravity, and others is that, according to Piagetian theory, understanding of these concepts requires formal thought. Similarly, according to Piaget, most 11- to 13-year-olds are still thinking in a concrete operational mode, while some 13-year-olds may be making the transition to formal thought in some aspects of their thinking, and others may not. A small proportion of this age group is able to manipulate abstract ideas and entertain a number of different viewpoints other than their own. However, the majority are not, and this determines the way you structure learning activities.

As mentioned earlier, there is also the danger that because of the level of difficulty of such concepts, children may memorize definitions. Verbalizations or definitions and premature naming of concepts by students are often mistaken for understanding.

One point should be understood very clearly before you focus on the implications of this for instruction. It has to do with the constructivist nature of concept development and the tentative nature of our understandings as our concepts are continually open to change and refinement:

> All concepts are constructions of the mind. Concepts are more or less useful to us, and we may decide to retain some and discard others. We may learn concepts largely through our own efforts, or they may be imposed on us in the sense that we may be led by other people to form some concepts and not others. But we must not forget that all concepts are constructs, and that our personal and collective concepts are never likely to be fixed and unchanging.

The question is: Who makes the construction? If the answer is the teacher, then the curriculum will be transmission-oriented and a transmission-oriented psychology will prevail. If the child is helped to discover or construct concepts for himself or herself (although in reality those discoveries are largely contrived by the teacher or text), then the approach will be transactional. If the answer is that children will be encouraged to create concepts largely through their own efforts, with minimal interference from teacher or text, then the approach will be transformational.

Of course, in the reality of classroom life, real students following real curricula in real schools with the aid of real teachers will be exposed to a mixture of approaches varying with the particular content under study. In what follows, you will consider how concepts are formed and how the development of process skills is inextricably interwoven with the development of concepts. You'll explore the views of different educators on how curriculum and instruction should be structured to facilitate concept development. You'll also become familiar with a portion of the voluminous evidence that now exists about the alternative conceptions that children bring to their experiences in science, and appreciate the need to work toward changing these conceptions so that they are more in line with scientific concepts. Consider, first of all, how concept formation begins in early childhood, and then think about how children's engagement in school experiences encourages the development of scientific concepts and prepares them to continue to expand on these concepts throughout life.

◆ ◆ ◆ ◆ ◆

HOW CONCEPTS ARE FORMED

Concept development begins within the early months of life. Nathan Isaacs, in a classic article written in 1962 and reprinted later in a collection of readings on primary science (Richards and Holford 1983), insists that the

> basic essentials of the methods that build up science ... are not a late and sophisticated discovery of the human mind, but a crucial part of its initial equipment. They are put to vital use during the earliest years of every infant. They actually build up in his mind, tier upon tier, a first fundamental scheme of knowledge, all new to him, but mainly dependable, precisely in the sense that it can be acted upon and further built upon (106).

What Isaacs is describing is the process of concept development in early childhood. He points to the need for the primary school to take advantage of these basic active learning drives as well as the "finding out" questions of young children. Concept building continues in a more organized way as the school fosters the interests and activities that are the "living roots from which growth towards developed science can spring" (107).

Gough (1977) emphasizes the need for children to be actively involved, physically and intellectually. She suggests that "children acquire concepts over time as they are actively involved in learning experiences which invite them to explore their environment, engage in play, use all their senses, manipulate objects, investigate, inquire and obtain knowledge through the use of their own minds" (2).

Lundgren (1979) views concept formation in children as an "open-ended process that begins through concrete experiences in early infancy. Children use their senses ... and observe and handle, classify and compare, verify and explain, and finally generalize" (39). She suggests that the process is a gradual one, involving irregular stages of limited comprehension along the way.

Simply stated, the process of concept development begun in infancy continues for children as you take advantage of their natural curiosity and inclination to explore, and as you provide concrete experiences designed to build a foundation of ideas that lead, much later, to understandings of theoretical concepts. Through the openness in your classroom and the way you set up conditions for them to observe, gather evidence, record, classify, and compare, children begin to see common features and regularities in a class of objects, events, and situations. When this happens they become able to generalize about certain parts of their world — to think about their experiences, construct meaning from them, and form concepts that are extended through repeated and related experiences.

"Stepping Stone" Ideas

Ann Squires (1980) refers to beginning concepts or emerging understandings as "stepping stone ideas" from which "official scientific ideas" later develop. She suggests that it is important that the patterns children see, the regularities they perceive, and the ideas they develop should be their own, expressed in their own words, by talking and writing, and perhaps by drawing and modelling, all of which facilitate concept development. Quoting a 10-year-old's description of science as "finding out about things" (investigating) and "saying what you think about things" (understanding), she emphasizes the connection between these two aspects of science. The relationship between investigating and the development of understanding is represented in Figure 4.2.

Squires suggests that as children are involved in scientific ways of investigating, they develop, revise, and test their understandings of the natural and physical world and gradually acquire more sophisticated understandings of scientific concepts. Using the concept of density as an example, she shows how children take steps toward understanding the accepted scientific concept through repeated, unhurried encounters with related experiences, coupled with opportunities to think through what is happening. A child's sequence of ideas might flow like this (Squires 1980):

1. "Big things are heavy and small things are light" (weight depends upon size).
2. "Some big things are light and some small things are heavy" (weight depends upon size but also on something else).
3. "Certain materials like plastics are light and other materials like metals are usually heavy" (weight depends upon size and upon the material).
4. "We can make a fair test of weight by weighing equal-sized pieces of different materials."
5. "We can make a fair test by calculating the weight of 1 cm^3 of each material."

FIGURE 4.2

What Is Science?

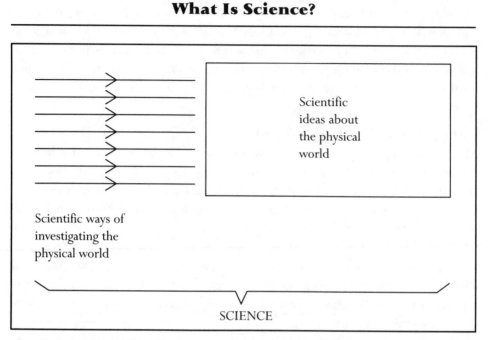

Scientific ideas about the physical world

Scientific ways of investigating the physical world

SCIENCE

Source: A. Squires (1983). What is science for primary school children? In C. Richards and D. Holford, eds., *The teaching of primary science: Policy and practice,* 57–58. Sussex: Falmer Press.

6. "We call the weight of 1 cm³ of a material its density and to calculate density we divide the mass by the volume of a piece of material."
7. "The density of a material is related to the characteristics of the atoms and molecules of which it is built up" (57–58).

This journey is the foundation on which the scientific concept of density may be built. The idea that big things are heavy and small things light is the starting point for most children. A large, light piece of plastic is an anomaly and stimulates the child to continue the journey. By the end of elementary school, children may have progressed to the notion that "we can make a fair test of weight by weighing equal-sized pieces of different materials." The remaining steps await the middle school years, or later.

Selection of Content

When you think back to Activities 4.2 and 4.4, you can see the similarity between Squires's "stepping stones ideas" and students' progression from beginning awareness of magnetic and nonmagnetic materials toward eventual understanding of concepts such as magnetic field and, much later, the domain theory of magnetism. The question for you as a teacher is how to select the learning experiences that have the greatest potential for concept development.

Wynne Harlen (1978, 1985, 1987) addresses some of the problems of selecting learning experiences that are developmentally appropriate yet intellectually challenging. The activities for students should be concrete, in that they involve the manipulation of concrete materials and are meaningful and relevant to students' lives. Harlen suggests that the child's ability to see patterns in the natural world grows as new facts and experiences are linked to an evolving structure. The ability to conceptualize from related experiences becomes a powerful learning tool that can lead to "habits of mind" that can be applied to lifelong learning — to *science for life*.

CONTENT VERSUS CONCEPTS

Harlen and Jelly (1985) distinguish between content and concepts. *Content* is the "subject matter of an activity or topic, the particular objects, materials and events that it concerns." For example, content may include observing a mealworm culture over a number of weeks or setting up a snail terrarium to observe the growth, movement, and reproduction of snails. The *concepts* are the "ideas which these activities help children to build [and] which have a wider relevance than just to the particular content studied" (52). The concepts that are built from the snail and mealworm experiences relate to the wider context of the needs, behaviour, and life cycles of living things. The concepts or important ideas are the first consideration in the teaching of concepts. The content is chosen to facilitate children's understanding. The same concept can be taught through many different activities or topics, and can be reinforced in a variety of ways. This range and variety are necessary so that patterns and generalizations emerge from the investigations.

Think about the relationship between content and concepts as you review the discussion of outcomes for science learning in Chapter 1. In that chapter, you identified classroom experiences that would be useful for developing outcomes related to concept development. These experiences are used as a starting point for the next activity.

- - - - - - - - - - - - - - -

activity 4.5 BUILDING CONCEPTS

The following are classroom activities that you identified in Chapter 1 as having potential for concept development:

(a) A Grade 3 class investigates objects that produce sound and finds that sound is produced by objects that vibrate.

(b) To illustrate how sensory inputs are transmitted through the nervous system, Grade 5 children stand in line and hold hands. Starting at one end, each child squeezes the right hand of the next child as soon as his or her own right hand has been squeezed.

(c) Grade 4 children perform a number of activities designed to show the existence of air pressure.

Working on your own, identify from the descriptions in statements (a), (b), and (c) some of the concepts that children can be helped to build. Add to the experiences in each of these statements any other related activities you can think of to help children develop these concepts.

❏ Reflecting and Sharing

Your answers will vary. You may have come up with an all-inclusive concept for each statement, such as (a) sound, (b) the nervous system, and (c) air pressure. Or you may have suggested concepts that are a little more explicit or that indicate relationships, such as (a) sound as vibrations, (b) stimulus-response in nerve pathways, and (c) air exerts pressure on things. The more general and inclusive the concept, the greater the need to break it down into smaller concepts and to plan a variety of classroom experiences for children that gradually lead to understanding.

The following are some additional classroom activities and some of the concepts that could be learned. Compare them with yours and then make a more complete list of the activities.

(a) From noting the effect of striking a ruler held in place at one end, or from sounds produced by plucking stretched rubber bands or from blowing across tin whistles, etc., children could learn the following concepts:

- ◆ When something moves back and forth, it produces vibrations.
- ◆ These vibrations are detected by the human ear as sound.
- ◆ Sounds differ; some are high and some are low.
- ◆ High sounds are produced when vibrations are fast; low sounds are produced when vibrations are slow.

(b) After a series of repeated experiences with the hand-squeeze activity (in which children propose and test various hypotheses on how to decrease the time taken for the stimulus to pass along the line), these concepts may emerge:

- ◆ It takes a certain amount of time for an impulse (stimulus) to pass along a nerve path and for a muscle to react to the impulse (response).
- ◆ The length of time between stimulus and response is called the "reaction time."

- Average reaction time is calculated by dividing the time taken for the hand-squeeze by the number of students.
- After the first few trials, more practice does not improve reaction time.

(c) From several experiences, including scooping air into plastic bags; blowing air into balloons; lifting stacks of books by blowing into a plastic bag beneath the books; sitting on inflated garbage bags; blowing up balloons inside large juice cans and lifting the cans holding onto the necks of the balloons; and observing the effect of air on a large sheet of cardboard as it is dropped from a horizontal position, the following concepts may develop:

- Air is real; there is something inside the bag that is as real as water or pebbles.
- Air inside a plastic bag seems to push in all directions.
- Air can lift things up.
- Air can slow things down.
- The greater the surface area on which air pushes, the greater the push.

In each case, you have recorded specific activities or *content* you could choose, and listed the *concepts* that these activities can help children to build. It is easy to think of other activities to help to extend the learning and make the concepts more inclusive. When selecting these activities, you are extending the exposure to similar experiences that children have had in earlier grades, and anticipating other learning experiences that will follow.

Selection of Concept Areas

Harlen (1985) proposes the following criteria when selecting concept areas for primary and elementary science:

TABLE 4.1

Selection of Concept Areas

Relevance to everyday life	Concept areas should relate to children's everyday experience, e.g., properties of matter such as colour, size, shape, texture, instead of things they cannot see (atoms, molecules) and classifications (acids, bases, salts) they aren't aware of.
Developmental appropriateness	Concept areas should be at a developmental level appropriate to the children. Concrete concepts, e.g., pushes and pulls, mass, volume, provide a foundation for understanding abstractions, e.g., gravity, density. *(continued)*

Table 4.1 (continued)

Ability to be tested scientifically	Concept areas should be scientific ones accessible to children and testable using science process skills, e.g., observing, making hypotheses, setting up fair tests. Concepts such as the effects of light and water on plant growth should be capable of being tested through further observations, pooling and interpreting data, further reading and study of other variables that influence plant growth.
Preparation for later learning in science	Concepts introduced at the primary level should be able to be extended for further learning in science. For example, concepts developed through concrete experiences with various forms of energy (light, sound, magnetism, and electricity) should lead to a broad, generalized concept of energy in the junior-high years.

✍ From a Teacher's Journal

Problems with learning arise when children try to learn new concepts by rote rather than through the physical experiences so necessary in the primary and elementary grades. Concepts are best learned through experiences in science that allow children to be active learners and to work co-operatively with others. At the same time, they develop thoughtful reasoning processes, and there is also a great probability of success and growth of self-esteem.

The thinking strategy "I know ... I wonder ... I learned" allows teachers to access prior knowledge and to find out what the children are interested in learning. From the questions generated, activities can be planned to help them solve problems they feel are relevant and important to them. Concepts are meaningful when they are derived from experience and ideas can be linked to prior knowledge.

Sharron Cooke

Richmond, BC

In Chapter 9, you will examine in detail the resources that are available to you to help with the process of concept development. Whatever resources you use, you will find that a well-balanced curriculum plan will span a variety of science areas, with basic concepts developed in each of these areas as children progress through the grades. With careful planning, there is ample time over the primary and elementary years for the gradual consolidation of ideas.

The next activity invites you to browse through some of the curriculum materials in your library to see how the materials are organized for concept development.

---

activity 4.6 CHECKING SCOPE AND SEQUENCE

1. Select a teacher's guide for any level of an elementary science program.
2. Check the introductory pages to see how the content is organized for concept development. Is there a balance among the major science areas?
3. Browse through one of the units to see whether the ways in which concepts are developed satisfy the other criteria proposed by Harlen — concreteness, attention to prior knowledge, relevance to life, testability, etc.

❏ Reflecting and Sharing

Notice that some of the criteria relate to the *development of the concept areas,* while others focus on the general *intellectual development of the learner.* The two emphases reflect different views of educators as to how curricula and instruction should be organized for concept development. As a teacher, you need to be aware of these views and how they are translated into various approaches and suggestions for instruction.

◆ ◆ ◆ ◆ ◆

APPROACHES TO CONCEPT DEVELOPMENT

The balance among science areas is often referred to as the *scope* of the curriculum, whereas the vertical organization, or the way concepts are ordered for children's learning, is referred to as the *sequence* of the curriculum. The scope and sequence of the curriculum are related closely to an approach to concept development that depends on the development of themes of related concepts, and is known as a *conceptual themes approach.*

A Conceptual Themes Approach

The conceptual themes approach is associated with *The Process of Education* (Bruner 1960), the report of the Woods Hole conference of scientists and educators that initiated the curriculum reform of the 1960s. At that conference, and in the programs that were subsequently developed, the emphasis was on conveying the structure of the discipline. The new curricula were based on what the authors believed to be the most fundamental concepts that give structure to a discipline: "the concepts, theories, laws and modes of inquiry" (Hurd 1970). The arrangement of concepts in conceptual themes remains a major approach to the development of curriculum. In programs based on this approach, conceptual strands in earth–space science, life science, and physical science are developed vertically through the grades.

The arrangement of content within developing conceptual themes provides a logical organization for the curriculum. New learning can be linked to old and related to a developing conceptual theme. Conceptual themes provide a sense of continuity and support. Without such a structure, new concepts may take on the character of isolated bits of information. With such a structure, existing concepts develop into revised and extended concepts. The conceptual themes approach reinforces the idea that concepts are not formed in isolation and, in a practical sense, encourages the understanding that concepts develop continuously, and that they are intertwined with other concepts. The importance of such a developing pattern is captured by Schwab (1974):

> In brief, the structures of the disciplines are twice important to education. First, they are necessary to teachers and educators: they must be taken into account as we plan curriculum and prepare our teaching materials; otherwise, our plans are likely to miscarry and our materials to misteach. Second, they are necessary in some part and degree within the curriculum, as elements of what we teach. Otherwise, there will be failure of learning or gross mislearning by our students (163).

A growing trend in elementary science is to build curricula that nurture conceptual understanding (Loucks-Horsley et al. 1990) by incorporating major scientific topics and themes into transdisciplinary study topics for children.

Project 2061 — a national effort begun in 1989 by the American Association for the Advancement of Science (AAAS) — identifies six common themes that pervade science, technology, and mathematics. The themes are systems, models, constancy, patterns of change, evolution, and scale. Project 2061 is named for the year in which Halley's comet will next return. It is an attempt to define what the well-educated citizen should know at that point in the twenty-first century.

The Canadian authors of *Explorations in Science* (Campbell et al. 1992) have selected five major themes: form and function, patterns and cycles, systems and interactions, energy, and change through time. In the teacher's guide for level four, the authors present the following rationale for the organization of the program in conceptual themes:

> Themes are the big ideas of science. These themes transcend disciplinary boundaries and show the interconnections of concepts in various units of study. As students experience different facets of themes throughout the year's study and through succeeding years, they become increasingly motivated to transfer and apply basic knowledge and concepts. As well, they take an integrative approach to learning that will extend to their daily lives (11).

As with all curriculum approaches, there are risks involved in using the conceptual themes approach to concept development. For adequate concept development, themes must be developed coherently and consistently. Most elements of the planned curriculum must be included or, all too easily, the structure is lost, and, since the themes become inevitably intertwined, the loss would not be restricted to a particular theme.

Constructivist Approaches

In the constructivist view, children are actively involved in generating ideas, linking newly generated ideas with prior knowledge and continually checking and restructuring knowledge through further learning experiences.

New programs with a constructivist approach to concept development tend to cover fewer concepts in greater depth. They recognize the importance of time for unhurried explorations and investigations, time to mull over emerging ideas and plan ways to test them. Children need time to discover likenesses and differences as they linger over the shell collection in the learning centre. They need time to add to the collection of floaters and sinkers some interesting objects of their own choosing, or to design their very best model of a foilboat, working intuitively at first, and then with the knowledge that comes from experience. They need time in the elementary years, as Osborne and Freyberg (1985) point out, to rearrange their ideas, to reinterpret information, to draw different inferences, and to try out alternative ideas. In short, students need to learn how to learn, to initiate a process that will go on throughout their lives. This is the essence of the constructivist view of learning — that learning occurs through active involvement inside children's minds, rather than by being imposed from outside.

This student has been given plenty of time to concentrate on his work and try out new ideas. Children need time to mull over emerging ideas and plan ways to test them.

Many of the approaches that have their primary focus on the learner have elements of constructivism, although some are more constructivist than others. A major criterion is the extent to which children are responsible for their own learning.

Heading the list of constructivist approaches are curricula based on an *inquiry–discovery approach*. Inquiry–discovery approaches to curriculum and instruction have great potential for encouraging individual learners to use their minds to solve problems and construct new ideas. Teachers using this approach, rather than explain concepts right away, facilitate students' construction of ideas by making materials available and posing questions that initiate inquiry. As the investigations proceed, more questions are posed that encourage children to continue their explorations and to think deeply about their observations and experiences. As children revise and test and revise again, they arrive at different levels of understanding. A *developmental approach* focusses on the learner and attempts to match learning experiences to Piagetian stages of development and to involve students actively in their own learning. A *concept mapping approach* encourages children to learn how knowledge is constructed and to establish relationships between what they know and the new concepts to be learned. A *personal directions approach* allows concept development to begin with children's interests and creatively reinforces science concepts as disciplinary barriers are freely crossed.

AN INQUIRY–DISCOVERY APPROACH

Bruner's ideas on discovery learning and Vygotsky's ideas on the value of "inner speech" in leading to reflective thinking have both contributed to the inquiry–discovery approach to the organization of curriculum and instruction. "Hands-on" experiences are combined with "minds-on" opportunities to think about, talk about, and make sense of their observations. In this way concepts are progressively differentiated and defined.

A contemporary example of a constructivist approach to concept development is a fourth-grade unit in the program *Explorations in Science* (Campbell et al. 1992). The unit, "Fantastic Plastic!" (212–39), begins with free exploration of a variety of materials so that children can pursue individual interests. Activities contain questions that spark the students' interests and motivate inquiry. As they are encouraged to discover attributes of plastic, they come to see that the attributes of the materials relate directly to the uses to which plastic is put and also the environmental problems that may result from its disposal.

A DEVELOPMENTAL APPROACH

In a sense, Piaget was the first constructivist, believing that learners should be actively involved in constructing their own learning from experience. In Chapter 2, four aspects of Piagetian theory are presented. All of these are considered central to curriculum structure.

Developmental Level. A curriculum based on Piagetian theory focusses, first of all, on the anticipated developmental level of the learner. The curriculum content should match the developmental level of the learners by trying to obtain a reasonable fit between the demands of the content and the anticipated average level of intellectual development of the members of the class.

Concrete Experience. Piagetian theory and the findings of related research suggest that most activities in the primary and elementary grades should be concrete in nature, and that curriculum should be based on a concrete, activity-oriented approach.

Social Interaction. Interaction with others also plays a significant role in concept development. Piaget points out the value of such interaction in reducing egocentricity. Children listen to one another in groups and entertain viewpoints other than their own. As they talk, children reflect upon their own ideas, change their ideas in the light of new evidence, and try to make sense of everyday events.

Equilibration. Piaget's notion of equilibration suggests that children need to be pushed to perform at a level slightly higher than their existing level — to be faced with overcoming a slight mismatch between what can already be done and what they are being asked to do.

Equilibration is the basis of the *learning cycle approach* to concept development. The Science Curriculum Improvement Study (SCIS) is one example of a concept-oriented program based on Piaget's notion of equilibration. SCIS uses the learning cycle approach — *exploration, conceptual invention,* and *discovery* — to foster concept development. In each of the SCIS teaching modules, children are encouraged to make a conceptual invention after a series of concrete experiences related to that concept. For example, in the Grade 4 unit "Environments" students observe changes in terraria populations, such as snails, sow bugs, beetles, grass, clover, and beans, for several weeks. To explain changes in these populations, the teacher invents the concept of environment. In subsequent activities, children extend this concept by exploring the favoured environments of these organisms in more detail, by applying what they have learned to other populations, or by discovering new applications of the concept.

The following activity, adapted from the SCIS "Environments" unit, illustrates the learning cycle approach to concept development. In this activity, children set up a ramp, with a range of light intensity from dark to bright, to study the preferred environment of isopods.

activity 4.7 ISOPODS' RESPONSE TO LIGHT

Exploration
- Make a 7.5 x 40 cm runway with black paper, as in Figure 4.3, folding up sides and ends. Draw lines with marker to divide runway into four equal sections.
- Fold a black paper cover to fit over runway, leaving a hole at one end to allow light in. The opposite end of the runway will be the darkest area, with light intensity changing from dark to bright as the lighted end is approached.
- Prepare a diagram of the runway on which to record data.

FIGURE 4.3

Isopods' Reponse to Light

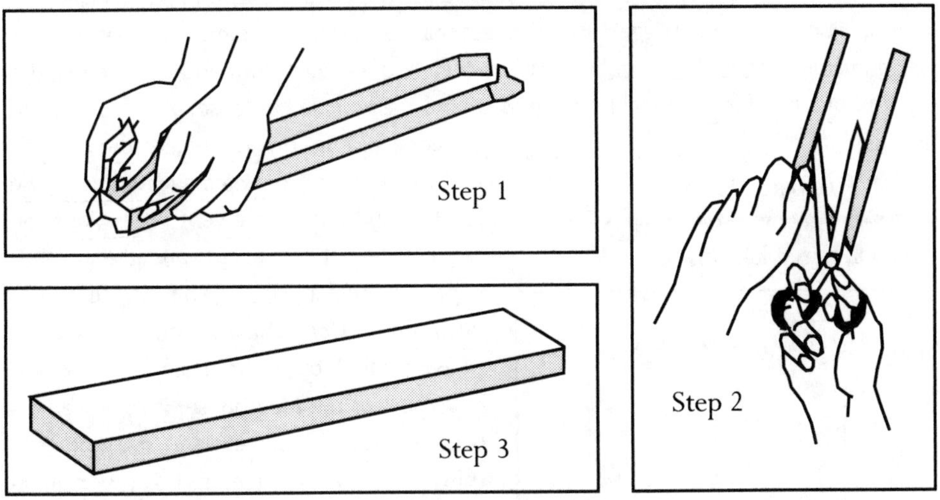

Step 1

Step 2

Step 3

Source: Environments (1970). Science Curriculum Improvement Study Teacher's Guide, 50. Chicago: Rand McNally. Copyright by Delta Education, Inc. Hudson, NH 03051. Reprinted by permission of copyright holder.

◆ Each team has ten isopods. Lift cover and drop isopods on to the lighted end of the runway, recording starting positions on the diagram as dots. After five minutes, carefully lift cover while other group members quickly mark X's on the diagram to record positions of isopods.

◆ Record on class histogram (Figure 4.4) the number of isopods in positions bright, medium, dim, and dark. Where are most isopods found at the end of five minutes?

Inventing the Concept of "Optimum Range"

◆ The segment where most of the organisms are found at the end of five minutes is called the *optimum range* for isopods. Think about the advantages to organisms of being able to move to their optimum light range.

Discovering Applications of the Concept

◆ Where on the school grounds would you expect to find most isopods? Would the optimum light range for isopods differ from the optimum range for other organisms? Repeat the investigation for another organism found on the school grounds.

❏ **Reflecting and Sharing**

Renner and Marek (1988) refer to the model on which the learning cycle is based as the *developmental,* or *knowledge construction, model.* They use slightly different terminology for the three phases, and stress the parallels with Piaget's notion of equilibration. They suggest that the less teacher-directed the exploratory or *data-gathering* phase, the more intense the feeling of diseqilibrium and the greater the opportunity for personal learning as children assimilate or "absorb the essence of the concept." In the next phase, the conceptual invention, or *getting the idea,* phase, the teacher and students invent an explanation representing the concept, and the teacher supplies the language. This phase is the *accommodation* phase. The application phase, called by Renner and Marek the *expansion of the idea* phase, involves equilibration, as students expand the concept, using the new language, and discover applications for the learning.

A CONCEPT MAP APPROACH

Novak and Gowin (1984), in their book *Learning How to Learn*, describe strategies for helping students to construct meaning by using a technique known as concept mapping. Concept mapping is based on David Ausubel's (1963) theory of meaningful learning, which suggests that concept learning depends upon assimilating new concepts into existing intellectual frameworks. Students learn best when they grasp the meaning of what is to be learned and link it to what they already know. New concepts are incorporated into the frameworks hierarchically, thereby modifying them in the process. The frameworks are arranged from the most general concept(s) to the most specific. Each concept is related to other concepts by propositional statements. The resulting structure is what Novak and Gowin (1984) call a *concept map.*

FIGURE 4.4

Class Data

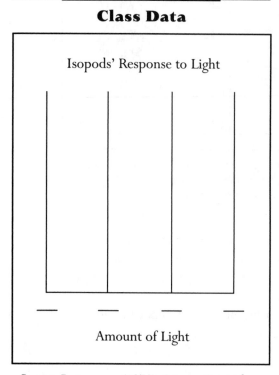

Source: *Environments* (1970). Science Curriculum Improvement Study Teacher's Guide, 51. Chicago: Rand McNally. Copyright by Delta Education, Inc. Hudson, NH 03051. Reprinted by permission of copyright holder.

In a recent publication, Novak (1990) provides a sample concept map of the concept "concept map." It is reproduced in Figure 4.5. Note, in particular, the hierarchy — from the most inclusive concept, "concept map," to more specific concepts, culminating in specific examples. Note also that there are several levels of concepts. Finally, note that each concept is linked to others by propositional statements. The concept of a concept map is illustrated further in Figure 4.6 by the reproduction of an elementary child's concept map for "water."

The uses of concept mapping, to both students and teachers, are outlined in Table 4.2.

The next activity invites you to practise the concept mapping technique by browsing through a primary or elementary science text or module, selecting a lesson, and constructing a concept map to illustrate the main concepts. Arrange the concepts hierarchically, showing the linkages between them.

TABLE 4.2

Uses of Concept Mapping

Students	*Teachers*
Identifying from content of a section of text the key concepts to be learned	Organizing curriculum and planning instruction
Making linkages between the new concepts	Evaluating students' conceptual understanding before and after instruction
Establishing linkages between new learning and what is already known	Organizing curriculum and planning instruction
Clarifying ideas	Measuring success of instruction
Improving self-concept through insights, understandings	Identifying students' misconceptions
	Negotiating meaning with students
	Revealing students' creativity through novel responses

FIGURE 4.5

A Concept Map of a Concept Map

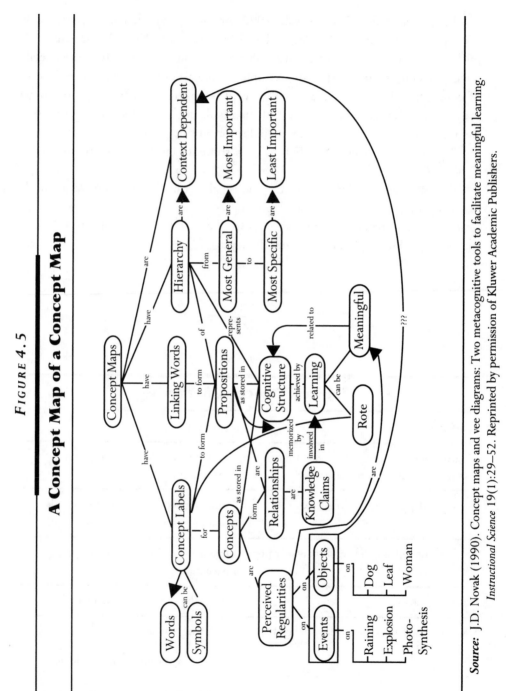

Source: J.D. Novak (1990). Concept maps and vee diagrams: Two metacognitive tools to facilitate meaningful learning. *Instructional Science* 19(1):29–52. Reprinted by permission of Kluwer Academic Publishers.

FIGURE 4.6

A Concept Map for Water

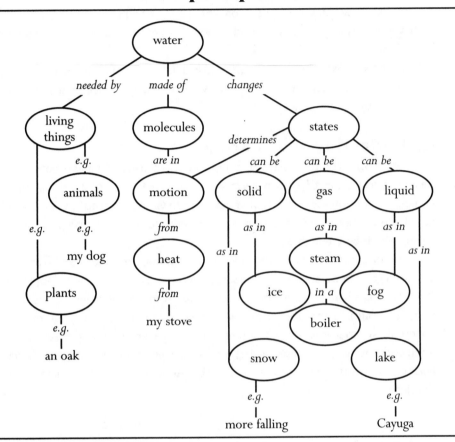

Source: J.D. Novak and D.B. Gowin (1984). *Learning how to learn,* 16. New York: Cambridge University Press.

activity 4.8   CONCEPT MAPPING

◆ Read the science lesson carefully and identify the main concepts to be covered.

◆ Print labels for the main concepts on yellow stickers, so that they can be easily moved around if you decide to change their positions in the hierarchy. Order the concepts from the most general concepts (at the top of the map) to the most specific concepts (at the bottom of the map).

◆ Think about the relationships between the concepts as you position them on the map. Concepts that are of equal importance should be positioned at the same horizontal level on the map.

◆ Once you have designed your concept map, write in the connecting words that give meaning to the relationships existing between concepts or groups of concepts.

◆ Don't be surprised if your concept map is different from a classmate's concept map. There is often more than one way to arrange concepts and the links between them on a concept map.

❑ Reflecting and Sharing

It probably occurred to you as you completed this activity that a concept map can be an important part of a teacher's lesson plan. A great deal of the preparation is complete once you assign levels of importance to various concepts, think carefully about the relationships between them, and indicate the relationships by writing linking words between them.

Ask for constructive criticism of your concept map from others who are likely to have a good understanding of the same concepts. This technique takes practice. You probably changed your first concept map arrangement several times before you were satisfied that the order was indeed hierarchical, that your map was coherent, symmetrical, and consistent with the generally accepted structure of good concept mapping. In particular, a good concept map contains clear, precise, linking statements. Vague or missing linking statements show inadequate concept development.

A PERSONAL DIRECTIONS APPROACH

Consider one final approach that has elements of constructivism. The *personal directions approach* is reminiscent of Carl Rogers (1969) and the transformational orientation to curriculum and instruction. Rogers's ideas are reflected in a learning environment conducive to inquiry learning, one in which children are allowed and trusted to make choices about their own learning.

This approach centres on the interests of the children, perhaps prompted initially by the teacher. An example of a personal directions approach is the *Nuffield Junior Science* program (Wastnedge 1967). The flowchart in Figure 4.7 represents the development of ideas and experiences for a whole term after a visit by a class of 7-year-olds to the local bay.

FIGURE 4.7

An Interest Map: The Bay

THE SEA SHORE

Source: E.R. Wastnedge, ed. (1967). *Nuffield Junior Science Teacher's Guide 2*, 97. London: Collins.

Clearly, this approach demands great flexibility and confidence on the part of the teacher. The rewards are great because of its potential for teaching new concepts that go beyond the boundaries of a discipline and for reinforcing concepts children have already met.

◆ ◆ ◆ ◆ ◆

OTHER APPROACHES TO CONCEPT DEVELOPMENT

In addition to the constructivist approaches to concept development there are other approaches that reflect the ideas of learning theorists introduced in chapter two. The *learning hierarchy approach* is associated with Robert Gagné, while the *meaningful learning approach* is based on the work of David Ausubel. Note that these approaches are less child-centred, more content-oriented, and more prescriptive than the approaches discussed so far. They approach concept development in different ways.

A Learning Hierarchy Approach

For Gagné, the most important factor influencing the learning of new content is what the learner knows and what the learner is able to do with this knowledge. Gagné (1970) suggests that learning can be considered in terms of five distinct domains. The most important of these five domains is the domain of *intellectual skills*. This domain includes concept learning; indeed, concept learning is its core. Gagné maintains that, within this domain, knowledge is hierarchically structured.

The practising teacher is less likely than the researcher to devote time to empirically validating hierarchies of learning, and, indeed, few well-validated conceptual hierarchies exist. Nevertheless, as a teacher you should ask the question "What should the learner already be able to do in order to learn this new concept or skill?" Repeat for each prerequisite concept or skill. Teach the resulting hierarchy, beginning with the simplest concept.

Careful attention to sequencing is essential, but the approach to classroom interaction is still very much in the hands of the teacher. When introducing new concepts to your class, you may find it useful to keep asking yourself what the learner should already be able to do. For example, suppose you are teaching children how to separate objects such as leaves or buttons according to a number of observable characteristics. You intend for the children to eventually develop a key, including separation according to colour, shape, size, and other characteristics if they wish. A simple hierarchy based on colour, shape, and size may look like the one shown in Figure 4.8.

Using a content hierarchy approach, you, the teacher, would be directive, while the children would be largely receptive. As such, it is a transmission-oriented approach. The basic nature of a learning hierarchy is that it represents a prescription for success, in that success with a particular intellectual skill is enhanced by successful prerequisite learning. The corollary of this is that failure

FIGURE 4.8

A Specimen Hierarchy: Separation of Objects

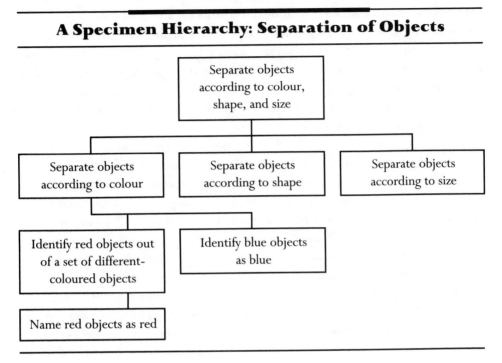

to learn prerequisite concepts is very likely to lead to failure in related dependent learning. You would minimize failure by offering remediation to the individuals within the class who require it. The content of the curriculum, or its core, at least, would be relatively fixed. It would be made up of small components that would be integrated into a larger whole.

A Meaningful Learning Approach

Although David Ausubel (1963, 1978) believes in the value of concrete experiences, he is a proponent of meaningful reception learning, which he distinguishes from rote learning. In contrast with inductive approaches in which understanding of complex concepts is built over a number of years through many experiences, Ausubel believes that learning is most successful when content is first presented in its most general form. General, more inclusive concepts, or *advance organizers,* act as organizing frameworks to which prior knowledge and subsequent learning can be linked. An integrative review at the end of a lesson links new learning with the advance organizer by summarizing the main points and stressing general integrative concepts.

The theory of meaningful reception learning translates into traditional approaches usually associated with direct instruction and textbook learning. The approach is useful in teaching content to students at the level of formal operations. However, in the elementary years science learning is initiated not with the verbal presentation of an advance organizer, but through engagement with concrete, hands-on approaches, followed by minds-on opportunities to think and talk about these experiences and construct meaning from them. Such approaches are closer to the way children learn.

The importance of Ausubel's thinking lies in its emphasis on the need for new learning to be linked to children's existing knowledge and to be subsumed under larger, more inclusive concepts as they progress through school. Ausubel was among the first to stress the importance of finding out about preconceptions held by children so that teachers are aware of them and can either build on them or try to correct those that need correcting. Also, as mentioned earlier, Novak and others attribute to Ausubel the concept mapping approach, which is so valuable in revealing children's thinking. Concept mapping incorporates his idea that new concepts to be learned can be "subsumed" under more inclusive concepts. You have seen that making a map helps students to arrange concepts in hierarchies and to see relationships among them. Concept maps also perform a diagnostic function in revealing the extent of children's understanding of scientific concepts and in identifying alternative conceptions.

◆ ◆ ◆ ◆ ◆

CHILDREN'S ALTERNATIVE CONCEPTIONS

In the treatment of concept development in this chapter, the importance of starting from "what the learner already knows" has been highlighted. This raises another interesting field of inquiry in science education because "what the learner already knows" may be alternative conceptions that can interfere with subsequent learning of scientific concepts. The research into alternative conceptions shows that children often build concepts or ideas that are nonscientific and not useful to them in understanding the natural and physical world.

One of the enduring legacies of Piaget's work has been the widespread appreciation that children's conceptions of scientific and natural phenomena are extremely varied and idiosyncratic. Especially in the 1980s, a large body of research has been conducted by the science education community. This research documents thousands of conceptions held by children, adolescents, and adults that differ from current understandings of a range of scientific concepts. It is not possible to document these in the space available, but excellent accounts are to

From a Teacher's Journal

Once upon a time, teaching was information-oriented and the goal was to learn and remember sets of facts. Students read about science concepts, copied notes, and occasionally worked on activities designed to confirm specific knowledge. They worked competitively to discover the correct point of view. Understandings were hoarded and selectively rewarded through the assignment of letter grades.

Students now work actively and collaboratively on investigations that embody process skills (observing, inferring, hypothesizing, interpreting data, etc.). Understandings, supported by evidence, are shared and lead to new investigations. Evaluation involves observing student engagement and product, and noting development in skill and understanding. The process of making meaning through the activity of sciencing is much more fruitful than memorizing factual information.

Neil McAllister

Vancouver, BC

be found in books by Driver (1983); Driver, Guesne, and Tiberghein (1985); and Osborne and Freyberg (1985). They provide informative and fascinating accounts. Some examples of the findings of several related studies follow.

What is Rain?

In a study of children's conceptions of weather, Stepans and Kuehn (1985) report that one 11-year-old responded to this question and a series of follow-up questions as follows:

INTERVIEWER:	What is rain?
CHILD:	It's water that falls out of a cloud when the clouds evaporate.

INTERVIEWER:	What do you mean clouds evaporate?
CHILD:	That means water goes up in the air and then it makes clouds and then, when it gets too heavy up there, then the water comes and they call it rain.

INTERVIEWER:	Does the water stay in the sky?
CHILD:	Yes, and then it comes down when it rains. It gets too heavy.

INTERVIEWER:	Why does it get too heavy?
CHILD:	'Cause there's too much water up there.

INTERVIEWER:	Why does it rain?
CHILD:	'Cause the water gets too heavy and then it comes down.

INTERVIEWER:	Why doesn't the whole thing come down?
CHILD:	Well, 'cause it comes down a little at a time like a salt shaker when you turn it upside down. It doesn't all come down at once 'cause there's little holes and it just comes out.

INTERVIEWER:	What are the little holes in the sky?
CHILD:	Umm, holes in the clouds, letting the water out (44–45).

Source: J. Stepans and C. Kuehn (1985). Children's conception of weather. *Science and Children* 23(1):44–47. Reprinted with permission from NSTA Publications, copyright 1985, *Science and Children,* 23. National Science Teachers Asociation, 1840 Wilson Boulevard, Arlington, VA 22201–3000.

You may think that such ideas are unusual and reflect the views of just one child. Wrong. Such naïve conceptions, as they are often called in the literature, are genuine and widespread. These naïve conceptions, or alternative conceptions or preconceptions, as they are also frequently called, are often very strongly held and cannot usually be eliminated by the teacher just "telling it the way it really is." There is evidence also that many teachers (and, to a lesser extent, curriculum writers) share many of the erroneous ideas held by children.

Change of State in Water

In a study of children's conceptions of change of state in water, Osborne and Cosgrove (1983) observed the following viewpoints:

When water boils, the bubbles are made of heat; the bubbles are made of air; the bubbles are hydrogen or oxygen. Only about 10 percent of children up to 15 years of age suggested the correct answer that the bubbles are made of steam. When asked to explain what happens to the water on a wet plate when it is allowed to dry, the same group of children said that the water went into the plate, that it ceased to exist, and that it changed into air. Below 15 years of age only a minority held a reasonably acceptable view. Finally, when asked to explain why the outside of a jar filled with ice becomes wet on the outside after a few minutes, children suggested that melted ice becomes water that leaks through the glass, that coldness comes through the glass to produce water, and that the cold surface causes oxygen and hydrogen to stick together on the glass to form water.

Living and Nonliving

In a study of children's conceptions of life, Joseph Stepans (1985) interviewed 30 fifth-grade children about eleven living and nonliving objects. In each case, the children were asked whether the objects were alive. The children had no difficulty identifying objects such as a tree, a flower, a worm, and a leaf as living, and gave conventional reasons, such as movement, growth, and need for food and water, to explain their decision. This success was illusory, however, because the children typically focussed on just one attribute of an object. When the same criteria were applied to nonliving objects, such as the sun, a candle, water, lightning, wind, a volcano, and a bicycle, they too were frequently considered to be alive. The children's explanations are illuminating, and are represented in Figure 4.9.

Stepans examined the way concepts of "living" and "nonliving" were presented in the science textbooks that the children were using. He found that although the children had studied concepts related to the nature of life for several years, they clearly did not understand the concepts. The lesson to be learned, again, is that children do not necessarily absorb the ideas presented to them. Instead, they are likely to maintain their own ideas unless they are actively encouraged by their teachers to re-examine these ideas for themselves.

Earth as a Cosmic Body

Joseph Nussbaum (1985) describes children's views of the earth as a cosmic body. Nussbaum's data were obtained from interviews with children between 8 and 14 years of age. Five conceptions were widely held, but only one is scientifically acceptable.

Conception one was that the earth is flat. The children began by stating that the earth is round like a ball. However, when questioned further it became apparent that they were repeating what they had previously been told.

FIGURE 4.9

Children's Conceptions of Life

Is the sun alive?	Is a candle alive?	Is a bicycle alive?	Is water alive?	Is lightning alive?	Is wind alive?	Is a volcano alive?
Yes, because …	Yes, because …	Yes, because …	Yes, because …	Yes, because …	Yes, because …	Yes, because …
◆ It shines.	◆ It has fire.	◆ It moves and it turns.	◆ It moves.	◆ It strikes.	◆ It moves.	◆ It can explode.
◆ It pours heat.	◆ The flame is.	◆ When you ride it, it is.	◆ It flows.	◆ It moves.	◆ It blows. If it didn't it would be dead.	◆ It can erupt.
◆ It is moving.	◆ It burns.	◆ You can pedal it.	◆ Running water is.	◆ It's full of electricity.	◆ It can grow.	◆ It erupts when it wants to.
◆ It has energy which keeps us alive.	◆ It is moving.	◆ Chains and gears work.	◆ It has insects, fish, bacteria, and plants living in it.	◆ It gives out light and can show you things.	◆ It has molecules.	◆ We say it's "active."
◆ It got earth together to it.	◆ When you light it you give life to it.		◆ It is made of living molecules.	◆ It's partly fire and fire is alive, because humans can't make it.		
◆ It keeps the solar system and universe alive.	◆ It is made of wax and wax was once a living thing.		◆ It dissolves.	◆ It can shock you.		
			◆ It gets hot, evaporates, goes to the sky, gets big, and then gets down.	◆ It makes noise.		

Source: J. Stepans (1985). Biology in elementary schools: Children's conceptions of "life." *American Biology Teacher* 47(4):422. Reprinted by permission of the National Association of Biology Teachers, Reston, VA.

Conception two was that the earth is a huge ball composed of two hemispheres. The lower hemisphere is solid, made up basically of soil and rocks, and is where people live. The upper hemisphere is not solid and is made up of "air" or "sky" or "air and sky." Children holding conception two believed that we live inside the earth, not on it.

Conception three involved an idea of unlimited space surrounding a solid earth. The earth was not seen as a frame of reference for up-down direction. Objects were seen as falling off and away from the earth.

Conception four included a number of acceptable aspects. The earth was believed to be largely spherical, with space all around it. It was seen as the frame of reference for up-down motions, and in some cases the concept of gravity was used to explain falling. However, up-down motions did not relate to the earth's centre. Therefore, an object falling through a hypothetical shaft from one side of the earth to the other through the earth's centre would not stop at the centre but would continue to fall to the other side.

Finally, some children held a fifth conception, which, in this case, is scientifically acceptable. These children considered the earth to be spherical, to be surrounded by space, and to attract falling objects to its centre.

◆　◆　◆　◆　◆

CHANGING CHILDREN'S CONCEPTIONS

What can you, the teacher, do when children hold conceptions that are unacceptable within the context of today's science? Some possibilities follow.

Researchers holding various perspectives all indicate the importance of identifying the child's existing understanding. A teacher following Gagné would identify missing content prerequisites and attempt to provide instruction of these. A teacher following Piaget would focus on the intellectual demands of learning the concept and on the match with the learner's existing developmental capabilities. A teacher following Ausubel and Novak would try to tease out a child's existing understanding by asking the child to construct a concept map.

Commonly suggested approaches to concept development and conceptual change include those of Posner et al. (1982), Nussbaum and Novick (1982), Rowell and Dawson (1983), as well as the scis materials (1970). All include exposure of the learner's existing concept, followed by conceptual conflict when the learner's concept is inadequate or incomplete, and, finally, encouragement toward accommodation of a "new improved" conception. Consider Nussbaum and Novick's study.

Nussbaum and Novick worked with children between 11 and 13 years of age in Israel and the United States. The exposing event (the event designed to bring children's conceptions out into the open) involved a flask of air connected to a simple evacuating pump. The children were encouraged to feel the suction effect on their finger when a similar pump was drawn out. Children were asked to imagine that they had a pair of magic magnifying spectacles and could see the air. They were asked to draw two diagrams, one representing what they would see before partial evacuation of the air inside the flask, and the other representing what they would see after partial evacuation. The teacher accepted all of their drawings encouragingly and reproduced them on the chalkboard.

Before examining Figure 4.10, which represents the children's responses, explore your own conceptions of the same phenomenon by following the steps in Activity 4.9.

activity 4.9

EXPLORING ALTERNATIVE CONCEPTIONS

- ◆ Draw a pair of identical flasks, with the words *before* and *after* under the first and second drawing. Recall that the first diagram in the pair represents the air before half the air was removed, and the second represents the way the air might look after partial evacuation.
- ◆ Working completely on your own, draw the air inside the flask before and after the partial evacuation.
- ◆ Beneath your sketch, write an explanation for why you drew it as you did.
- ◆ Share your drawings with those of other class members, and record on the chalkboard all the suggestions that evolved from the activity.
- ◆ Discuss the pros and cons of each suggestion. Which seems to offer the most satisfactory explanation of what is happening?
- ◆ Think of a related situation. In the activity you have just experienced, air was being withdrawn from a flask. This time, take a plastic syringe, draw out the syringe until it holds 40 mL of air. Now hold your finger over the opening and compress the air in the syringe until it has a volume of 20 mL. Which of the models presented best explains how this can happen?

❏ Reflecting and Sharing

Compare your results with the drawings and explanations in Figure 4.10, from Nussbaum and Novick's study. Nussbaum and Novick found that typically, in any class, four or five responses were suggested, and seven different responses emerged in all.

The procedure used was followed in Activity 4.9, with students encouraged to debate the merits of each of the explanations and challenged to use the ideas to explain why air in a syringe can be squeezed into a smaller space. They were asked which of their drawings would reflect this. With some help from the teacher, the children chose diagram 6, the particulate model in Figure 4.10.

Studies of misconceptions have been conducted at all levels of schooling, from primary and elementary through to university-level science majors. The prevalence of these misconceptions, their resistance to change, and the interfering role they play in science learning are all reasons for identifying them early and working toward replacing them with scientific concepts.

Harlen (1987) sees "an important role for primary science in challenging these ideas when they are being formed and helping children to consider alternative ways of looking at things" (57). To facilitate this process, children should be given experiences related to their alternative conceptions so that they can begin to construct basic scientific concepts. Conceptual change must *involve* learners in the construction of understanding. Hands-on activities are important, but activities alone are not enough. If students are to replace their alternative conceptions with scientific concepts there must be ample opportunity as well for dialogue with teacher and peers, for argument and debate. Children's understanding of theoretical science concepts involves encouraging them to think about their experiences and construct meaning from them.

Mary Budd Rowe (1983), writing in an issue of *Daedalus* devoted to scientific literacy, emphasizes the importance of exposure to science throughout elementary school, with direct experience with phenomena, discussion and argument, examples and counterexamples. This kind of exposure can help students establish more appropriate explanatory systems and therefore lessen the need to do so much "unlearning" in later years.

How to change alternative conceptions is not yet fully understood, but it may be that the same components that lead to effective concept development may be the basic ingredients of conceptual change. These include:

FIGURE 4.10

Children's Conceptions of Air in a Partial Vacuum

	1 David	2 Sara	3 Ruth	4 Gideon	5 Miriam	6 Dan	7 Benny
Description	Air remains on the bottom; above it there is a vacuum.	Air fills the flask, but there is less of it.	The air that is left is on the top; below it there is a vacuum.	The air remains near the side arm.	Most of the air is on the bottom, then less and less and on top — a vacuum.	Air fills the flask, but there is less of it.	The remaining air is in the middle and around it there is a vacuum.
before evacuation after	after	after	after	after	after	after	after
Reasons	The air sinks because its specific gravity is greater than the vacuum.	The gas flows, so the air flows to fill the flask.	Air has nearly no weight; very light things rise.	We pulled the air from the opening; the remaining air concentrates there and wants to push out.	It's like what we learned about the atmosphere in our geography lessons.	This is like the second drawing, but it would look like this if a little dwarf could get in and see.	I can't give a reason; I just feel it should be that way.

Source: J. Nussbaum and S. Novick (1982). Alternative frameworks, conceptual conflict, and accommodation: Toward a principled strategy. *Instructional Science* 11:192. Reprinted by permission of Kluwer Academic Publishers.

- starting from prior knowledge;
- providing first-hand, challenging experiences related to the conception;
- giving children opportunities for talking and writing about the experiences;
- encouraging and accepting a diversity of viewpoints;
- noting all explanations and presenting the scientific view as just another explanation;
- allowing time for thinking reflectively about the pros and cons of each view presented;
- helping children to search for the most satisfactory explanation;
- experimenting further to see whether the scientific concept also explains related phenomena; and
- encouraging the consolidation of ideas that have not been fully understood.

There is a need for cataloguing commonly held alternative conceptions and for curriculum developers to make this information available to classroom teachers. Some of the newer programs include in their teachers' guides information on "children's ideas in science." As you teach, add to your awareness of alternative conceptions through one-on-one interviews with children, listening to children as they share ideas in groups, and checking ideas that are evident in their writing and concept mapping. Keep track of any alternative conceptions you encounter, bring them out into the open when you introduce new material, contrast scientific explanations of phenomena with students' conceptions, and begin the process of conceptual change. The evidence indicates that if these ideas are not confronted, alternative conceptions will continue to play an interfering role with subsequent learning in science. As an elementary teacher, you have a unique opportunity to begin the gradual development of scientific concepts, and to include in your instructional planning opportunities for unlearning of ideas that may retard the process of conceptual change.

◆ ◆ ◆ ◆ ◆

LOOKING BACK AND LOOKING FORWARD

A major accomplishment of scientists has been, and continues to be, the gradual development of a network of concepts and conceptual themes that explain the natural and physical world. In the same way, children seek explanations and strive to bring order and coherence to their experiences and to make sense of their world.

In Chapter 2, you were introduced to the views on learning of several psychologists and others who have been influential in helping educators understand the developmental characteristics and learning capabilities of children. This chapter has drawn upon and extended some of these views as they apply specifically to an important outcome of learning in science — the development of scientific concepts.

In this chapter, you have considered what concepts are, how they are formed, as well as the levels of conceptualization that are appropriate for children in the primary and elementary grades. By exploring the ideas that might evolve from specific learning experiences, you have thought about the connection between content (learning experiences) and concepts (the ideas that are built through these experiences). You have explored the merits of building a primary program from a number of concept areas spanning the life, physical, and earth/space sciences. Ideas that evolve from such experiences are thought of as "stepping stone ideas." These lay the foundation for later understanding of abstract scientific concepts.

Approaches to concept development have two main emphases — those that concentrate on organizing the subject matter for optimal learning, and those that are based on how children learn. In practice, the two kinds of approaches inevitably become interwoven, with careful attention given to the selection of content and the developmental appropriateness of learning experiences. Among the major emphases that have evolved is the trend toward organization of curricula either under conceptual themes that reflect each of the main science disciplines or under overriding themes that cut across several disciplines.

An increasing emphasis in curriculum and instruction is on the direct, active involvement of the learner in constructing meaning from experience. This is facilitated by studying fewer concepts in greater depth and by providing a rich environment for learning, with carefully chosen, developmentally appropriate experiences relevant to the lives of children. Children are given plenty of unhurried time to use science process skills to test and revise the ideas that emerge and link them to growing concepts. It is important for you to be aware of different approaches, so that you understand teaching strategies suggested by others and use this theory base to make appropriate instructional decisions with respect to the particular children involved.

The question of the role of prior knowledge in learning has directed attention to the growing body of research on the alternative conceptions children bring to the learning situation, the interfering role these conceptions play in the development of scientific concepts, and efforts that are being made to deal with this problem. This research has shown that learning is not simply addition or integration of new concepts into cognitive structure, but sometimes calls for major revisions of existing ideas or for a conceptual change.

Early attention to building scientific concepts is important as preparation for further learning in school science, and equally important as preparation for the scientific literacy children will need to be effective decision-makers as adults. Familiarity with the concepts of science will enable them to read and understand science-based articles and to be aware of the implications of science/technology/society-related problems. Concept building in science in the primary school begins to prepare children to be comfortable with science throughout their lives.

The next chapter begins a new section of the book — one that will help you to make the transition from theory to practice, from the curriculum-as-planned to the curriculum-in-action in your classroom. The climate for learning that you create in your classroom will determine how well affective outcomes are realized as well as ensure success in cognitive goals. The next chapter will explore ways of making your classroom a positive environment for learning as you begin the adventure of "sciencing" with children.

CANADIAN ACHIEVEMENTS IN SCIENCE

FREDERICK BANTING (1891–1941)

Frederick Grant Banting was born of hard-working parents on a farm near Alliston, Ontario. After medical training at the University of Toronto, followed by war service and the award of the Military Cross, he established a practice in London, Ontario, and taught part-time at the University of Western Ontario, instructing in orthopedic surgery and physiology.

Preparing for a lecture on the pancreas, Banting read with interest an article reporting atrophy of the glands that produce the external or digestive secretion in the pancreas when the ducts are blocked with gallstones. He immediately wondered whether ligating the pancreatic ducts of experimental animals might be a way of isolating the internal secretion in the islets of Langerhans believed to control the level of blood sugar in the body. He took his idea to Dr. J.J.R. Macleod, head of the physiology department at the University of Toronto medical school, who gave him the use of the lab the following summer and assigned Charles Best to work with him and carry out the chemical tests. By the end of that summer, Banting and Best had discovered that when the extract from dogs that had had the ligation was injected into diabetic dogs, blood sugar levels were lowered to normal, and that while injections were continued the dogs were free of the symptoms of diabetes. Late in 1922, Dr. J.B. Collip, a biochemist from the University of Alberta, was assigned by Macleod to work on the purification and standardization of the extract.

Human testing began just eight months after Banting and Best had begun their work, and in 1923 Banting and Macleod received the Nobel Prize for the discovery of insulin. Banting immediately gave half of his share to Best, and Macleod shared his with Collip. Further recognition included the directorship of the Banting–Best Institute, a Fellowship in the Royal Society, and knighthood. During World War II, Banting was engaged in military medical research. In 1941, his life ended tragically when his RCAF bomber bound for England crashed in Newfoundland. The house on Adelaide Street in London, where he began his medical practice, has been restored by the Canadian Diabetes Association as a museum and education centre commemorating Banting's life and work.

☐ REFERENCES

Ausubel, D.P. (1963). *The psychology of meaningful verbal learning: An introduction to school learning.* New York: Grune & Stratton.

Ausubel, D.P., J.D. Novak, and H. Hanesan (1978). *Educational psychology: A cognitive view.* New York: Holt, Rinehart and Winston.

Bruner, J.S. (1960). *The process of education.* Cambridge, MA: Harvard University Press.

Campbell, S., et al. (1992). *Explorations in Science, Level 4.* Don Mills, ON: Addison-Wesley.

Cornell Alumni News (1984). How we learn (March): 33–37.

Driver, R. (1983). *The pupil as scientist?* Milton Keynes, UK: Open University Press.

Driver, R., E. Guesne, and A. Tiberghein (1985). *Children's ideas in science.* Milton Keynes, UK: Open University Press.

Environments (1970). Science Curriculum Improvement Study Teacher's Guide 50. Chicago: Rand McNally.

Gagné, R. (1970). *The conditions of learning.* 2d ed. New York: Holt, Rinehart and Winston.

Gough, R.L. (1977). *Manual for workshop leaders: STEM Science in-service.* Toronto: Addison-Wesley.

Harlen, W. (1978). Does content matter in primary science? *School Science Review* 60 (209): 614–25.

————. (1985). *Teaching and learning primary science.* New York: Teachers College, Columbia University.

————. (1987). Primary school science: The foundation of science education. *Physical Education* 22:56–62.

Harlen, W. and S. Jelly (1985). *Developing science in the primary classroom.* Portsmouth, NH: Heinemann.

Hurd, P.D. (1970). *New directions in teaching secondary school science.* Chicago: Rand McNally.

Isaacs, N. (1983). The case for bringing science into the primary school. In C. Richards and D. Holford, eds., *The teaching of primary science: Policy and practice.* Sussex: Falmer Press.

Loucks-Horsley, S., et al. (1990). *Elementary school science for the '90s.* Andover, MA: The Network.

Lundgren, R. (1979). Look for happenings. *Science and Children* (October): 39.

Novak, J.D. (1990). Concept maps and vee diagrams: Two metacognitive tools to facilitate meaningful learning. *Instructional Science* 19(1):29–52.

Novak, J.D., and D.B. Gowin (1984). *Learning how to learn.* New York: Cambridge University Press.

Nussbaum, J. (1985). The Earth as a cosmic body. In R. Driver, E. Guesne, and A. Tiberghien, eds., *Children's ideas in science.* Milton Keynes, UK: Open University Press.

Nussbaum, J., and S. Novick (1982). Alternative frameworks, conceptual conflict, and accommodation: Toward a principled teaching strategy. *Instructional Science* 11:183–200.

Osborne, R., and M.M. Cosgrove (1983). Children's conceptions of the changes of state in water. *Journal of Research in Science Teaching* 20(9):825–38.

Osborne, R., and P. Freyberg (1985). *Learning in science: The implications of children's science.* London: Heinemann.

Pines, A.L. (1980). On concepts and their acquisition. Paper presented at the International Congress on Education. June 1–4, Montreal, Canada, 1–28.

Posner, G.J., K.A. Strike, P.W. Hewson, and W.A. Gertzog (1982). Accommodation of a scientific conceptual: Toward a theory of conceptual change. *Science Education* 66:211–27.

Renner, J.W., and E.A. Marek (1988). *The learning cycle and elementary school science teaching.* Portsmouth, NH: Heinemann.

Richards, C., and D. Holford, eds. (1983). *The teaching of primary science: Policy and practice.* London: Falmer Press.

Rockcastle, V.N., B.V. McKnight, F.R. Salamon, and V.E. Schmidt (1984). *Addison-Wesley Science.* Menlo Park, CA: Addison-Wesley.

Rogers, C. (1969). *Freedom to learn.* Columbus, OH: Merrill.

Rowe, M.B. (1983). Science education: A framework for decision-makers. In A.B. Arons et al., eds., *Scientific literacy,* 123–42. *Daedalus* (Spring). The American Academy of Arts and Sciences.

Rowell, J., and C.J. Dawson (1983). Teaching about floating and sinking: An attempt to link cognitive psychology with classroom practice. *Science Education* 61(2):245–53.

Rutherford, F.J. et al. (1986) Project 2061: Education for a changing future. In *This year in school science 1986: The science curriculum*, 61–65. Washington, DC: American Association for the Advancement of Science.

Schwab, J. (1974). The concept of the structure of a discipline. In E. Eisner and E. Valance, eds., *Conflicting conceptions of curriculum*. Berkeley, CA: McCutchan.

Science Curriculum Improvement Study (scis) Teacher's Guides (1970–74). Chicago: Rand McNally.

Squires, A. (1980). What is science for primary school children? In C. Richards and D. Holford, eds., *The teaching of primary science: Policy and practice* (1983), 57–58. Sussex: Falmer Press.

Stepans, J. (1985). Biology in elementary schools: Children's conceptions of "life." *American Biology Teacher* 47(4):222–25.

Stepans, J., and C. Kuehn (1985). Children's conceptions of weather. *Science and Children* 23(1):44–47.

Wastnedge, E.R., ed. (1967). *Nuffield Junior Science: Teacher's Guide 2*. London: Collins.

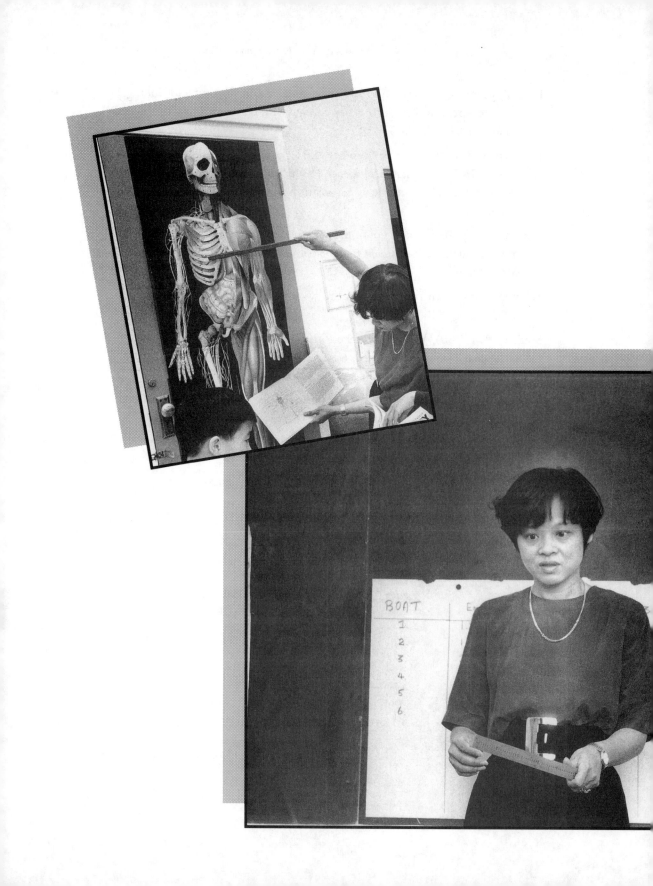

PART 2

From Theory to Practice

■ ■ ■ ■ ■ ■

CHAPTER 5   *Creating a Positive Climate for Learning Science*

CHAPTER 6   *Planning for Instruction: Teaching Strategies*

CHAPTER 7   *Developing Science Teaching Skills*

CHAPTER 8   *Evaluation of Sciencing*

CHAPTER 9   *Selecting Curriculum Resources*

Insights from noted educators, as well as studies of exemplary science teaching, provide the basis for identifying the characteristics of a positive climate for learning science. Teaching strategies are suggested along a continuum of orientations from transmission to transaction to transformational modes. Specific teaching skills are the focus of a second chapter on science teaching methods. Skills involved in developing concepts and thinking skills are followed by suggestions on techniques for evaluation of student progress toward intended outcomes, and by guidelines for selection from the resources available to help teachers implement the elementary science curriculum.

CHAPTER 5

Creating a Positive Climate for Learning Science

Toward a Definition of
POSITIVE CLASSROOM CLIMATE
with the help of
INSIGHTS FROM SCIENCE EDUCATORS
and
STUDIES OF CLASSROOM INTERACTIONS
such as

SEARCHING FOR EXCELLENCE	EXEMPLARY PRACTICE IN SCIENCE AND MATHEMATICS EDUCATION	CHILD-CENTRED ENVIRONMENTS

which show that exemplary teachers
have these in common

FACILITATING ENGAGEMENT, GROWTH, AND SELF-DIRECTION	PROMOTING UNDERSTANDING	SETTING RULES AND ROUTINES

and highlight
THE ROLE OF MANAGEMENT
in attending to

ORDERLINESS vs. CHAOS	EFFICIENT PHYSICAL ARRANGEMENTS	SAFETY CONSIDERATIONS	DISCIPLINE WITH DIGNITY

and extending learning
BEYOND THE CLASSROOM

◆ ◆ ◆ ◆ ◆

We must provide for children those kinds of

environments which elicit their interests

and talents, and deepen their engagement in

practice and thought.

DAVID HAWKINS (1969)

From the beginning of this book, you have been, in the constructivist and Piagetian sense, actively structuring your own meaning about the teaching of science in the elementary grades. As you explored potential outcomes for elementary science and how these relate to what science is (the nature of science) and how children learn (the nature of children), you were building a foundation of ideas. Among the insights gained was an awareness of the mutually reinforcing aspects of the two faces of science — science as a body of knowledge and science as the process by which that knowledge comes into being and is continually refined. You have related these ideas to the classroom by considering in depth how cognitive outcomes, such as the development of process skills and concepts, are realized through various approaches to curriculum organization.

This chapter extends your frame of reference and sets the tone for "sciencing" by emphasizing the importance of affective outcomes. Affective goals include not only attitudes, interests, and values that are characteristic of science and scientists, but more elusive ones that have to do with the way children respond to a learning situation and are favourably disposed toward it — the absence of anxiety and the sense of excitement, interest, satisfaction, and sheer enjoyment that accompany the experience. This chapter invites you to imagine how your classroom and other environments for learning will look and sound as you establish and maintain a classroom climate in which affective outcomes are seen as integral components of successful learning.

The term "sciencing" captures the essence of elementary science. It evokes images of an active, busy classroom, with children questioning, searching, exploring, working with materials, observing and making sense of their observations, talking to one another about them, and enlisting the help of the teacher in supplying the feedback to enable them to continue their learning. The constructivist view of learning highlights the central role of the learner and the role of the teacher in setting up the conditions that promote children's active engagement in learning. This is resulting in more and more interest in studying the interactions that take place at the classroom level, the role of the teacher in stimulating and sustaining such engagement, and the features of the classroom environment that enhance learning in science.

As a prospective teacher, the classroom you think about most often is the one that will be your own, and the occupants of that imagined classroom are your own students. When these images become reality, your teaching will reflect the special person you are, your concern for children, and your growing confidence, enthusiasm, and genuine liking for what you are doing. These attributes will contribute positively to the environment for learning that you create and sustain through the interactions that take place within your classroom and between school and home, and school and community.

This chapter focusses on these interactions and explores ways you can create an inviting, child-involving atmosphere for children's learning. It invites you to explore the characteristics of a positive learning environment through

- your own reflections;
- the reflections of science educators; and
- the research on exemplary practice.

Finally, it aims to help you as well to organize your classroom and other instructional settings so that intended outcomes are realized and children are encouraged to develop attitudes, interests, concepts, and skills that will remain with them long after their elementary school years.

♦ ♦ ♦ ♦ ♦

CHARACTERISTICS OF A POSITIVE LEARNING ENVIRONMENT

What are the characteristics of a positive climate for learning science? As a teacher, you will know intuitively when a particular lesson or unit has gone really well, when you have sustained the "fun" of the initial investigations, and when students have shown progress toward expected outcomes. Think of the potential for children's learning and for creating a positive learning environment as you imagine yourself in the situation described in Activity 5.1.

activity 5.1 SNAILS AND TRAILS

It is Monday morning, and you have spent part of the weekend planning the day's activities. Something happens that makes you decide quickly to change the science lesson you had planned. A child has brought a container with some wet leaves and garden snails to school, and several children cluster around her as she carefully places her "gift" on the science interest table. You have a feeling that she and her friends have been watching the snails for a long time and would like to find out more about them. Other students in the classroom are bound to be curious as well, and some may already know a little more about snails and may be anxious to share their knowledge. The child's gift has become a natural starting point for learning, one in which the whole class can be involved.

You may know very little about snails at this point, but you feel you should capitalize on this child's interest and the potential that exists not only for cognitive growth but for affective outcomes as well. You develop a tentative plan for the next few weeks.

◆ Working in a small group, imagine possible directions the unit might take. Begin by writing the word "snails" in the middle of a sheet of blank paper. Use your imagination and a "webbing" technique to think of questions to guide the possible paths the learning might take. Record the web for your group on an overhead transparency.

◆ Share the web produced by your group with those of other groups, projecting them on the screen one by one and taking note of new ideas that arise.

◆ Later, compare your ideas with the possible sequence of events described in "Reflecting and Sharing."

❑ Reflecting and Sharing

In each group the web will be different, as it would be in each class, with the teacher planning the initial activities, but structuring the unit as much as possible around the questions the children have — what *they* want to find out about snails. Think of yourself as involved in a co-operative venture — as a learner along with the children in a sequence of events inspired by the container of snails brought in by the young student. As you read about how this unit might develop in your classroom (a possible sequence of learning experiences that could occur), sense the children's obvious enjoyment of the activities and think about other characteristics of the learning environment that make this unit a success.

First of all, to find out about snails you would need to borrow from the environment enough of these small creatures for six to eight groups of children.

One source is the neighbour's garden where the original snails were found. The children quickly suggest other locations. You plan a field trip and alert parents to the need for clear, plastic containers to be made into terraria. Some parents volunteer to help with the field trip.

Picture the scene as you and your students return to the classroom, discuss excitedly where the snails were found (whether the environment was wet or dry, what food they were eating, etc.), and plan together how to re-create in the classroom the same conditions.

Space is found in an already crowded science centre for the "homes" to be constructed for the snails, the books and pictures to be gathered, the collections of shells. Carefully, working in groups of three or four and helped by the parent volunteers who had accompanied the students on the field trips, children take turns adding to the containers moist soil, stones and twigs for the snails to cling to as they move along, and food (lettuce, cabbage, a raw carrot). When the small animals are placed in the terraria, cheesecloth is stretched across the top and secured with an oversized elastic band. There is great excitement as the children watch the snails exploring their new homes, moving up the sides and along the underside of the cheescloth, leaving "shiny, silvery trails."

Hand lenses on the trays are quickly put to use as children examine more closely the small animals exploring their environment. Excited conversations ensue as they watch the snails using their tentacles as feelers, using the "foot" to propel themselves along and withdrawing now and then into their shells for protection.

By the next day there is no doubt about the level of interest. There are new trails on the cheesecloth, some of the snails are "hiding" under the debris in the terraria, and children wonder whether new lettuce leaves should be added, or whether cabbage leaves would be better, because they'd found their snails on cabbage leaves originally.

There is a need now for making notes and drawings in science logs to record new observations as children find "eyes" on the tentacles and wonder about this new discovery. One child decides to place a snail on a clear glass plate and watch its movement from underneath. Others quickly follow suit.

The question of animal care becomes very important. Should the snails on the glass plates be returned fairly quickly to the moist environment of their homes? How moist is "moist"? Can the answer to this be found by thinking back to the field trip and where the animals were found? Do the books in the interest centre have further information on land snails? Are there water snails, too? Could these be found and a home made for them in the classroom?

By now, you are entirely caught up in the children's interest and desire to find out more, and while browsing through some books you find just the right poem.

The poem is about snails and the title is "Hide and Seek." You reproduce the poem on a large chart to be displayed in the interest centre when the students come into the classroom the next day. With the help of a guitar-playing friend, the poem is set to music, and you make a tape of the "song." Later, as the children get the lilt of the song, they read the words and sing along with the music. They talk about the title of the song and during the day add stones and large leaves to their terraria to make hiding places. And so the learning continues, limited only by the children's interest and freely crossing any artificial barriers that exist between subject areas.

You discover that the glass plates make excellent race tracks, as snails from different terraria are placed at the same starting point and the distance they travel in one minute is measured. There is renewed interest in the anatomy of the snail, when it is noticed that some shells are small and some are big. Do the shells get bigger as the snails grow? Are the small ones baby snails? Is there a connection between the small snails and the masses of small round things on the underside of a leaf?

Once again there's a need to go back to the books in the classroom, or to find more information in the school resource centre. In fact, so much information has been gathered that one student volunteers to compile a database titled "All We Know about Snails" and everyone's contributions are entered in the computer for future reference.

Much importance is given to the care and feeding of the snails, as well as to their safe return to the environment after having been borrowed for a while. The field trip for this purpose leads to a discussion of other habitats that should not be disturbed, that should be respected and enjoyed, with the expectation of choosing another to study some day.

The children's experiences, with your guidance, have answered questions on the environment snails prefer, how they respond to different elements of that environment, the foods they eat, how they move, how they grow, and how they protect themselves. A new avenue for exploration is initiated — how they reproduce. On the second field trip, the sight of birds hovering nearby raises questions of who their natural enemies are. And so on.

◆ ◆ ◆ ◆ ◆

CLASSROOM CLIMATE

The potential of the experiences depicted in Activity 5.1 in a primary or elementary classroom has been considered in depth to help you develop some understanding of the concept of "classroom climate" and its importance in children's learning. There have been many attempts to define this concept, and a generally accepted definition is that classroom climate consists of the *social-psychological environment in the classroom as perceived by students*. The *social aspects* include the teacher–student and student–student interactions that take place there, as well as interactions between school and home, and school and community. The *psychological aspects* include the effects of these interactions on children's learning.

Johnson and Johnson (1975) elaborate on these patterns of interaction:

> Every school, classroom, and instructional group has its own climate. In one classroom, students will be having discussions, sharing materials, giving support and help to each other, communicating openly and freely, and involving themselves in instructional activities; in another class students will be working by themselves, ignoring other students, avoiding communication, hiding materials from each other, and withdrawing from instructional activities. These patterns of interaction among students are the climate of the classroom, and that climate will have a large impact on the behavior of students and the amount of learning that takes place (26).

The next activity invites you to think back to the "Snails and Trails" unit and the patterns of interaction that contributed to the climate for learning.

Feeling confident about communicating with the teacher and with other students contributes to a positive classroom climate.

r - - - - - - - - - - - - - -

activity 5.2 CREATING A POSITIVE LEARNING ENVIRONMENT

◆ In small groups, discuss the factors that you feel were important contributors to the obvious success of the "Snails and Trails" unit. When you have finished, share your ideas with other groups.

◆ Reflect on the definition of "classroom climate." How would the factors you identified as important to the success of the unit fit into this definition?

◆ Read the following review of the thoughts of educators who have studied inter-actions at the classroom level and the effect of these interactions on classroom climate. Compare their thoughts with yours.

Studying Classroom Interactions

In a comprehensive review of research in science education, Welch (1985) sug-gested that the investigation of the environmental effects of home, school, and classroom was one of the three avenues for research that appear to offer "the most hope ... for improving the teaching and learning of science" (443).

Studies of the effects of classroom environment on learning have been pur-sued fairly extensively by a number of researchers, among them Johnson and Johnson (1975, 1982, 1987), studying classroom interactions in the context of their work on co-operative learning; Penick and Johnson (1983), and others, in the Search for Excellence in Science Education project of the National Science Teachers Association (NSTA); and Tobin and Fraser (1987, 1990), and others, in the Exemplary Practice in Science and Mathematics Education project. In addition, there is evidence of a renewed interest in the whole question of attitudes toward science and the crucial role of the teacher in stimulating students' interest.

Other educators have written extensively on the importance of establishing an environment conducive to children's learning. Their insights are valuable as well in helping you to create a positive environment in your classroom.

JOHNSON AND JOHNSON: CO-OPERATION AND COMMUNICATION

In the course of their studies of co-operative learning in classrooms, Johnson and Johnson (1975, 1987) have written extensively on schooling as a social process. Their studies focus on the interdependence that exists among the indivi-duals interacting within the educational setting, and their "deep, human need to respond to others and to operate jointly with them toward mutual goals" (1975, 25).

Johnson and Johnson propose that interpersonal interaction patterns important to a positive climate for learning are mutual liking, co-operation and communication, sharing and helping, and emotional involvement in an open, accepting, supporting environment where divergent thinking and risk taking are encouraged. The research on co-operative learning indicates that a greater sense of psychological security and greater motivation to learn result when children work together in co-operative groups in science, rather than compete or work alone. There is increasing evidence that constructive argument within groups enhances learning, and that co-operative learning encourages retention of content as students discuss material with peers.

PENICK AND JOHNSON: POSITIVE ATTITUDES

Elementary science was one of five focus areas in the NSTA's Search for Excellence in Science Education. Penick and Johnson (1983) report that in the classes rated as excellent, students felt very positive about science, while programs emphasized hands-on science and inquiry strategies and focussed on "educating students to appreciate and use science in all walks of life" (152). Common characteristics of the centres of excellence were support of the programs from parents and the community. Reviewing the research, Bonnstetter and Yager (1985) suggest that "better science instruction in elementary school means teachers who are involved with science — and are having fun with it — perhaps in ways that are entirely new to them. It means teachers who are curious and who just can't rest until they satisfy their curiosity" (46).

TOBIN AND FRASER: A CONSTRUCTIVIST CLASSROOM

When Tobin and Fraser (1987) began their large-scale study of Exemplary Practice in Science and Mathematics Education, they hypothesized that the classrooms of teachers perceived by students to be exemplary would be constructivist classrooms, where students are mentally active, involved in activities, and discussing ideas and problems. They contrasted this type of setting with "siphon" classrooms, where learning is more teacher-directed and there is less peer interaction.

At the elementary level, the investigators were impressed with the exemplary teachers' concern for the students they taught and their understanding of the students' needs, interests, and abilities. The teachers worried about their own lack of scientific background and the challenges posed by the group management and inquiry skills they felt to be necessary for teaching science effectively. However, they dealt with these concerns by working from their students' understanding of the world, using ordinary equipment and simple activities that developed in complexity as the children worked with the materials. The teachers all motivated children to learn and participate in hands-on activities. They demonstrated caring and respect for the children, asking thoughtful questions and often using humour in their classes. The students seemed to have a strong interest in science and pride in their work, and liked their teachers.

GOLDBERG: INTERESTING AND SIGNIFICANT ACTIVITY

Goldberg (1970) derives the essential features of a climate for children's learning in science from the practice of science and the experiences of children. For Goldberg, the optimal environment is an anti-authoritarian, co-operative, democratic climate in which there is high tolerance for dissent, argument, error, and failure; where there are aesthetic rewards, "respect for manual as well as intellectual effort, and, above all, interesting and significant activity" (14).

Goldberg points to the need for unhurried blocks of time, uninterrupted by school bells or other pressing matters, in which children can continue their play. For Goldberg, school is a place where delight in questioning is sustained, where "children transform bits of their environment and in the process transform themselves" (23).

HAWKINS: THE "I, THOU, IT" RELATIONSHIP

For Hawkins (1965), this kind of classroom creates for children a state of "liberating involvement" (40). In an essay aptly titled "I, Thou, It," Hawkins (1969) points also to the mutual respect that grows between "I," the teacher, and "Thou," the student, once the involvement with "It" — the concrete materials — begins. The teacher's respect grows for the child as it becomes more and more apparent how much the child is capable of learning; respect for the teacher grows because of the feedback and guidance provided at crucial points as the child goes about his or her own learning and is enabled to pursue questions that have been generated in the course of the investigations. This relationship occurs because of their mutual involvement with the materials and whatever investigation is in progress.

BERGEN: LEARNING THROUGH PLAY

Bergen (1988) reflects in her writing and research the value of an environment that encourages playful learning, allowing children to initiate their learning, with the teacher responsive to their needs and engaging with children in the construction of knowledge. In such an atmosphere, there are frequent opportunities for social interactions through collaborative and co-operative learning in games and constructive play. Through play, according to Bergen, children grow in creative thinking abilities, emotional maturity, and social competence.

BARNES: THE SOUNDS OF CHILDREN TALKING

According to Barnes (1976), classrooms should not be quiet places. Rather, they should be full of the sounds of children talking, places where children are encouraged to think out loud and to learn by talking themselves into understanding. Through thinking out loud, children bridge the gap between what they know and what they are trying to understand. This happens most easily in a nurturing classroom environment where students have frequent opportunities for such exploratory talk, either on their own or in small groups with their peers.

ABRUSCATO AND HASSARD: A SAFE, SECURE ENVIRONMENT

Abruscato and Hassard (1976) stress the value of a humanistic approach to teaching/learning — one in which teachers consciously explore ways of improving the classroom climate by recording their own reactions and feelings, and by acquiring sensitivity to children's need for a safe, secure environment. They suggest that opportunities should abound for teacher and children to learn together, discovering, valuing, and exploring in an atmosphere in which learning is fun. *Discovering* can be facilitated through a rich environment, with an abundance of materials to encourage the development of inquiry skills. The teacher can encourage the expression of feelings, attitudes, and emotions through *valuing* activities. *Exploring* includes opportunities for children to have enriched experiences in learning centres, and to explore topics in depth through activities involving project work, science fairs, and field trips.

... AND YOU

As you begin to teach, you will work toward creating a nurturing environment in which all elements discussed above will come together. A good way to prepare for this is to abstract from your reading of the views of educators the characteristics of the positive climate for learning that you will try to create. This will be the focus of the next activity.

---

activity 5.3   **PUTTING IT TOGETHER**

◆ Make a chart, listing in the left column each of the educators whose views have been presented, and in the right column the characteristics they deem important in creating a positive learning environment.

◆ Using these ideas and any you would like to add, describe your classroom as you and your students become involved in a new science unit.

❏ Reflecting and Sharing

You have just shared some of your perceptions of the climate you would like to create in your classroom and carry through to the out-of-school experiences that will be part of your students' education in science. You'll want your classes to be child-involving, and to accomplish this you'll want to try a number of teaching strategies, each of which will place demands on you as a teacher because of the freedom your students will have to work in different locations and with different groups on different projects and learning tasks.

You have also shared your impressions of how your classroom will look and sound as these dreams are translated into reality. There will be movement and noise, as children pick up and return materials, and talk to one another in small groups, clarifying directions and sharing results. In your classroom, there will be children at learning centres working individually and in pairs, sometimes independently, sometimes requiring feedback and guidance from you. With your guidance, and through involvement with materials and significant activity, children will be constructing their own learning, either through individual learning activities or as members of co-operative groups, listening to one another, criticizing one another's views, arguing and debating, and making sense of their observations. There will be other times when the whole class comes together to get started on an investigation or for activities such as role playing, planning a field trip, making student presentations, or discussing the data they have gathered.

It is important to encourage interest in science and positive attitudes toward science in the early years. There is a growing body of research that highlights the importance of feelings of success in the early years of school, and of the positive results that accrue from exposure to a good science program and especially from exposure to teachers who themselves enjoy teaching science and are perceived by their students as liking science and as being good teachers of science.

The studies of exemplary science teaching mentioned earlier in this chapter focussed on a number of grade levels, one of which was science in the elementary years.

◆ ◆ ◆ ◆ ◆

SEARCHING FOR EXCELLENCE

In the early 1980s, the National Science Teachers Association (NSTA) began a search for innovative programs in school science, with elementary science as one of five focus areas. The study, Search for Excellence in Science Education, grew out of Project Synthesis, a research project involving 23 science educators who synthesized several national reports in science education in the United States.

The goal clusters derived from these reports were used as criteria for defining excellence in school science programs. It was felt that knowing the nature of exemplary programs and the critical factors that accompanied their successful implementation would guide and provide support for similar innovations.

The goals for school science delineated by the Project Synthesis team (Penick 1983) centred around four broad areas:

◆ Goals concerned with meeting the *personal needs* of students, for preparing them to cope with an increasingly technological world.

◆ Goals that addressed current *societal issues,* preparing children to deal responsibly as adults with science and society issues.

From a Teacher's Journal

I have found that developing and maintaining a positive classroom climate is an ongoing but extremely worthwhile goal for a teacher. It is a goal that is reachable when the learning experiences invite children's involvement in learning and are perceived as relevant to their daily lives and the issues of today. Some examples of motivating experiences in the primary and elementary grades that help to create such an atmosphere for learning are:

◆ having animals in the classroom. Class pets create a natural atmosphere that is highly motivating for learning. An aquarium, hamster, and a singing bird attract children, especially when they are responsible for care of the animals and are encouraged to observe through task cards, questions, placed near the animal homes.

◆ ensuring that courses of study relate to everyday life, including in themes discussion of media coverage of the garbage crisis, the three R's, composting, ecological damage, etc.

(continued)

> ### From a Teacher's Journal (continued)
>
> ◆ including in such themes "hands-on" activities that are fun, such as cleaning up not only the classroom but also the school yard and/or a natural area in their community, and/or initiating composting and recycling programs at school.
>
> *Alan Nesbitt*
>
> *Windsor, ON*

◆ Goals related to the aptitudes and *career interests* of students, designed to increase students' awareness of a wide variety of science- and technology-related careers.

◆ Goals related to preparing students for *further study in science* at the school level and professionally as adults.

The following characteristics of teachers, students, administrators, and the community in an exemplary elementary science program were identified and suggested to schools wishing to create their own exemplary programs. They are reproduced in Table 5.1.

In the fourth year of the project, further information was revealed about the teachers whose programs had been identified as being exemplary. Exemplary teachers at the elementary level generally had a long period of involvement with the program, and although only 11 percent of the sample had completed a concentration in science, all had confidence in their ability to teach science. Most placed a high value on professional journals and on interaction with other teachers in in-service sessions, and had positive feelings about their schools, their students, and their science teaching.

◆ ◆ ◆ ◆ ◆

EXEMPLARY PRACTICE IN SCIENCE AND MATHEMATICS EDUCATION

Tobin and Fraser (1987), noting the enthusiasm, optimism, and motivation inspired in teachers by the Search for Excellence project in the United

TABLE 5.1

Exemplary Elementary Science Programs

Teachers in exemplary elementary science programs:

◆ Provide a stimulating environment.
◆ Promote inquiry strategies.
◆ Are very professional.
◆ Play a major role in their own curriculum.
◆ Include many aspects of the synthesis criteria from Chapter 1.
◆ Provide systematically for feelings, reflections, and assessment.
◆ Encourage pragmatism while expecting students to question facts, teachers, authority, and knowledge.
◆ Want to see students apply knowledge rather than merely know it.

Students in exemplary elementary science programs:

◆ Actively do science.
◆ Identify problems as well as solve them.
◆ Make decisions relating to their science study and their science activities.
◆ Learn how to learn.
◆ Do not view the classroom walls as a boundary.
◆ Develop effective communication skills, understanding of science and the scientific enterprise, and use of their science knowledge.

Administrators of exemplary elementary science programs:

◆ Support good science programs.
◆ Become involved in elementary science.
◆ Provide systematically for availability of science materials and in-service related to science teaching.
◆ Identify key science teachers as leaders in the Search for Excellence in elementary science.

The community desiring an exemplary elementary science program will:

◆ Recognize the importance of good elementary science programs.
◆ Support science programs both at the developmental and maintenance stages.
◆ Demand their children receive a science education that assures them of science literacy and an ability to live and work in the technological age of the future.

Source: J.E. Penick and R.T. Johnson (1983). Excellence in teaching elementary science: Some generalizations and recommendations. In J.E. Penick, ed., *Focus on excellence: Elementary science* 1(2):156–57. Washington, DC: National Science Teachers Association, 1840 Wilson Boulevard, Arlington, VA 22201–3000.

States, began a similar study in Western Australia. Their study focussed on the classroom and especially the teaching and learning strategies in the classes of teachers identified by others as outstanding.

Classroom observers examined the layout of the classroom, teacher planning, science equipment and materials, the structure of the lessons, use of groupings, handling of classroom discussions, written work, and evaluation. It was found that, in every case, teachers established a positive, productive learning environment in which students were actively engaged in constructing their own learning, and in which interactions were relaxed, friendly, and respectful. Teachers were well versed in the content, possessed a range of teaching strategies, and facilitated and actively monitored students' understanding.

An adaptation of an instrument, "My Class Inventory" (MCI), was used to measure the psychosocial environment in classes of exemplary primary and elementary teachers. The MCI assessed students' perceptions of five components of the learning environment. These were the degree of satisfaction felt by the students, the amount of friction, the degree of competitiveness, the level of difficulty of the work, and the cohesiveness in the classroom. These dimensions are further elaborated in Table 5.2.

The questionnaire, "My Class Inventory," which is reproduced in Figure 5.1, is composed of five groups, each consisting of five statements. In each group, the

TABLE 5.2

Scale Description of Each Dimension of the MCI Questionnaire

Scale	Scale Description
Cohesiveness	Extent to which students know, help, and are friendly toward each other
Friction	Amount of tension and quarrelling among students
Difficulty	Extent to which students have difficulty with the work of the class
Satisfaction	Extent of enjoyment of class work
Competitiveness	Emphasis on students competing with each other

Source: B.J. Fraser (1987). Psychosocial environment in classrooms of exemplary teachers. In K. Tobin and B.J. Fraser, eds., *Exemplary practice in science and mathematics education,* 178. Perth, Western Australia: Curtin University of Technology.

first item represents "satisfaction," the second item "friction," the third item "competitiveness," the fourth "difficulty," and the fifth "cohesiveness." For example, statements 1, 6, 11, 16, and 21 represent satisfaction. Children respond "yes" or "no" to each statement.

Scoring is simple. Each "yes" response receives a score of one point and each "no" response receives a score of minus one point, *except* for the questions whose numbers are underlined. For these the scoring is reversed. The total score for each subscale is obtained by adding the scores for the five statements representing the scale. For example, the total score for an individual for the "satisfaction" scale is obtained by adding the score for the first statement in each of the five blocks. In addition to obtaining a total score for each subscale and for the questionnaire as a whole, the teacher may want to focus on particular items. For example, if a substantial number of children responded "yes" to the statement "some children are not happy in class," the teacher may wish to pursue the reasons for this with the individual children concerned.

The MCI has been shown to have good reliability and validity, and is worth considering as a means of enabling the teacher to step back and receive the children's view of life in the classroom. As a written instrument, MCI is likely to be of more use to elementary teachers than to primary teachers, although it would be possible to administer it orally to primary children.

The evidence from all the studies of exemplary practice in Australia showed that exemplary and nonexemplary teachers can be differentiated in terms of the perceptions held by students, who favour the classroom environment of the exemplary teachers. The results support the data from the NSTA-sponsored research in the United States and the findings of a later American study (Vargaz-Gomez and Yager 1987), which revealed that students in exemplary programs hold more favourable attitudes toward their science teachers than do students in comparison groups.

activity 5.4 A CLASSROOM ENVIRONMENT PROFILE

- Refer to Table 5.2 to review the scale description for each dimension of My Class Inventory (MCI). The entire MCI questionnaire appears in Figure 5.1.
- Imagine that you are a student in the classroom of one of the exemplary teachers in the Australian study, or in *your* classroom as you put into practice the ideas here.

◆ Complete the MCI questionnaire; remember that the questions are designed to find out what the classroom is *really* like.

◆ Circle the hypothetical answers that might be given by a student in such a classroom. Circle *yes* if the student agrees with the sentence, or *no* if the student does not agree with the sentence.

◆ Create a profile of the classroom; describe what might be going on and how a positive classroom environment might be created and sustained.

FIGURE 5.1

My Class Inventory (MCI)

Name _____ School _____ Class _____

Remember you are describing your actual classroom	Circle your answer		Teacher use only
1. The pupils enjoy their schoolwork in my class.	Yes	No	
2. Children are always fighting with each other.	Yes	No	
3. Children often race to see who can finish first.	Yes	No	
4. In our class the work is hard to do.	Yes	No	
5. In my class everybody is my friend.	Yes	No	
6. Some pupils are not happy in class.	Yes	No	
7. Some of the children in our class are mean.	Yes	No	
8. Most children want their work to be better than their friend's work.	Yes	No	
9. Most children can do their schoolwork without help.	Yes	No	
10. Some people in my class are not my friends.	Yes	No	
11. Children seem to like the class.	Yes	No	
12. Many children in our class like to fight.	Yes	No	
13. Some pupils feel bad when they don't do as well as the others.	Yes	No	
14. Only the smart pupils can do their work.	Yes	No	
15. All pupils in my class are close friends.	Yes	No	
16. Some of the pupils don't like the class.	Yes	No	
17. Certain pupils always want to have their own way.	Yes	No	
18. Some pupils always try to do their work better than the others.	Yes	No	
19. Schoolwork is hard to do.	Yes	No	
20. All of the pupils in my class like one another.	Yes	No	*(continued)*

Figure 5.1 (continued)

Remember you are describing your actual classroom	Circle your answer	Teacher use only
21. The class is fun.	Yes No	
22. Children in our class fight a lot.	Yes No	
23. A few children in my class want to be first all of the time.	Yes No Yes No	
<u>24</u>. Most of the pupils in my class know how to do their work.	Yes No	
25. Children in our class like each other as friends.		

Source: K. Tobin and B.J. Fraser, eds. (1987). *Exemplary practice in science and mathematics education,* Appendix A, 199. Perth, Western Australia: Curtin University of Technology.

◆ ◆ ◆ ◆ ◆

CLASSROOM ENVIRONMENT: THE EARLY YEARS

The importance of creating a positive environment for learning science in the early years of school cannot be overestimated. Studies of classroom climate at the primary level conducted by psychologists and groups of early childhood professionals all emphasize the need for curriculum and instruction to be responsive to the differing learning and developmental needs of young children, and to promote a sense of self-worth and motivation for learning.

The members of the National Association for the Education of Young Children (NAEYC), while acknowledging these needs, nevertheless point to problems of translating theory into practice and creating a truly child-centred environment in the classroom. Whatever the grade level, a child-centred classroom poses a much greater challenge than a teacher-centred one, and involves infinitely more preparation on the part of the teacher. But the rewards are great and the psychological climate a healthy, happy one for you and your students when you give them the freedom to become their own teachers, and seek to prepare them for lifelong learning in science.

For early childhood educators, a child-centred environment and a positive classroom climate are very closely linked. Understanding the characteristics of one inevitably brings one close to understanding the other.

◆ ◆ ◆ ◆ ◆

CHARACTERISTICS OF A CHILD-CENTRED ENVIRONMENT

Schwartz and Pollishuke (1989), two Canadian primary teachers who have shared their ideas in a comprehensive resource book on child-centred instruction in the early years, begin by posing the question "What is a child-centred classroom, and what would I see if I walked into one?" The authors guide other teachers toward the answer by offering ideas on which they can build their own beliefs, understandings, and philosophy.

> You will bring your own learning style, your own life experiences and your own unique feelings into the classroom. You will bring all available information and resources together, some old, some new, to create a classroom that is truly your own (1).

To create a climate for learning that is "truly your own" and truly child-centred, requires, first of all, an understanding of the needs, interests, and developmental level of the children in your classroom. It will help to reflect on what you know about how children learn, the learning activities that are appropriate to the child's stage of development, the potential for learning through play, the possibilities in a rich environment for stimulating and encouraging child-initiated learning.

A Nurturing Environment

An interesting study at the primary level by Regan and Weininger (1988) of the Ontario Institute for Studies in Education involved classroom observation and videotaping of exemplary child-centred practice. The beliefs that guided practice for the teachers in the study were as follows:

1. Children have unique personalities and different ways and rates of learning, and this is a paramount concern.
2. They learn through play experiences and interaction with one another.
3. Successful experiences in the early years motivate and support learning and lead to a satisfying self-concept.

The exemplary teachers in the study provided a nurturing environment, with materials in abundance and many opportunities for children to make choices and feel that they have control and ownership in their work. Clear directions, routines, and limits were considered important because of the child's need for structure. Unhurried blocks of time maximized learning.

A Climate for Growth

To create an atmosphere in which children continue their play and are actively involved in constructing their own learning, the classroom should be one in which error is accepted as a natural part of learning, where risks can be taken without fear of undesirable consequences, where there are choices, where children feel a measure of control over what happens in the classroom rather than being overly dependent on or directed by the teacher. Mary Budd Rowe (1973) has written extensively on the importance to children of a sense of "fate control," the feeling that they have some influence on what happens in their lives, that what they do in the classroom makes a difference. Alan Wheeler (1971) writes about the need for attention to the "wholesome climate for growth" that is prerequisite to providing for individual needs and differences among the students in your classroom. He describes the teacher's role in this process as that of an "organizer-enabler." In individualized primary classrooms, the environment must be truly flexible, and the teachers partners in investigation, helping students to make decisions on their individual growth and collaborating in their learning.

In individualized primary classrooms, the environment must be truly flexible, and the teachers should be partners in investigation, helping students to make decisions on their individual growth and collaborating in their learning.

Your classroom, then, will be an active, child-involving one in which there is time for exploration and investigation with real materials and with activities that are concrete because of their relevance to the everyday life and world of the child.

A Climate for Self-Direction

Although in this kind of classroom children are free to move around the classroom, with the noise level growing as they talk to one another in small groups, the environment is by no means chaotic. The National Association for the Education of Young Children (NAEYC 1987) suggests that instead there is the impression of orderliness because rules have been established and their rationale explained so that children understand limits and acquire a sense of responsibility and self-direction. This sense is enhanced through children's total involvement in integrated units, with increased opportunities for student selection of directions for learning. A variety of learning centres and a variety of grouping arrangements for experiential learning provide for individual interests and aptitudes. There is a balance of teacher-directed and child-initiated activities, with the teacher playing a facilitative role and encouraging independence. In this climate of respect and nurture, the child's feeling of self-worth flourishes and continues to grow.

◆ ◆ ◆ ◆ ◆

EXEMPLARY PRACTICE: REVIEWING THE DATA

These characteristics of effective learning environments — nurturance, child-centred instruction, and an atmosphere that encourages growth and self-directed learning — are supported by Tobin and Fraser in their 1990 review of the series of case studies of exemplary teaching. The data from classroom observation and from questionnaires assessing students' perceptions of classroom psychosocial environment revealed four major trends. The results showed that outstanding teachers:

1. used management strategies that facilitated sustained student engagement;
2. used strategies designed to increase student understanding of science;
3. utilized strategies that encouraged students to participate in learning activities; and
4. maintained a favourable classroom learning environment (3).

Tobin and Fraser reported that managerial skills were high on the list of attributes of the teachers in the study. Managerial efficiency was evident in:

◆ the way student behaviour was actively monitored as teachers moved around the room, speaking quietly with specific students as necessary, but retaining the ability to control simultaneously the whole class.

◆ the way students were working with a high degree of self-direction, and also as co-operative learners within small groups, seeking help when needed from peers or the teacher.

◆ the way students appeared to be aware of and to respect a previously arranged and accepted rule structure, so that there was little evidence of rule breaking and few signs of misbehaviour or time off task.

◆ the way students seemed to be aware of the teacher's expectations of them.

◆ the pleasant interactions within the classroom; the teacher's relaxed manner, confidence, and subtle use of humour; and the students' obvious enjoyment of what was going on.

◆ the establishment of an atmosphere in which students were not embarrassed if they made errors. Rather, their answers were treated with respect as steps on the road to understanding.

◆ ◆ ◆ ◆ ◆

THE ROLE OF MANAGEMENT IN CLASSROOM CLIMATE

An important question is how these exemplary teachers were able to maintain an extremely pleasant environment and sustain children's enjoyment in learning. Surely, to begin with, classes are very much alike in the potential for behaviour problems among students and for mishandling of critical incidents as they occur. What other qualities did these teachers possess and what were the reasons for the low incidence of behaviour problems in their classes?

When one looks back on the studies of exemplary practice, it becomes apparent that there was one feature common to all of the teachers who were selected for the study. That feature was classroom management. Their classes were well ordered and taught in a pleasant, relaxed manner, and, because of the freedom from behaviour problems, they were able to concentrate on teaching and learning, and on the active engagement of their students in the learning process. Because of their management skills they were able to organize instruction in various groupings for whole-class, small-group, and individualized learning; to be adventurous with their teaching strategies; and to continue to enlarge their repertoire and vary modes of instruction within lessons and units.

A Common Factor: Orderliness

A common factor, then, in studies of exemplary teaching in science at various levels of schooling and studies of truly child-centred instruction is the high degree of involvement of students and at the same time the virtual absence of discipline problems. The word "orderliness" appears often in descriptions of such classrooms, and yet it is an enjoyable orderliness — not one that is imposed through arrangement of furniture in neat rows of desks and involving children in quietly listening and completing well-planned written exercises, although this is part of what happens.

There is evidence of planning in the way the children know what to do and how to go about it. Directions for a group activity or learning centre task have been clearly explained, and children know where to find things in the classroom, how to work with each other in small groups, or independently, on a learning centre task. There is respect for students, teachers, and other helpers in the classroom and a sharing, relaxed kind of humour that is enhanced by a sense of responsibility on the part of everyone for the way the classroom runs.

What are the secrets of teachers who are effective managers? Are management skills something you have from the beginning or are they learned through experience? What are the specific tasks you do beforehand to ensure that you are free to concentrate on student understanding rather than on problems of behaviour?

The next activity invites you to consider this question and to plan ways in which effective organization can anticipate problems and prevent them before they occur. The title of the activity is borrowed from Farmer and Farrell (1979), whose science methods book has an extremely practical chapter focussing on solutions to the problem of "control or chaos in your classroom." You may like to read this chapter to start you thinking about discipline in any classroom situation and some ways to ensure that disruptions are kept to a minimum.

CONTROL OR CHAOS?

5.5

1. Choose a science topic and grade level, and imagine that you are planning lessons for the coming week.
2. Suppose that the lesson for tomorrow involves an activity with a variety of

concrete materials, one that has the potential for being a bit messy and stimulating a fair amount of discussion among group members as they collect data
and discuss their findings.

3. Think about the old adage "An ounce of prevention is worth a pound of
   cure."

4. Develop a tentative lesson plan and think of ways of managing the learning
   environment so that your lesson will run smoothly and productively, and will
   be perceived by students to be an enjoyable and satisfying learning experience.

❑ Reflecting and Sharing

What considerations were first on your list? Equipment and materials? Storage
space for both? Work spaces? Arrangement of centres? Flexibility of furniture to
make different grouping arrangements possible?

Did you think of the behind-the-scenes preparation? Going through the activity beforehand, thinking of possible questions that might be generated and additional materials that might be needed? Soliciting the help of parents with obtaining
recyclable materials that you might substitute?

Did you think of setting out the materials for easy pickup and return? Perhaps
preparing an activity sheet to supplement oral directions? Adding a chart for the
data to be gathered? Preparing a class data chart now instead of while the children
are working?

Congratulations! You are well on your way to setting up the conditions that
may make you, too, an efficient manager and perhaps an "exemplary teacher" of
science. You have learned that preparation is everything, that once you are ready
you will enjoy the activity along with the children, savouring the directions it may
take, being alert to possibilities for tomorrow's learning centre tasks, of extending
the activity for some and allowing further play and practice for others. A more
detailed look at some of the elements of classroom organization follows. Management is an essential part of the climate for learning in the exemplary classes; it will
be an essential component of the climate in your classrooms as well.

◆ ◆ ◆ ◆ ◆

COMPONENTS OF EFFECTIVE MANAGEMENT

As you thought through the last activity, you were trying to imagine the behind-
the-scenes preparations that contribute to the "ounce of prevention" — the
things you would do as a teacher to open your classroom and facilitate the
smooth running of activities, the setting up and effective use of learning centres,

the healthy, involved learning. Collectively, you were thinking of practical ways of translating these ideas into the reality of the classroom where you will one day involve children in science learning. Compare your ideas now with the following discussion of some of the components of effective management.

A good place to begin is with the *physical setup* of that classroom, and then to focus on the resources you will need, the *equipment and materials* needed for the teaching of science in the early years, and the arrangements for *storage and accessibility* of these materials. Other considerations in the smooth running of the classroom are the *procedures and routines* set up for distribution of materials; organization of group activities and use of learning centres; and planning for *out-of-classroom experiences*.

From a Teacher's Journal

Children in a primary classroom like the "orderliness" and predictability that come from routines and procedures that have been established and that they come to expect. Many of the unplanned experiences during the day, as well as the routines and procedures that are established in the primary classroom, promote the objectives of the science curriculum, often without the teacher's awareness. Before class begins each morning, children may be scattered throughout the room, looking for new things that have been added to the learning centres, checking out the aquarium and the hamster cage, adding a leaf or rock or shell to a growing collection in the science centre. The morning routine of checking the calendar for a new date, and identifying the day, the week, and the month helps to build concepts that are basic to learning science and mathematics, such as time relations, ordering of

(continued)

From a Teacher's Journal (continued)

events, and so on. Perhaps included in the morning routine is the practice of pasting a weather symbol on the chart, or referring to the temperature and the changing seasons. As I began to build themes around science, I was surprised to find out how much science I had unconsciously included in everyday classroom events.

Finally, the very practice of "orderliness" in the running of my classroom made it easy to set up other routines specific to science, such as group activities, learning centre tasks, and rotations of chores such as picking up materials, clean-up, feeding the animals, watering the plants, and so on. Children grow in responsibility and independence in practising these routines, and the potential for learning increases.

Karen Keough
St. John's, NF

Physical Setup of the Classroom

In the study of exemplary teaching in upper primary science classes (Goodrum 1987), it was reported that each of the classrooms had a "dynamic, childlike quality [with] all of the classrooms bright and festooned with displays of children's work interspersed with commercial posters or charts prepared by the teachers" (83). Desks were pushed together to form tables for groups of four to six, and each room had an open carpeted area used for starting the lessons or getting children together for discussion after an investigation. There were some nontraditional placements of the teacher's desk, and variety in the approaches and strategies used in any one day. It was apparent that the *physical setup* of the classroom was an important aspect of the climate for learning.

The change to less traditional and more fluid types of furniture arrangement has been a corollary of the emphasis on the uniqueness of each child and attempts to individualize learning experiences to take this into account. New ways of teaching have led to more flexible arrangements for work at centres and with small groups, and classrooms have become more open, with centres and individual projects spilling out into adjacent corridors and taking in the school grounds and often the community. Children are encouraged to communicate with one another, to move to adjoining classrooms, and to share information on special projects with other classes through displays and newsletters.

FLEXIBILITY

The keynote to effective management is flexibility — flexibility of furniture placement and use of space, so that the arrangements you try can be adapted quickly for small- or large-group instruction, or changed completely when a new science unit or an integrated theme calls for a fresh look and correspondingly different setting. Nothing is more motivating for children than to walk into their

Exemplary classrooms are set up to encourage group activities and stimulate discussion. In this classroom, the desks have been pushed into groups and the walls are covered with motivational pictures and student work.

classroom some morning and find it transformed, with all the old centres gone and an inviting display promising an exciting adventure into something new and different. Think of the following scenarios:

1. Autumn colours and smells permeate the classroom as the momentum increases on a "Harvest" theme begun last week when a child brought in a freshly picked apple. A flowchart on the bulletin board indicates the directions the unit may take and its potential for encompassing and enriching all areas of the curriculum.

2. The occasion is "Halloween," and children enter the room and find that desks or tables have been pushed back to the perimeter, and in the centre of the classroom floor a huge white sheet covers a bumpy pile of — you've guessed it — pumpkins. The challenge is to make as many observations as possible, beginning with the outside of the pumpkin, and relating those observations to what is found inside as the exploration continues.

3. The beginnings of a space station are displayed as children sit on the floor, watching the day-to-day communication with the *Discovery* and sharing the fulfilment of a childhood dream with the second Canadian pioneer in space — Canadian astronaut Roberta Bondar.

activity 5.6 **THEME SCENARIOS**

Using the scenarios above, let your imagination run wild as you visualize the physical setup that these units would require, and how the setting might change as learning proceeds. Think of how you would prepare your classroom to ensure that maximum learning for children would result from each of these exciting beginnings.

❑ Reflecting and Sharing

This exercise may have been a challenge in a number of ways as you thought through classroom arrangements for activities and learning centres, possible avenues the exploration might take for different students, the resources that would be required, and how your planning would have to provide for smooth transition from one arrangement to the next. Once again, the keynote is flexibility, and you probably realize that the same flexibility is necessary also on more routine days, so that a class can move quickly from whole-class instruction for the introduction to an activity or a teacher demonstration, to small work areas for the group activity, and perhaps back in a semicircle to allow children to discuss the class data that have been placed on a chart on the board.

Circumstances will differ for each class. It may be that desks have to be pushed together to make separate work areas, that desks or tables have to be pushed back to allow primary children to find working spaces on the floor. An innovative teacher with only desks to work with might find that a circular arrangement of the desks works best, leaving a circular area of floor space in the middle and corners free for learning centres and supply areas. Sometimes the children can suggest a floor plan that may take into consideration the need for a quiet corner for browsing through science books; improve the traffic flow to water and sand play areas; allow freedom of movement within the classroom for easy access to the larger equipment; facilitate the pickup and return of materials; or enable the teacher to move easily from group to group.

Equipment and Materials

A good way to begin this section is to start the following activity:

activity 5.7 ## ORDERING SUPPLIES

◆ In groups, choose a teacher's guide from a variety of primary and elementary science programs available to you in the library or from your co-operating teachers. Choose one that has a master list of the supplies and equipment that will be needed for the suggested activities. At times, these lists will also indicate the frequency with which certain items will be used.

◆ Imagine that you have the responsibility of ordering the materials that you see listed in the guide, and decide among yourselves where you might procure the needed items.

❑ Reflecting and Sharing

You have often heard of the motivating influence of a rich environment for learning. "Richness" in an environment for science learning can range from an abundance of free and recyclable materials and the availability of a petty-cash float for "consumables" to a budget that allows the purchase of a few expensive items each year. Preferably, all these components would be included.

How did you make out with your shopping list? How many categories of materials did you discover on the master list?

EVERYDAY THINGS

Were you surprised by the number of "everyday things" that were on the list? You probably found that the master list at times read more like a shopping list for a supermarket or hardware store. A master list of equipment for elementary science will include, first of all, a number of items that are readily recognizable as "science" equipment; but there will be many more items that are "everyday things." Indeed, the shopping list for these items would be a far longer one than the list that would need to be ordered from a scientific supply catalogue. There are several advantages to this:

1. Teaching science with everyday things makes science seem relevant to everyday life.
2. Experiments done in class can often be repeated or extended at home using materials that are readily available there. This increases the potential for reinforcing and extending the learning.
3. The "recycling" of ordinary household materials for the science program makes good sense environmentally, especially as these materials are used again and again.
4. The budget for science can be stretched by the use of everyday things.

"SCIENCE" SUPPLIES

A few expensive items can be added each year until there are sufficient for distribution to six to eight groups working on the same activity, with specific items purchased as needed for individual use as children rotate through learning centre tasks. Items most frequently needed are microscopes and other magnifiers; microscope supplies; batteries and bulbs and wire; magnets; lenses; balances; thermometers; metric measuring equipment; rock, mineral, and fossil collections; and models of various types.

A petty-cash float should be available to purchase consumables such as fruits for seed counting, foods for testing and tasting, supplies for growing plants, and kitchen chemicals. Equipment that is relatively expensive to purchase in quantity commercially can be constructed by students or parents. Be resourceful — a friendly maintenance person may have scraps of wood to make blocks of various sizes and shapes, homemade balances, inclined planes, and other useful apparatus.

Since science supplies and "classroom supplies" frequently overlap, you will find that you need additional quantities of paper towels, masking tape, markers, chalk, and art paper, all of which are a drain on your total budget. Once again, your ingenuity will be needed as you think of creative ways either to improvise or substitute lower-cost or recyclable materials for the expensive items on your list.

Recycling: Enlisting Parents' Help

To balance the drain on classroom supplies a note can be sent to parents asking them to save certain materials they would normally discard. Among the materials that can be recycled for use in the program are styrofoam and aluminum trays, bottles of all sizes, egg cartons, pill vials, film cans, paper towel tubes, shoeboxes, newspapers, and other paper products.

Parents could clean out their sheds and basements, and send along to the school on a designated day scraps of wire, assorted nuts and bolts, rusty hinges, washers, springs, flashlights, old eyeglasses, alarm clocks, flower pots, and many other useful items. They could donate bulbs and cuttings for planting, tools for the science lab, and so forth. Collecting the materials may not be a problem; a greater problem may be deciding where such materials, once collected, can be stored for maximum accessibility to both teacher and students.

Storage of Equipment and Materials

Storage and accessibility of materials are crucial to the success of the program. The more accessible materials are to teachers and students, the greater the

Organizing materials for easy access encourages children to return things to the same place each time.

likelihood that children will have the opportunity and incentive to construct knowledge. Organizing materials for easy access is important because knowing where things are encourages exploration beyond the original activities, and also encourages children to return things to the same place each time.

FACILITIES

Facilities differ in different schools. For the most part, primary science takes place in classrooms, or in corridors outside classrooms, or on the school grounds, where it fits easily into the integrated day that is characteristic of many primary schools. Children are small, and there are tables or the floor for group activities. Centres lend themselves to individual projects in science and to topic work in which science is an integral part. Often primary teachers share a central storage facility where items such as bucket balances, metric measuring equipment, slinkies, microscopes, magnets, and toy cars are stored and checked out when needed.

ACCESSIBILITY

It is important for the most commonly used items to be stored in labelled containers, perhaps in drawers or bins stacked against whatever wall space is available. Sometimes schools have inherited durable boxes from previous science kit programs. These, too, can be relabelled, recycled, and alphabetically arranged for current use.

Banks of drawers, or old chests of drawers, are ideal for grouping all materials used for certain units, such as a unit on sound, or for certain purposes, such as microscope work or sensory observations. Drawers can be fitted with dividers that facilitate pickup and return of separate items. For example, a drawer clearly labelled "Microscope Supplies" could hold slides, cover glasses, dropper bottles, forceps, and lens paper, while a drawer labelled "Electricity and Magnetism" would contain all materials related to these topics.

Locating supplies close to the place where they will be most used also helps with efficient management. Supplies for growing plants would be located near a window area and replenished often. And, by the same token, good organization involves having a collection of funnels and tubing and plastic containers of various sizes near water and sand play areas, with balances and metric equipment stored nearby. Science and number-related activities would be set up in these areas.

It is useful also to save from year to year items collected for floating and sinking, and to keep collections of classroom materials (for use with magnets) in plastic bags ready for distribution to six or eight groups, rather than have to assemble them each time they are needed.

◆ ◆ ◆ ◆ ◆

SAFETY IN THE ELEMENTARY CLASSROOM

Closely connected with rules for care, handling, and storage of equipment and apparatus are rules for safe conduct of science activities in the elementary classroom. The best rule of thumb in a classroom of groups of busy children involved in science activities is to avoid potentially dangerous situations. Below are some general procedures that could be discussed in a class at the beginning of the year and brought up again as specific activities are begun.

Orderliness and Cleanliness

Recall that a common factor in the classrooms of exemplary teachers was orderliness. When this is combined with cleanliness the safe conduct of group activities is almost assured. Both orderliness and cleanliness are important factors in ensuring that group activities are safe and enjoyable, and in preparing young students for the more structured lab activities of the high-school years.

A rota for "pick-up and clean-up" duties works really well in elementary classes and is excellent for building awareness of the need for establishing general precautions for health and satety. Encourage children to wash hands after handling moulds, hay infusions (pond water cultures), animal cages, and so on, or cleaning microscope slides. Children should be taught not to leave used microscope supplies on the counter, but rather to wash slides, medicine droppers, and cover glasses in detergent and to rinse and then dry them on paper towels.

ALLERGIES

Be conscious of allergies that some children may have. Check information on house plants growing in the classroom, and cover mould gardens with plastic wrap, opening only when there is a need to make a slide for examining with a hand lens or a microscope. Destroy moulds and pond water cultures after observations are made.

Care with Open Flames

A challenge to groups of children, seated in small groups, to make as many observations as possible of a candle before, during, and after lighting should be accompanied by sometimes exaggerated safety precautions. Tying back long hair and placing a small pan of water at each table help to build awareness that there could be a problem. The proper use of hot plates and care when using matches should also be demonstrated.

Electrical Safety

When interest in electrical circuits is kindled, students tend to repeat the activities at home. It is wise to discuss electrical safety, such as the extreme danger of using wall outlets for any experiments, and the proper way to insert and withdraw plugs when using household appliances. Students should be taught to use only low-voltage batteries for electricity and magnetism experiments. Children readily accept counsel when reasons are given, not when they are simply told, "Don't do that — it's dangerous!"

Plastic versus Glassware

Elementary science involves teaching with everyday things. Whenever possible, use plastic instead of glass containers and measuring equipment. Encourage children to bring from home recycled plastic bottles (of all sizes) rather than glass ones, which are easily broken. Use plastic mirrors, or tape the edges of glass ones. Storage of glass containers is also important. Overcrowding of shelves invites dropping and breakage.

Lenses and Light Beams

Students should not look directly at the sun, or focus the light from a sunny window by means of a microscope mirror through the lenses to the eye. Students should be told that lenses can focus light and heat.

Water Play and Spills

With floaters and sinkers and other activities involving water, there are bound to be spills that could cause accidents if not wiped up promptly. Children can be taught the importance of taking care of spills and/or reporting immediately to the teacher. One way to reinforce safe practice is to have children walk around the classroom holding a test tube full of water, trying not to spill the contents.

Plastic Bags and Balloons

The use of plastic bags is almost a necessity in elementary science. For example, think of their uses in catching air in bags and demonstrating properties of air and air pressure. Similarly, balloons are often used for demonstrating expansion and contraction of air, air pressure, and so on. A warning is in order because of the danger of suffocation with plastic bags and the possibility of breakage as balloons are inflated. Precautions are especially important with young children.

Using the Senses

Encourage observation with all the senses, but allow children to use taste only with permission. Smells should be wafted toward the nose; on field trips, use discretion with the sense of touch until safely back in the classroom, where you can monitor observations more closely.

Eye Protection

Good safety practices should begin early. One practice that should become automatic as children progress through school is the use of safety goggles. Activities such as breaking up small rocks to show how soil is made, or to conduct mineral tests, should never be done without wearing goggles. Ice cubes can be crushed within a cloth bag for activities on melting, and so on.

A First-Aid Kit

A first-aid kit is a necessity in an elementary classroom, not just for science. Children should know its location and contents, and be instructed in its use.

A Positive Approach to Safety

Lest all these precautions seem to take the joy from elementary science experiences, think of the consequences of *not* attending to these very simple rules. Children are reasonable people, and they too will see the need for such routines when you give them explanations beforehand and model safe behaviours. Any safety considerations pertaining to a specific activity should be dealt with at the start of the activity. There are more subtle ways of keeping safety in mind, such as posting a set of rules on the backdrop of a learning centre, affirming in a positive way: "We keep our centre clean. We return everything to where we found it. We wipe up spills as soon as they happen."

You'll find that children will develop an intuitive awareness that these rules are reasonable and necessary if they, too, are to get the most from their experiences in active learning in science.

◆ ◆ ◆ ◆ ◆

PROCEDURES AND ROUTINES

Efficient management will involve careful planning beforehand, and having a clear idea of where you are going and the expected (as well as some unexpected) outcomes of all activities set up for children, both individually and in groups.

You will need to teach the skills of following directions, with children attending well as you demonstrate the use of materials, equipment, and apparatus — for example, how to use a microscope, a two-pan balance, or a thermometer, or how to construct instruments for a weather station.

Efficient management will include setting up *science interest centres* as new units begin, and individualizing within these centres by adding, one by one, *learning centre tasks* for specific student needs and then monitoring their use. You will develop skills in managing *small-group activities* by setting up groups and teaching children ways of working co-operatively and getting to know one another as they get to know science.

To return for a moment to the "physical setup," it is obvious that, just as a commitment to co-operative learning in groups requires careful attention to the composition of groups, so also functioning of groups is facilitated by providing work spaces and spacing these for ease of traffic flow when children pick up and return materials and clean up afterward. Prearranged signals, with the rationale for their use carefully explained to students, also help to keep activities running smoothly.

Preparing and Organizing Learning Centres

The potential of learning centres to provide for individual needs will be discussed thoroughly in Chapter 11. The focus here is on preparing the centres and organizing their use. There should be a variety of tasks ranging from simple to complex and concrete to abstract. Your success in realizing expected outcomes for children's learning will depend greatly on how carefully you prepare beforehand the settings and the learning centre tasks.

PREPARATION

A good idea is to prepare these tasks — activities, games, puzzles, boxes of questions or task cards, materials for practice with science processes — as they are needed, and to store them for future use. Shoebox kits are particularly good for storing materials needed for individual activities, because the ends can be labelled clearly and they can be stacked under a table and retrieved as needed. A materials list taped to the cover of the box indicates the contents of the kit and also lists extra materials, consumable or nonconsumable, that should be picked up in another location.

For each learning centre activity, there should be:

◆ clear directions, with pictorial aids or audiotaped directions to assist poor readers;

◆ all needed materials, including manipulative materials, paper, pencils, crayons, etc; and

◆ some means of recording responses for self-checking or later discussion and evaluation by the teacher.

If the preparation at the beginning seems overwhelming, remember that you can't do everything at once. Start with just one activity for one student and add others as time allows and necessity dictates. Gradually you will accumulate materials and ideas for an assortment of centres based on the areas you plan to include in your curriculum.

ORGANIZATION

It is important to spend some time introducing the centre to children and giving clear directions for its use. Guidelines can be posted for the use of the centre, and safety rules where applicable, encouraging responsibility and fostering independence of learning. Activities should be carefully monitored, and completed work can be placed in folders and unfinished work in an open basket or accordion file, to be picked up and resumed the following day.

Children can work individually or in pairs at the centre, or in some cases take a set of materials back to their tables. Usually no more than four or five children, working alone or in pairs, can be accommodated at any one centre; but, with centres set up as well in social studies, math, language arts, and integrated topics, the whole class can be involved at centre time each day. Also, children should be allowed to continue their work at unscheduled times. A "buddy system" works well for learning centre tasks, and groups of two are appropriate in a number of situations — peer tutoring, games, checking each other's work.

Group Activities

Again, careful preparation and management are the hallmarks of success. Thinking through the activity and its potential for fulfilling your expectations and achieving certain outcomes for children's learning will help to build your own enthusiasm and confidence in your lesson plan. Below are some guidelines for science investigations that other teachers have found useful:

1. Go through the activity beforehand and think of ways to ensure that things go smoothly.

2. Have all materials ready, including additional materials you may need if children want to extend the learning by pursuing either student- or teacher-generated questions.

*Students file ongoing learning centre activities in bins to be resumed
at a later date.*

3. Sort materials on trays, with each tray containing sufficient materials for each group, and place in the supply area. Think of incidental materials the activity may call for, such as paper towels, newspapers, masking tape, and have these available in the same location. All additional material can be located in another area.

4. Give clear directions for the activity, including any safety considerations. It is a good idea to supplement oral directions with a simple activity sheet that also highlights safety precautions and perhaps includes a chart on which to record data, as well as follow-up questions to guide the group's thinking about the purpose of the activity. If necessary, demonstrate the use of any apparatus with which children may not be familiar. *Give all directions before distributing materials!*

5. Try to keep all children involved by assigning roles to individual group members, with one person from each group picking up the materials, another responsible for returning them, one acting as timer, all involved in recording the group data, and one responsible for reporting to the class. If equipment or a model needs to be constructed, give a child who may be interested in this type of activity a chance to shine.

6. Circulate quietly while the activity is in progress, observing and listening, supplying extra materials as needed, but generally withholding suggestions or advice unless feedback is requested.

7. Allow as much time as possible for completion of the activity, but have ready a signal for returning materials, to allow time for post-activity discussion. (Clean-up may have to wait until after class, with teams rotating chores.) Again, *wait until all materials have been returned to a designated location* before entering group data on a class chart and beginning discussion of the results.

8. Make sure that every group is heard from. Entering the group findings on the class chart may be a way of involving the only group member who was not assigned something to do.

9. Reshuffle groups now and then to allow children to interact with a variety of personalities. Skills associated with being productive members of co-operative groups take time to develop, but are well worth the time taken in working individually with group members to achieve this goal.

10. Remember that a word of praise for the way children worked together in groups and also contributed to the class results will set a positive tone for subsequent learning activities.

11. Encourage suggestions from the children for tomorrow's investigations.

◆ ◆ ◆ ◆ ◆

MINIMIZING MISBEHAVIOUR

An important aim of education is to encourage children to be self-directing and responsible for their behaviour. Dr. Richard Curwin has spent a number of years helping preservice and in-service teachers, as well as parents, with ways of minimizing disruptive and off-task behaviour. *Discovering Your Teaching Self* (Curwin and Fuhrmann 1975) is a unique book that offers a program of self-improvement designed to help you to clarify your values and beliefs, and to develop humanistic approaches to effective teaching. Self-knowledge is purported to lead to greater creativity and personal growth by offering a wide range of choices in relating with other people.

Discipline with Dignity

More recently, the views of Curwin and Mendler (1989) have been presented in counselling sessions and in a treatise on discipline with dignity. Their thesis is that locus of control is a central factor in discipline problems, that, by and large, problems are caused by boredom and low self-concept when children have low hopes of success and therefore acquire a sense of powerlessness and lose the motivation to learn. Giving students choices, in homework, in activities, in questions on a quiz, increases control and decreases their tendency to act out. Clear limits are important, with children involved with the teacher in developing rules that make sense with respect to the running of a classroom, and consequences that are clear, specific, and well understood. Curwin and Mendler make this statement:

> When we treat students with dignity, we have a better chance of helping them learn, both about behavior and over the long run, about academics. When we attack students' dignity we might get them to follow rules, but we will lose them as students, and as lovers of learning (5).

Exemplary teachers everywhere would admit that this is not an easy task. But if there is a commitment to child-centred instruction and the notion that children must be allowed to construct their own learning, then effective management will involve setting up in your classroom the conditions that will make it possible. To those who are not convinced that it can be done, exemplary teachers would point out that the greater children's engagement in learning, the fewer the discipline problems. Classroom management techniques grow with experience, and you will develop your own ways of using effective management to free you to become the best teacher you can be and to make your classroom a motivating, happy learning place.

◆ ◆ ◆ ◆ ◆

BEYOND THE CLASSROOM

Creative preplanning and extra help are important aspects of learning experiences that extend beyond the classroom, such as field trips to natural areas, project work, and visits to museums, science centres, and other places of interest within the community.

Field Trips

Field trips can be as simple as a short excursion to the school grounds to play shadow tag; to begin the setting up of a sundial; to test the wind speed with anemometers made in class; to measure the length of the playground with student-made trundle wheels; or to compare differences in vegetation in travelled versus nontravelled sections. Or they may take you and your students, and a parent or two, farther afield for a scavenger hunt; an alphabet hike; a trip to a nature park or the seashore; or a visit to a planetarium, science centre, or museum. Field trips with a science–technology–society–environment emphasis are an integral component of environmental education, and important in relating science to everyday life and developing outcomes related to scientific literacy. Careful planning maximizes the potential of such experiences, either as starting points for new learning or to complement a unit already in progress.

Organization

Planning for a field trip includes following accepted school protocol, such as getting approval from the school principal, sending a letter to parents, arranging for transportation, and visiting the site beforehand to plan the major activities. Students and parents should be well informed about equipment needed for the trip. It is wise to spend class time to develop beginning concepts and to establish rules for outdoor safety and acceptable behaviour, stressing the importance of preserving the environment: "Take nothing but photographs; leave nothing but footprints." Classroom follow-up should be based on each of the on-site activities, to increase interest and to maximize learning.

Planning for Project Work

Organization is also the key to the success of project work, whether the project is a poster display in the science corner or a full-scale investigation of a problem that results in participation in a school or regional science fair. Students need help with both, and at the elementary level should be given clear directions on the nature of the undertaking and provided with a great number of resources and fruitful day-to-day experiences from which they can choose areas of interest. Many of the questions raised in the course of classroom activities in science are well worth further investigation through project work or science fairs. For example, during a unit on the environment, young children may investigate which items in garbage are biodegradable and which are not by burying items in a garden plot and recording changes a month later. Students in another class may extend their observations of water drops to an investigation of which fabrics are most suitable for rainwear.

The low-risk environment that encourages children's questions also encourages creative approaches to problem solving. Once again, the interweaving of classroom management and climate for learning is evident, as is borne out well in the studies of exemplary practice described earlier in this chapter.

◆ ◆ ◆ ◆ ◆

INVOLVING PARENTS IN SCHOOL SCIENCE

The importance of enlisting parental help with gathering materials for science has already been mentioned. Having parents become involved in this way not only increases their awareness of what is going on in classrooms, but often stimulates interest and invites involvement in science-related projects in which their children are engaged.

Teachers can capitalize on this by deliberately taking advantage of opportunities at home for reinforcement of school learning. A colourful newsletter sent once a month to parents of primary children — telling about what's happening at school, and suggesting science activities that families might do, books they might read together, and television programs they can share — is an excellent way of reaching out to home and community.

You may discover that the flow of communication will no longer be one-directional once you find out more about parents and enlist their help as resource people who can share their expertise with your classes or willingly volunteer their help with science activities and learning centre tasks, science days, science fairs, and science olympics.

◆ ◆ ◆ ◆ ◆

LOOKING BACK AND LOOKING FORWARD

This chapter has emphasized the importance of creating a positive environment for learning science. It has explored ways of establishing routines and organizing your classroom so that expected outcomes can be realized and children's perceptions of the classroom climate are pleasant and sufficiently motivating to encourage them to continue to question and to try to find answers.

Classroom climate is defined as the social-psychological environment in the classroom, and the characteristics of a positive climate for learning are identified by several science educators. You have been invited to explore your own feelings about the environment you would like to create and sustain, and you have discovered that effective classroom management also plays an important part in the psychosocial environment as perceived by students. This was supported in the Search for Excellence in Science Education project in the United States and the Exemplary Practice in Science and Mathematics Education in Australia, as well as in policy statements by the National Association for the Education of Young Children (NAEYC) and research by Canadian educators.

An examination of the role of management in classroom climate brought you closer still to the practical realities of the classroom — the physical setup, ordering and storing supplies, planning for in-class and out-of-classroom activities, and involving parents in children's science.

The aim of education is to establish an environment where children are motivated to learn and are stimulated to learn how to learn so that throughout their lives they can become their own teachers. This chapter dealt with creating such an environment for children, emphasizing its importance in setting the tone for the learning activities that occur. In the next chapter, you will consider a whole range of teaching strategies you can use to enhance still further the atmosphere for learning as you make science come alive for the children in your classroom.

CANADIAN ACHIEVEMENTS IN SCIENCE

GERHARD HERZBERG (B. 1904)

Gerhard Herzberg came to Saskatoon from Germany in 1935, already an established figure in the field of spectroscopy, a blend of physics and chemistry that yields important information about the structure of atoms, molecules, and other particles. From 1948 to 1969, he was Director of Physics at the National Research Council in Ottawa. Since his "retirement," he has been Distinguished Research Scientist in that division.

Herzberg received the Nobel Prize for chemistry in 1971 for his work on the spectroscopic determination of the structure of very short-lived particles called "free radi-

cals," which have since become vitally important to scientists' understanding of how chemical reactions proceed. This includes understanding of the spectra of the outer planets and the stars, making Herzberg's work as well known to astronomers as to physical chemists.

In its simplest form a spectrum is what you see as light passes through a prism, or what you see as you observe a rainbow. However, this visible spectrum represents only a small part of a much larger spectrum that can only be detected by sensitive scientific instruments specially designed for this purpose. Spectroscopists are concerned with the development and use of such instruments, and through them they have been able to determine much about what happens in the minute fraction of a second in which atoms and molecules react to form new substances.

As one of Canada's most prominent scientists of all time, Herzberg has been influential not only within his science but also in the wider field of scientific policy in Canada. He has been a strong proponent of the view that scientists must be allowed to pursue their basic research interests, whether or not the results are directly useful to society.

◻ R E F E R E N C E S

Abruscato, J., and J. Hassard (1976). *Loving and beyond: Science teaching for the humanistic classroom*. Santa Monica, CA: Goodyear Publishing.

Barnes, D. (1976). *From communication to curriculum*. Harmondsworth: Penguin Educational.

Bergen, D., ed. (1988). *Play as a medium for learning and development*. Portsmouth, NH: Heinemann Educational Books.

Bonnstetter, R.J., and R.E. Yager (1985). A profile of excellence: Teachers of exemplary programs in elementary science. *Science and Children* (May): 45–46.

Curwin, R.L., and B.S. Fuhrmann (1975). *Discovering your teaching self: Humanistic approaches to effective teaching*. Englewood Cliffs, NJ: Prentice-Hall.

Curwin, R.L., and A. Mendler (1989). *Discipline with dignity*. Washington, DC: Association of Supervision and Curriculum Development.

Farmer, W.A., and M.A. Farrell (1979). *Systematic instruction in science for the middle and high school years*. Reading, MA: Addison-Wesley.

Fraser, B.J. (1987). Psychosocial environment in classrooms of exemplary teachers. In R. Tobin and B.J. Fraser, *Exemplary practice in science and mathematics education,* chap. 13. Perth, Western Australia: Curtin University of Technology.

Goldberg, L. (1970). *Children and science*. New York: Scribner's.

Goodrum, D. (1987). Exemplary teaching in upper primary science classes. In K. Tobin and B.J. Fraser, *Exemplary practice in science and mathematics education,* 81–94. Perth, Australia: Curtin University of Technology.

Hawkins, D. (1965). Messing about in science. Reprinted in *The ESS reader,* 37–44. Newton, MA: Elementary Science Study of Educational Development Center, 1970.

———. (1969). I, thou, it. Reprinted in *The ESS reader,* 45–51. Newton, MA: Elementary Science Study of Educational Development Center, 1970.

Johnson, D.W., and R.T. Johnson (1975). *Learning together and alone: Cooperation, competition and individualization*. Englewood Cliffs, NJ: Prentice-Hall.

————. (1982). What research says about student–student interaction in science classrooms. In M. Rowe, ed. *Education in the 80s: Science.* Washington, DC: National Education Association.

————. (1987). *Learning together and alone: Cooperative, competitive and individualistic learning.* Englewood Cliffs, NJ: Prentice-Hall.

National Association for the Education of Young Children (1987). Appropriate education in the primary grades: A position statement. Washington, DC: NAEYC.

Penick, J.E. (1983). *Focus on excellence: Elementary science* 1(2). Washington, DC: National Science Teachers Association.

Penick, J.E., and R.T. Johnson (1983). Excellence in teaching elementary science: Some generalizations and recommendations. In J.E. Penick, ed., *Focus on excellence: Elementary science.* 1(2) Washington, DC: NSTA.

Regan, E., and O. Weininger (1988). Toward defining and defending child-centered curriculum and practice. *International Journal of Early Childhood* 20(2):1–10.

Rowe, M.B. (1973). *The teaching of science as continuous inquiry.* New York: McGraw-Hill.

Schwartz, S., and M. Pollishuke (1989). *Creating the child-centered classroom.* Toronto: Irwin.

Tobin, K., and B.J. Fraser (1987). Results and discussion. In *Exemplary practice in science and mathematics education* (EPSME), chap. 14. Perth, Western Australia: Curtin University of Technology.

————. (1990). What does it mean to be an exemplary science teacher? *Journal of Research in Science Teaching* 27(1):3–25.

Vargaz-Gomez, R.G., and R.E. Yager (1987). Attitude of students in exemplary programs toward their science teachers. *Journal of Research in Science Teaching* 24:87–91.

Welch, W.W. (1985). Research in science education: Review and recommendations. *Science Education* 69(3):421–48.

Wheeler, A.A. (1971). Creating a climate for individualizing instruction. *Young Children* 27(1):12–16.

CHAPTER 6

Planning for Instruction: Teaching Strategies

BEGINNING THE ADVENTURE

takes into account

| THE SCIENCE OF CHILDREN | THE SCIENCE OF SCIENTISTS |

to set the scene for

ELEMENTARY SCIENCE

by

PLANNING UNITS AND LESSONS

using

TEACHING STRATEGIES

based on a continuum of

CURRICULUM ORIENTATIONS

including

TRANSMISSION	TRANSACTION	TRANSFORMATION
represented by	*represented by*	*represented by*
EXPOSITORY METHODS	INQUIRY/DISCOVERY METHODS	SELF-ACTUALIZATION METHODS

and emphasizing

SCIENCE
ACROSS THE
CURRICULUM

making up a

REPERTOIRE OF TEACHING MODES

and

IMAGES

of

HOW YOUR CLASSROOM WILL
LOOK AND SOUND

◆ ◆ ◆ ◆

There is an approach to education which treats

it primarily as ... so much intellectual content,

which is first in the teacher's head, and then

transmitted to the student's head. Now, one does

not have to be content with this kind of education.

One can develop an approach that enables

children to learn things for themselves through

being involved, being able to shape, change,

manipulate the subject matter they are

studying ... from playing with blocks to playing

with microscopes.

J e r o l d R. Z a c c h a r i a s (1965)

In Chapter 5, you explored ways of establishing a positive climate for learning in your classroom and other instructional settings, and reflected on the importance of attending to affective outcomes — children's attitudes and interests — as a first step toward growth in other domains of learning. Crucial to stimulating interest in science in the early school years, and sustaining that interest through the years that follow, is the ability to use a variety of approaches to instruction. This chapter aims to help you do this by introducing you to teaching strategies that represent each of the orientations to curriculum and instruction proposed by Miller and Seller (1985) — transmission, transaction, and transformation — and weighing the merits of each in achieving important outcomes of elementary science.

You'll continue to use these orientations as a framework as you become involved in planning units and day-to-day lessons, and sample a variety of lesson plans from teacher-centred to child-centred in approach. This will help you to choose from many exciting possibilities the teaching strategies that can make elementary science a joyous adventure for you and your students.

◆ ◆ ◆ ◆ ◆

BEGINNING THE ADVENTURE

A story is always a good way to begin an adventure; two stories may be even better. To establish these teaching and learning strategies firmly within the foundations of science education in the nature of science and the nature of the child, think of the implications of these two stories. One story is about a scientist; the other is about a child.

Scientists as Children

In March 1990, Dr. Richard Taylor, a physicist who shared the Nobel Prize for his work on subatomic particles, was asked on the CBC program "Front Page Challenge" why he and other scientists continued their work on quarks, and what they hoped to get from it. Dr. Taylor explained to the panelists that he wasn't at all sure what might come from the work, but that he and others are doing it for the same reason that scientists in the early nineteenth century had occupied their time conducting experiments on electricity. These scientists had no idea what they would get out of it or that one day there would be an electric light bulb and whole cities would operate on electricity. They were just "playing around with the world — trying to find out how the world is put together."

Children as Scientists

In the second story, Lazer Goldberg (1970) tells about one of his students, an 8-year-old boy who had asked a worker why he was putting acoustic tiles in the school library and was told that the tiles trapped noise and would make the library quieter. Immediately the boy asked Goldberg to confirm what the worker had told him, and then shared with him the thoughts that were crowding into his mind. He was thinking that if he made a box from the acoustic tiles, put an electric bell inside the box, and connected it to a battery, plugging tightly the hole the wire made, the bell would ring but wouldn't be heard. The boy continued his line of thought, to the point where he would let the bell keep ringing until the battery got used up, and then asked Goldberg whether all that trapped noise still inside the box would come out with a terrible noise if the box was suddenly opened. When he was told that it would not, the boy wanted to know where the sound went.

Goldberg resisted the temptation to give an impromptu lecture on energy conversions and the conservation laws, and instead gave his student another example to think about. He asked him to think of the sound in the music room in the school when all the instruments were playing, and whether the sound could be heard all over the school. The boy said that he guessed the music got all used up, and Goldberg suggested to him that perhaps the sound from the ringing of the bell in the imaginary box also got used up. Since the boy was clearly not satisfied, Goldberg gave him a book on sound to take along with him and felt, as the boy left, that if the question continued to interest him sufficiently, he would build the box and try, to the best of his ability, to find the answers he was seeking. "The school," wrote Goldberg, "would provide encouragement, time and materials" (4).

There is a parallel here between the science of scientists and the science of children, and also a message to you as a teacher. Keep this parallel and Goldberg's message in mind throughout this chapter as you decide on teaching strategies that will encourage children to question and to continue their explorations and investigations. At times, the questions will be those that your students bring to your classroom from their everyday experience with the world — for example, the child's wonder about the acoustic tiles in the school library. At other times, the questions will arise from more contrived experiences as you set up the conditions that encourage the same longing to know and understand.

In both stories, there is a picture of science as "playing around with the world" and the recognition that the potential for learning this way is as great for children as it is for scientists, but only if there are significant adults to listen to children's musings and to guide and give feedback as needed. A curriculum that reflects the nature of science also reflects a good part of a young child's world, and the same emphases must find their way into the classroom in the lessons you plan, the climate for learning you create, and the teaching strategies you employ. A curriculum that is based on how children learn will be the most fruitful. Just as scientists are perpetual learners who are perpetually curious, children in school must be given the freedom to inquire, to be curious, to continue the joy in learning that has characterized their preschool years. The experiences that you provide to get this started must be carefully chosen, so that their very openness will allow children to choose from a variety of options.

After reading these two stories, you may wish to read the rest of Lazer Goldberg's book, *Children and Science: How to Awaken and Sustain the Interest of the Young in the World Around Them*. The subtitle sets the tone for the rest of this chapter and, for that matter, for the remaining chapters of the book. You may wish to read further about Richard Taylor and his search for the smallest particles in the nucleus of the atom — particles that are being given names like "up," "down," "strange," "charm," "bottom," and "truth" until their nature is more fully understood. Many of your students will share with the boy in the school library and with scientists like Richard Taylor the same compelling curiosity about puzzling events and phenomena. You have that on your side as you begin to plan your strategies for teaching.

◆ ◆ ◆ ◆ ◆

PLANNING INSTRUCTION

As suggested in Chapter 1, one way to approach the teaching of science is to think of teaching methods within the framework of curriculum orientations, identifying teaching strategies that fall under each of the three orientations to curriculum proposed by Miller and Seller (1985). This model of curriculum development begins by clarifying the orientation — whether *transmission, transaction,* or *transformation* — and, once that is established, proceeds from that context to implications for contemporary educational practice. This classification is useful because a variety of strategies can be included under each orientation, all of which are useful and can become part of your repertoire for teaching science. In planning curriculum and instruction for children in the primary and elementary grades, you will need to embrace all of the orientations at different times and for different purposes. You will find yourself adopting a particular orientation depending on the nature of what is to be learned, the developmental stage of the children, their need for variety, and a host of other variables. For example, your commitment to the constructivist view of children's learning will determine the extent to which you will choose transaction and transformation over the more traditional transmission approaches. It is the balance between approaches that is important. However, in preparation for choosing, it is important that you become familiar with teaching strategies that reflect each of these orientations.

Activity 6.1 presents a situation that is fairly common in elementary science. A hamster is brought into the classroom, and you are asked to consider questions and possible pathways for children's learning that could result from such an experience. The same project will be used in subsequent activities to illustrate in turn each of the three orientations to curriculum and instruction.

- - - - - - - - - - -

activity `6.1` **A PET PROJECT**

Many schools or individual teachers have a tradition of keeping small animals — rabbits, mice, hamsters, fish, birds, and so on. In this activity, focus your attention on one animal, a hamster. Imagine you are a teacher with a class of your own. Consider the possible outcomes of this activity for the children you may teach, but think about it as a series of questions that you and the children may wish to consider. Write down these questions before reading on.

☐ Reflecting and Sharing

You may have thought of the following kinds of questions:

Appearance:

Does the hamster have hair (fur)? If so, does it cover all of the body? If not, which parts? Is it all the same colour? Is it all the same length? Is the hamster shedding?

Does the hamster have a tail? If so, how long is it? Is the tail hairy? What is the hamster's shape? How many legs does it have? What are its feet like? Does it have toes? If so, how many?

Does the hamster have whiskers? If so, how many? What colour are its eyes? What are its teeth like? What else do you observe?

As follow-up questions, you may consider: Why does the hamster have fur? Are its senses like ours? Does it see colour, distinguish tastes, etc.? How could you find out?

Nutrition:

What does the hamster eat? Does it like human food? What does it like most? How much does it eat? Does it eat whenever food is available? [Note: Hamsters have large pouches in their cheeks and use these to collect food, which is later deposited in a safe storage place.]

Hygiene:

Does the hamster have good personal hygiene? Does it wash itself? Does it defecate just anywhere, or is it selective?

Communication:

Does the hamster communicate with other hamsters? If so, how? Does it communicate with people? If so, how? Is it friendly or aggressive?

Gender:

Is the hamster male or female? How can you tell? How do hamsters reproduce? How often? What are baby hamsters like? Do they have hair? How do baby hamsters feed?

Movement:

How do hamsters move? Do they walk, run, hop? Do they leave tracks? If so, what do their tracks look like? How might you find out?

Feelings:

What is it like to be a hamster? What is it like to be restricted to a cage?

You probably came up with some different questions. You may have approached the task in the same way you did in Chapter 1, by thinking in terms of cognitive, affective, psychomotor, and social outcomes. This time, however, the purpose is a little different. The focus now is on how the questions asked and the teaching strategies used fit into Miller and Seller's three orientations.

◆ ◆ ◆ ◆ ◆

THE TRANSMISSION ORIENTATION

When applying the transmission orientation, the teacher is very much in control of the learning situation. The teacher decides what will be learned and what approach will be taken to learning in terms of both motivation and learning strategies. Teaching is directed at the class as a group, and it is anticipated that all children will learn in basically the same way, with little attempt to provide for individual differences except, perhaps, for rate of learning and remediation. Problem solving may be a part of the curriculum, but problems will be such that they are intended to produce or reinforce routines rather than to develop a question-

In the transmission orientation to curriculum, teaching is directed at the class as a whole, rather than at small groups and individuals.

ing approach or the ability to identify or solve novel problems. The teacher is director, the learner receptor. The overall aim is to transmit knowledge, routine skills, and routine problem-solving strategies and attitudes to the learner, and to do so as directly as possible.

activity 6.2 PET PROJECT: TRANSMISSION ORIENTATION

Assume that you are a teacher of a grade of your choice, and that you are teaching in a transmission mode. You have just introduced two hamsters, a male and a female, to your class. Think about how you might develop a class project involving the two hamsters. What are some questions you would have the children consider? Make some notes on your thoughts before you read on.

❏ Reflecting and Sharing

Perhaps you would ask the children to consider the following:

1. What do the hamsters look like? Examine their shape, hair colour, amount of hair coverage. Write down these characteristics. Try to describe their tails, even if they are very short. How many legs do the hamsters have? Do they have toes? How many? Do they have whiskers? How many? What colour are their eyes?

2. What do hamsters eat? Try them with different kinds of food. Do they eat all of the time? Watch carefully over a period of time. You will see that hamsters collect food in large pouches in their cheeks, and then deposit it somewhere safe to be eaten at some future time.

3. Over a period of two weeks, each time you see a hamster washing itself write down the date and time. Make a table in your notebook to help you record these times. When you have finished, try to decide whether hamsters are clean or dirty animals.

4. Read the section about hamsters in your science text. What do the authors say about how hamsters "talk" to one another?

5. Hamsters are *mammals*, which means that their young are fed milk from their mother's mammary glands, just like human babies. Mammals share five common features. Read about them in your text. Write about them in your notebook.

6. What kinds of tracks do hamsters make? Find out by putting some water paint on their feet and having them walk on a sheet of white paper.

7. Write about a day in the life of a hamster.

Your suggestions may be quite different from these, but if you captured the essence of the transmission orientation, you, as teacher, would be very much in control — telling the children what to do, what to look for, what sources to consult, and so on.

◆ ◆ ◆ ◆ ◆

THE TRANSACTION ORIENTATION

Consider what it means to be a transactional teacher. As a transactionally oriented teacher, you are much less directive than if you were operating in a transmission orientation. You are prepared to grant the children more autonomy as you encourage them to learn to recognize problems, to invent strategies for their solution, and to generalize these strategies so that they can be adopted in other situations. Consistent with these goals is an atmosphere in which you entertain and encourage children's questions about the nature of science itself as well as its products in the world around us. What is implied here is that your focus is on creating an investigative spirit, a willingness to be wrong, and an awareness of the tentative nature of scientific knowledge. At this level, the focus is on the use of an appropriate word here and there, rather than on an overtly philosophical approach. In general, the degree of control you exert over your students is likely to be greater in reality than they perceive. You are still in control of the general directions taken, and of the specific problems to be investigated. Each child is likely to feel unique, and will be governed by an intrinsic motivation. Overall, your role is less directive and more facilitative than the role of a transmission-oriented teacher, but you are still very much in charge. Because it is less structured, your role is likely to be more difficult than that of the transmission-oriented teacher. Return now to the hamsters.

activity 6.3 PET TRANSMISSION: TRANSACTION ORIENTATION

Your task here is to set out a plan for how you will operate in a transactional mode, starting again with the introduction of two hamsters into your classroom. In this case, you will find you cannot be as detailed and specific as you were when operating in a transmission mode. In the transaction mode, it is more appropriate to lay out a tentative plan for how events may unfold. Please do this now, before you read on.

❏ Reflecting and Sharing

Here is one suggested plan. Compare it with yours:

1. Introduce two caged hamsters. Cage with food and water trays and a small transparent house filled with loose paper. No discussion for a few days.

2. After a few days, determine what the children "know" about hamsters. How sure are they? How can they check? [Ask for suggestions about how to proceed.]

3. (a) Physical characteristics — obvious ones such as eye colour, hair colour, etc.; less obvious ones such as length of tail, length of hair. [How to measure?]

   (b) What do they eat? How will you find out? [Ask for plans.]

   (c) What kinds of personal habits do hamsters have — for example, are they clean? How will you find out? [Look for development of a systematic plan.]

   (d) Do hamsters communicate with other hamsters? How will you find out? [Ask for plans.]

   (e) Do hamsters like light or darkness, quiet or noise? How will you find out? [Ask for plans.]

   (f) Do hamsters leave tracks? How will you find out? [Ask for plans.]

   (g) What else might it be interesting to find out? For example, do hamsters belong to any larger families? What other animals are they like? [Lead to mammals.] How might you find out? [Library search.] How do hamsters spend their day (and night)? How will you find out? [Look for schedule.] Suggest video camera overnight.

The essential point here is that the children are challenged to come up with their own questions and suggestions for how to answer these questions. Interest centres on the identification of interesting questions and possible ways to answer these questions. Some unexpected avenues will probably be explored, but the teacher will have in mind a number of possibilities as well. For the teacher, there are different levels of potential involvement. This will vary from teacher to teacher, but the children will do much more than receive information and learn routine skills.

◆ ◆ ◆ ◆ ◆

THE TRANSFORMATION ORIENTATION

The transformation orientation is less precisely defined than either of the other two orientations, and it is also further removed from the ways in which most teachers have traditionally operated. Your teaching will be child-centred as you seek to help your students develop a feeling of self-worth and the ability to evaluate personal progress in this direction. The process of learning is more important than the content to be learned, which is not to say that content is unimportant. You recognize the uniqueness of each child in your class, but you also want to show that we can all have common concerns. Motivation is primarily intrinsic, rather than based upon external rewards. You endeavour to help children develop a foundation, a beginning, for a satisfying aesthetic, spiritual, and emotional life within the wider community.

Your orientation is interdisciplinary. You recognize that diverse viewpoints and traditions are acceptable. To illustrate this orientation further, return again to the hamsters.

activity 6.4 PET PROJECT: TRANSFORMATION ORIENTATION

Consider how you might operate with the two hamsters, this time in a transformation mode. Record your thoughts on how you might do this. When you have finished, compare your thoughts with the ideas that follow.

❑ Reflecting and Sharing

If you were a child faced with two hamsters that were left in a cage for you to think about as you liked, would you be interested in finding out more about these creatures? Almost certainly you would. What would you do? How would you progress? Your teacher would not provide you with a number of questions to enable you to find out a wealth of factual information about hamsters. Nor would your teacher lead you along within a prepared framework of problems to be solved.

Your transformationally oriented teacher would help you find some interesting questions to consider and to investigate. They would most likely be the same questions you have already considered, especially in the transactional orientation. But now the questions would have to come from you, the child. You might be more concerned with getting inside the mind of the hamster, with seeing life from a very different perspective from your own. But for most teachers in most educational situations in the early years of schooling, there is likely to be little overt difference between transformation-oriented classrooms and those under the influence of the transaction orientation. The difference is likely to be subtle — a word here or there, a slight shift of focus, a greater willingness on the part of the teacher to depart from "the script," a greater likelihood of real democracy, a greater concern for the larger world, and a subtle yet significant difference in what is deemed important.

ORIENTATIONS AS A CONTINUUM

It is useful to think of the curriculum orientations as a continuum ranging from the most teacher-centred (transmission) to a teacher-facilitative, child-active mode (transaction), to the decreasing teacher direction and greater child involvement in the transformation orientation. This classification scheme is not a perfect one; but, although a specific teaching method may not always fall neatly under the umbrella of a single orientation, the scheme will provide a useful framework for discussing methods of teaching.

Teaching strategies that fall under these orientations are characterized by the same philosophical, psychological, and pedagogical foundations, and can also be placed on a continuum, as shown in Figure 6.1.

Consider a whole range of possibilities, beginning with transmission-oriented approaches (exposition and mastery learning). As you progress along the continuum, other possibilities come into view — methods that increase children's involvement as they construct their own learning, generate and pursue new questions, and initiate inquiries in a transaction mode. Finally, there are ways of teaching that allow more and more freedom and encourage children to evolve paths that may lead to a transformation in their ways of perceiving themselves and viewing the world.

◆ ◆ ◆ ◆ ◆

PLANNING UNITS AND LESSONS

Whatever the degree of structure and whatever orientation you decide to adopt as you begin to teach science, it is good to have a plan — preferably a written one — that will give you a purpose and a sequence for instruction. In *unit planning,* a tentative outline is necessary to help you sort out the possibilities and provide an overall structure for the unit. The process of *lesson planning* will be part of a larger plan for children's learning. Both lessons and units will reflect the objectives for the grade level you are teaching and the goals of the overall plan for elementary science.

FIGURE 6.1

Teaching Strategies: A Continuum

---

from most teacher-directed	to least teacher-directed;
from whole-class instruction	to co-operative learning in groups;
from whole-class instruction	to individualization of instruction;
from acquiring public knowledge	to acquiring personal knowledge;
from child relatively passive	to child constructing meaning;
from largely verbal learning	to concrete experiences;
from emphasis on basics	to societal, global applications;
from discrete subject areas	to integrated approaches;
from largely cognitive emphases	to holistic learning.

Unit Planning

Each time you begin to develop a unit you will need a tentative plan that will take into account what your students already know about the topic, as well as what they would like to know. The plan will take advantage of opportunities to extend learning by providing experiences that are developmentally appropriate but provide for a variety of interests and abilities. The unit may be designed to extend children's knowledge in science and develop competencies and attitudes, or it may be an interdisciplinary unit in which a theme is developed, barriers between subject areas are freely crossed, and the wholeness and interconnectedness of knowledge are emphasized. In either case, you should find out about related in-school and out-of-school experiences children have had, brainstorming to ascertain starting points for learning.

Sometimes the idea for a theme may spring spontaneously from children's interests, perhaps expressed in something fascinating to them that has been found at home, in the garden, or on the way to school (as in the "Snails and Trails" unit discussed in Chapter 5). Sometimes the starting point is the immediate environment, such as the unit on snow described in Chapter 3, which has tremendous potential for both process and concept development. Sometimes the topic may be a teacher-chosen one that has been found to be particularly productive with earlier classes. Whatever the origin of the topic, you will need to think about which areas of the curriculum can be included productively and which outcomes for children's learning can be achieved. Some general guidelines for unit planning follow.

PREPARING CONTENT AND METHODS OF TEACHING

- Start by making a flowchart or outline of the directions the unit may take.
- Think of concepts, skills, attitudes, and values that might come out of the experiences.
- Divide the content into curriculum areas.
- Decide on possible subtopics within curriculum areas.
- Talk to the students about their choices of ideas and interests to pursue.
- Add these options to the flowchart.

From a Teacher's Journal

As an elementary teacher with a background of training in resource-based teaching and learning, the instructional strategies I use are primarily influenced by my belief in the value of this approach. This belief has been reinforced again and again when I have observed children's excitement as they experience and enjoy independence in learning and the satisfaction of accomplishing goals.

Resource-based learning is most effective when teachers, in co-operation with a resource teacher, plan integrated units in which children learn in different activity groupings and a variety of settings, using a wide range of resources. The emphasis shifts from the teacher as the primary source of information, placing students at the centre of the learning process in an active rather than a passive role. Children are allowed to function at an appropriate developmental level and at the same time are

(continued)

> ### From a Teacher's Journal (continued)
>
> challenged to learn more. Emphasis is placed as well on the interaction between the learner and the learning environment, which includes a variety of settings inside the school (classroom, corridors, resource centre) and outside (field trips, the public library, the community). The student learns how to access and use information, exploring a wide range of resources that may or may not include the teacher and the traditional textbook.
>
> Although I, as teacher and facilitator, retain responsibility for ensuring that learning occurs, student ownership of and involvement in learning are emphasized. Through choices, challenges, and successful experiences, children are equipped with skills they will need for lifelong learning.
>
> *Janet Case-Cadigan*
> *St. John's, NF*

GATHERING RESOURCES AND EQUIPMENT

◆ Gather books, filmstrips, videotapes, and study prints, some for children and some for your own information.
◆ Enlist the help of the resource teacher in locating such materials, as well as computer software at appropriate levels.
◆ Encourage children to collect needed materials.
◆ Secure permissions if a field trip is needed.
◆ Collect needed equipment.
◆ Prepare a folder for each child's drawings and records.

PREPARING THE CLASSROOM

♦ Arrange a display area for pictures, poems, books, etc.
♦ Prepare space in the display area for equipment and collections.
♦ Arrange furniture for initial explorations.
♦ Plan for monitoring of children's progress and evaluation of the success of the unit.

Lesson Planning

Your daily lessons will reflect the specific objectives of a science-based unit, or the broad goals of a multidisciplinary or thematic unit.

Guidelines for lesson planning include:

♦ a statement of purpose and a listing of the main concepts to be taught and skills to be developed;
♦ a motivating beginning, focussing on the lesson and giving its main purpose and an overview of what the lesson will be about;
♦ some way to find out the entry level of the students, what they now know about the concept under consideration, what skills they already have or may need to develop;
♦ a tentative sequence of instructional events, including the teaching strategies to be used, questions to be asked and anticipated student questions, student participation, activities, etc.;
♦ a listing of materials needed, audiovisual resources, etc.;
♦ a plan for assessing children's progress toward expected outcomes;
♦ a closure of the lesson, with a summary of what has been learned;
♦ a discussion of questions that still remain, avenues for further exploration;
♦ a formative check of the lesson, with space for notes on what went well and what you might improve next time;
♦ and, for future reference, a note or two on unanticipated outcomes that have evolved during the learning experience.

This format will change with the kind of lesson, as you'll see when you discuss specific lessons. However, the basic components will be the same, and you will find it useful also to keep notes on how well a particular plan worked, how you modified it in actual practice, and, especially, students' reaction to it. Gradually you will build up a repertoire of lesson plans in which you will find yourself varying the teaching strategies, using your creative ingenuity and your artistry as a teacher to keep lessons interesting and to ensure that expected outcomes are realized.

With any lesson you plan there will be different degrees of child involvement, different ways your lesson will be perceived by children, different ways in which your carefully planned lesson will be translated into reality, and different degrees of progress toward achieving the desired outcomes.

◆ ◆ ◆ ◆ ◆

TEACHING STRATEGIES: THE TRANSMISSION ORIENTATION

If you consider actual practice in many primary and elementary classrooms in Canada, you will find that science is frequently taught in a transmission mode. Leithwood (1986) and colleagues at the Ontario Institute for Studies in Education suggest that most actual practice at all levels of schooling is transmission-oriented and that there is a significant gap between the intended curriculum and the curriculum as delivered. They suggest that there is an urgent need for teachers to incorporate a much more substantial element of transaction in the curriculum as practised. As you begin to teach, you will need to ask yourself which teaching strategies best reflect the nature of science and how children learn science, which strategies are most likely to achieve the goals of elementary science, and you will need to decide how often and for what purposes you would use each approach.

Expository Methods

Traditional ways of teaching are usually referred to as *expository methods* or *direct instruction*. Examples are the teacher's talking or "telling," showing a film, students' listening to a presentation by a resource person, and so on. Expository methods are associated with the *mastery of content,* especially in curriculum materials in which there are long, descriptive passages to read and relatively few activities as the basis for concept building.

In expository lessons, information is presented verbally without overt interaction between learners and the presenter. David Ausubel (1963) believes that even though interaction is hidden, it is present if someone is learning through the presentation and therefore is participating mentally. As pointed out in Chapter 4, Ausubel believes that if the information is clearly presented and linked to an already existing cognitive framework (or to what the learner already knows), it will be meaningful. He advocates the use of an outline of the main points to be covered in a lesson — an *advance organizer* — when presenting new material, so that the learner is given a framework to which subsequent learning can be linked. The remainder of the lesson is then presented in the same sequence in which the points were made in the advance organizer. If the learner already possesses knowledge related to the new material, Ausubel suggests starting with a *comparative organizer,* in which new material is linked or compared with what has been taught earlier. The extent of pupil involvement in expository teaching will depend on how meaningful and interesting the material is, how logical the order appears to the student, and the appropriateness of the level of abstraction in which the material is presented.

INCREASING PUPIL–TEACHER INTERACTION

To allow for more interaction, students' questions can be interspersed with the steps in the presentation. Students are involved to a greater extent as the teacher seeks input from them and tries to ensure that each step of the lesson has been understood before moving along to the next. To heighten interest, the overhead projector can be used or more concreteness added through charts, models, animation, sharing segments of a film, and so forth.

Your final decisions on when to use expository methods of instruction with children in the elementary grades will be made in the context of whatever you are teaching. Note that in the list that follows, each of the potential uses refers to a part of a lesson, rather than to a whole lesson. In other words, even if the thrust of a lesson is transactional or transformational, there are specific times within lessons when it is appropriate to present information and give instructions in a transmission mode.

SOME USES OF EXPOSITORY METHODS

Think about these possible uses of expository methods:

◆ Reviewing background material for the day's lesson, for example, going through the instructions for performing an activity.
◆ Presenting the key points of the lesson in the form of an "advance organizer," for example, outlining the purposes of a field trip and what the children will be doing.
◆ Demonstrating the steps children will follow in assembling apparatus, for example, setting up a cloud chamber.
◆ Demonstrating the use of a piece of equipment, for example, a balance, a microscope, or a wet and dry bulb thermometer.

Encouraging students' questions increases interaction and heightens interest in expository teaching methods.

- ◆ Demonstrating an experiment that would be unsafe for children to do on their own.
- ◆ "Wrapping up," or summarizing a lesson or the results of an investigation.

A WORD OF CAUTION

Verbal presentations, for whatever purpose, should be short. No matter how interesting the material, not all children will be attentive. Another difficulty may be that the sequence in which you present the material may be logical to you but not equally logical to the child.

There is also the danger that what is being heard may be clouded by the alternative frameworks children bring to the learning situation. In Chapter 4, you considered ways of dealing with children's misconceptions. Remember that a number of different strategies, including relevant concrete experiences, are sometimes needed to bring students' conceptions out into the open and help to clarify them.

activity 6.5 **A TRUE STORY**

Read the following selection from the Level 5 teacher's guide for the unit "Rocks in Layers" in the *Addison-Wesley Science* textbook series (Rockcastle et al. 1984). Reflect on the benefits of beginning an expository lesson in this way. Think about positive outcomes from using this approach. List a few.

FIGURE 6.2

A True Story

Dave's Discoveries

When Dave was about 10 years old, he liked to explore the vacant lots near his home. Here he discovered pieces of rock with shells and other interesting things in them. The best ones came from gullies and from old stone walls.

Sometimes in deep holes dug for new houses, Dave could see layers of bedrock in the ground. These were firm and solid far down. But higher up they were soft and crumbling. On top, the crumbling bedrock was covered by soil.

The firm rock had shells in it. But it was hard to get them. It was easier to pick them up where they had come loose from crumbling rock.

To protect the things he found, Dave wrapped them in newspaper. When he got home, he washed them carefully and put labels on them. Then he took some of the best ones to show at school.

It seemed to Dave that the layers of bedrock must once have been sediment under water. He supposed that the shells came from animals that lived in the water. When these animals died, their shells became buried by sediment. Then this later hardened into rock.

To find out more, Dave got books from the library. He read that shells and other remains of animals and plants in rock are called *fossils*.

Jobs Using Science

In time, Dave learned that most of his fossils were the shells of *brachiopods*. These animals live only in the sea. They are still living in the sea today. But they are not as common as they were long ago.
(continued)

Figure 6.2 (continued)

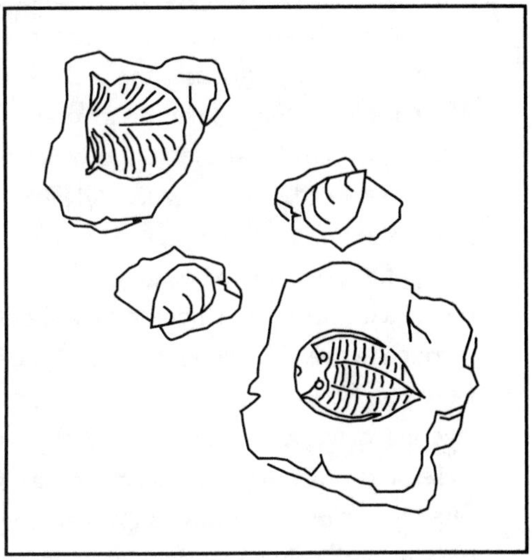

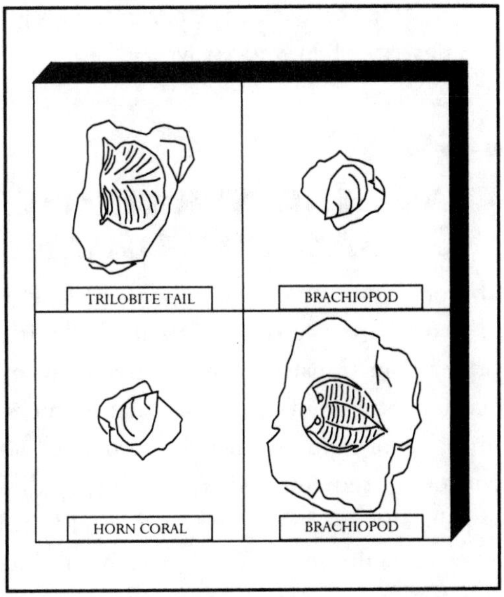

Dave also learned that some of his fossils were the skeletons of *corals*. Corals, too, are animals that live only in the sea.

One thing puzzled Dave. Why was he able to find fossils of sea animals near his home? He lived hundreds of kilometres from the sea, and many metres above sea level! Could it be that the sea covered his home area at one time? If so, why was it no longer there?

Dave found fossils of other kinds of sea animals too. These had strange names, like *trilobites, crinoids,* and *bryozoans*. Trilobites became very interesting to him because he read that these animals are no longer living. He was able to collect many fossils of trilobites. Mostly these were just pieces of skeletons. But he studied all the parts he could find — even their eyes!

Later, Dave became greatly interested in fossil crinoids, or "sea lilies." He learned that these were not plants, but animals related to sea stars. Many of them may have looked like flowers attached to the sea bottom by long stalks. Unlike trilobites, crinoids are still living today in the sea.

While in high school, Dave received top honours at the State Science Fair for his study of crinoids. He even discovered a kind of fossil crinoid that nobody had ever found before!

In time, Dave went to college to study geology. Best of all, he liked to go on fossil-collecting trips to faraway places. He kept finding out more about crinoids. He was even able to dive to the bottom of the sea to study living crinoids.

Today Dave is a college professor. He still studies fossils and teaches others about them. Now his students make their own discoveries!

Source: V.N. Rockcastle et al. (1984). *Addison-Wesley Science, Teacher's Guide, Level 5,* 60−61. Menlo Park, CA: Addison-Wesley. © Addison-Wesley Publishing Company, Menlo, CA.

❑ Reflecting and Sharing

Reading aloud "A True Story" is a unique way of introducing an expository lesson, one that has been employed by teachers often in the context of language development, but perhaps not as often in the context of science teaching. The story puts a 10-year-old's interest in his discoveries at the centre of the picture and gives other children a focus for the lesson to which they can relate. Best of all, the story about this 10-year-old, Dave, is true, and all the illustrations on the pages of the teacher's guide, shown in Figure 6.2, are Dave's own illustrations of his fossil specimens.

In this case, the expository lesson is appropriately placed since it comes at the end of a unit in which students have spent weeks learning about sedimentary rocks through active involvement in a series of real-life, concrete experiences, including field trips to look for layers in bedrock and rock cuts; activities on settling and layering of rock particles; and opportunities to collect and observe sandstone, shale, and other sedimentary rocks, as well as to look at various types of fossils. The "true story" is a way of bringing together and reinforcing the ideas that have been gained from a unit that has been largely transactional in nature.

Do you think the story of Dave's interest in fossils has transformational qualities as well? In which ways?

◆ ◆ ◆ ◆ ◆

TEACHING STRATEGIES: THE TRANSACTION ORIENTATION

Underlying transactional models of teaching/learning is the constructivist theory of knowledge, the view that knowledge is constructed in the mind of the learner, rather than transferred intact from the mind of the teacher to the mind of the learner. The theory proposes that learners construct understanding as they try to organize new knowledge in terms of what they already know, and that they constantly redefine existing concepts through interaction with their peers and objects and events in the environment. Bodner (1986) suggests that to apply this view to children's learning means a shift in perspective for the teacher from someone who "teaches" to someone who tries to facilitate learning — a shift from a passive role for the student to one of active involvement in learning. The constructivist model calls for a dialogue between teacher and student in which the teacher requires students to explain their answers, whether they are right or wrong, and to reflect on their knowledge.

Inquiry/discovery-based methods of teaching and learning facilitate the construction of knowledge. In Chapter 7, in the context of more specific inquiring,

---

✏️ **From a Teacher's Journal**

Great science lessons are those in which students take command of the situation and expand the lesson beyond the parameters established by the teacher. I remember one occasion when the lesson had begun with the challenge to design a paper airplane that would glide longer than any other, or fly the farthest. After thinking of a number of variables that might affect the length of time the paper airplane would stay in the air, the class had tested one variable, weight, by adding paper clips to the body of the plane to determine the effect of increased weight. The class was left with the question of what other things might make a difference to the flight. It was rewarding to go out at recess time and see the students flying paper airplanes all over the playground, expanding the first experiment to include the testing of slight changes in the design of the planes — different kinds of paper, flaps on the back of the wings, different angles for the flaps, how to make the tests fair — all of this from the simple challenge, with the promise of a great discussion next day on experimental design, controlling variables, and so on. To see the students take this beginning and expand it to further play and further possibilities for problem solving was extremely satisfying.

Bob Benmore

Gibsons, BC

---

problem-solving, motivating, and questioning skills and techniques, you will explore the use of discrepant events (puzzling phenomena that seem to defy common sense) in initiating inquiry. There are many ways in which children can be involved in inquiry-based learning. Children's experiences can range from simple explorations of the environment in the early years to opportunities in the elementary grades to find answers to questions and solutions to problems in which they become interested. Interests may evolve either from child-initiated experiences or from starting points for inquiry they will find in the rich environment for learning that is provided in your classroom.

Learning through Inquiry/Discovery

In inquiry/discovery-based lessons, teacher and student are fellow investigators, partners in discovery. The classroom is one in which children are working in threes and fours with concrete materials, while the teacher circulates from group to group, listening to children and supplying the feedback and extra materials they need to pursue new questions that arise. There is the notion of learning by doing, of hands-on, minds-on science, where the answers come not so much from the teacher or other authority but from what is there in 3-D, as Verne Rockcastle (1974) puts it, as children work together in groups on science investigations.

The next activity will involve you in an instructional method that falls under the transaction orientation and guided-discovery methodology. You'll examine the *Science 5/13* approach and follow one of the starting points for learning in the teacher's guide for the unit "Science from Toys."

In inquiry/discovery-based lessons, the teacher circulates from group to group, listening to children and supplying the feedback and extra materials they need to pursue new questions that arise.

SCIENCE 5/13

In *Science 5/13,* children gather experiences by exploring the physical and biological environment, and teachers guide these explorations by encouraging their students to develop inquiring minds, to ask questions, and to find answers, freely communicating what they feel and what they find. A variety of teaching techniques are used, including discussion between teacher and child, and between child and child. Children are encouraged to communicate their observations by talking about them, writing, building up a whole new vocabulary of words and phrases based on their experiences. Although "practical discovery" is important, it is recognized that "looking," "reading," and "asking" are other ways in which children discover something new to them. The theme of the unit from which this lesson is drawn is that science lies hidden in toys — in spinning toys; in toys that use springs; in toys that make noises, sounds, or music; in dolls and dollhouses; in boats and bouncing balls; in trains and cars and playground toys.

---

activity 6.6 — BOUNCING BALLS: A SCIENCE 5/13 DISCOVERY LESSON

The investigation can arise naturally from a game on the playground or the teacher's picking up a ball on a desk and bouncing it on the floor. The question that arises is: What can you find out about the bounciness of a ball?

Children will tackle this problem in different ways depending on their age and development. These are some directions that the inquiry may take:

- ◆ Children may drop the ball and see how high it bounces.
- ◆ They may go on to relate the height of bounce to the height from which it is dropped.
- ◆ Children may investigate surfaces of various materials and kinds — pieces of wood, foam rubber, tiles, two sides of corrugated cardboard, metal, sand, linoleum, carpet.
- ◆ They may use balls of various types — rubber balls of different types, ball bearings of different sizes, Plasticine balls.
- ◆ They may investigate the paths of bouncing balls.

Remember that the teacher's role is to watch and listen, to help and guide, to ask the right questions at the right time, and to stimulate discussion.

Some of the questions generated by teachers and/or pupils during the bouncing balls activity, in the section "Using a Rubber Ball," are:

- ◆ How high does the ball bounce?
- ◆ How can you measure it?
- ◆ How many times does the ball bounce?
- ◆ Does the surface on which you bounce the ball have any effect on the height of the bounce? Does the ball mark the surface?
- ◆ Does the ball bounce on sand? Collect a number of rubber balls of different colours and sizes. Do they all bounce to the same height if dropped the same distance?
- ◆ How many things can you change to alter the bounce of balls? (55)

Figure 6.3 shows a chart of topics that have arisen from bouncing balls when

FIGURE 6.3

Topics That Have Arisen from Bouncing Balls

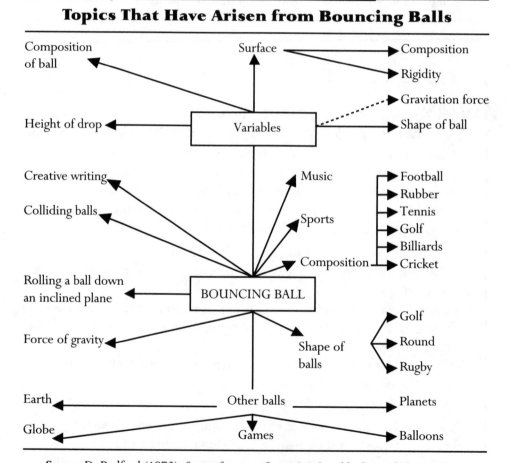

Source: D. Radford (1972). *Science from toys: Stages 1 & 2 and background. Science 5/13.* Unit for Teachers, 56. London: Macdonald Educational. Reproduced with permission from Simon & Schuster Education, Hemel Hampstead, UK.

this unit has been taught in Britain. Could you add any other possible topics? Think of some questions you could use to stimulate interest and encourage investigations of the bounce of the ball bearings. Do you think that this approach would work well with the whole class, or, because of the teacher guidance needed, would be better done in small groups, while the rest of the class is occupied with other things?

☐ Reflecting and Sharing

Imagine yourself as a teacher in the style of *Science 5/13*. Three girls have just broken away from a group of seven or eight students who had been clustered around you. One has a notebook, and sketches what she sees as the other two throw the ball back and forth to each other. You are still spending time with the rest of the "bouncing ball" group. One child has ball bearings in his hand and you begin to improvise a ramp, using a hinged board and a stack of books.

A larger group that has been exploring the topic of "dolls" from the same unit on toys is busy wiring a dollhouse. Some children are making switches and others are installing bulb holders and connecting wires. At the art table, children are making curtains and floor rugs for the dollhouse, which occupies a space just inside the classroom door. There is a large chart on the wall of the corridor outside the classroom, on which children have recorded the bounce heights of different rubber balls. One child has written a paragraph about how the experiment was done and what the results were. It all looks confusing yet there is order there as well — perhaps from the impression of busyness that pervades, the sense that everyone has a job to do.

Perhaps you could carry this notion a little further now as you examine a view of science teaching that, while recognizing that science sometimes needs to be taught purely as science, and that there is a need within the school curriculum to preserve its integrity as a vehicle for gradual development of science concepts, skills, and attitudes, also recognizes the potential for mutual reinforcement of science and other areas of the curriculum. Your next teaching strategy in a transactional mode is one that models and takes into account the wholeness of knowledge and uses topical themes as an integrating framework for presenting science experiences and making connections across traditional subject lines.

Science across the Curriculum

The potential of science for integration with and enhancement of other subject areas has often been overlooked. And yet, if learning is to be meaningful, it must be applicable to a young child's world. Beginning a thematic unit broadens the opportunity for constructing knowledge by encouraging children to pursue in depth an interest in a specific topic that can be extended across the curriculum and enrich all areas in the process.

Science in our daily lives is not compartmentalized, but permeates our society and freely crosses artificial subject-matter barriers. In the teaching of science, we should therefore take full advantage of the natural bridges that exist between science and language arts, science and social studies, science and drama, science and music, science and art. Whatever the topic chosen, the rewards for both children and teachers will be great, because learning is enhanced as new interests and new directions evolve from the original investigation. In a holistic approach to curriculum, the barriers disappear as concepts are built and skills acquired that enrich all areas of learning.

From a Teacher's Journal

I have found that integrated units are a great method of teaching. Although there is a lot more work in the initial planning, the success of the units and the children's excitement more than make up for the additional effort.

A unit on water is always a favourite. One that I have used began with a reading unit, "I Like Water," and led to a variety of learning experiences inside and outside the classroom, involving a number of subject areas. One of the main activities I would recommend to teachers is to arrange a bus trip to look for water in the environment. If the trip takes place in late fall, children may encounter half-frozen puddles on the ground as they walk to the school bus. If your school is near the coast, the bus route could take you where children can see the ocean and a river. You may also see a lake, and note that the lake, like the puddles, is also beginning to freeze, while the river and

(continued)

✎ **From a Teacher's Journal (continued)**

the ocean as yet show no signs of freezing, and children wonder why.

Back at school, the unit goes on as children find interesting books in the resource centre, use water colours and washes to depict what they have seen, and include in their illustrations water as rain, water as snow, and water as ice. There are a multitude of science experiments with water, and these can be set up at work stations, along with measurement activities. The paintings and the records of the day's activities go into simple journals as children are encouraged by these high-interest experiences to write about their discoveries. The learning in such a unit is almost unlimited and can encompass goals in many subject areas, depending on the teacher's imagination and the choices children make along the way.

Brenda Dunsmore

Hampton, NB

Science and Language Development

Science and language arts are mutually reinforcing and mutually enhancing. Starting points for language development are present in all stages of science investigations, from the motivation to read the directions for a science activity to the desire to put into words what is observed and what is discovered in the course of that activity. The very acts of observing, of putting things into classes on the basis of observed properties, and of ordering things from light to dark, from smooth to rough, from short to tall are all pre-reading skills. It has been suggested that science could very well be the backbone of the curriculum in the primary and elementary grades, providing the enjoyable experiences that encourage discussion, writing, reading, spelling, and listening. Reading becomes meaningful when children read what the teacher has written, with their prompting, on an experience chart, and when they read science trade books to find out more about a science topic in which they have become interested. Writing becomes meaningful when children record in their own words and share with others the results of their observations, when they enter data on a chart, write a descriptive narrative in a science log, or are inspired to compose poetry on a nature theme such as the poem on "Clouds" in Figure 6.4. Speaking and listening skills are enhanced during a discussion or role-play on an environmental issue, or as children interact in co-operative learning groups or explain their projects at a science fair. In science, accurate observation and precise description are encouraged. Vocabulary development is a natural outcome of science learning as new words and their meanings are derived from concrete experiences.

FIGURE 6.4

Clouds

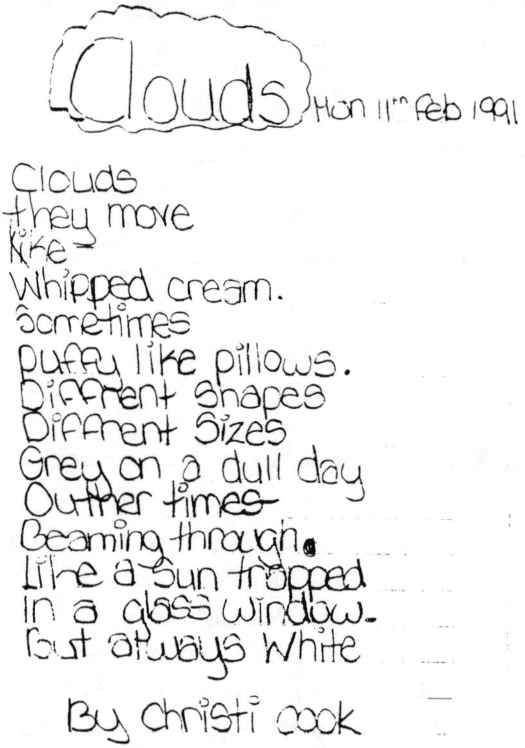

Clouds   Mon 11ᵗʰ Feb 1991

Clouds
they move
like
Whipped cream.
Sometimes
puffy like pillows.
Diffrent shapes
Diffrent Sizes
Grey on a dull day
Outher times
Beaming through
like a Sun trapped
in a glass window.
But always white

By Christi cook

Source: Reprinted with permission from Christi, Orde Street Public School, Toronto.

Science 5/13 recognizes this potential in the mapping and semantic webbing that develop in almost every unit as teacher and child explore together directions that learning can take. The *Science 5/13* teachers' guides, some of the newer provincially developed materials, and a number of large-scale programs developed recently in the United States (such as the *Insights* modules) and Canada (such as *Innovations in Science*) are all representative of the trend toward a holistic curriculum in which science and language are seen as natural partners in learning.

Language Arts and Science

The trend is most noticeable in the *Innovations in Science* materials, where poetry and stories become entry points into science explorations, where children's journals are a record of their observations, and where bridges between science and other subject areas are freely crossed. Children explore problems that have significance to them because they are part of their everyday life and the environment in which they live and work and play. Language development and communication are integral components of science learning, and in turn science experiences provide a meaningful experience base that children want to write, talk, read, and construct new meanings about.

A thematic unit on trees can broaden learning potential in many subject areas. Children are motivated to read and experiment on their own. A book about trees can add to science learning and develop language skills.

INNOVATIONS IN SCIENCE

When an environmental ethic is interwoven with these themes, as in *Innovations in Science*, and when knowledge is seen not as fragmented but as part of a totality of experience, the approach is closer and closer to the transformation orientation. Watch for shades of both orientations — transaction and transformation — in the next activity.

activity 6.7

WANTED—DEAD OR ALIVE: AN *INNOVATIONS IN SCIENCE* LESSON

This lesson is the fifth in a series of seven lessons that over the school year make up the Grade 2 theme "A Tree for All Seasons" (Figure 6.5). Children are invited to adopt trees in their community and observe them all year. Suggestions for establishing the theme are a walk around the neighbourhood to locate their trees for adoption, setting up a tree centre in the classroom, inviting a gardener or forester to speak to the children, and using a list of reference books and story books with a science focus. The concept is growth and change over time as the seasons come and go, and the experiences and related literature are designed to build ideas, skills, appreciations, and aesthetic awareness.

Before this lesson, children have observed their trees in late summer, autumn, and winter; compared and measured and kept records of seasonal changes; made bark rubbings; shared information about their trees; mapped their locations; made a class book about trees, with a picture and a piece of writing on each page; classified fallen leaves gathered on a leaf walk; made leaf prints; and looked at twigs. They have looked for basic tree shapes, made silhouettes, twig sculptures, and abstract pictures, and are now ready to learn about the usefulness of trees. In subsequent lessons, they will revisit their trees in the spring, observe budding twigs, plant tree seeds, and finally translate knowledge and appreciation into concern as they learn about the importance of trees and the need for conservation and reforestation.

Here are the steps in the lesson plan:

1. Read aloud "Once There Was a Tree," by Natalia Romanova, which portrays how even after a woodcutter has cut down an old tree it is still a home and source of food for many kinds of wildlife.
2. Have children identify in the classroom and around the school objects made of wood. They learn that paper is made from wood and how to make their own paper as well as recycle scrap paper.
3. An art project develops as the handmade paper is used to make paintings and notepaper gifts.

4. Children are encouraged to write compositions about trees, copy them into their Tree Journals, record them on tape, and share them in small groups. Drama is introduced as each child pretends to be an animal and tells how the tree provides a home and food.

5. Everyone brings in pieces of rotting wood, and groups examine the wood and look for evidence of life, temporarily housing creatures in pill bottles until they are released into the environment.

6. In anticipation of spring and the next lesson in this theme, children write a poem that describes the sights, sounds, smells, and textures they will sense when spring arrives. They compare their poems with this poem:

I'll know it's spring when
I can see buds swell
I can hear birds sing
I can smell the scent of blossoms
I can touch smooth new leaves
And then I'll feel like walking in the rain.

Think about your reaction to this sequence of activities. What outcomes for children would you anticipate from this lesson? from the whole unit as described above? Remember to include affective and social outcomes (attitudes, appreciations, interests, values), psychomotor outcomes (manipulative skills), along with the cognitive outcomes (concepts, processes, thinking skills).

Source: Rod Peturson et al. (1990). *Innovations in Science — Level 2,* 25. Copyright © Holt, Rinehart and Winston of Canada, Limited. Reproduced by kind permission.

❑ Reflecting and Sharing

To help you reflect further on instructional planning for a unit such as the one described, think of yourself as the teacher at this point in the unit, and imagine how your classroom might look and sound.

It is February. The theme "A Tree for All Seasons" is evident in the classroom. The large theme cards decorate the room and serve as a focal point for the lessons and a composite framework for the unit. The story "Once There Was a Tree" is reproduced in a large format in the library centre, along with a number of other books about trees. There are sand tables and a water area and a science table with newspapers. On the newspapers are pieces of bark and rotting wood, with hand lenses close by and pill vials with damp leaves to make temporary homes for captured creatures. On the bulletin board are samples of children's writing and some of the bark rubbings from earlier lessons.

FIGURE 6.5

A Tree for All Seasons

Title of learning event/focus	Objectives — The children will have opportunities to:	Theme cards
Adopt a Tree Children adopt neighbourhood trees for study during the year and make observations about the physical characteristics of the trees.	◆ observe and record the characteristics of selected trees. ◆ measure the parts of their trees using standard and nonstandard measurement tools.	**Adopt a Tree — 1** A discussion picture showing young children among a variety of trees. The children will be shown observing trees from various angles and positions, measuring the trees using standard and nonstandard units (e.g., metric measuring tape, hands, string, etc.), and drawing the trees.
Autumn Leaves By examining and classifying, children identify the characteristics of leaves.	◆ examine and classify leaves. ◆ measure the area of a leaf using non-standard units. ◆ discover that leaves contain moisture.	**Leaves — 2** Labelled illustrations of leaves from a variety of Canadian trees. The trees represented will include: pine, tamarack, spruce, fir, cedar, polar, birch, oak, elm, maple, ash.
Tree Shapes By observing the shapes of their adopted trees and comparing them with others in the neighbourhood, children discover that trees have many different shapes.	◆ identify different types of leaves. ◆ compare tree shapes to basic geometric shapes. ◆ observe how branches determine shape.	**What Kind of Tree Are You? — 3** Several verses of a song by Charlotte Diamond.

Figure 6.5 (continued)

Winter Watch Children observe trees in winter, and study and compare tree trunks. ◆ identify the seasonal changes that occur in trees from fall to winter. ◆ examine the trunks of trees to study bark and growth rings.	***The Most Important Thing about Bark — 4*** An illustration of a tree with the bark and the limbs as the focal point, and a variety of facts and observations pertaining to bark.
Wanted: Dead or Alive Using both observation and prior knowledge, children investigate the usefulness of trees. ◆ discover the usefulness and importance of trees. ◆ identify objects in their environment that are made from trees.	
Spring Has Sprung By observing branches and buds, children become aware of the ways that trees change in springtime. ◆ observe the ways trees change in the spring. ◆ examine tree branches for buds and bud scars.	***The Seasons of Arnold's Apple Tree — 5*** Illustrations from the story by Gail Gibbons, depicting an apple tree during spring, summer, winter, and fall.
Helping Trees Children discover how to care for trees and contribute to the conservation of this valuable resource. ◆ explore ways in which trees can be protected and preserved. ◆ practise ways of helping trees through role playing. ◆ discuss what they have learned about trees.	***How Do You Treat a Tree? — 6*** A discussion picture showing people helping and hurting trees.

Source: Rod Peturson et al. (1990). *Innovations in Science — Level 2,* 1–3. Copyright © 1990 Holt, Rinehart and Winston of Canada, Limited. Reproduced by kind permission.

You have assigned roles to the group members. The "equipment manager" picks up the materials needed, distributes them to the others in her group, and later returns them to the science centre. The "organizer" makes sure that everyone in the group has an opportunity to do the activity; the "recorder" is responsible for deciding how to record the data and keep notes; and the "sharer" obtains information from other groups and decides how they can share the group's results.

The children are seated together at round tables, and the "equipment manager" from one group has just picked up the materials for today's activity from the work area near the centre, which seems to have lots of materials still for extended activities. Today there is a large collection of articles that have been brought from home. They are all made from wood, and one group is busy making labels for the articles and writing brief descriptions about their usefulness in everyday life. Other groups have begun to examine the pieces of rotting wood and bark. There is a clear area where the children will gather around you at the end of the activity and talk about their observations. Later they will write about what spring will be like — how it will look and sound and smell and feel, and what changes they will see in their trees when spring comes. The poem "Spring Is Sprung," printed on a huge poster, is near your chair, waiting to be read aloud.

Cognitive outcomes? Affective outcomes? Psychomotor outcomes? Social outcomes? Share and compare your lists, and continue to think about expected outcomes not just for science but for all areas of the curriculum.

◆ ◆ ◆ ◆ ◆

TEACHING STRATEGIES: THE TRANSFORMATION ORIENTATION

Did you think that some of the potential outcomes of the last lesson were close to the transformation orientation to curriculum? Carl Rogers, who is associated with this orientation, is noted in psychiatry for his belief in client-centred therapy, which is characterized by "genuineness, unconditioned positive regard for the patient and empathic understanding" (Freedman, Kaplan, and Sadock 1977, 36). The patient is believed to have the ability to improve. The therapist merely helps the client to clarify his or her own thinking and feelings.

As mentioned earlier, this orientation translates in education into an emphasis on the needs and interests of the learner rather than subject matter as the primary source of learning objectives, although subject matter may be chosen that focusses on and promotes basic literacy skills, problem-solving skills, and self-awareness. According to the Weinstein and Fantini (1970) transformation model of curriculum development, diagnosis of the needs of the learner is a basic first step, and instruction is aimed at self-determination. *Social concerns* and *envi-*

ronmental ethics are the domain of this orientation, and an important aspect is the reconciliation of the child's inner and outer worlds — the self and the community. In Canada's multicultural society, this is particularly important. Children from a non-Western background may relate more readily than do children of Western families to the transformation orientation. To illustrate the transformation orientation, two units are chosen. The *Insights* module focusses on social concerns and the appreciation of individual differences. The Earth Day ceremony, "Ceremony of the Rock," focusses on the development of environmental ethics and appreciation for the environment.

INSIGHTS

At times an example is worth a thousand words, and with that in mind it is worthwhile to work through a unit from a new American elementary science curriculum, *Insights*, produced at the Educational Development Center in Newton, Massachusetts, where the original Elementary Science Study (ESS) units had been developed and tested 30 years earlier. Instead of being organized by subject matter, five organizing themes run through the program — structure and function, diversity, change, growth, and cause and effect. As shown in Figure 6.6, the teaching–learning framework guides each lesson through four phases: Getting Started, Exploring and Discovering, Processing for Meaning, and Extending Ideas.

FIGURE 6.6

Insights: Teaching–Learning Framework

Teaching–Learning Framework

The "Myself and Others" module is organized around a series of "learning experiences," science activities that you guide your students through to explore and discover science concepts. Any given learning experience will include all or some combination of the following four phases: Getting Started, Exploring and Discovering, Processing for Meaning, and Extending Ideas.

Phase 1: Getting Started	
TEACHER	**STUDENTS**
probes for current knowledge and understanding	*share ideas*
	raise questions
	make connections
motivates and stimulates	*predict*
sets challenges and poses problems	*set goals*

Figure 6.6 (continued)

Children's involvement in an experience usually begins with a full discussion in which they share with you and their classmates their experience and knowledge about the topic. By creating an open atmosphere in which children feel free to express their ideas (even those that may be incorrect) and ask questions, you can assess their prior knowledge and experience, and at the same time set challenges and stimulate their curiosity about the subject. Discussions also encourage children to think about *how* they think, a valuable exercise for the developing scientific mind.

Phase 2: Exploring and Discovering

TEACHER	STUDENTS	CO-OPERATIVE GROUPS
observes	*observe*	*discuss ideas*
facilitates	*explore*	
mediates	*collect data*	*divide, share, and*
assesses	*compare*	*complete tasks*
	organize	
	question	*prepare reports*
	problem solve	
	interpret and analyze	
	communicate	

During Phase 2, children work directly with science materials, using their observation and inquiry skills to explore phenomena. Adequate time for exploration is crucial so that children can learn to work with materials and engage in trial and retrial as they close in on their discoveries. Most often children work in small groups (which, keep in mind, do make noise), in which they have the opportunity to trade ideas, share tasks and strategies, and prepare reports they present to the class. During exploration, children record their ideas and discoveries on Science Notebook Pages, using words, graphs, and pictures.

Phase 3: Processing for Meaning

TEACHER	STUDENTS
questions	*organize*
	evaluate
guides students	*problem solve*
assesses student	*use models*
understanding	*interpret and analyze*
	synthesize

Figure 6.6 *(continued)*

In Phase 3, children come together as a class to discuss what they observed and experienced during their explorations. The discussion focusses on helping children identify and articulate science concepts. As discussion leader, your role is to guide children as they clarify ideas, organize their thinking, compare different solutions, and analyze and interpret results. They often use their Science Notebook Pages to go into greater detail to explain their results or illustrate their understanding of a particular science concept.

Phase 4: Extending Ideas

TEACHER	STUDENTS
facilitates	*apply*
	integrate
assesses student	*question*
understanding	*infer*
	create and invent

In the last phase of a learning experience, children relate new ideas to old ones and connect their learning in the module to other curricular areas and to life outside the classroom. Extension activities are intended for the classroom. Home–school work suggestions allow children the opportunity to share their discoveries with their families and community.

Source: Insights: A Hands-On Elementary Science Curriculum (1990), 10–11.
Education Development Center, Scotts Valley, CA: Wings for Learning.

In the last two phases, children have opportunities to clarify their thinking and build structures, and finally to relate new ideas to life outside the classroom as well as to new curriculum areas, raising new questions that have evolved since the Getting Started phase.

activity 6.8 AN *INSIGHTS* LESSON (GRADE 1)

The "Myself and Others" module "encourages the development of positive attitudes and values, a sense of uniqueness and self-esteem, an appreciation of diversity, and specifically an appreciation of others who are different" (44). It begins with an introductory interview with each child, in which students discuss how they think about themselves. This helps teachers to focus their teaching, and at the end of the module to determine through a repeat of the interview how much growth there has been. Learning experiences throughout the unit give children the opportunity to highlight things that are special about themselves, to look at physical characteristics and classify them as shared by all, shared by a few, or unique to individuals.

Children draw self-portraits, share experiences about feelings, make body outlines, measure each other, make handprints and fingerprints, discuss hands, handfuls, eyes, hair, the texture and colour of their skin, and extend their concept of time in relation to themselves (making a chart about what they were like as babies, the things they have learned since then, and things they will be able to do when they are bigger and have learned more). They complete their body outlines, putting in additional features and clues so that someone else can recognize them, and discuss their outlines to determine in which ways they are the same as others, different from others, and unique.

Imagine the classroom, with children of different racial and ethnic origins working together in groups involved in Learning Experience 11, which has to do with the colour of their skin. The teacher's guide gives this advice: "Skin colour can be a sensitive issue. Young children are very aware of differences and may already have negative responses to skin darker or lighter than their own. Respond directly to any negative comments. Also highlight the diversity and variation in the class and use the poster, pictures, and books to create a positive climate for discussion about differences" (44). Now follow the sequence for learning that is repeated in each module of the program.

Getting Started. The teacher reviews the chart from the previous lesson that focussed on skin texture and fingerprints, highlighting words and phrases that describe color. The children are told that they are going to be using special crayons to find a colour or colour mixture that matches their skin.

Exploring and Discovering. Materials trays are distributed to children working in pairs. They are asked to try to find a colour or colour mixture that matches the skin on the back of their hands. The children work together on each other's skin colour and experiment on pieces of paper, describing in their science notebooks the colour they chose for themselves and for their partners. If time permits, they draw their faces, using the skin colour.

Processing for Meaning. Children discuss similarities and variations of skin colour. The teacher ends this session with a discussion of study prints, and reads aloud the poem "Your Skin and Mine" by Paul Showers.

Extending Ideas. The children generate as many words and phrases as they can to describe a series of colours. At home, using books and study prints, the children and their families explore cultural similarities and differences between people of diverse backgrounds. They explore relationships between hair, eye, and skin colour.

Reflect on the differences between the "Myself and Others" approach to instruction and others that have been discussed in this chapter.

❑ Reflecting and Sharing

Imagine the classroom in which all this is occurring as your own. Imagine that the unit is about two-thirds over, and the results of all the explorations and discoveries are hung on a clothesline strung across the room. There are height charts, children's drawings of themselves, a large poster displaying hand prints, and another titled "Our Hair Type," with children's names arranged under three headings — curly, wavy, and straight — as shown in Figure 6.7.

Today the topic is "the colour of our skin," and you are exploring along with the children, joining the groups of two as they mix their colours and try to reproduce the colour of their skin and their partners' skin. Right now you are handling a question a child has asked about whether a black person tans. You recognize it as a question that needs to be answered in a common-sense way, and deal with it in this light. You make a mental note to respond directly to any hurtful comments and handle those on the spot as well, bringing all problems and concerns out into the open, and emphasizing qualities and characteristics that contribute positively to a child's uniqueness.

You hope that the final interviews at the end of the unit will show not only an improvement in the quality and richness of the descriptive language children will use, but also growth in their understanding and appreciation of human differences. You have involved parents from the beginning of this unit, so that they too could help their children with the expansion of self-awareness that the module has made possible.

The transformation orientation lends itself to interdisciplinary units with starting points such as the "Myself and Others" theme just discussed, or a topic just as relevant to children's lives — the environment in which they live. The unit on trees

FIGURE 6.7

"Myself and Others": Our Hair Type

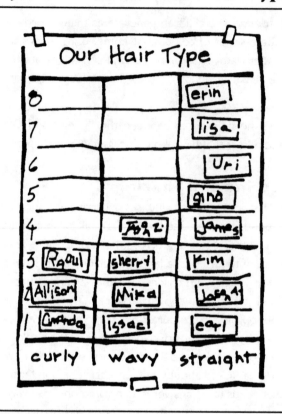

Source: Insights: An Elementary Hands-On Inquiry Science Curriculum Preview Packet, Grades K–1 (1992), 115. Education Development Center, Scotts Valley, CA: Wings for Learning.

from the *Innovations in Science* program focussed on the environment, with the potential for cultivating in the early school years attitudes of aesthetic awareness and appreciation of nature. Consider now the potential in the following Earth Day ceremony for building concepts and developing attitudes and appreciations in science, and also for extending beyond science into the whole of life on this planet, creating environmental awareness and clarifying values for elementary students.

activity
6.9
EARTH DAY, 1990:
THE CEREMONY OF THE ROCK

1. Read Dr. Susan Ahearn's account (Figure 6.8) of the ceremony to celebrate Earth Day that took place in St. John's, Newfoundland, in 1990.
2. Think of the elements that went into the planning for this special day, and think of ways you could prepare a group of elementary students to take part meaningfully in the ceremony. Could it be, for example, the culminating activity in a science unit begun a few weeks earlier? If so, what might have been the content of such a unit? Remember, there are a number of ways the unit can be approached and developed. Use your collective imaginations.
3. Jot down the ideas that your group came up with, and later compare them with the ideas of other groups.
4. Dr. Ahearn suggests the opportunity for values clarification afforded by these experiences. Comment on this and think about how you might handle the next lesson after the ceremony.

FIGURE 6.8

The Ceremony of the Rock

On Earth Day, 1990, many local residents of St. John's, Newfoundland, met on Signal Hill, overlooking the harbour and the city, to welcome the rising sun as it appeared over the Atlantic Ocean. Organizers of these Earth Day festivities wanted to create an opportunity for people to make a personal commitment to work for the betterment of the planet. Drawing upon my knowledge of values clarification, I developed "The Ceremony of the Rock."

The idea was to build on the symbolism of "Rock." Newfoundlanders are surrounded by rock, the island of Newfoundland has been dubbed "the Rock," and rock represents strength, endurance, having survived throughout the ages. Indeed, many of the rocks of the island are some of the oldest in the world. Most people are attracted to certain rocks because of their colour, shape, or size, and most people are fascinated by beach stones because they are round and smooth, with regular patterns.

My children and I selected one hundred of the most magnificent beach pebbles we could find from a local cove and carried them up to Signal Hill for the sunrise events. At the appropriate moment in the program, I came forward to share a story of rock, told to me by Oglala Lakota (Sioux) oral historian Charlotte Black Elk and considered sacred by these people. *(continued)*

Figure 6.8 (continued)

"The Lakota tell of Inyan who existed at the time of first motion, before anything had meaning. Within Inyan was the spirit beyond understanding, known as Wakan Tanka. Inyan was soft and supple and his blood was blue. Inyan became lonely so he created others from himself, containing some of his power, spirit, and motion, and these others were forever attached to himself. First he created Maka (Earth), a disc which he wrapped around himself and allowed his blood (Mini) to run throughout (waters of Earth). The rest of his power was sent upwards and is known as Marpiyo To (Sky). Inyan reduced himself so much that he became hard, brittle, and still. Now he is inyan (rock). Maka, Mini, and Marpiyo To each co-create a source of light (Amp) which has no heat and no meaning. Maka is cold so they again co-create Wi (Sun) who is placed above for heat and light. Maka is sent circling throughout the realm of Marpiyo To so as to give her some rest from heat. Maka is barren and decides to cover herself. She creates her children which are a part of her, nourished from her and attached to her forever. These children are: (1) those who move and grow (Plants and Fishes), (2) the winged, (3) the four-legged, and (4) Mato with quiet wisdom (Bear). Then she creates the Maker of Choices, Winyan, whose name means "you are complete," and this is Woman. As a companion to Winyan, Maka creates Wica who is a step from completion, and this is Man."

After the story, I encouraged all participants to select a beach pebble from the pile and to make a thumb print on it, using the ink pad provided. Each person was asked to silently make a commitment to participate in some future action on behalf of the Earth. The personalization of the thumb print and the personal statement were combined with the individual action of throwing the pebble over the cliffs into the sea. I assumed that every-one loves to throw rocks, and everyone could easily accomplish this feat. Indeed everyone at that sunrise ceremony on Signal Hill climbed the short distance to the summit to throw a rock into the sea. Although they were not asked to share their personal statements of commitment, many chose to do so as they tossed their rocks. We left the unused rocks at the visitors' centre and later I heard that throughout the day, visitors who heard of the sunrise ceremony tossed selected beach pebbles into the sea as well.

This personal act involved a large crowd of people, of all ages, in a collective action that heightened their environmental awareness. Participants could choose to be private or public about their commitments. A small action such as this, which is memorable, exciting ("How far can I make my rock fly?" "Will it reach the water?" "Who can throw their rock the farthest?"), highly participatory, inclusive, and easy, can do much to change the way people think about themselves, their planet, and their responsibilities.

Source: S. Ahearn (1990). Earth Day. The Ceremony of the Rock. Typescript. Faculty of Education, Memorial University of Newfoundland. Director, The Field School and Athene Expeditions International.

❑ Reflecting and Sharing

This Earth Day experience takes the students out of the classroom for the preliminary preparation as well as for the ceremony. In many rural schools in Newfoundland, it would be relatively easy to transport a class of Grade 4 or 5 students to a nearby beach to gather a collection of beautifully rounded beach rocks. (Even in St. John's, a school bus could be at a beach in less than twenty minutes.)

You may envisage this value-laden ceremony as the culminating activity, though not the last lesson, in an integrated unit on "Water and the Land." The topic may have evolved from remembered experiences in earlier grades when children had compared handfuls of soil and sand, or experienced water as rain and snow and hail; water in basins and oceans; running water in streams and rivers and its effects on the land; invisible water escaping into the air and becoming visible again as clouds and rain. Expanding these ideas into an integrated unit would heighten interest and enhance learning and understanding, especially in view of the timing of the unit just before the Earth Day celebration.

There would be no end to the questions. How many waves must have pounded on the shore to make stones as smooth and round as those we picked up on the beach? How old are these rocks, anyway? How could we find out? Did the ocean do all of the rounding or did it begin in the river beds? Perhaps with heavy rain or snow or ice?

It is only a step to cross the bridge to social studies as maps are consulted to locate nearby rivers, and science activities on rainfall lead to discussions on weather and weather forecasting. There is a need, then, to make a chart on which to record the rainfall each day, and a need to enter in science journals what has been found out about the possible age of these Newfoundland rocks. The maps and charts can be placed on a bulletin board in a rapidly growing thematic centre. On one end of the interest table there is a beginning collection of other "worn" objects that the children have been bringing to school — shells of snails and sea urchins and sand dollars blanched and smoothed by sun and wind and sea.

The incentive to write stories and poems about these objects, about the rocks and the sea, is just a child's thought away, and you, the teacher, encourage this by collecting poetry to read aloud and enjoy in class and afterward add to the bulletin board. The Indian legend becomes an incentive for children to find other stories related to nature and how people of different origins perceive nature.

A final lesson or two gives students an opportunity to discuss the way they felt about the experience; the way it moved them; the attitudes that may have been either confirmed or strengthened through the story; the personalization of the act as they put their thumbprints on the stones and acknowledged responsibility for the future of the planet; and the symbolism of the ceremony of throwing stones into the ocean, returning them to the environment from which they had been taken.

With such an experience excitement grows and so does the learning, which is no longer restricted to one topic or one subject area, but has dimensions as large as life itself — a good life, on this planet — if there is respect for the environment and if the cycle of earth and wind and water is preserved.

◆ ◆ ◆ ◆ ◆

LOOKING BACK AND LOOKING FORWARD

This chapter has introduced you to a variety of teaching strategies you may use as you begin the adventure of teaching primary and elementary science. The roots of that adventure lie deep in the nature of science and the nature of children, and have been illustrated by two stories, one about a scientist and the other about a child.

The three orientations to curriculum and instruction proposed by Miller and Sellar — transmission, transaction, and transformation — have been used as a framework for planning instruction. A fairly common project in elementary classrooms — the introduction of a hamster — was used to illustrate how lessons modelled on each of these orientations would differ in the approach to instruction, the role of the teacher, and the kinds of questions that would guide the learning experiences.

You were then introduced to guidelines for unit and lesson planning, and the orientations were once more used to introduce you to a continuum of teaching strategies ranging from teacher-centred to more and more child-centred and representing each of these orientations.

Examples of units and lesson plans were selected to illustrate teaching strategies reflecting the various approaches.

Your walk beneath the transmission umbrella suggested appropriate uses of direct instruction or expository methods at certain points and for specific purposes. You reflected on the value of an expository approach, using a true story about a child's interest in fossils and how it led to a lifetime interest and a career in geology.

For the transaction orientation you re-examined the constructivist theory of knowledge and investigated the science in bouncing balls, and the potential of such experiences for integration with other areas.

You detected shades of both transaction and transformation as you worked through a lesson on the beauty and usefulness of trees. Here the power of language was evident, not only for communication in science but for its affective value in developing aesthetic awareness and enhancing the richness of the unit.

Finally, through the module "Myself and Others," you became involved in a challenging unit as a Grade 1 class explored with great sensitivity similarities and differences among themselves and their friends, and discovered characteristics that expanded their awareness of themselves and others as unique individuals. The transformation approach and its alliance with holistic learning were further illustrated through an Earth Day ceremony with great potential for attitude development and values clarification.

In addition to becoming familiar with a number of teaching strategies representing a continuum of instructional approaches, you will need to acquire a repertoire of specific skills and techniques for teaching science. These will be the focus of the next chapter.

CANADIAN ACHIEVEMENTS IN SCIENCE

URSULA FRANKLIN (B. 1921)

Women are even less represented in technology than in science. Ursula Franklin is one of the exceptions. She is exceptional in other ways too.

The daughter of a Jewish mother, Dr. Franklin spent the war years in a German concentration camp. This experience may have influenced her strong humanitarian concerns throughout her career.

Following the war, Dr. Franklin studied at the Technical University of Berlin and later emigrated to Canada. Her work links technology and archaeology, for example in her high-temperature techniques used to analyze ancient pottery shards. She is best known for her extensive research into prehistoric copper mining, early metallurgy, and Peruvian metal working. Until her retirement, she was a professor of metallurgy and materials science at the University of Toronto. Dr.

Franklin's work provides a link between past and present, and illustrates that sometimes we know less today than we may think, and that in some instances we know less than ancient peoples. For example, Dr. Franklin tells of a Chinese technology of about 2000 years ago through which extremely corrosion-resistant mirrors were produced, and which we are unable to replicate today, and of a long-lost technology for providing copper scraping knives in the high Arctic.

With respect to her concerns for contemporary society, Dr. Franklin has been a prominent spokeswoman about the dangers of testing nuclear weapons in the atmosphere. In the 1960s, in the wake of widespread testing of this kind, she studied the effect of radioactive strontium 90 on children's teeth. This by-product of nuclear explosions fell to earth in rain, was taken up by cows in the grass they ate, and passed into their stomachs and into their milk. As young children drank this milk, the strontium, being very similar to calcium, entered children's developing bone structure, including their teeth. The strontium, being radioactive, caused a high incidence of bone cancer in children who lived in areas affected by high rainfall and certain prevailing wind directions.

Since that time, Dr. Franklin has been active in leading citizens' concerns about peace issues as well as about the effects of nuclear-weapons testing and other environmental issues.

▢ REFERENCES

Ahearn, S.K. (1990). Earth Day. The Ceremony of the Rock. Typescript.

Ausubel, D.P. (1963). *The psychology of meaningful verbal learning: An introduction to school learning.* New York: Grune & Stratton.

Bodner, G.M. (1986). Constructivism: A theory of knowledge. *Journal of Chemical Education* 63(10):873–78.

Freedman, A.M., H.T. Kaplan, and B.J. Sadock (1977). *Modern synopsis of comprehensive textbook of psychiatry II.* Baltimore: Williams and Wilkins.

Goldberg, L. (1970). *Children and science: How to awaken and sustain the interest of the young in the world around them.* New York: Scribner's.

Innovations in Science (1990). Level Two. Wanted: Dead or Alive. Toronto: HBJ-Holt.

Insights: An Elementary Hands-On Inquiry Science Curriculum (1992). Developed by Educational Development Center. Scotts Valley, CA: Wings for Learning.

Leithwood, K.A., ed. (1986). *Planned educational change.* Toronto: Ontario Institute for Studies in Education.

Miller, J.P., and S. Seller (1985). *Curriculum perspectives and practice.* New York: Longman.

Rockcastle, V.N. (1974). Curriculum in the open classroom: Strcuture or Stricture? *Science and Children* (September): 9–13.

Rockcastle, V.N., B.J. McKnight, F.R. Salamon, and V.E. Schmidt (1984). *Addison-Wesley Science, Teacher's Guide, Level 5.* Don Mills, ON: Addison-Wesley.

"Science from Toys" (1977). *Science 5/13 Teacher's Guide,* 52–57. Schools Council Publication. London: Macdonald Educational.

Weinstein, G., and M. Fantini (1970). *Toward humanistic education.* New York: Praeger.

Zaccharias, J.R. (1965). Cited in J. McGavack and D.P. La Salle, *Crystals, insects and unknown objects,* 39. New York: John Day.

CHAPTER 7

Developing Science Teaching Skills

TEACHING ELEMENTARY SCIENCE
involves
CREATING ENCOURAGING ENVIRONMENTS
and
ACQUIRING TEACHING SKILLS
which include

SPECIFIC TEACHING MODELS *for* DEVELOPING CONCEPTS *and* DEVELOPING THINKING SKILLS *through* DISCOVERY LESSONS, PROBLEM SOLVING, *and* INQUIRY	MOTIVATIONAL TECHNIQUES *such as* DISCREPANT EVENTS *and* OPEN-ENDED PROBLEMS *and* ROLE PLAYING *and* LEARNING THROUGH PLAY	QUESTIONING SKILLS *such as* INCREASING WAIT-TIME *and* IMPROVING TEACHER QUESTIONS *and* ENCOURAGING PUPIL QUESTIONS

as well as
EXTENDING EXPERIENCES
through

SCIENCE DAYS	POSTER SESSIONS	SCIENCE CHALLENGES	SCIENCE OLYMPICS

all of which involve
PROBLEM SOLVING IN ACTION

◆ ◆ ◆ ◆ ◆

The challenge is to gain control over the

knowledge base of teaching, develop a repertoire

of best practice, acquire attitudes and skills for

reflection and problem solving, and approach

this whole process as a lifelong quest.

RICHARD I. ARENDS (1988)

You are now familiar with unit and lesson planning, and a variety of teaching strategies. These include teacher-directed or expository methods associated with the transmission approach; inquiry/discovery and other transactional modes of teaching; and personalized approaches characteristic of the transformation orientation to curriculum and instruction. Having worked through examples of each of these teaching orientations, you should now have a sense of the flow of lessons and units that reflect these approaches and a mental picture of how your classroom will look and sound as you model teaching strategies in a transmission mode, a transaction mode, or a transformation mode. Depending on the purpose of the lesson and the nature of the content or skills to be taught, your teaching strategies will emphasize one approach over the others. Many times you will combine all three approaches, shifting easily from one to the other so that the experiences are varied and interesting to children and take into account their individual differences.

This chapter goes beyond lesson planning and focusses on the more specific teaching skills, techniques, and capabilities that you will need to develop to increase the effectiveness of your lessons. These teaching skills are important components of every lesson in science, setting the tone for the experiences you provide and determining the quality of the interactions that take place and how well children are encouraged and empowered to learn. The first teaching skill on the list that follows — the skill of creating a positive environment for children's learning — has been dealt with in Chapter 5, but is included here to underscore its importance to your success as a teacher and to help you achieve other skills and techniques. Some of the skills that are the hallmark of effective science teaching are listed as follows.

- The ability to *create encouraging environments* for learning science — environments in which children develop favourable attitudes and construct their own knowledge and skills.
- The ability to select from and use a variety of teaching strategies to help children *develop concepts in science*.
- The ability to select from and use a variety of teaching strategies to help children *develop thinking skills* and apply them in problem solving, inquiry, and creative thinking.
- The ability to *use motivational techniques* to stimulate and sustain learning in science and across the curriculum.
- The ability to *use appropriate questioning techniques* and to encourage students' questions.
- The ability to *encourage participation in science projects* beyond the classroom.

◆ ◆ ◆ ◆ ◆

CREATING ENCOURAGING ENVIRONMENTS

If you are committed to the idea that children must construct their own knowledge (that the role of the learner is an active one in which cognitive structures emerge and change with experience and interaction with peers and adults), then the settings you arrange, the materials you provide, and the starting points for thinking and learning are very important. Often learning will be initiated by the questions you ask and the rich environment you provide; at other times, learning will be spontaneous and self-directed. Sometimes learning experiences will extend and enrich science content and skills; at other times, starting points in science will encompass and enrich many subject areas, as topics are explored that emphasize the wholeness of knowledge. Since science encompasses the whole of life, science skills and knowledge that are acquired are transferable to other areas of the curriculum and to "science for life."

The climate that you create is crucial to successful learning. Not only should it be a stimulating environment, but it should also be an accepting and empathic environment. Just as creative thinking and problem solving are fostered in an inquiry-based classroom, the way children learn is also determined by the way they perceive the learning environment — their attitudes toward themselves, their peers, their teachers, and the subject. Carl Rogers (1983) points to the need for genuineness or realness, for learning experiences to be perceived as meaningful and relevant to students' lives.

Whatever the topic or investigation, you are the organizer and facilitator, the one who carefully plans the motivational beginnings, the playlike environments, the questions and the challenges that initiate learning. Children will model your enthusiasm for science and appreciate your role as a collaborator in their investigations — a partner in discovery. You are the one who listens, observes, gives feedback, assesses children's progress, and plans the follow-up experiences that encourage them to continue their discoveries and their interest in science. The decisions you make, the lessons you plan, and the techniques you use will be based on your growing knowledge of how children learn and your reflective thinking on how well each of the techniques and models of teaching accomplishes your goals.

Your feelings of satisfaction and success as a teacher will be largely determined by the teaching models and motivating beginnings you choose for lessons and units, the questioning techniques you develop, and the opportunities you provide for inquiry and problem solving. Cognitive, affective, and social outcomes will be realized as you encourage your students to extend their science learning into independent projects and group projects. These projects take students beyond the everyday routine of the science classroom and encourage them to become involved in following to the full extent of their curiosity and interest the starting points in science for interdisciplinary learning. All of these components of instruction are designed to keep children's curiosity alive, to sustain their interest in science through the primary and elementary grades, and to encourage them to acquire "learning how to learn" habits that will last throughout their lives.

◆ ◆ ◆ ◆ ◆

DEVELOPING CONCEPTS

When you encourage children to acquire "learning how to learn" habits, you are encouraging the development of thinking skills and, at the same time, the development of scientific concepts. Recall from Chapter 4 that concepts are the key ideas that serve as a foundation for higher-order thinking skills (creative thinking, critical thinking, and problem solving). Familiarity with concepts also helps children to feel comfortable with the language of science.

In the primary years, children's natural curiosity, their wide interests, and their concern with the here and now provide excellent opportunities for nurturing favourable attitudes and introducing scientific ways of thinking. Concepts are gained gradually over a long period of time through repeated and related "happenings" that encourage children to discover their world. It is important to take advantage of their innate sense of wonder and their natural inclination to explore, to see patterns in diversity, and to make sense of their world.

A child's natural curiosity is an excellent starting point for introducing scientific ways of thinking. A visit to a petting farm can lead to important questions about animals and their care.

Teachers can select from several models for teaching concepts. A *model* is a plan or pattern that organizes teaching and determines how the curriculum is planned and how instructional materials (concrete materials, books, modules, audiovisual resources, computers, etc.) are used.

Concept Teaching Models

It will be useful to you as you begin this chapter to review briefly a number of teaching models that are associated with concept development. Among these are *concept attainment models* (which present examples and nonexamples of the concept), *concept formation models* (which require students to generate lists or groupings from their own information or experience base), and *conceptual change models* (which focus on the ideas children bring to a learning situation and broaden their experience through related concrete experiences).

CONCEPT ATTAINMENT MODELS

The attributes or common features of a concept enable us to place concepts in certain classes or categories. Joyce and Weil (1986) attribute the concept attainment model to Bruner's work on concepts, in which he uses the terms name, examples, attributes (common characteristics), and attribute values (essential and non-essential attributes) to denote the elements of a concept.

Teachers using the concept attainment model provide students with *examples* and *nonexamples* of the concept. Positive examples (examples of the concept) are clearly labelled *yes,* and negative examples (nonexamples of the concept) are labelled *no*. Children are asked to compare attributes of the examples and non-examples and to make hypotheses about the attributes that distinguish the categories. When the concept is identified, children are asked to identify additional examples as *yes* or *no*.

The concept attainment model can be used successfully at all levels for teaching facts and simple concepts, and is especially effective when related concrete experiences are provided through group activities, learning centre tasks, and so on. For example, when a collection of shells is shown to a primary class, the children are led to the concept of univalves by showing the univalves as examples of the category and the bivalves as nonexamples. Children then apply the concept through further experience with identifying univalves, for example, in another shell collection.

CONCEPT FORMATION MODELS

Children develop categorization and discrimination skills leading to concept formation when they are encouraged to *group objects or events in categories,* according to their own classification schemes, and to suggest labels by which to identify the groupings. A more complex model for concept formation involves children actively in investigations with their own senses, accompanied by opportunities to try out ideas, to analyze their interpretations of things, to consider alternatives, and to *discover concepts* for themselves.

Concept Formation through Grouping Objects and Events. This model dates back to the 1960s, when Hilda Taba (1967) developed a series of strategies to help students learn to categorize. Her beliefs were that children can be taught to think, to organize facts into conceptual systems, and that thought levels can be lifted as one thinking skill builds on another. The steps are *identifying data* related to the problem (What do you see?), *developing categories* (What belongs together?), and *developing labels for the categories* (What would we call this group?).

Imagine you are teaching a unit on animal diversity, and the lesson topic is the classification of animals into vertebrates (animals with backbones) and invertebrates (animals without backbones). To arrive at the classes of vertebrates, you ask the students to name as many animals with backbones as they can think of and list their responses on the chalkboard. Children are then asked to discriminate further, considering similarities and differences and identifying subgroups with common characteristics. Eventually, through questioning and teacher–student dialogue they distinguish five groups, each with different properties, and give the groups identifying labels — fish, birds, reptiles, amphibians, and mammals. The children discuss the attributes or common characteristics that led them to identify five different groups, and are encouraged then to think about the thinking processes that led them to choose these categories. To reinforce the growing concepts, you could decide on a follow-up activity with animal picture cards to involve the students once more in the categorization process.

Concept Formation through Discovery. In this model, experiences are provided and children learn through active involvement and teacher guidance. There can be different degrees of structure and openness, depending on the amount of teacher direction. You can begin the lesson in a fairly unstructured way, by providing children with materials and by initiating the learning with a lead-off question and then encouraging children to tackle the problem in any way they choose. Alternatively, the lead-off question can be followed with some directions for the activity, with discussion and feedback at intervals to ascertain the level of progress toward concept development.

activity 7.1 CHOOSING A MODEL

Choose a topic from the following list of concepts in science, and develop a lesson plan using either the concept attainment model, or one of the concept formation models. Teach the lesson to a small group of your peers.

- Solids, liquids, and gases
- Living and nonliving
- Types of rocks: sedimentary, metamorphic, and igneous
- Pushes and pulls
- Animal cells and plant cells

❑ Reflecting and Sharing

The potential for building basic concepts that help children to understand further experiences is present in all models, especially if help is given to children to develop their ideas.

Harlen and Jelly (1990) offer the following advice for helping children with concept development:

- Provide opportunities for children to tell you what they think about things.
- Analyze what children are likely to mean by the things they tell you, especially when their comments seem strange.
- Organize class discussion in which you show that you value children's contributions, however odd, and through which children can be helped to analyze their own interpretations of things and consider alternatives.
- Continue to develop your ability to plan work "through the mind of a child," i.e., to anticipate what children are likely to think about the things they investigate (57).

Harlen and Jelly suggest that you listen to children as they are involved in science investigations, try to interpret the meaning of their comments, and then provide opportunities for them to analyze their own interpretations of things and to consider alternatives. Their suggestions are similar to those on which "conceptual change models" of teaching are based.

CONCEPTUAL CHANGE MODELS

In earlier chapters, the importance of starting from what children already know (Ausubel 1963; Novak and Gowin 1984) was emphasized. "What children know," however, is frequently clouded by misconceptions that differ from the scientific notions you aim to teach. Obviously these misconceptions must be taken into account when planning instruction, and the lessons you plan should be aimed at restructuring students' existing knowledge and bringing about *conceptual change*.

Children's alternative conceptions are identified through interviews, through "exposing events" (Nussbaum and Novick 1982), or by encouraging children to "think out loud" (Barnes 1976) as they interpret their observations of a phenomenon they are investigating. Questioning strategies, experiments, and discussion encourage children to test the "new" conception, so that they are led to "change" by replacing their previously held ideas with the scientifically accepted ones. Two conceptual change models are the *generative learning model* and the *learning cycle model*.

The Generative Learning Model. Harlen and Osborne (1985) advocate a constructivist model — a generative learning model — in which learning is generated as "links are made between children's existing ideas, new experiences, and tentative explanations" (138). A preliminary phase precedes the three main phases — exploration, investigation, and reflection. In this preliminary phase, students' existing ideas are identified through questioning, discussion, or a short diagnostic test.

The generative learning model is a practical one in which the whole class works on a particular topic, but not everyone is doing the same things. The contact with objects and events in the *exploration phase* determines the directions that students will follow in the next two phases. Activities relate to the new concepts to be learned. Children in small groups work out tentative procedures for finding answers to the questions generated in the exploration stage. From the close contact with materials, questions emerge and hypotheses are made that are tested in the *investigation phase.* The pooling of results and exchange of ideas constitute the *reflection phase,* which may lead to further investigations. The reflection and testing of ideas against those of other children are important components of this model. Figure 7.1 presents the framework for the teaching sequence based on this generative model.

FIGURE 7.1

Framework for Teaching Primary Science

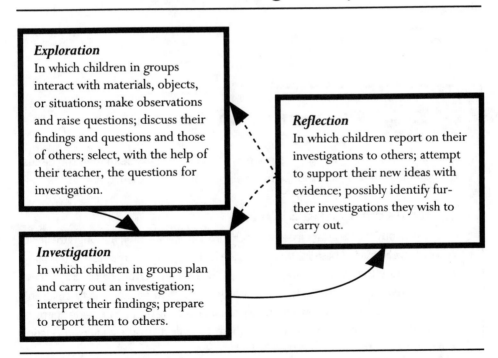

Exploration
In which children in groups interact with materials, objects, or situations; make observations and raise questions; discuss their findings and questions and those of others; select, with the help of their teacher, the questions for investigation.

Reflection
In which children report on their investigations to others; attempt to support their new ideas with evidence; possibly identify further investigations they wish to carry out.

Investigation
In which children in groups plan and carry out an investigation; interpret their findings; prepare to report them to others.

Source: W. Harlen (1985). A model for learning and teaching applied to primary science. *Journal of Curriculum Studies* 17(2):142. Washington, DC: Taylor and Francis.

The Learning Cycle Model. The learning cycle, which you are familiar with through the Science Curriculum Improvement Study (SCIS) materials, is another example of a conceptual change model. Recall from Chapter 4 that this model is built on the belief that students' prior learning should be considered when new concepts are introduced, and opportunities should be given for them to explore the concept at first with concrete materials (*exploration phase*). The exploratory phase sets the stage for what is to follow in the *invention phase,* in which the teacher assumes an active role in helping students to use their concrete experiences to "invent" the new concept. In the final *discovery phase,* students are encouraged to apply and extend the invented concept.

Various modifications of the learning cycle have been proposed, with new terminology used for the three phases and new knowledge about children's alternative conceptions incorporated into the rationale for what happens in each of the three phases. More and more, the first phase is used for free exploration of a new concept or phenomenon, and the second is used to introduce children to the scientific view of the concept. The third phase is again student-centred as growing concepts are extended through further related experiences and discussion.

---

activity 7.2 **PLANNING FOR CONCEPTUAL CHANGE**

Compare the generative learning model with the learning cycle model, and discuss the potential of each model for bringing about conceptual change.

❏ Reflecting and Sharing

Note that both models start from what children already know, although the inclusion of a preliminary phase in the generative learning model emphasizes this starting point more than the learning cycle does. Harlen and Osborne (1985) believe that "for generative learning to occur, it is important to gain access to children's existing ideas by encouraging them to ask questions, by encouraging them to explain their reasoning and by helping them to reflect on their ideas in relation to evidence and the ideas of others" (139).

What other differences are there? Think about the two models in the light of the constructivist view of learning. Which of the models places more responsibility on the learner?

The learning of concepts is an active, generative process that is tied in with the use of science processes for finding answers to questions that children are curious about. Concepts become more useful and inclusive as tools of thinking as new information is linked to what is already known. One of the most important outcomes of science teaching/learning is the development of thinking skills.

◆ ◆ ◆ ◆ ◆
DEVELOPING THINKING SKILLS

As a teacher, you now have certain expectations of the influence your teaching will have on children's ability to use process skills to investigate phenomena in which they become interested, and to find answers to questions about their world through activities that allow them to build their own understandings and meanings. In other words, you hope that their learning experiences in science will help them to develop thinking skills that will lead to lifelong learning.

Higher-order thinking skills and deeper levels of understanding develop as children are involved in *learning through discovery,* in *problem solving using process skills,* and in *developing inquiry skills*. The ability to think creatively is also stimulated and enhanced as children are involved in open-ended investigations and discussions that encourage divergent thinking.

Learning through Discovery

"Science in its purest form," writes Verne Rockcastle (1975), "is seeking of information *not* already known. It is discovery. Not necessarily discovery insulated from all reception learning. But certainly discovery where discovery is the central focus of the learning effort" (1).

Think of the possibilities for children's learning by discovery as you work through the following investigation.

activity | **7.3** | **WATER DROPS: A DISCOVERY LESSON**

Materials (for each person)
Newspapers, waxpaper sheet, medicine dropper, medicine cup, petri dish, pencil, nuts and bolts, pennies, glass jar containing tap water.

Part 1
 1. Spread newspapers on table. Fill the medicine cup by dipping it into the water in the glass jar, so that the water level is level with the top of the medicine cup.

2. Place the medicine cup on a petri dish and drop in the nuts and bolts one by one until the water overflows.

3. Draw the shape of the water in the medicine cup.

Part 2

1. Place a medicine cup on a petri dish and use the jar of water to fill the medicine cup.

2. How many drops of water do you think you can add to the full cup before it spills over? Make a guess.

3. Use the medicine dropper to add drops of water, counting the number of drops you add. Compare your results with those of others in your group.

Part 3

1. Think back to your first guess about the number of drops you thought you could safely add before the water in the medicine cup spilled over.

2. Revise your estimate and repeat Part 2. Was your estimate closer this time?

3. Were you more confident this time about the number of drops you could add?

Part 4

1. Children often refer to the property of water that you have been observing as "heapiness." Find out more about the "heapiness" of the water by dropping some onto the piece of waxpaper.

2. Play with the drops, pushing the water around with a pencil point. What happens when you push the pencil point into a water droplet? What happens when you push several drops together?

3. How do the drops look from the side? From the top? Sketch some of the drops.

Part 5

1. How many water drops do you think you can heap onto the surface of a coin?

2. Compare your estimate with those of others in your group. Now, transfer several coins to a petri dish and check your estimate by adding water drops to one or more of the coins.

3. What factors might affect the number of drops you can add? List as many as you can. Choose one of these factors for your group to investigate further. Record your results.

4. Keep your list at hand and share your ideas with the class, recording all ideas on the chalkboard. Sort the list of factors into groups according to whether they relate to the drops, the coins, the droppers, or perhaps to you!

☐ Reflecting and Sharing

To do all this in a class of elementary students would take much longer than it has taken you to follow the directions and to experience some of the discoveries. Were there surprises for you, as there would be for children? If there *were* surprises, think back to the way you felt when you experienced them — the water in the medicine cup that didn't overflow even when one, two, three ... or eight nuts and bolts were added; the full medicine cup that allowed you to add not three or four drops but 30, 40, 50 ... 90, 100, or more before overflowing.

Listen to the musings of a boy in an elementary classroom who is engrossed in finding out how many drops he can fit on the "heads" side of a penny, and becomes even more engrossed with the properties of water that allow this to happen. As you "listen," think of the potential in this discovery lesson for the development of concepts and thinking skills.

> I take my snub-nosed eye dropper, and begin dropping drops of water on the penny. Nineteen, pretty good ... 25, hmm, better yet ... 35, good, I think. Things begin to bother me: What is good? ... One of my friends could get 46 drops of ordinary water on the penny. I wonder why? ...
>
> I continue to wonder about what is in this water that allows it to heap up like this ... Deep within myself I expect that I'm going to have to do something to find out why this happens, even if it takes me a long time to do so" (DeBruin 1975, 16).

The boy's words capture the spirit of discovery learning and the power of puzzling or discrepant events in initiating the process. Nor do his questions end there. He wonders about the skinlike effect on the surface of the water, identifies in his mind the variables that might make a difference to the number of drops he can add, and plans "heads vs. tails" and "Canadian vs. American penny" experiments that he and his friends can try. He continues:

> Some of my friends are attempting to make connections ... they are using terms like "surface tension" and "adhesion" and "cohesion" of molecules to explain this heapiness. I'm wondering if my friends using these terms actually know and understand what they mean.
>
> I'm encouraged by a friendly voice to try soapy water and see if it will heap as high as regular water (17).

The initial exploratory phase of Activity 7.3 takes time, time for delight in what is happening, time for the disequilibrium that the child is obviously experiencing, and time for the chance to think it through. The opportunity to think and talk through possible explanations of what they are observing is an important component of children's discovery learning. Driver (1983) expresses it as follows:

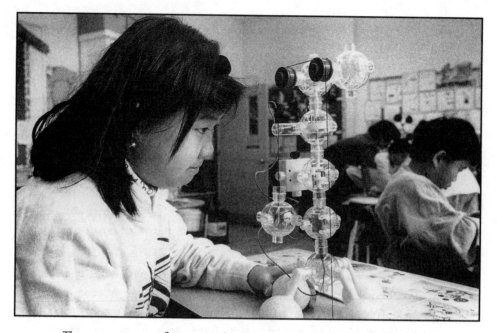

The opportunity to reflect on an observation is an important part of discovery.

Activity by itself is not enough. It is the sense that is made of it that matters. Teaching strategies are needed which help pupils think and talk about the significance of their experiences, and, most important, time for teachers to talk through pupils' experiences with them (49).

Problem Solving Using Process Skills

As with many investigations that, like the water drops activity, begin with free exploration, the question of "What makes a difference?" is bound to arise, as well as the need to find out through testing whether certain factors *do* make a difference. Once this happens, the question becomes a problem worth pursuing, and the thinking skills that are used to find a solution are the science process skills that you were introduced to in Chapter 3.

Problem solving in life usually means defining the problem and applying knowledge and skills to achieve a goal or find a solution. In the science education literature, problem-solving and process skills are closely linked. Problem solving is equated with using the skills involved in making and testing hypotheses and collecting and analyzing data. The scientific processes are the thinking skills needed for problem solving in the science classroom, or for engaging in a science project.

Robbie Case (1985) has been involved for a number of years in building on the developmental theory of Piaget, the discovery-oriented perspective of Bruner, and information-processing perspectives, to develop a new conceptualization of how children learn and how they may be taught so that intellectual development at any stage is maximized. The basic aim of his approach to education is to "provide children with the sort of high level problem-solving structures most valued in their own particular culture, and the basic method is to involve them in actual problem-solving, at their own developmental level — from the outset" (408). The eventual goal is to design educational activities that are appropriate for children at each of the developmental levels posed by Piaget, and to facilitate their ultimate transition to the next level.

Roberta Barba (1990) agrees that problem solving can be taught. Students learn to solve problems through having the opportunity to solve problems at a level of complexity suited to their stage of development. Because children differ within the same age group, co-operative problem solving is often productive. Brainstorming can be used to identify the variables in an experiment or as a means of thinking of possible solutions. Finally, reflective thinking can reap dividends as pupils reflect on the strategies they use and why they chose these strategies.

Even in the early years of school, children have an intuitive sense of what constitutes a "fair test" when it is related to real life, and when the number of variables is low. Nancy Kaplan (1984) describes an early childhood class where she sets out, with the help of the students, to find out which of the gym balls is the best bouncer. The students set her straight as she deliberately makes the test "unfair," and they point out to her one by one all the factors that might make a difference and insist that each of these factors has to be the *same* if the test is to be a fair one. Even kindergarten children have already had experiences, in their games and playing, of what is "fair."

Think back for a moment to the water drop investigation. Did the behaviour of the water drops on the waxpaper help to interpret your earlier observations of the water in the medicine cup as you added carefully, and sometimes not so carefully, drop after drop after drop?

On what did you base your prediction of the number of drops that could be heaped on the surface of a penny?

How many factors did you identify that might make a difference to the results? Students in one class came up with these:

Coins: Surface (heads vs. tails); condition (worn vs. mint); age (year); type (Canadian vs. U.S.)

Drops: Size; speed; position of drops on coin

Dropper: Angle of dropper; height

You: Force exerted on the bulb of the water dropper

activity **7.3** **(CONTINUED)**

Part 6 invites you to pursue the investigation a little further. Reflect on your thinking as you go through the science processes that are involved.

Part 6

1. Select one of the above-mentioned factors to investigate. This time, try to make the investigation a "fair test" by keeping everything the same except the factor you are manipulating.
2. Within your group, plan your experiment and jot down the plan. Conduct the test and record your findings. How reliable do you think your results are this time?
3. Did some of your findings lead to further questions you would like to explore?
4. Think of real-life problems children could explore that are related to these initial investigations.

❏ Reflecting and Sharing

The processes involved in this activity are *higher-order thinking skills* that can be practised often in your classroom. Children are given a problem, or a problem arises that they choose to investigate. There is no set sequence of steps, and the answer is as yet unknown. The major emphasis is on the thinking skills that are developed and practised. One of the compelling arguments for the inclusion of process skills in which children are engaged in pursuing answers to questions, making hypotheses, and collecting and interpreting data is that the skills involved can be used for problem solving in real-life situations.

You can help your students by beginning with simple questions related to their own environment, and by giving them the opportunity to practise the thinking skills at each phase of the inquiry. Children can make connections between the tendency of water to "ball" on certain materials and the best fabrics for rainwear. Questions that arise from the claims made in television advertisements are good starting points for problem solving. The whole class can get involved in checking the claim made in a television commercial that a certain detergent is indeed the "best" one. What is "best," anyway? It becomes necessary to define operationally *best* detergent, *best* bouncer, *best* fabric. And so the thinking process goes on, and thinking habits form that carry through into "science for life." As you pursue one of these investigations, think about its potential for helping children toward this long-range goal.

activity 7.4 FURTHER PRACTICE WITH PROCESS SKILLS

Select one of the above-mentioned questions to investigate, or choose another from the list that follows.

- ◆ Which is the best fabric for rainwear?
- ◆ Which ball is the best bouncer?
- ◆ Which is the best detergent?
- ◆ What proportion of radish seeds will germinate on a wet paper towel?
- ◆ Which brand of paper towel is the most absorbent?

Review the science processes in Chapter 3 and use the following outline for the design of your experiment. Think about how you will initiate the inquiry and help children with finding answers.

1. Question or problem _____

2. Method or strategy to be used in answering question _____
   _____

3. Hypothesis _____

4. Manipulated variable _____

5. Responding variable _____

6. Operational definitions of each _____
   _____

7. Variables to be held constant _____
   _____

8. Data _____
   _____

9. Was your hypothesis supported or not supported by your data? _____
   _____

10. Can you make a generalization based on your data? State the generalization.
    _____
    _____

11. Discuss your experiment with your colleagues. Can you think of ways to improve the investigation, reduce errors, make results more reliable? _____
    _____

❑ Reflecting and Sharing

"Fair test" activities in the primary grades should involve relatively simple or familiar problem situations. Young children can participate in investigations that can be related easily to their experience, and in which the number of variables is low. For example, they can make a hypothesis about the effect on the distance a toy car moves when the number of turns of the winding mechanism is increased. Children in the intermediate grades can be helped to identify the variables that affect the brightness of a bulb in an electric circuit, and to hold all of these constant while testing the effect of changing one of the variables. When facility grows with practice, the teacher can introduce more complex investigations.

Developing Inquiry Skills

The problem solving in which you have just been engaged can be included under the broader concept of *inquiry*. Both discovery learning and problem solving can be considered part of inquiry, in the sense that knowledge new to the learner is discovered and creative solutions to problems are derived. In an effort to come close to a definition of inquiry, Howard Birnie and Alan Ryan (1984) cite a number of propositional statements, each of which includes the use of thinking skills to attain knowledge or to solve problems.

◆ Inquiry is the process of investigating a problem.
◆ Inquiry is a search for truth or knowledge that involves critical thinking.
◆ The end product of inquiry may be a discovery, but discovery is only a part of inquiry.
◆ Inquiry involves making observations, asking questions, performing experiments, and stating conclusions.
◆ Inquiry can be idiosyncratic and creative. An individual may develop his or her own strategies and may take intuitive approaches to the problem (31).

The last statement may be the very reason inquiry is difficult to define, and also the reason for its motivational value. The processes involved in inquiry methods are open-ended, and intuitive and creative solutions are often involved. However difficult it may be to define, inquiry is a highly interactive mode of teaching and learning, with the potential for intrinsic motivation and feelings of success as underlying ideas are discovered. Inquiry is first and foremost a process by which students can develop the skills to raise questions and search for answers about phenomena that interest them.

Through inquiry, students learn how to raise questions and search for answers about what interests them.

INQUIRY TRAINING

Over a quarter of a century ago, Richard Suchman (1966) saw the potential for motivation and for developing students' question-asking skills in using puzzling or discrepant events to initiate inquiry. He developed a series of silent films that focussed on puzzling events or phenomena, such as a bimetallic strip bending when heated, a Cartesian diver, a collapsing can, and so on. To arrive at the explanation, the students were taught to ask questions that could be answered "yes" or "no" by the teacher. Part of the training was aimed at teaching children to listen to one another and to follow what was being discovered as the questions were answered. After fifteen minutes of inquiry, the group reviewed what was known to that point, following which the questions continued until the correct explanation was proposed. Studies indicated conceptual growth and improvement in students' question-asking skills.

In many of Suchman's original films, the explanations are too abstract for elementary students. However, you can use some of them productively, or, better still, substitute a silent demonstration of any appropriate counterintuitive event. The intrinsic rewards are great when the explanation is arrived at as a result of the students' own questions. Care must be exercised that the conceptual level of the explanation is appropriate for the developmental level of the students participating in the inquiry session, but sufficiently challenging to require a little mind stretching. Add a touch of drama to heighten interest.

Phenomena for Inquiry. A Canadian source of demonstrations suitable for inquiry sessions is Tik Liem's (1981) book, *Invitations to Science Inquiry*. The Bimetallic Strip, the Cartesian Diver, and the Collapsing Can inquiries are examples drawn from this source. The Collapsing Can inquiry is reproduced in Figure 7.2.

FIGURE 7.2

The Collapsing Can

Materials

1. One empty gallon (or 4–5 liter) can, or any other tin can that can be closed off airtight.
2. A hot plate or burner and tripod.

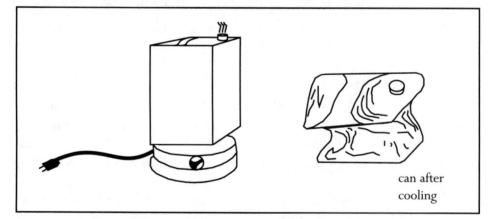

can after
cooling

Procedure

1. Put about 20 mL of water in the can (just enough to cover the bottom) and heat it over the hot plate or burner.
2. Let the water boil vigorously for about 2 minutes (vapours should come out of the can).
3. Take the can with the boiling water off the heat (don't burn your fingers!) and immediately close off with the cap very tightly.
4. Let it stand upright on the table and cool off to room temperature, or for faster results: cool off with wet towel.

Questions

1. What was in the can besides the water?
2. What happens when water is boiled? *(continued)*

Figure 7.2 (continued)

3. What will the air in the can do when much water vapour is formed?
4. What would happen if we did not close the can very tightly?
5. What is the total force that is working on the outside of the can?

Explanation

Before heating, the can was filled with water and air. By boiling the water, it changed states, from liquid to gaseous state (water vapour). The water vapour or steam pushed the air that was inside, out of the can. In closing off the can with an airtight cap, we are actually trapping the air out of the can: we are preventing it from going back into the can. The cooling condenses the water vapour back to water. All the vapour that took up the interior space of the can before is now turned into a few drops of water, which take up much less space. This causes the pressure to drop; the atmospheric pressure is therefore pushing on the can and crushing it.

The total force working on the outside of the can is the total of the can's surface area in cm² multiplied by 1 kg.

Source: Tik L. Liem (1981). *Invitations to Science Inquiry,* 20. Needham, MA: Ginn.

A second edition (1990) of *Invitations to Science Inquiry* is now available, and other sources of "discrepant events" to initiate inquiry are *Bet You Can't! Science Impossibilities to Fool You* (Cobb and Darling 1980) and Wright's (1981) list of fifteen discrepant events that teach science principles and concepts. Because of the high interest of children in puzzling events, you will find yourself creating a file of your own. Good sources are the "Phenomena for Inquiry" section of *Science and Children* and occasional articles in *Science Scope*, such as "Science Startlers" (Selnes 1986) and "Inquiry Investigations" (Potter and Horak 1987). Once you have found a suitable number, choose one as an inquiry demonstration and practise the technique with a group of your classmates or with the whole class.

activity 7.5 AN INQUIRY SESSION

The following perplexing situations may help you get started:

◆ Water boils in a paper lunch bag over a flame without burning the bag.
◆ A cutout figure appears headless when immersed to the neck in water in a transparent container.
◆ Mothballs bounce up and down in a clear liquid in which bubbles are visible.

Using one of these situations, or a situation drawn from one of the other sources, practise the technique with your group or the whole class.

Imagine what it will be like to involve your class one day in an inquiry session. Think of ways of adapting the technique so that it is suitable for young students.

Remember that questions must be constructed to elicit "yes" or "no" answers. You may find it useful to add to your "yes" and "no" responses a third response, "irrelevant." This saves a lot of time and helps students to focus their questions.

Suggest, after the first round of questioning, that the group summarize "what they know" up to that point. This often results in a fresh look at the phenomenon and more productive questions.

❏ Reflecting and Sharing

One difference that you may have perceived between this and other teaching strategies is a change in the traditional role of the teacher as question asker. Rather, the emphasis in inquiry training is on encouraging students to ask well-thought-out questions that lead them eventually to an explanation of the puzzling phenomenon or "discrepant event" that was used to initiate the inquiry.

It is important that the explanation is not too abstract — that the students are capable of understanding the concepts and principles involved. It is important, too, for the teacher to have a good grasp of the principles involved in the phenomenon used to initiate the inquiry.

As you conducted the inquiry session with your classmates, you may have thought of the value of a discrepant event as a motivating strategy. Such a beginning stimulates a high level of interest and sustains curiosity until the explanation is finally reached and the discrepancy resolved.

With any learning experiences in science that you plan, you will be conscious of the importance of motivating beginnings — of invitations to learning that encourage participation and involvement. The ability to use a variety of *motivational techniques* is another science teaching skill that will become part of your repertoire. As you read this section, continue to reflect on the thinking skills that will be enhanced as you use each of these motivational techniques. You will find that the very nature of the suggested teaching activities will stimulate another dimension of thinking — the *creative dimension* — and emphasize its importance in science learning.

OPEN INQUIRY

Open inquiry is also known as unguided inductive inquiry. It is usually initiated by the teacher at the elementary level, but the students are encouraged from that focus to use any methods they like to arrive at solutions. As children pursue their investigations, the teacher listens and supports, supplying additional material as needed.

A question such as "What determines how a paper airplane flies?" can initiate an inquiry that can go on for days as children design and test different models, at first at random and then more systematically, keeping records of what they have discovered.

With younger children, inquiry can begin when the class returns from a field trip to a meadow with a large variety of seeds and pods and fruits. For one group the question may be: "How can we make the seeds germinate?" Another may notice different ways in which the seeds are equipped to travel, and decide to find out more about seed dispersal. Self-confidence grows as children find, from the seeds, answers to their own problems. The teacher listens and guides, having created a situation where children identify problems and find their own ways of solving them.

From a Teacher's Journal

Science education lends itself to the development of thinking skills. By organizing a classroom in a manner that encourages risk taking, students are encouraged to use their minds to find solutions to problems, without the fear of being wrong. When the concept of a "fair test" is used as a framework and students are given practice with science processes, they have a set of parameters within which to work. The task then becomes one of using these parameters to find a solution to an identified problem.

Bob Benmore

Gibsons, BC

◆ ◆ ◆ ◆ ◆

USING MOTIVATIONAL TECHNIQUES

Motivation is the energizing influence that encourages learning to begin and sustains it through a series of activities making up a lesson or a unit. Whereas extrinsic motivation depends on rewards — tangible symbols such as stickers in the early years and letter grades in the later years of schooling — intrinsic motivation is the inner drive that is stimulated by curiosity and sustained by the satisfaction of learning and the joy of discovery. As Bruner (1966) suggests, the rewards are great when learning is intrinsically motivated, and the learning is much more likely to be retained.

As you were involved with the last inquiry activity, either as a "teacher" or a "student," you were probably impressed with the high level of interest that was evident throughout. The use of *discrepant events* to initiate inquiry is one of a number of motivational beginnings that you can include in your lesson planning. Other strategies for stimulating and sustaining learning in groups include teaching/learning through *co-operative learning, open-ended problems, brainstorming, buzz groups, dilemma analysis,* and *role playing.* The motivating quality of *play* as the initiating phase of learning is also well known.

Discrepant Events

Because puzzles, or events that defy common sense, are always intriguing to children, the use of discrepant events can be a tremendously motivating strategy. Children are encouraged to satisfy their curiosity through "finding out" how such events happen. Suchman (1966) believes that individuals faced with a puzzling event are naturally motivated to solve the puzzle. The potential of puzzling phenomena or discrepant events for initiating inquiry is evident in experiences such as the heaping of water drops or the demonstration of the "collapsing can."

The same effect occurs in a primary class when children enter the classroom to find a bar magnet protruding from the top of a stack of books, with a paper clip tied to a thread suspended in midair a short distance beneath, as shown in Figure 7.3. For children, objects that defy common sense include a "rock" that floats, or two ice cubes, each in a container of a colourless liquid, one floating, one sinking. In all cases, there is cognitive dissonance or disequilibrium, which is not resolved until an explanation is forthcoming. Shrigley (1987) suggests that "knowing the motivating power of the discrepant event and understanding its base in consistency theory may inspire us to take full advantage of this teaching strategy." By "full advantage," he means its potential for "surprise, challenge, thought and inquiry" (25).

FIGURE 7.3

A Discrepant Event

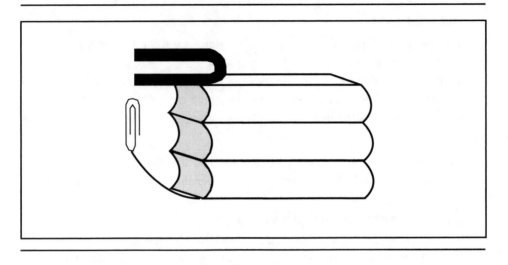

Co-operative Learning

The motivational aspects of learning co-operatively in groups is receiving much attention in educational circles. The research of Johnson and Johnson (1988) suggests that groups can be made more productive by acquiring co-operative learning skills such as active listening, checking other group members for understanding, shared group goals, individual accountability, and so on. Their 1982 meta-analysis of studies over more than a century indicates that having students work in co-operative groups is much more powerful than having them work alone, competitively or individually. The work of Johnson and Johnson is discussed more thoroughly in Chapter 11 in the context of providing for individual differences. In this chapter, co-operative learning is viewed as a powerful means of motivating children's learning and developing thinking skills and conscious problem-solving strategies.

Open-Ended Problems

An open-ended problem is one that has more than one possible solution. Because a number of responses or solutions are possible, interest is quickly sparked and investigations willingly begun when suggestions such as those by Tom Graika (1989) in Activity 7.6 are used to begin the inquiry.

----

activity 7.6   OPEN-ENDED PROBLEMS

Form a group and think of possible solutions to one of the following problems:

- Using any materials available in the classroom, try to find a method to determine which soil type can hold the most water.
- You are provided with water samples that have been contaminated with soil and plant debris. Design an apparatus and procedure that will clean up the water.
- Find out who has the strongest grip in the class. Design several ways to test grip strength.

Look through a textbook program and find the directions for one or two textbook activities. Rewrite them so that they become open-ended problems.

❑ Reflecting and Sharing

To stimulate children's interest in science and to help them develop creative- and critical-thinking skills, attention must be paid to the "minds-on" of "hands-on" science activities. One way to accomplish this is to involve your students in open-ended learning experiences such as the activities you have just completed. Another way is to modify typical textbook investigations so that they encourage a variety of acceptable solutions. Compare your modified textbook activities with the suggestions in Figure 7.4.

FIGURE 7.4

Modifications to
Typical Textbook Investigations

Laboratory Investigation: Root Growth in Seedlings
The textbook investigation has students study root growth by marking lines on the emerging root and observing them over time.

Redesigned: Ask students to determine a method to find out where root growth occurs on a sprouting seed and at what rate the growth occurs.

Laboratory Investigation: Strength of Electromagnets
The textbook investigation has the students study the effect of the number of coils of wire on the strength of an electromagnet.

Redesigned: Ask students to find different ways to increase the strength of an electromagnet.

(continued)

Figure 7.4 (continued)

Laboratory Investigation: Dissolving Rates
The textbook has students compare the dissolving rate of two solutes by following carefully designed instructions.

Redesigned: Ask students to find out which will dissolve faster: sugar or salt.

Laboratory Investigation: Strength of Magnets
To compare the strength of several magnets, the textbook has students hang paper clips on the magnets.

Redesigned: Ask students to find a number of methods to test the strength of magnets.

Source: T. Graika (1989). Minds-on, hands-on science. Reprinted with permission from NSTA Publications, copyright March 1989 from *Science Scope,* 20. National Science Teachers Association, 1840 Wilson Boulevard, Arlington, VA 22201–3000.

The more open the questions, the greater the involvement and the possibilities for creative solutions. When you use this technique in class, look for fluency (many responses) as well as novel and unusual responses (originality). Both are evidence of creative thinking.

Brainstorming

An effective way to begin a lesson is to use a divergent question as a brainstorming technique. Brainstorming can be used to ascertain what pupils already know about a topic, or to get them to think of relevant examples of a concept from their own experience, such as asking for examples of their own observations of the effects of static electricity. New concepts can then be linked to the old to make them more understandable.

activity 7.7 BRAINSTORMING

In a small group, or with the whole class, do one of the following brainstorming activities:

- Imagine you are introducing an integrated unit on weather. Brainstorm within your group for examples of "weather lore," which you will return to later in the unit, and discuss their possible origins and validity.
- Use the following question to elicit a variety of responses: How many different uses can you think of for magnets?

☐ Reflecting and Sharing

Brainstorming is a creative-thinking technique that can be used to increase the number of responses when a problem is posed. When you use this technique in your classroom, remember to accept all responses in a nonjudgemental manner, and to encourage students to piggyback on each other's responses. Accept wild or unconventional ideas, and ensure that the atmosphere is nonthreatening, so that as many children as possible are encouraged to participate.

Buzz Groups

This technique involves dividing the class into groups, no larger than five children, and posing a question or problem to each group. The groups discuss the problem for five to ten minutes, debating pros and cons and trying to find answers or solutions to the problem. Ideas are pooled, recorded on the chalkboard or a transparency, and become the basis for a class discussion in which all groups participate. Newspaper clippings on local issues relating to the environment are excellent topics for group discussions. Students are encouraged to search for information, to take sides on an issue, defend their positions, and work toward a group consensus on the best way to solve the problem. More creative solutions are possible because there are more children involved, and the controversy presents a challenge that is motivating to children.

A nonthreatening atmosphere will facilitate a brainstorming session. This teacher's informal and enthusiastic manner excites her students and encourages them to participate.

Dilemma Analysis Cards

An alternative to newspaper clippings to initiate discussion on problem situations such as issues relating to connections between science, technology, and society is the use of *dilemma analysis cards*. In dilemma analysis, open-ended problem situations are described on a card. Students are invited to read, analyze, and take a position. Examples of this technique are given in Chapter 13.

It is important to accept all solutions, but students are required to provide the reasons for their thoughts.

Whatever the starting point for this type of debate, there are positive affective outcomes as well as cognitive gains as issues are discussed and values clarified.

Role Playing

Role playing in groups is another particularly effective motivational technique for lessons related to social and human dimensions. A problem is posed and children are encouraged to assume the roles of persons involved in the problem situations. To do this they seek to understand the problem by acquiring additional information. Feelings are explored, insights are gained, and problem-solving abilities enhanced as the students project themselves into real-life situations. Joyce and Weil (1986) point out that "the collective reactions of the peer group can bring out new ideas and provide directions for growth and change. The model de-emphasizes the traditional role of teacher and encourages listening and learning from one's peers" (243).

activity 7.8 ## DILEMMA ANALYSIS: ROLE PLAYING

- ◆ Create a dilemma analysis card, describing a hypothetical issue on the environment that concerns you as a member of the community.
- ◆ Assign roles to group members and have each dramatize the part of community members who are for and against the issue.

❏ Reflecting and Sharing

You probably had no difficulty thinking of an issue and dramatizing the roles of different community members who would be affected by it.

More preparation is necessary when this technique is introduced in an elementary classroom. A good way to begin is to have role cards ready, as in the Society, Environment and Energy Development Studies (SEEDS) Activity reproduced in Appendix B.

All of these motivational techniques have a number of elements in common. All have a playfulness about them, challenging children to become part of a game in which ideas are generated and creative solutions to problems sought, in a relatively low-risk environment in which divergent thinking is encouraged and answers and answerers are treated with respect. They are techniques that can work well at higher levels of schooling, but because of their gamelike nature they are particularly appropriate for the early grades. The next section invites you to continue your exploration of motivational techniques by considering the role of play in science.

Play as a Motivational Technique

By the time children come to school, they have mastered the infinitely complex task of learning a language, simply by interacting with other human beings. Inspired by an innate sense of wonder and delighted by novelty, they have been exploring their environment since birth, sensing, learning, experimenting, repeating happenings that interest or challenge them, playing with the world, and through this exploratory play gradually bringing order to their experiences. This natural inclination for children to play and learn can enrich the kindergarten and primary years, and the potential of play for stimulating involvement, enhancing problem solving, and generating new ideas makes it a necessary component of science learning in the elementary years as well.

Many of the models for teaching science have been developed with this in mind. Recognizing the motivating value of play and the potential of developmentally appropriate experiences for enhancing learning, the introductory exploratory phase is often playlike in nature. Two models that incorporate an exploratory, playlike initial phase are the generative learning model and the learning cycle model, which were presented earlier as conceptual change models. You will find that the degree of openness and the time allowed for exploration varies in these models. There is no doubt, however, that beginning lessons in this way has an extremely motivating influence on learning, as well as great potential for encouraging creative thinking and problem solving.

THE ROLE OF PLAY IN SCIENCE

Discussing work and play in the light of Piaget's writings, George Hein (1973) states that the distinction between work and play is an adult one and does not exist for children. He suggests that Piaget's criteria for the kinds of experiences that lead to learning — active involvement, enthusiasm, questioning, and puzzlement — cut across the work–play distinction.

✍️ **From a Teacher's Journal**

Children are motivated to learn if they have a good feeling about themselves, if they have a feeling of confidence in their ability to succeed — a positive self-concept. When children are placed in problem-solving situations, encouraged to succeed, and assured that they can succeed, they are motivated to attack science challenges persistently and to develop competence in doing so. It is important to create an atmosphere in which risk taking is encouraged. Let children know that you think they can do it, and they will.

My experience has shown me that motivation is developed and sustained in science lessons when science challenges are used frequently, for example, "Which soup can will roll the farthest off the ramp?" and when predictions offered by each child are treated with respect and not criticized later if they do not correspond to experimental results. Injecting a little history of science and relating opposing views to views held tenaciously by scientists over the centuries also helps children realize that it is all right to be wrong, and that sometimes we learn more from mistakes because at least they force us to take another look at what is happening.

Ronald Mutton

Windsor, ON

Severeide and Pizzini's (1984) review of the research on play points to the importance of play in creating a risk-free environment within which problem-solving skills such as fluency and flexibility can flourish. They report that children participating in play groups exhibit positive attitudes toward learning, showing enthusiasm, spontaneity, self-directedness, imaginativeness, divergent thinking, and relative independence from adult guidance.

Severeide and Pizzini's summary of the research findings, with suggested actions, is reproduced in Table 7.1.

TABLE 7.1

Play in the Classroom: Theory and Practice

Research Findings	*Suggested Actions*
◆ Play helps develop skills and attitudes that are important for effective thinking.	◆ Provide a wide variety of play materials on a topic and allow the children time to "experiment" with them.
◆ Make-believe play increases the number of solutions children generate.	◆ Use imaginary stories and settings, imagery, roleplaying, and what-if games in science lessons.
◆ Play helps children develop flexible problem-solving strategies as well as a wide range of solutions.	◆ Let the children become acquainted with materials before providing structure for the activity. Let them imagine what they will do before you begin the activity.
◆ Play lessens the risk of failure and reduces frustration.	◆ Include play in lessons that are new and/or difficult.
◆ Play promotes positive learning attitudes at all ages, but especially in young children.	◆ Begin guided play in preschools and primary classrooms and maintain it throughout the grades.
◆ Playtime is most effective and innovative when adults observe before offering guidance.	◆ Watch for repetition of play activities and then redirect play to extensions or elaborations of the play theme.
◆ Playful and open teaching strategies can facilitate productive play.	◆ Be a playful model: ask open-ended and/or higher-level questions, be receptive to spontaneous ideas, and suspend judgement until after the play period.

Source: R.C. Severeide and E.L. Pizzini (1984). The role of play in science. Reprinted with permission from NSTA Publications, copyright May 1984 from *Science and Children,* 61. National Science Teachers Association, 1840 Wilson Boulevard, Arlington VA 22201–3000.

PLAY AS AN INITIATING PHASE OF INSTRUCTION

The Elementary Science Study (ESS) was one of the first to initiate children's learning with a playful examination of their environment. The units are based on a three-phase model (Hawkins 1965) that begins with free, exploratory learning through play — "Messing About" in Science — and progresses through two other more guided and structured phases, culminating in concept development.

Another interesting model is the Play–Debrief–Replay sequence for science learning developed by Wasserman and Ivany (1988).

Each of these teaching models is discussed in detail below.

Play as "Messing About" in Science. Hawkins (1965) believes that "children's play evolves from their experience, and learning through play is a necessary component of science education and playfulness a condition of understanding science" (40). Children's natural affinity for science is related to this, and the curiosity and sense of wonder that they bring to the school experience are akin to the playful approach that scientists find effective in problem solving.

The "messing about" phase is one of three phases that, according to Hawkins, should be included in all good science teaching. In the experience of the ESS developers, the longer the time devoted to messing about, the greater the diversity of experiments that result. As children explore with the materials, new questions are generated, and the teacher is the facilitator in the process, encouraging children along new paths of learning. In the third phase, the teacher and children pull together the discoveries that have been made and the ideas that have evolved from the explorations.

To capture the flavour of this approach, begin the following ESS activity in the spirit of "messing about in science" — in the spirit of play. Think about how a child would respond to these experiences.

- - - - - - - - - - - - - -

activity 7.9 "MESSING ABOUT" WITH MEALWORMS

1. In front of you is a glass dish with a mixture of bran and cornflakes, a small piece of apple, and a half-dozen active mealworms. On the tray beside the glass dish are popsicle sticks and hand lenses. A large culture of mealworms is on the science table, together with an assortment of other cereals, pieces of potato, carrot, some wooden blocks, cardboard of different colours, plastic containers, styrofoam trays, petri dishes, larger magnifiers, and two or three stereomicroscopes.

2. Make as many observations as you can about the mealworms. What can you find out about them in the next half-hour or so? Use your hand lenses to examine them more closely. Please be gentle when handling them and don't put anything directly on their bodies. Make drawings and other records of your observations.

3. Do you see anything else, living or nonliving, in the containers, besides the mealworms and cereal? in the culture on the supply table? Make a record of your observations. Share them with other group members and see if they have noticed anything different. Take a closer look and add any new findings to your list. Draw and record your observations.

4. What would you like to know about mealworms that you have not yet discovered? How do you think children would react to these experiences? What might *they* find out in the first encounter? What questions about mealworm behaviour would they have that could be answered by long-term investigations? How would the questions differ in Grade 2 and Grade 4 classrooms?

❏ Reflecting and Sharing

Children are enthralled with the segmented, slow-moving larvae, and in their "play" will count segments and the number of legs, antennae, and eye spots; notice how the mealworms feel to the touch; notice how it feels to have them crawl along their hands; observe the way they move; and check the way they move along walls and around barriers. They will place little piles of bran or perhaps sugar or a drop of water nearby to see whether the mealworms will move toward the food. One day they will find quiet, resting pupae and will try to explain this discovery. And when a young child finds a darkling beetle in her container, everyone will wonder how it got there and all kinds of theories will be proposed to explain the "discrepant event." Think back to the chapter on the nature of science. Are there stirrings and a feeling of déjà vu?

A Grade 4 child who has had wider experience with life cycles and metamorphosis will have different questions, different comparisons to make, and different avenues for exploration. Your role as a teacher will be all-important at every grade level, as you listen and provide the feedback and encouragement that allows your students to pursue the paths that they themselves have chosen.

The paths they choose will call for explorations that will extend learning in directions unforeseen at the beginning, and you, too, will see the potential in such explorations for enhancement of other areas of the curriculum, for counting and measuring, drawing and keeping accurate records, telling and writing about their experiences, and reading to find more information. Judith Newman (1985) writes about a child who came to her for help because his parents were concerned about his reading development. Her moving description begins the story of J.P. and his learning about language in the context of learning about the world:

> I have just sat down with J.P., an eight-year-old having some difficulty at school and on the table in front of us is a glass dish with some mealworm larvae crawling around. J.P.'s eyes light up as he bends over the dish to watch these creatures move.
>
> "Can I pick one up?" he asks me.
>
> "Certainly," I answer.
>
> "Look at it wiggle," he comments. "I can hardly feel it moving, though."
>
> "What can you tell me about this creature?" I ask him.
>
> With that query we began an exploration which finished with J.P.'s authoring his first book (151).

During the course of instruction, J.P. investigated frogs, mealworms, magnets, and batteries and bulbs, each time recording his observations, reading whatever appropriate material he could find, and writing his own book. By the time the sessions ended, he had written four books, each one more detailed and longer than the preceding one. By becoming involved enthusiastically in these learning activities in which "language was serving some real, practical purpose" (152), he was able to sustain his own learning about written language. Figure 7.5 is a sample page from J.P.'s first book.

Figure 7.6 illustrates further the desire to communicate that accompanies such experiences. This Grade 3 student uses the "This is the house that Jack built" model for his poetic description of the stages of mealworm development, and adds the drawings and arrows to complete his record of what he has learned.

Play–Debrief–Replay Learning Sequence. Selma Wasserman and George Ivany (1988), working in elementary schools in British Columbia, conducted a two-year study aimed at retraining teachers on the principles of sciencing and teaching for thinking. They are convinced of the value of *investigative play* in capitalizing on children's curiosity and initiating inquiries from which conceptual understanding may grow. In using this method, you would supply the materials, as in ESS, and let the investigation evolve from your pupils' own inquiries.

After a half-hour's play with the materials, in which you would not intervene except perhaps to facilitate the process, you would call the group together for a *debriefing session*. Then you would help the students to extract meaning from the

FIGURE 7.5

J.P.'s First Book: A Sample Page

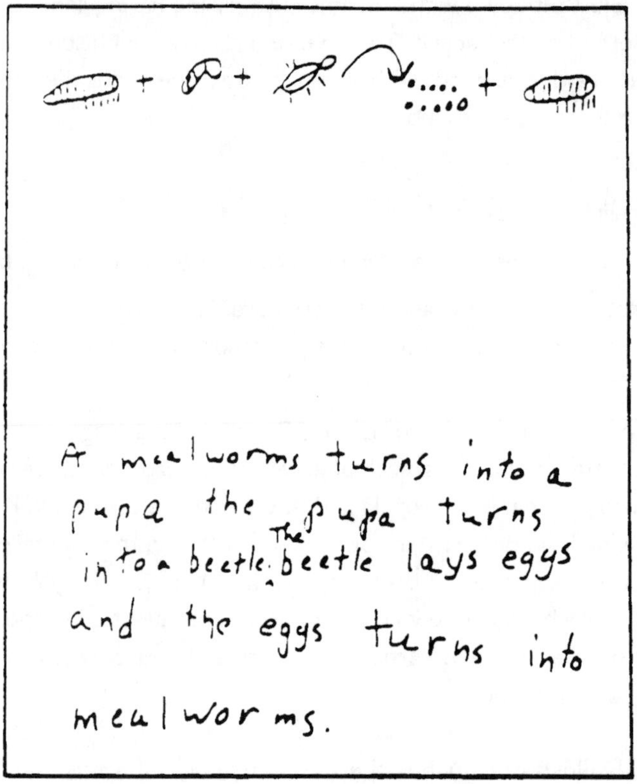

A mealworms turns into a
papa the pupa turns
into a beetle, the beetle lays eggs
and the eggs turns into
mealworms.

Source: J.M. Newman (1985). Mealworms: Learning about written language through
science activities. In J.M. Newman, ed., *Whole language theory in use,* 151.
Portsmouth, NH: Heinemann, A Division of Reed Publishing (USA), Inc.
Reprinted by permission of Judith M. Newman.

experiences, using a questioning strategy that begins with low-level questions
such as "What are some of your observations?" You would ask the children to
look for relationships within the data and make generalizations and extend ideas.
This period of reflective questioning lays the ground for the third stage, *replay,* in
which investigations of the first phase are sometimes repeated, or questions that have
arisen stimulate new inquiries and explorations. In this stage, bridges are crossed
into other curriculum areas and further creative explorations are encouraged.

The next activity is one of the 60 investigations developed by Wasserman and
Ivany for the "teaching for thinking" study. These investigations begin with play

FIGURE 7.6

This Is the Egg

This is the egg
that hatched into a larva
that nibbled the leaves
that turned into a pupa
that rested awhile on a branch
that turned into an adult butterfly
that sucked the flowers nectar
that laid the egg to start again

Rick Maharaj
Grade 3

Source: Reprinted with permission from Rick, Grade 3, Queenston Drive Public School, Toronto.

and "move from the hands-on manipulation of material into the realm of cognitive play, where groups discuss and play with ideas" (99). During this activity, children find out all they can about soap bubbles. Play is initiated by placing an activity card in the centre; the card instructs the children what to do and encourages them to think of other ways of using the materials and other investigations they may choose to pursue.

In your groups, work through the play–debrief–replay sequence to envisage the nature of the children's learning experiences in this program.

activity 7.10 BUBBLES

At the bubble centre, the children work with soapy water to make some observations about bubbles.

FIGURE 7.7

Activity Card

- Use the materials in this centre to find out what you can about bubbles.
- What observations did you make?
- Talk to each other about what you found.
- Then write about your observations.

You may wish to use the materials in this centre to create some other investigations. Try out your ideas and see what happens.

Source: S. Wasserman and J.W.G. Ivany (1988). *Teaching elementary science: Who's afraid of spiders?*, 147. New York: Harper & Row.

Materials

A solution made of a few drops of glycerine in a gallon of water, with a capful of liquid detergent, in a plastic bucket or container; straws; flexible wire and cutters; a few funnels of different sizes.

Debriefing

Here are some questions that may be raised during initial debriefing sessions:

- What observations did you make about bubbles?
- What did you observe about their size? shape? colour?
- What observations did you make about the "life" of a bubble? Which bubbles lasted longer? How do you explain this?
- What makes a bubble pop more quickly? How do you know this?

Extending

When the initial play periods begin to lose their productivity, extend the inquiry in one or more of the following ways:

1. Add new materials to the bubble centre, such as bubble pipes, sponges, waxed paper with holes of various sizes, paper cones, wire frames of different shapes.
2. Introduce new activity cards.

3. Introduce more challenging questions in later debriefing sessions, for example:

   ◆ Why are bubbles always round?
   ◆ How could you make a square bubble?
   ◆ Why do bubbles have colours? Where does the colouring come from? What explanations do you have for this?
   ◆ Why do bubbles pop so quickly? How might you extend the life of a bubble? Conduct some investigations to see how this might be done.
   ◆ What makes the biggest bubble? How do you explain this?

Creating

To bring these studies to a conclusion, invite the students to carry out one or more of the following creative activities:

1. Work with a friend. Design a house made of bubbles. Draw a picture of it.
2. Write a poem or make up a song about bubbles.
3. Make up a story called "The Bubble That Never Popped."

Source: "Bubbles Activity" from *Teaching Elementary Science: Who's Afraid of Spiders?* by S. Wasserman and J.W.G. Ivany. Copyright © 1988 by Harper & Row, Publishers, Inc. Reprinted by permission of HarperCollins Publishers.

❏ Reflecting and Sharing

You will probably agree that the playfulness with which the play phase of this learning sequence begins is sustained through the play–debrief–replay and extending activities. This is mostly because of the high intrinsic interest of the experiences, the mixture of convergent and divergent problem-solving activities that provide for a range of ability levels, and the fun-packed nature of the suggested avenues for exploration. The creating component at the end extends the learning beyond the science program and enhances and enriches other curriculum areas as well.

Both models of teaching have the play component in common, but they are very different in structure. Both try to encourage active learning and foster independence, and both use strategies designed to capitalize on children's interest in science and continue to stimulate and sustain that interest through the primary and elementary years.

In both models, pupil questions play a significant role. This is not surprising, because science begins with questions, and it is by asking questions that children are most likely to make sense of their world. Initiating activities in the spirit of play and providing a rich environment for science learning will encourage creativity and help to develop children's ability to ask questions. Class discussion of results after science activities also provides a fertile ground for further inquiries. One way to develop question-asking skills is to ask children at the end of the discussion whether there remain questions they would like to pursue or related information they would like to find out about — perhaps to list the things they are still curious about.

And what about the role of teacher questions? You have seen that many of the motivational techniques suggested in this chapter are initiated with teacher questions. Teacher questions play a critical role in teaching and an often underestimated role in the teaching of thinking. Yet the research on teacher questions indicates that the art of questioning is one that needs a great deal of attention in our schools. Although there are many aspects of teacher questioning that are not fully understood, techniques can be improved by taking cues from the research findings.

◆ ◆ ◆ ◆ ◆

DEVELOPING QUESTIONING SKILLS

Research on Teacher Questioning

Research on teacher questions indicates that, for the most part, teachers ask questions that are at a very low cognitive level, eliciting responses that simply require the learner to recall information previously learned, rather than to analyze or synthesize information or to think through problems.

Mary Budd Rowe's pioneer research in 1973 showed a rapid question–answer pattern. An analysis of 200 recorded tapes of a variety of elementary classrooms led to further study of the length of the pauses during the teacher–student interaction.

WAIT-TIME

Rowe (1973) found that teachers allowed less than a second for a student to begin an answer to a question (the first potential wait-time), and if the student response did not begin within that time the teacher repeated the question or called on another student. Even after a response (another potential wait-time), the teacher waited an average of only 0.9 seconds before reacting or moving on to another question or another topic.

Rarely were the students the questioners, and rarely, with so short a time allowed for a response, were their responses complete sentences. Rarely did the exchange lead to a fruitful discussion.

Effects of Increased Wait-Time. In subsequent studies, Wait-Time 1 (the pause after a teacher move) and Wait-Time 2 (the pause after a student move) were increased through training to a mean of three to five seconds. When 900 tapes were analyzed there were significantly improved values on ten student variables:

- an increase in the length of student responses;
- an increase in the number of unsolicited but appropriate student responses;
- a decrease in the number of students failing to respond, with fewer "I don't know" answers;
- an increase in confidence, as indicated by the decreased number of inflected responses;
- an increase in the number of speculative responses;
- an increase in the number of child–child comparisons of data;
- an increase in the number of inferences (statements supported by evidence);
- an increase in the frequency of student questions and an increase in the number of experiments proposed by students;
- an increase in the frequency of responses from children rated as slow learners;
- an increase in the variety of moves made by students.

Teacher behaviour changed in three ways:

- Teachers exhibited more flexibility in the range of responses they allowed.
- Teachers' expectations of students rated as slow learners seemed to increase.
- The number of teacher questions decreased and the quality and variety increased.

SCIENCE, SILENCE, AND SANCTIONS

Another interesting factor in these exploratory studies of the classroom was an interaction between wait-time and overt verbal rewards and punishments (positive and negative sanctions). Just as wait-times that are too brief may have a negative effect on students' ability to inquire and reason, verbal rewards also tend to have an inhibiting effect on the quality of explanations in science.

When teachers reduce verbal "rewards," dependence on the teacher lessens and children spend more time discussing and thinking through problems and planning experiments on their own. Children inquire best and suggest most creative answers in a risk-free environment where they are not afraid to be wrong, where they feel that they can control or change things, and where they feel that their opinions are valued. In a too-directed, too-rushed environment, where the final authority is always the teacher, pupils have a low sense of "fate control" — control of their own destiny. The five seconds of silence during wait-time gives children a chance to think, to formulate responses with confidence.

Silences, rather than sanctions, as the teacher circulates among groups can also give children the freedom to speculate, to listen to one another, to change their views, and to explore paths of their own choosing.

activity **7.11** **THE WAITING GAME**

Make arrangements to tape-record a lesson in science as you would normally teach it. Then teach and record another lesson, this time deliberately increasing the wait-time after each of your questions and student responses to three to five seconds. As you listen afterward to the two lessons on tape, note any differences in the pattern of questions and responses, in the quality of student responses, and in the child-to-child interaction within your class.

The next time you teach an inquiry-based lesson, think about changing your usual pattern of sanctions. Make a note of any differences you observe in the success of the lesson.

☐ Reflecting and Sharing

You may have found it difficult to wait for an interval of three to five seconds after asking a question, and then to wait again after the first student response. If so, you are not alone. Teachers generally dislike "dead time" and want to fill it, usually with words. It may have been difficult not to praise, quickly, a "correct" answer, rather than wait until a number of other children had offered responses and then reward all of them together with a positive comment about how well everyone was thinking today. Similarly, it may have been difficult to circulate from group to group, listening and observing, resisting the temptation to ask questions or offer suggestions until you were asked for help or feedback. However, you probably agree that the increased wait-time and the judicious use of silence and sanctions make good sense if you are trying to make your students less dependent on you and more responsible for their own learning.

Rowe's research on the effects of extending the average wait-time after questions and responses has been continued, not only by her own further study, but by a number of other researchers in different countries and at many levels of education. Extensive research by Ken Tobin (1984) revealed that with wait-times of less than three seconds the desired changes in student and teacher verbal behaviour did not occur. However, when wait-times of from three to five seconds were consistently maintained, thus giving students time to think and teachers time to frame better questions and reactions to student comments, there was a significant relationship between teacher wait-time and student achievement. The quality of teacher and student discourse was also found to be substantially improved in both whole-class and small-group settings.

Improving Teacher Questioning Patterns

To maximize thinking for most students in a whole-class setting, such as when an investigation is planned or data are being interpreted, Tobin suggests the following strategy:

1. Present a question clearly at a relevant time during the lesson.
2. Give all students three to five seconds of silence in which to consider a response.
3. Call upon one student to respond to the question.
4. Allow the student three to five seconds to commence a response. If the student doesn't respond, repeat or rephrase the question or redirect it to another student.
5. After a response to a question, provide three to five seconds for the student to elaborate or evaluate the response and for others in the class to consider the appropriateness of the response.
6. Redirect the question or the response to another student in the class. The redirecting strategy may be used for a maximum of three or four occasions (62).

Tobin suggests that when students know that a question or a response will be redirected for additional discussion, they tend to listen to one another. At the conclusion, students should have a clear idea of responses that are acceptable and those that are not, and the input will have come from their own ideas. Tobin warns, however, that wait-time alone is not a panacea, that classroom interactions are infinitely complex, and that there are times when wait-time should be shorter, as in drill and practice when the goal is rote memorization of factual material. However, the research of twenty years now indicates that when the goal is to stimulate higher cognitive processes, extended wait-time has great potential for improving teacher–student discourse and for enhancing achievement in science from kindergarten to the college level.

Improving the Quality of Teacher Questions

Good questioning can enhance all areas of science instruction. Science begins with questions, and skilful questioning can start discussions, stimulate involve-

Give all students three to five seconds of silence in which to consider a response.

ment and interaction, initiate investigations, and sustain inquiries. Wait-time has been found to encourage children to think critically and to come up with creative responses.

One well-known way to classify questions is according to whether they are convergent or divergent; another system is according to the levels of Bloom's taxonomy. Let's consider each of these and think of their application to successful science teaching.

Convergent versus Divergent Questions

Convergent Questions. To "converge" means to "come to a point," so that convergent questions centre or focus on one "correct" response rather than spread out to accept a number of responses. Answers to convergent or "closed" questions may involve recall of previously memorized information. Convergent questions may also call for "yes" or "no" answers. Although convergent questions are usually associated with recall, they can also require students to put together known facts before replying. Some examples of convergent questions are:

"Who was the first Canadian astronaut?"

"What are the four stages of mealworm development?"

From a Teacher's Journal

When I first started teaching, I emphasized the traditional "who," "what," "when," and "where" questions, but seldom asked those that start with phrases such as "What would happen if?" or "What do you think?" or "How are these alike?" or "How are they different?" or "How could we find out?" which are so characteristic of sciencing. Over the years, I have become much more conscious of formulating my questions so that students have lots of opportunities to share, discuss, and explain their opinions and ideas. During the last few years, I have also been more aware of the need for the students to be the ones asking the questions, and I try to build time into my daily lessons to allow this to happen.

When I first read about the "wait-time" research, it really made me think about whether I, too, was guilty of the rapid-fire questioning found by Mary Budd Rowe in her studies. I still wonder at times whether I am allowing enough time after my questions, especially for those students for whom English is a second language. I encourage the children to let me know if they need more time to think. (They usually say: "Come back to me!") It's important for them to have that thinking time.

Cynthia Clarke

Richmond, BC

Convergent questions may be used to review background information before starting a lesson, or perhaps to ascertain understanding at various points in the lesson, or to elicit the main points made. An obvious disadvantage is that having to know the "right" answer may be threatening to children who are afraid to risk answering in case they are wrong.

Divergent Questions. To "diverge" is to "spread out," so that divergent questions are open-ended and encourage a number of acceptable responses. Examples of divergent or "open" questions are:

"In how many different ways can you measure a ball?"

"How many animal adaptations can you think of?"

Because many replies are acceptable, divergent questions are less threatening, and children join in more readily during class discussions. When making the transition to more divergent questions, give children time to develop fluency of response. Don't make judgements, and from the beginning accept all responses.

USING DIVERGENT QUESTIONS:
IN HOW MANY DIFFERENT WAYS?

Ed Labinowich (1973) suggests another way of generating and recording divergent responses. He uses the familiar ESS unit "Batteries and Bulbs," and the familiar question "In how many different ways," but the follow-up is different. Try this way of encouraging divergence as you work in groups, following the steps and conducting experiments to determine "how many different ways" the brightness of a bulb can change.

activity 7.12 IN HOW MANY DIFFERENT WAYS?

1. You have been introduced to electrical circuits and have experienced some basic activities with batteries, bulbs, and wires. You are familiar with a simple circuit, as illustrated in Figure 7.8. To show how familiar you are, connect the wires so that you light the bulb.

2. In how many different ways can you change the brightness of a bulb? Within your group, list as many possibilities as you can think of. When you are ready, put your suggestions on the chalkboard and other groups will do the same.

3. If any other ideas occur to you after everyone has finished, add these to the list.

4. Look at Figure 7.9 — Idea Tree with Three Limbs. Each of the limbs of the tree could be a major part of a circuit, and each might affect the brightness of the bulb and therefore represent a *general solution* to the problem. Start by labelling each of the limbs on the tree.

5. The multitude of small branches growing out of the limbs suggests the possibility of a number of *variations of each general solution*. See how many variations you can come up with. Add them to the idea tree shown in Figure 7.9.

FIGURE 7.8

Simple Circuit (3 Components)

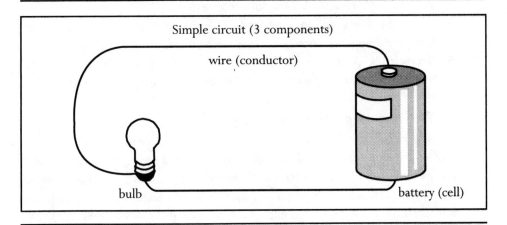

Simple circuit (3 components)

wire (conductor)

bulb

battery (cell)

Source: E. Labinowich (1973). In how many different ways ...? Divergent questions as springboards for "opening" your classroom. Reprinted with permission from NSTA Publications, copyright October 1973 from *Science and Children,* 18. National Science Teachers Association, 1840 Wilson Boulevard, Arlington, VA 22201–3000.

FIGURE 7.9

Idea Tree with Three Limbs

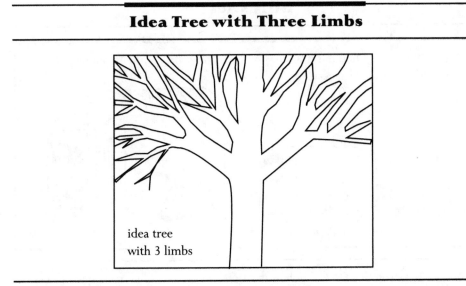

idea tree
with 3 limbs

Source: E. Labinowich (1973). In how many different ways ...? Divergent questions as springboards for "opening" your classroom. Reprinted with permission from NSTA Publications, copyright October 1973 from *Science and Children,* 18. National Science Teachers Association, 1840 Wilson Boulevard, Arlington, VA 22201–3000.

6. Return to your battery and bulb, and test your variations. Be sure that your plan is a fair test of one of your ideas. Figure 7.10 shows how Bill tested the effect of battery size on the brightness of the bulb. What is wrong with Bill's approach? Which variables are not controlled?

7. Choose another variation to test and think of different procedures for investigating the same idea. Share your ideas with others.

8. Afterward, look at Figure 7.11, which is the result of one elementary teacher's adventure into "opening" her classroom with divergent questions.

❏ Reflecting and Sharing

As you become an experienced teacher, you will be the best judge of what you consider to be the optimal mixture of convergent and divergent questions, and you will know which children are most comfortable with each approach. One of the strengths of "excursions into divergence" is that while no one child is required to generate all or even most possible solutions, a group of children interacting with their classmates will come up *collectively* with a host of ideas and gain valuable practice in approaching problems creatively.

FIGURE 7.10

Bills's Test

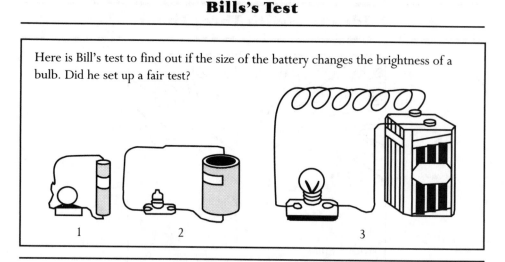

Here is Bill's test to find out if the size of the battery changes the brightness of a bulb. Did he set up a fair test?

1   2   3

Source: E. Labinowich (1973). In how many different ways ...? Divergent questions as springboards for "opening" your classroom. Reprinted with permission from NSTA Publications, copyright October 1973 from *Science and Children,* 19. National Science Teachers Association, 1840 Wilson Boulevard, Arlington, VA 22201–3000.

FIGURE 7.11

In How Many Different Ways Can You Change the Brightness of a Bulb?

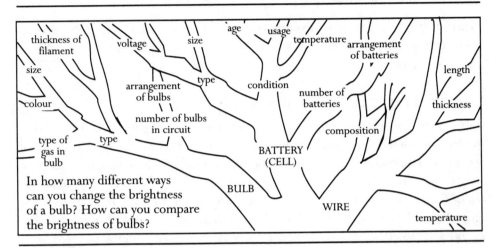

Source: E. Labinowich (1973). In how many different ways ...? Divergent questions as springboards for "opening" your classroom. Reprinted with permission from NSTA Publications, copyright October 1973 from *Science and Children,* 19. National Science Teachers Association, 1840 Wilson Boulevard, Arlington, VA 22201–3000.

LEVELS OF QUESTIONING: BLOOM'S TAXONOMY

Another way to vary the types and level of questions is to model them according to the levels of Bloom's taxonomy — from the level of *knowledge* (recall) through *comprehension* (understanding), and along a continuum where understanding would lead to *application* (to a new situation), *analysis* (breaking into component parts to see relationships), *synthesis* (putting together parts to make a whole), and *evaluation* (making judgements or comparisons according to certain standards or values). The examples of questions that follow illustrate how each step in the taxonomy calls for a higher level of thinking:

Knowledge. What are the functions of the stem of a plant?

Comprehension. You have been studying communities in science class. Explain why the rotting log on the science table could be called a community.

Application. You have been learning about minerals and their properties, such as hardness, streak, colour, lustre, and so on. Can you identify the "mystery mineral" on the science table?

Analysis. The dandelion is one of our most successful weeds. Can you think of some reasons for its survival?

Synthesis. How would you design an experiment to find out the effect that music has on a plant's growth?

Evaluation. You have been experimenting with two methods of growing trees from cuttings. Which method was more successful? What criteria did you use to help you decide?

LIFTING LEVELS OF QUESTIONING: TABA

Taba (1967) suggests a sequence for questions that begins with a low-level, general-knowledge question that focusses on the topic and allows a number of acceptable responses, so that a good number of students can respond. It must be worded so that the factual knowledge elicited can be used as a base for *lifting the thought levels* of the students and encouraging them to look for relationships among the data collected. Children who cannot respond in this manner are encouraged to elaborate on the first responses, perhaps by adding to the data or giving additional examples. The teacher works momentarily with students who are on the verge of seeing relationships, and tries to raise the level of their responses and guide them to greater understanding. The third step involves teacher questions that attempt to raise the level still further toward generalizations and patterns, to draw together what has been learned, and to determine whether the evidence supports a hypothesis or whether a concept is more clearly understood. The progression is from fairly specific and concrete to more general and abstract. Students are told about the process so that they, too, are trying to raise the quality of the discourse and to become better at thinking through problem situations.

IMPLICATIONS FOR PRACTICE

Looking back over the ideas of Rowe, Tobin, Bloom, and Taba, you can see similarities in their thinking and draw implications for practice from all of them. Your mode of questioning will vary, depending on the topic under consideration and the students with whom you are creating a dialogue or conversation. It will be in practising these techniques now and some day in your own classrooms that your competence will grow and you will know that you have been successful in involving all your students, reinforcing for them the awareness that they *are* learning, and challenging as many as possible to attain higher levels of thinking and problem solving.

Despite indications of earlier studies that achievement and interest improve when teachers use questions of varying levels of difficulty, results are still inconclusive. Tischer (1985) reports that painstaking reviews of studies to determine the effect on students' understanding of higher-level questions show no conclusive results. There is a great deal to be learned, and perhaps the answers will come as you and other teachers become involved in action research in your own classrooms, gathering data from taped segments of your lessons and reflecting on the results you obtain as you experiment with different patterns of questioning.

If you model various levels of questioning and open up your classroom to a host of creative responses, there is a good chance that you will find ways to realize your goals of developing your pupils' thinking skills and stimulating further interest in science. In primary and elementary science, a *focus on students' questions* is a very fruitful approach.

Encouraging and Refining Pupils' Questions

It has been suggested (White 1977) that teachers may need to show children how to form questions and how to refine their questions so that they are investigable. Dorothy Alfke (1974) coined the term "operational questions" for questions that arise in the course of an investigation and that can be made into testable statements or hypotheses and answered by going back to the materials. Biddulph and Osborne (1984) have produced a set of guidebooks designed to help teachers make use of children's questions as a basis for investigations in primary and elementary science. As teachers, encourage children to generate questions, and supply the feedback needed to refine the questions and the additional materials they will need to help them find answers. Your help can make the difference between interest that wanes for lack of a nurturing environment and interest that finds expression in a variety of science projects at all levels.

◆ ◆ ◆ ◆ ◆

PROBLEM SOLVING IN ACTION

Projects are a form of problem solving in action. They can take the form of a library search for information about a topic in which a student has become interested, a take-home science activity to share with parents on a weekend, a poster project for the science learning centre, or participation in science olympics or school science fairs. These are usually highlights in a student's life that are remembered long after elementary school is over and may spark interest that will lead to further participation in science projects in the middle and secondary school years. Think of the following possibilities.

Science Days

The flow of communication from school to the home is important, as well as from the home to the school. This can begin very early with parents' involvement as helpers in the science classroom and with science activities at home that enhance and extend school experiences. Children in the early grades love to "show and tell" what they are involved with at school, and a science day brings parents and siblings together to share science experiences with students. Later this can be extended to the science fair or some modification of the science fair suitable for the elementary grades.

Poster Sessions

Michael Padilla and Edward Shaw (1983) recommend poster sessions as a project that can give intermediate students practice with conducting experiments and thinking a problem through from the hypothesis stage to interpreting data. Students explain an experiment to their classmates with the help of a poster that outlines the steps in the experimental procedure. Poster sessions are also good practice for participation in a school science fair at the junior-high level. Other advantages are additional science learning and practice with public speaking. Posters can be displayed in corridors or in the classroom to interest other children in the science projects. Figure 7.12 shows a poster that outlines a classic experiment appropriate for the upper elementary level.

Science Challenges and Science Olympics

Community and parental involvement are assured when science fairs get underway at school. Usually competitive science fairs begin at the junior-high level, but there is a growing interest in noncompetitive fairs in the elementary grades, and even primary children (and their parents) delight in a "show and tell" exhibition of their work in science.

SCIENCE CHALLENGES

Donald Maxwell and Glenn Berkheimer (1987) suggest having a school-wide or district-wide science "challenge" at this level that involves all students and includes a variety of events. Elementary students who participate have a broad choice of events to enter, and all participating students receive a certificate. Primary-grade events are included and may demonstrate mastery of skills or replicate an activity done in class.

Ideas can be gathered from science trade books, collections of science activities (which are found quite often now in curriculum materials centres), or modular and textbook programs. Problems are solved using only the materials provided, and there is a set time limit to complete the challenge.

SCIENCE OLYMPICS

A similar sort of event has been endorsed by the Youth Science Foundation. Science olympics are problem-solving events that demonstrate the fun side of science, and the solutions depend more on creativity and imagination in problem solving than on research skills such as those emphasized in science fairs. An example of a science olympic challenge is to use a variety of materials, such as one sheet of newspaper, straws, scissors, popsicle sticks, paper clips, glue,

FIGURE 7.12

How Does the Number of Coils Affect the Strength of an Electromagnet?

Hypothesis:
The greater the number of coils in an electromagnet, the stronger the magnetic force will be.

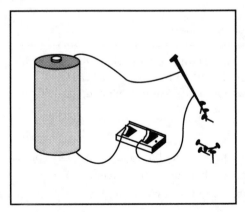

Data Table	
Manipulated Variable	*Responding Variable*
Number of Coils on Nail	Number of Pins Picked Up
10	0
20	10
30	27
40	39
50	64

Figure 7.12 (continued)

Variables:

Manipulated variable — the number of coils on the nail

Responding variable — the strength of the magnet

Controlled variables — the type of wire and nail used; the size and strength of the battery

Materials Needed:

Large (20-penny) common wire nail

Insulated wire (preferably copper wire)

6-volt dry-cell battery

Knife switch

Steel straight pins

Procedure:

Cut 2 pieces of wire — one 0.5 meter (m), one 1.5 m.

Carefully strip the insulation from the ends of the wires.

Attach the wires to the battery terminals and the knife switch as shown on the diagram.

Coil the wire around the nail 10 times, close the switch to make electrical contact, and see how many pins can be lifted.

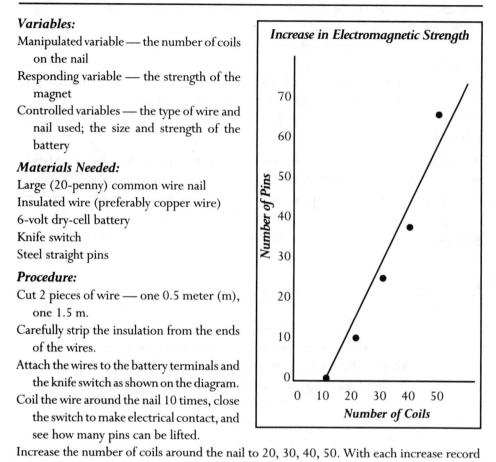

Increase the number of coils around the nail to 20, 30, 40, 50. With each increase record the number of pins that can be lifted.

Conclusion:

The more coils of wire are added, the stronger the magnet is.

Source: M.J. Padilla and E. Shaw (1983). Experiments with poster sessions. Reprinted with permission from NSTA Publications, copyright May 1983 from *Science and Children,* 61. National Science Teachers Association, 1840 Wilson Boulevard, Arlington, VA 22201-3000.

staples, and stapler to construct the strongest possible one-metre newspaper bridge. Both science olympics and science challenges are excellent for public relations with the community and for extending the science program beyond the classroom.

◆ ◆ ◆ ◆ ◆

LOOKING BACK AND LOOKING FORWARD

In this chapter, you have focussed on the development of specific skills, techniques, and capabilities that are the hallmark of effective teaching. If you begin with the premise that the role of the learner in science classrooms is an active one in which knowledge is constructed through experience, the first task is to create an encouraging environment for learning, in which children have opportunities to explore freely and gradually develop and refine their ideas.

You have been introduced to a number of concept teaching models, including concept attainment and concept formation models as well as models that facilitate conceptual change.

The teaching of thinking has been explored through a discovery lesson on water drops that led quickly to the use of process skills in problem solving and to inquiry-based teaching. You have considered the motivational aspects of co-operative learning and a number of ways of initiating inquiry in groups through discrepant events, open-ended problems, brainstorming, "buzz" sessions, dilemma analysis, and role playing. The role of play in science has been highlighted as a motivating beginning for children's learning and also for its value in providing a risk-free environment in which creativity and problem solving can flourish.

Another emphasis is the role played by verbal interactions in teaching and learning, and the research on questioning that has focussed on identifying ways in which these interactions can be improved. One way is to extend wait-time after teacher questions and student responses. Extending wait-time reduces children's risk of being wrong and increases their sense of fate control.

You have been introduced to a variety of types of questions to enlarge your repertoire and "open" your classroom: convergent and divergent questions; questions of varying levels of difficulty; questions to lift thought levels; questions to stimulate children's involvement in science; and questions to guide them through the steps of gathering and processing data and arriving at generalizations.

A neglected area of research has been the study of children's questions and how they can be refined and become the starting points for inquiring and discovering, pursuing interests, and solving problems. Science days, science olympics, science challenges, and science fairs have been explored as exciting possibilities for extending science into real-life situations and leading students to a lifelong interest in science.

It is clear that effective classroom practice will encompass a number of ways of teaching and many opportunities for children to become actively involved in learning. An important component of improving day-to-day decisions on teaching/learning is ongoing evaluation and assessment of the success of the teaching strategies used and the skills acquired in ensuring children's progress over time toward the achievement of cognitive, affective, psychomotor, and social outcomes and the overall goal of scientific literacy. This will be the focus of the next chapter.

CANADIAN ACHIEVEMENTS IN SCIENCE

JOHN POLANYI (B. 1929)

John Polanyi was born in Germany in 1929, but at the age of 4 emigrated to England when his father, an eminent chemist and widely read philosopher of science, took up an academic position in England. John Polanyi spent part of the war years in Canada, returned to England after the war, and completed a doctorate in chemistry before returning to Canada in 1952. He worked for two years in the National Research Council laboratories in Ottawa with Nobel Prize winner Gerhard Herzberg. Not surprisingly, Polanyi's work, like Herzberg's, was in the field of spectroscopy. Polanyi conceived the idea of vibrational and chemical lasers.

The word laser is an acronym for "light amplification by stimulated emission of radiation." A laser produces an intense beam of energy that can be finely focussed and made to travel millions of miles with little loss of focus. It can be used for microsurgery, for example, in the treatment of minute eye defects, for long-range communication, and is the basis of the successful formation of holograms. Polanyi used this intense beam of energy as a tool to help him understand and explain chemical reactions in terms of the motions of atoms and molecules as they engage in reactive collisions. In 1986, he was awarded the Nobel Prize for chemistry for his part in opening up this new field of research.

The stereotype of the dedicated scientist divorced from other aspects of life is nowhere less true than in the case of John Polanyi. He has a strong interest in painting, literature, and poetry, as well as more athletic pursuits. For over 30 years, he has been a vocal advocate of nuclear disarmament, a champion of the cause of science as a potential force for good in society, and a critic of Canada's inadequate investment in scientific research.

☐ R E F E R E N C E S

Alfke, D. (1974). Operational questions. *Science and Children* (April):18–19.

Arends, R.I. (1988). *Learning to teach,* 24. New York: Random House.

Ausubel, D.P. (1963). *The psychology of meaningful verbal learning: An introduction to school learning.* New York: Grune & Stratton.

Barba, R.H. (1990). Problem solving pointers: Techniques that can be taught. *The Science Teacher* (October):32–36.

Barnes, D. (1976). *From communication to curriculum.* Harmondsworth: Penguin.

Biddulph, F., and R. Osborne, eds. (1984). *Making sense of our world: An interactive teaching approach.* Hamilton, New Zealand: University of Waikato.

Birnie, H.H., and A. Ryan (1984). Inquiry/discovery revisited. *Science and Children* 21(7) (April):31–32.

Bloom, B. (1950). A taxonomy of educational objectives: Handbook I. *The cognitive domain.* New York: David McKay.

Bruner, J. (1966). *Toward a theory of instruction.* Cambridge, MA: Harvard University Press.

Case, R. (1985). *Intellectual development: Birth to adulthood.* Toronto: Academic Press.

Cobb, V., and K. Darling (1980). *Bet you can't! Science impossibilities to fool you.* New York: Lothrop, Lee & Shepard.

DeBruin, J. (1975). Messing with mysteries and minds. *Science and Children* 12(5):16–17.

Driver, R. (1983). *The pupil as scientist?* Milton Keynes, UK: Open University Press.

Elementary Science Study Teacher's Guide. (1966). Behavior of mealworms. St. Louis, MO: McGraw-Hill.

Graika, T. (1989). Minds-on, hands-on science. *Science Scope* (March): 18–20. Washington, DC: National Science Teachers Association.

Harlen, W. (1985). *Teaching and learning primary science.* New York: Teachers College, Columbia University.

Harlen, W., and S. Jelly (1990). *Developing science in the primary classroom.* Portsmouth, NH: Heinemann.

Harlen, W., and R. Osborne (1985). A model for teaching and learning applied to primary science. *Journal of Curriculum Studies* 17(2):133–46.

Hawkins, D. (1965). Messing about in science. *Science and Children* (February). Reprinted in *The ESS Reader,* 37–44. Newton, MA: Educational Development Center, 1970.

Hein, G. (1973). Piaget, materials and the open classroom. *EDC News* (Winter):7–10. Newton, MA: Educational Development Center.

Johnson, R.T., and D.W. Johnson (1982). What research says about student–student interaction in science classrooms. In M. Rowe, ed., *Education in the 80's*. Washington, DC: National Education Association.

———. (1988). Research matters ... to the science teacher: Encouraging student/student interaction. New York: National Association for Research in Science Education (NARST).

Joyce, B., and M. Weil (1986). *Models of teaching.* 3d ed. Englewood Cliffs, NJ: Prentice-Hall.

Kaplan, N. (1984). But that's not fair! *Science and Children* 21(7): 26–27.

Labinowich, E. (1973). In how many different ways ...? Divergent questions as springboards for "opening" your classroom. *Science and Children* 11(2):18–20.

Liem, T.K. (1981). *Invitations to science inquiry.* Needham, MA: Ginn.

———. (1990). *Invitations to science inquiry.* 2d ed. Chino Hills, CA: Science Inquiry Enterprises.

Maxwell, D.E., and G. Berkheimer (1987). Olympics achievement for your science program. *Science and Children* (April) 17–19.

Newman, J.M. (1985). Mealworms: Learning about written language through science activities. In J.M. Newman, ed., *Whole language theory in use,* 145–52. Portsmouth, NH: Heinemann.

Novak, J.D., and D.B. Gowin (1984). *Learning how to learn.* Cambridge, UK: Cambridge University Press.

Nussbaum, J., and S. Novick (1982). Alternative frameworks, conceptual conflict and accommodation: Toward a principled teaching strategy. *Instructional Science* 11:183–200.

Padilla, M.J., and E. Shaw (1983). Experiments with poster sessions. *Science and Children* 20(8):60–61.

Plowden Report (1967). *Children and their primary schools*. A report of the Central Advisory Board of Education. London: Her Majesty's Stationery Office.

Potter, T.G., and W.J. Horak (1987). Inquiry investigations. *Science Scope* (September):6–7.

Rockcastle, V.N. (1975). Science teaching — Its demands, freedoms and responsibilities. The demand for providing elementary science experiences. Typescript, personal communication.

Rogers, C. (1983). *Freedom to learn for the 1980s*. Columbus, OH: Merrill.

Rowe, M.B. (1969). Science, silence and sanctions. *Science and Children* 6(6):11–13.

————. (1973). *Teaching science as continuous inquiry*. New York: McGraw-Hill.

Science Olympics, Grades 4–6. Ottawa: Youth Science Foundation.

Selnes, M. (1986). Science startlers. *Science Scope* (September):5–7.

Severeide, R.C., and E.L. Pizzini (1984). The role of play in science. *Science and Children* 21(8):58–61.

Shrigley, R.L. (1987). Discrepant events: Why they fascinate students. *Science and Children* (May):24–25.

Society, Environment and Energy Development Studies (1987). SEEDS Newsletter no. 1:4–5.

Suchman, J.R. (1966). *Developing inquiry*. Chicago: Science Research Associates.

Taba, H. (1967). *A teacher's handbook for elementary social studies*. Reading, MA: Addison-Wesley.

Tischer, R.P. (1985). What are the effects of intellectually demanding questions? Perspectives on higher cognitive questions. *Australian Science Teachers Journal* 30(4):67–71.

Tobin, K. (1984). Applications of extended wait time in science classes. *Australian Science Teachers Journal* 30(4):61–66.

Wasserman, S., and J.W.G. Ivany (1988). *Teaching elementary science: Who's afraid of spiders?* New York: Harper & Row.

White, R.T. (1977). An overlooked objective. *Australian Science Teachers Journal* 23(2):124–25.

Wright, E.L. (1981). Fifteen simple discrepant events that teach science principles and concepts. *School Science and Mathematics* (November).

CHAPTER 8

Evaluation of Sciencing

EVALUATION

is

AN ONGOING AND INTEGRAL PART

of

TEACHING AND LEARNING

which relates to

FORMATIVE AND SUMMATIVE ASSESSMENT

of

children's

- **Cognitive Capabilities**
- **Affective Behaviours**
- **Psychomotor Skills**

through

EVALUATIVE TECHNIQUES

which include the use of

- **Checklists**
- **Rating Scales**
- **Anecdotal Records**
- **Portfolios**
- **Free-Response Tests**
- **Forced-Response Tests**
- **Questionnaires**

◆ ◆ ◆ ◆ ◆

When my children were in school, the end of

term always brought a report card which read

that one of them was "not living up to expecta-

tions." I could never sort out whose expectations

were not being met. Their own? The teacher's?

Mine? All three would be a safe bet in most cases.

ROY BONISTEEL (1983)

Throughout this book, a number of suggestions are offered that relate to the teaching and learning of primary and elementary science. This chapter will help you to evaluate the progress of your students in achieving a variety of potential outcomes in the cognitive, affective, and psychomotor domains. Consistent with the focus of this book, the chapter leans toward evaluation techniques that relate particularly well to science. However, it is important to realize that in primary and elementary classrooms, separation of teaching and assessment into science and nonscience is often likely to be artificial.

In the space available, this chapter cannot offer a comprehensive treatment of testing and measurement. If further detail is required, you will find many other more specialized resources. Useful examples include Bloom, Hastings, and Madaus (1971), Doran (1980), Gronlund (1985, 1988), and, particularly with respect to evaluation of primary children, North York Board of Education (1983) and Wortham (1990). Many provincial departments of education also have evaluation handbooks written with their own teachers in mind.

Evaluation is an integral part of good teaching, and for it to be effective it must be planned in advance of teaching. Evaluation of students is not an end-game. On the contrary, it is a vital component of the continuous development of children toward their maximum potential. Without wishing to burden you with technical terminology, a few technical terms are introduced to facilitate a link between the specific examples of classroom practice introduced below and general principles that are useful to a consideration of evaluation of children's performances.

◆ ◆ ◆ ◆ ◆

ASPECTS OF EVALUATION

Consider the following glimpses of teachers' evaluative activities in several typical classrooms. The examples are meant to be illustrative, and represent only a tiny fraction of actual practice. Yet, each represents a particular aspect of classroom life as it relates to evaluation of children.

Mary is a kindergarten teacher. It is mid-September, and once again Mary is faced with fifteen very different, very individual 5-year-olds. Some are happy to be "finally in school," while others are timid and afraid. Some come to school "knowing their colours" and the names of different shapes and so on; others may be as much as two years behind in terms of what they can do. The children are playing cheerful games, aided by Mary. Mary, however, is paying careful attention to what each child is doing. Although the children don't realize it, over a period of several weeks she makes careful observations of each child. These observations will be useful to Mary as she plans the year ahead for each of them. Mary is applying *formative evaluation*.

Margaret has been a Grade 2 teacher for many years, and has developed a set of worksheets that she uses throughout each year. Although the children don't realize it, the completed worksheets are used to obtain information about how each child is progressing in terms of generalized competencies. Collectively, Margaret's worksheets reflect a variety of possible outcomes including, for example, knowledge and understanding of specifics, attitude toward learning, and manipulative skills. Like Mary, the purpose of evaluation for Margaret is formative, as she strives to help children move forward.

Phil is a Grade 4 teacher. Phil organizes the content of his classes so that every few weeks a new unit is begun, usually corresponding to a new unit in the textbook. At the end of each chapter, the children are given written tests. Although the tests are not scored, the completed tests are used, when necessary, to provide individual suggestions for additional work to be completed before the class as a whole progresses to the next unit of work. Phil is diagnosing children's individual problems and prescribing appropriate remedial action. His approach is called *diagnostic-prescriptive evaluation*.

Alice teaches Grade 6. She is aware that when the children leave her class they are beginning a new phase of their education. As such, Alice aims to assess each child in terms of content knowledge, general intellectual ability, ability to perform specific intellectual and motor skills, attitude toward specific subjects, and attitude toward school in general and to other students. On several occasions throughout the year, including at the end of the year, Alice schedules regular tests and feeds back to students and their parents each student's score on the test, as well as information about the performance of the entire class. No suggestions for improvement are provided. Alice's approach to evaluation is called *summative evaluation*. The essential characteristic of summative evaluation is that it is intended to report a degree of success at the end of a unit of instruction.

The meanings of the terms formative evaluation, diagnostic-prescriptive evaluation, and summative evaluation are considered further in Activity 8.1.

activity 8.1   AN EVALUATION PROBLEM

Imagine that you have asked some children to design an experiment to find out which of several brands of paper towel is best at cleaning up spills of liquid. Better, ask some children to do this, if you can. Consider how you will evaluate children formatively, diagnostic-prescriptively, and summatively when they do this activity.

❏ Reflecting and Sharing

Perhaps you considered children who have little experience in designing experiments. In this case, your evaluation is probably formative. Your concern is to find out what, if anything, these children understand about experimental design and about the idea of a fair test. If their understanding is limited, you will consider exposing them to further similar situations.

Perhaps you considered children who have encountered similar situations before, but you may expect some children to have difficulty. You may be particularly interested in identifying the specific problems that individual children are having with the concept of controlling variables, and about designing experiments. You will use this information to design further instruction to help them overcome their specific difficulties. In this case, your evaluation is diagnostic-prescriptive.

Finally, you may be considering children at the end of their last year in elementary school. Although you know that children at this level typically have difficulty understanding the concept of controlling variables, you know that some of them are likely to have a reasonable understanding of this process. You decide that it should be included in a final test of the children's performance in science. In this case, your evaluation is summative.

Two further commonly used terms are norm-referenced evaluation and criterion-referenced evaluation.

The purpose of *norm-referenced evaluation* is to discriminate between individuals. When evaluation is norm-referenced, the performance of each child is typically expressed in terms of the child's rank within an overall group, and success or failure is relative to the performance of the rest of the group. On the other hand, the purpose of *criterion-referenced evaluation* is to determine a child's performance in relation to a preset standard, a criterion, rather than to determine the child's performance relative to others. As a primary or elementary teacher, you are more likely to be concerned with criterion-referenced evaluation than with norm-referenced evaluation. At this level, it usually matters less how an individual child compares with the rest of the class than how each individual is progressing.

◆ ◆ ◆ ◆ ◆
DOMAINS OF LEARNING

In Chapter 1, you were introduced to the idea that it is useful to consider different domains of learning as you plan instruction. It is also useful to consider evaluation of children's learning in terms of these same domains. Consider first the cognitive domain.

Cognitive Domain

Especially since the publication of Bloom's taxonomy of educational objectives in the cognitive domain (Bloom, Hastings, and Madaus 1956), educators have argued about the usefulness of behavioural objectives in instruction and learning. Some, such as Robert Mager (1962), argue strongly for their inclusion. Others, such as Elliott Eisner (1967), argue that stating objectives in precise terms is constricting and frequently counterproductive. It is reasonable to take an intermediate position. Although the detailed specification of objectives in minute detail is not a worthwhile use of the teacher's time, it is useful for the teacher to think in terms of the specific behaviours that are involved as she or he prepares both for instruction and for evaluation of children's learning. Bloom's taxonomy separates objectives in the cognitive domain into six major categories and a number of subcategories. The subcategories are not explored in detail here, but you will find them described in detail in Bloom's taxonomy.

In order of ascending complexity, the six major levels of Bloom's taxonomy represent *knowledge, comprehension, application, analysis, synthesis,* and *evaluation.* Each of these categories represents important and useful objectives of education, and it is possible to identify examples of them all in the curriculum of the primary and elementary grades. Each is now described briefly.

KNOWLEDGE

It is not difficult to create objectives and test items at the knowledge level. *Knowledge* involves the recall of previously learned material, including recall of facts, definitions, procedures, conventions, trends, and theories. Emphasis is on remembering, not understanding. For example, taking the order above and progressing generally from early primary to upper elementary levels, questions such as "What are the five senses?" "What is a square?" "What are the steps to be followed when using a microscope?" "What are the fixed points on the Celsius temperature scale?" "What are the stages in frog development from egg to adult?" and "How did Copernicus's view of the universe differ from Ptolemy's?" are representative of the knowledge level. In each case, whatever the format of the question, the response requires only recall of previously encountered information.

COMPREHENSION

Comprehension represents the ability to grasp meaning. It includes being able to translate, interpret, and extrapolate information. Examples include:

◆ a child's explaining, in his or her own words, the meaning of terms like hypothesizing, melting, sedimentary, acid, and inherited trait;
◆ a child's following instructions for drawing a graph, sorting the objects in a set, completing an electric circuit;
◆ a child's using data or information to make predictions, for example, extending a graph of the local temperature in July over the past five years to predict what it will be next July.

For the above examples to be classified as comprehension, they must involve more than repetition of previously learned information, as this represents only knowledge, and they must not involve kinds of situations different from those encountered by the individual previously, as this represents application. The difference between comprehension and application is that application involves situations new to the learner, while comprehension only requires the learner to work within familiar situations.

APPLICATION

The essence of *application* is that a situation that is new to the child must be involved. For example, being able to determine the area of a triangle, having already been shown how to do this, involves comprehension. In contrast, being able to determine the area of a nontriangular object by first realizing that the object can be broken down into a number of triangles, without being specifically

Testing knowledge places an emphasis on remembering rather than on understanding. Written tests should allow students to explain in their own words what they understand.

told to do this, involves application. Routine problems involve comprehension. Such "type" problems, common in mathematics throughout school and in the physical sciences in secondary grades, do not constitute application.

If children are to learn to think things through for themselves, it is clear that they need more than just comprehension, important though that is. Fortunately, opportunities abound in informal interactions between teachers and students. Consider the following examples:

◆ Having spent some time learning basic shapes, such as square, circle, and triangle, members of a kindergarten class are asked to find and talk about examples of each of these shapes in their homes.

◆ As part of a unit on weather, Grade 2 children are asked to design a weather bulletin board and use it to report the weather on the first day of each week for three months.

◆ After a unit on heat, Grade 4 children are challenged to compete to find the best way to keep an ice cube frozen.

◆ After learning to use a single pulley, Grade 6 children are challenged to find the best arrangement of two pulleys in terms of ability to lift a simple load.

Each of the above examples involves application. Some are more likely to be useful than others for evaluation, but there is no shortage of possibilities with which to measure children's ability to demonstrate application in the course of a normal school year.

ANALYSIS, SYNTHESIS, AND EVALUATION

The remaining three levels of Bloom's taxonomy include *analysis, synthesis,* and *evaluation*. Although they represent the highest levels of the taxonomy, each can occur in the primary and elementary grades, but they are likely to be much less prominent than in later years of school.

Analysis involves breaking down a situation or problem into its component parts — for example, breaking down a project, such as finding out the favoured environment of a species such as mealworms by testing their responses to humidity, temperature, and light.

Synthesis is the opposite of analysis. It involves putting components together to make a whole. An example is producing a plan to determine the preferred environment of a species.

Finally, evaluation is concerned with judgement. Judging the merits of a plan or the level of its success in providing a solution to the problem investigated represents evaluation.

Even when working with young children, there are opportunities for teachers to engage the children and evaluate their performance at each of these levels. All are worth the teacher's attention. As a starting point, it will be useful for you to make a conscious attempt to require children to operate at least at the level of application. Much evidence suggests that this represents an advance over many teachers' practice.

Affective Domain

With respect to evaluation within the *affective* domain, again the pioneering work was done by Bloom and colleagues (Krathwohl, Bloom, and Masia 1964). Krathwohl's taxonomy has five main levels, including, from most to least inclusive, *receiving, responding, valuing, organization,* and *characterization by a value complex*.

RECEIVING

Receiving is the lowest level of affective awareness and represents merely that the child pays attention to the subject at hand. For example, the child does not withdraw attention when science becomes the focus of interest in class.

RESPONDING

Responding requires a greater level of commitment than receiving. Responding involves active participation and reaction on the part of the learner. For example, the child who opts to be the leader in a science investigation, who volunteers to bring material to school for a science activity, or who willingly participates in additional learning tasks is responding and by so doing is showing a higher level of commitment than is represented by receiving.

VALUING

Valuing refers to a feeling of worth attached by the child to some specific activity. For example, the child who tries to invoke in class discussions scientific evidence of a potential environmental issue is exhibiting a value for science.

ORGANIZATION AND CHARACTERIZATION BY A VALUE COMPLEX

The remaining two levels of the affective taxonomy will only be referred to briefly here, as they represent a considerable step in the development of individuals with respect to their affective behaviours. They require an accompanying level of cognitive development that is unlikely to be found in many children by the end of elementary school. The first of these two levels is *organization,* which involves comparing, relating, and synthesizing values. The final level in the taxonomy, *characterization by a value complex,* involves the development of a characteristic life-style. Clearly this is unlikely to develop substantially by the end of elementary school.

Psychomotor Domain

The third domain of learning proposed by Bloom and colleagues in the mid-1950s is the *psychomotor domain*. Despite its potential appeal to early childhood educators, science educators, and others, this third taxonomy has not been as prominent in the educational literature as the other two taxonomies. One reason for this may be that, as educators, we are often concerned to focus upon specific skills rather than upon generalized competencies when considering outcomes in this domain. For example, although there are resemblances in the procedure, the ability to hit a baseball with a baseball bat does not necessarily carry over to hitting a cricket ball with a cricket bat. Similarly, the use of a simple dropping pipette to dispense a measured quantity of liquid is similar in some ways to the use of scissors. Yet the individual who can successfully use a pair of scissors may not be able to manipulate a dropping pipette.

Unlike the development of cognitive and affective behaviours, which are not generally developed through direct repetition, the essence of the development of psychomotor skills is guided repetition. Another difference is that, once learned, psychomotor skills tend to be retained and can be resurrected readily. Detailed specification of the structure of the psychomotor domain is provided by Simpson (1972). A brief representation follows.

Learning in the psychomotor domain begins with the use of the senses and progresses successively from the ability to demonstrate simple skills, such as pouring a liquid from one container to another; to the early stages of more complex skills, such as using a simple microscope under direct guidance from the teacher; to confident, habitual use of such skills; to correct demonstration of more complex skills, such as heating a liquid safely in a test tube; to being able to adapt existing skills to new situations, such as using a compound microscope after having used only a simple microscope previously; and, finally, to being able to create new techniques in novel situations, such as the construction of a unique piece of apparatus in the context of a science fair project.

There is evidence, for example, from the extensive studies of the Assessment of Performance Unit in Britain, that psychomotor skills are often poorly learned. Even by the end of school, performance of a number of routine practical skills, such as the use of measuring instruments like stopwatches, graduated cylinders, simple balances, and a variety of electrical meters, is inadequate. Clearly, there is a need for systematic monitoring of the use of these and other commonly used items of practical equipment. It is important to realize that children's learning of a psychomotor skill must be evaluated mainly by observing the application of the specific skill.

activity 8.2   IDENTIFYING DOMAIN EXAMPLES

Examine the textbook for a grade level of your choice. Find passages in the text (narrative, examples, activities, questions, etc.) representing each of the following:

- the first three levels of Bloom's taxonomy of the cognitive domain;
- the first three levels of Krathwohl's taxonomy of the affective domain; and
- three activities designed to develop or make substantial use of children's psychomotor skills.

Discuss each of your selections with a teacher or a peer.

❏ Reflecting and Sharing

You probably found this activity to be difficult, both in finding appropriate examples and in defending them. If so, you will find it useful to repeat the activity with another text or the text for another grade level.

In any realistic situation, the cognitive, affective, and psychomotor domains are not independent. Children have feelings about what they learn, and how they learn and apply that learning. At times, this will affect learning in all three domains. For example, the child who dislikes science is less likely to learn its content and its practical techniques than is the child who likes it. Similarly, development in the cognitive domain may influence development and application of specific and general psychomotor competencies. It is no accident that the latter domain is designated psychomotor, not just motor.

◆ ◆ ◆ ◆ ◆

PLANNING FOR EVALUATION

Before turning to specific evaluation techniques, it is worth considering how you can develop a plan to fit individual activities into the overall assessment of the progress of your students. Figure 8.1 lists some questions you should ask yourself.

Activity 8.3 provides a specific example of planning for evaluation.

FIGURE 8.1

Planning for Evaluation

◆ How does the activity relate to past activities?
◆ What is the focus of the activity?
◆ What are its anticipated major outcomes?
◆ What other outcomes may be important?
◆ Which outcomes should be the focus of evaluation?
◆ What techniques are appropriate to identify each child's success in achieving these outcomes?
◆ Which children should I focus upon primarily?
◆ How will the results of evaluation be recorded?

activity 8.3 PLANNING FOR EVALUATION: AN EXAMPLE

Consider again an activity that was considered in Chapter 1, namely "Filling a Foilboat." First, read the activity again. Then answer the questions listed in Figure 8.1. You will need to be speculative, especially if you are not teaching at the moment. Record your thoughts before you read on.

❑ Reflecting and Sharing

How does the activity relate to past activities?

Given that "Filling a Foilboat" is not found in any specific program, you would have to be speculative here. However, let us suppose that the activity is part of a developing theme relating to density, and that the activity is mainly a fun activity that will lead, sometime in the future, to consideration of why specific objects float in some liquids but sink in others. The activity was probably preceded by an activity that looked at the tendency of objects to sink or float in water and in solutions of different substances such as salt and sugar.

What is the specific focus of the activity?

The answer to this question will vary according to the nature of the particular lesson concerned. The focus of the activity may be the development of a specific concept — for example, that the shape of a hollow, floating object affects its load-carrying capacity.

What other outcomes may be important?

There are many possible answers to this. A number of scientific processes can be identified, such as controlling variables, defining (the load) operationally, and quantifying. There is clearly potential for attitude development, both in terms of attitude toward science and scientific attitude in the traditional sense of curiosity, perseverance, co-operation with others, and so on. There is also the potential of focussing upon manipulative skills, as when objects are dropped carefully into the foilboat. Finally, it is quite possible for the activity to lead to other curriculum areas, such as language arts (a story about a lost foilboat, perhaps), mathematics (units of measurement), and art (fantastic foilboat drawings, perhaps).

For evaluation, which outcomes shall I focus upon?

Clearly, the answer to this question will vary with the situation, the intent of the curriculum, the needs of the children, the interests of the teacher and the children, and so forth.

How can I identify the status of each child? What techniques are appropriate?

The previous questions are all important to evaluation considerations, but the last question is *the* central question in this chapter. The remainder of the chapter is concerned primarily with the development of techniques likely to be useful to you.

Which children will be the focus of evaluative attention?

Generally, it is not possible to focus closely on all of the children in the class at the same time. A plan for systematic selection of children should be in place before the activity starts.

✍️ **From a Teacher's Journal**

There are many ways to monitor children's progress, but for a new teacher there are four basic and helpful methods. Observation or "kid watching" is an easy enough thing to do, but knowing what and how to observe is a skill to be practised because of its great potential as a tool for evaluation. A daily routine for a teacher is to observe a child's behaviour, interaction with others, use of materials, facial expression, verbal communication, and so on, and to do it nonjudgementally and in a nonthreatening manner.

Once observations are made, a method of recording them is required. Anecdotal notes are the second essential method of monitoring progress. One system is to have a daily or weekly "At-a-Glance" record sheet of squares labelled with each child's name. Notes are made on Post-It notes that fit into each square and can be transferred later into a file on each student.

(continued)

> ✍ **From a Teacher's Journal (continued)**
>
> The third essential element of monitoring progress is tracking a child's progress through centres and activities. A tracking sheet on which the teacher uses checkmarks to record completion of tasks or a sheet on which the child keeps a record are both effective ways to track children.
>
> Finally, checklists and surveys that help the teacher to focus on specific skills or tasks should be completed several times a year for each child. These can be kept on file and compared to provide a means of assessing progress over time toward specific goals.
>
> *Judy Onody*
> *Scarborough, ON*

◆ ◆ ◆ ◆ ◆

EVALUATION TECHNIQUES

Observing

In a sense, all information collected by a teacher for the purpose of evaluating students involves observation. However, it is useful to distinguish between methods that involve observation directly from those that do not. For this reason, the use of checklists, anecdotal records, and rating scales will be included under the umbrella of "observation." Other techniques, such as the use of portfolios and formal testing, will be considered separately.

Observing involves much more than perception. What scientists observe is governed by what they choose to pay attention to, and what they choose to pay attention to is governed by what is already in their minds, that is, by their existing conceptual frameworks. The same is true for teachers. The teacher who has a good general understanding of children's intellectual, social, affective, and psychomotor development starts from a different base from the teacher who does not have this understanding. The former is empowered to make different and more profound observations. Similarly, the teacher who understands the science being taught, its place in the overall structure of the subject, and the different conceptions children may bring with them as they learn this science, will observe what is happening in class quite differently from the teacher who lacks this background. The teacher's mind is not a blank slate. It is vitally in control of the observations the teacher chooses to make, and of what the teacher makes of the observations. Moreover, the good teacher, like the good scientist, will not only be sensitive to what happens but will plan an appropriate schedule of observation. This is vital. Without such planning, the teacher will be overwhelmed by the number of potential observations that might be made. Typically, for the purpose of evaluation, it is possible to observe no more than a few children in any given lesson, and a systematic plan for recording observations is necessary to ensure success. Some of the factors to be considered are illustrated in Figure 8.2.

FIGURE 8.2

Effective Observations

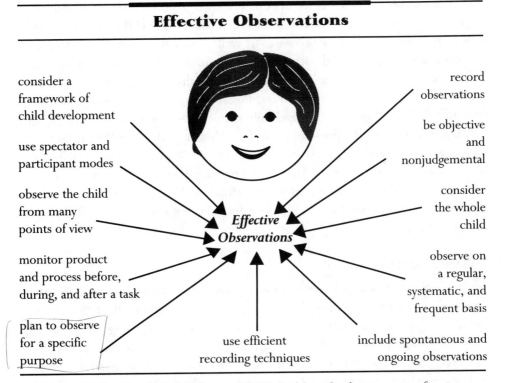

Source: North York Board of Education (1983). *Look hear: Developing programs for primary children based on observation of learning needs,* 37. North York, ON: Board of Education.

CHECKLISTS

Checklists are particularly suited to routine observation of predetermined skills, concepts, and behaviours. Sometimes checklists are provided as part of a curriculum package, but frequently the teacher will need to design a checklist personally. Checklists are not difficult to design, they are usually easy to use, and they can be monitored and updated continuously. However, they have disadvantages. For example, checklists often indicate that something has or has not been done successfully, but they don't indicate different levels of proficiency.

Checklists are ideal for monitoring repetitive situations, such as the development of process skills and motor skills. For example, it is relatively easy to design a process checklist including all processes encountered in all practical activities covered during the year. Figure 8.3 illustrates such as a checklist.

Suppose that, in Figure 8.3, Activity 2/1 is "Filling a Foilboat." This activity offers good opportunities for children to employ a number of processes. These include controlling variables, defining operationally, quantifying, and, to a lesser extent, several other processes. These three processes provide a major focus for the teacher to observe the degree of competency of a selected group of children, and of course the teacher may wish to include evaluation of children's capabilities with respect to several other processes as well. A way to record this is to mark the processes to be observed with a circle and, for each child observed, to mark success (✔) or lack of success (✘) on the child's individual record. For example, the record in Figure 8.3 shows successful exhibition of the processes "defining operationally" and "quantifying" and failure to exhibit "control of variables," in Activity 2/1. It is equally possible to prepare similar grids for different kinds of outcomes. For example, Figure 8.4 represents an illustrative checklist for the psychomotor events involved in an activity concerned with use of a thermometer. The checklist is designed to represent an individual child's performance, but it is possible to prepare a similar checklist that includes the performance of all members of the class.

RATING SCALES

An extension of the checklist procedure is to use rating scales. For example, each item in the table might be scored on a five-point scale from excellent (5) through average (3) to unsatisfactory (1). Rating scales have the advantage of providing more information than checklists, and they are easy to create and administer. However, they are relatively subjective and therefore error-prone. Like checklists, rating scales do not include reasons for any behaviour observed. Sample rating scales are represented in Figures 8.5 and 8.6.

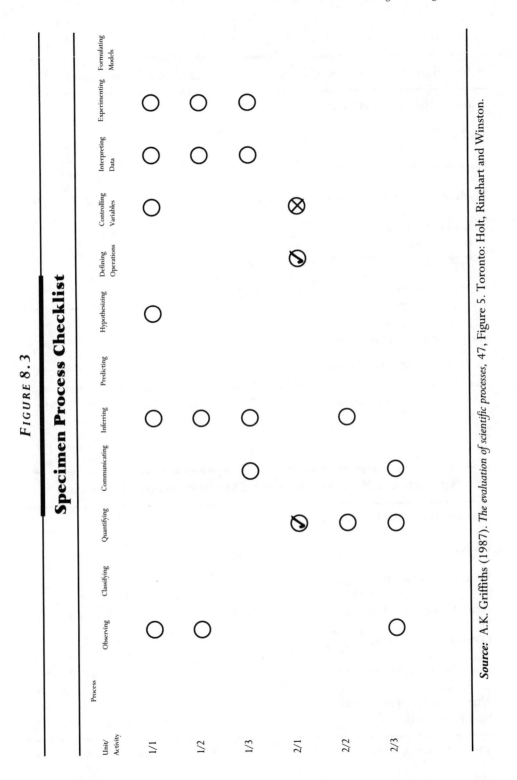

FIGURE 8.3

Specimen Process Checklist

Source: A.K. Griffiths (1987). *The evaluation of scientific processes*, 47, Figure 5. Toronto: Holt, Rinehart and Winston.

FIGURE 8.4

Specimen Checklist (Psychomotor Domain)

Activity: Using a Thermometer

Child:

Handles thermometer carefully   _____

Reads temperature with thermometer at eye level   _____

Obtains correct reading   _____

Does not use as a pointer or stirrer   _____

After use, places thermometer back in protective container   _____

ANECDOTAL RECORDS

In the course of a school year, primary and elementary teachers spend a substantial amount of time with the children in their class. Inevitably, the teacher makes many informal observations. It is valuable to record a selection of these. Much

FIGURE 8.5

Specimen Rating Scale (Psychomotor Domain)

Activity: Using a Thermometer

Child:

Handles thermometer carefully	5	4	3	2	1
Reads temperature with thermometer at eye level	5	4	3	2	1
Obtains correct reading	5	4	3	2	1
Does not use as a pointer or stirrer	5	4	3	2	1
After use, places thermometer back in protective container	5	4	3	2	1

5 = excellent   4 = above average   3 = average   2 = below average   1 = unsatisfactory

FIGURE 8.6

Specimen Rating Scale (Affective Domain)

Activity: Field Trip

Child:

Is excited beforehand	5	4	3	2	1
Lingers over exhibits	5	4	3	2	1
Selects handouts relating to exhibits	5	4	3	2	1
Does not wish to leave	5	4	3	2	1
Wishes to visit again	5	4	3	2	1

5 = excellent　4 = above average　3 = average　2 = below average　1 = unsatisfactory

information can be obtained when the teacher pays serious attention to children's drawings, informal writing, discussions and other interactions with others, concept maps, and so on. Unless it is systematically recorded, much of this information can be quickly lost. One way to minimize this loss is for the teacher to maintain an anecdotal record for each child, in which significant information is recorded at the time it is observed. A preplanned format is advisable. A specimen entry is illustrated in Figure 8.7.

FIGURE 8.7

Anecdotal Record

Name: _____　**Date:** _____

Observed Behaviour	*Interpretation*	*Proposed Action, if Any*
Peter repeatedly takes charge of data collection over partner Sue. Peter insists on being the one to fill the foilboat while Sue only keeps records.	Peter is being "masculine."	Ask Peter to share duties with Sue.

Anecdotal observations, especially if relatively ad hoc, can provide unreliable evidence and may reflect the predisposed biases of the teacher. However, they can also provide fine-grained evidence that is hard to obtain in any other way. Joseph Abruscato (1982) provides some hints that can help you create good anecdotal records:

1. Whenever you place an observation on paper be sure to write down the date. You may even want to include the time.
2. Make the writing of notes a habit. Prior to the lesson remind yourself that you are going to be writing down observations.
3. Consider focussing your observations on cognitive, affective, and psychomotor progress that you observe. Your notebook could take the form of a daily chart that has a column for each. Such a chart will help you keep track of your observations.
4. Be sure to tell the children that you will be writing notes to yourself about how things are going. You may even suggest that they do the same. If so, at the end of each week you can have a full-class discussion of your observations and their observations.
5. Review your anecdotal records in detail when you come to the end of a teaching unit. This will enable you to assess the effectiveness of the learning activities in which the children participated (69).

OBSERVATIONAL TECHNIQUES: CONCLUDING REMARKS

Each of the techniques discussed so far requires multiple observations of each child over the course of the school year. It is important to be objective, to avoid bias, and to be unobtrusive whenever possible. It is also important to be selective, or the sheer volume of data will be overwhelming. It is necessary for the teacher to produce a plan for recording observational data as early as possible in the school year, or even in advance of the year if possible. It is important to realize that traditional scoring techniques, which are useful in the later years of schooling and beyond, are not likely to be useful with primary children. Using a series of faces from happy to disappointed, or perhaps a point on a number line, will be appropriate feedback to younger children.

Most of the observational techniques listed in this section are just as useful for assessment of learning and development in all three domains of learning. In contrast, the remaining methods described, with the exception of the use of portfolios, are likely to be more useful for evaluation in the cognitive domain than in the affective and psychomotor domains. The truism "actions speak louder than words" applies particularly well to evaluation of affective and psychomotor outcomes. For instance, it is one thing to respond, "I like science," when asked directly, and another thing to demonstrate this by choosing to read a newspaper article about science or to visit a science centre, or opting to watch a television program relating to science, or volunteering to do a science fair project. Similarly, it is one thing to describe the right way to carry out an operation such as using a microscope or a dropping pipette. It is another thing to carry out these operations successfully. The focus of evaluation in the affective and psychomotor domains must primarily be on observation of actions.

Portfolios

A different evaluation technique that also requires consistent monitoring by the teacher, but which is more dependent on selective input by the children, is the development of individual portfolios. A portfolio is a child's selection of personal "best" work, rather like a portfolio an artist might generate. The child is encouraged to keep the work in some kind of separate folder or container. Initially, selection should be according to the child's own criteria, and could include selective reports of activities, drawings, paintings, stories, excursions, and any other interactions, including feelings, that seem important to the child. As time goes by, it is useful for the teacher to discuss these reports and, cautiously, to suggest criteria for what should be included. The child's portfolio is likely to be more useful for formative evaluation, if the necessary trust between teacher and student is to be maintained. It is also likely that portfolios will provide evidence useful to the teacher, as the teacher attempts to identify the kinds of informal as well as formal learning taking place in the classroom.

Testing Instruments and Formal Reports

The approaches discussed so far are likely to be the most useful evaluation techniques for primary and elementary teachers to use. However, most elementary teachers and, to a lesser extent, primary teachers will find occasions to create or use a variety of more formal test instruments. These include the use of both objective and free-response approaches.

Objective approaches to evaluation include the use of multiple-choice, multiple-completion, matching, and true–false questions. Free-response approaches involve the use of a written format, even when the response is no more than a few sentences long. It is important that teachers understand the construction of such tests and be able both to evaluate tests produced by others and construct their own.

> ### ✍ From a Teacher's Journal
>
> Monitoring science is similar to monitoring progress in other areas, but is related of course to the expectations and goals set specifically for science. For example, observations should assess the extent to which a child experiments, take risks, and demonstrates a sense of wonder. Anecdotal notes must take into account the extent to which children are using scientific vocabulary and learning to investigate science problems. Tracking must show that the child is moving through many different types of science activities and centre tasks. Checklists can also be used to record facility with the scientific processes — observing, classifying, communicating, predicting, inferring, experimenting, and so forth.
>
> *Judy Onody*
> *Scarborough, ON*

As you read this section, keep in mind that the ages, capabilities, and prior evaluation experiences of the children involved are paramount considerations. For example, for young children a written multiple-choice question may present sufficient difficulty with respect to reading that the child's understanding of what is tested may be obscured. Further, for a child not yet versed in the intricacies of test-taking strategies, understanding what a question is asking may itself be a major hurdle. Factors that must be considered include the language used; the underlying conceptual structure of the test question; the requirements for response, for example, whether a selection or a justification is required; and the length of answer that is needed. With these comments in mind, we turn now to a consideration of different types of test questions.

FREE-RESPONSE QUESTIONS

A *free-response* test question requires an answer in the child's own words. Good free-response questions are deceptively difficult to produce. It is often very easy to think of questions that relate loosely to a particular piece of content. However, loosely constructed questions often yield loosely constructed responses, which may have little bearing on the intent of the question. Free-response questions may require a sentence or so, or they may require several pages of writing. They can be constructed so that adequate response requires the child to operate at any level of Bloom's taxonomy. Free-response questions can require only direct recall of something, such as a recently performed practical activity, but generally they should be used to assess children's understanding at least. Free-response questions can be constructed to challenge children to perform at any level of Bloom's taxonomy.

Traditionally, answers to free-response questions are considered to be both difficult and time-consuming to assess, and the process is often considered to have low reliability in that different "examiners" will have different standards and will apply different criteria. This problem is less evident in the teacher-controlled environment of the primary and elementary grades. At this level, children's free-response answers are brief and take little of the teacher's time to read. It is usually possible to attend immediately to any misunderstandings both in the item itself and children's responses. Reliability may be difficult to establish in a technical sense, but it is likely that the teacher's feel for the efforts of the small number of children in the class in a given year will eliminate most misunderstandings and enhance reliability. Here are some guidelines that will help as you construct and use free-response test items:

◆ Take time to think of appropriate questions.
◆ Present the task explicitly.
◆ Indicate as much as possible about the form and length of an acceptable response.
◆ Allow ample time for the children to respond.
◆ Be clear in advance about what you are evaluating. For example, how much weight will you give to good style, good grammar, the correctness of the science involved, and children's innovative ideas.
◆ Although this is often not possible in the elementary grades, try to mark each children's answer without knowing which child is involved.

MAJOR REPORTS

For children nearing the end of elementary school, it is possible to incorporate a variation of a long essay in the form of a report on a moderately lengthy activity.

Major reports are excellent evaluative tools for teachers to assign students nearing the end of elementary school.

A good example in science would be a report on a science project, perhaps a report on a science fair project or on an extended activity that took a considerable amount of time. As is true for the assessment of longer essay questions, it is important to have established criteria for assessment in advance.

OBJECTIVE QUESTIONS

Objective test questions include *completion, true–false, matching,* and *multiple-choice* items. Each will be illustrated below.

Completion Questions. Completion questions have the form "incomplete sentence ... word(s) to complete sentences." Here are two examples:

1. Objects that sink in water have a _____ that is greater than that of water.
   and
2. Pure water freezes at _____ °C.

The completion word or phrase need not be at the end of a sentence, but it usually is placed there. Most completion questions test only at the knowledge level of Bloom's taxonomy because, usually, the questioner is seeking one very specific answer. The following may be useful when you are considering development of completion questions:

◆ Minimize ambiguity in wording.
◆ Require only one completion per question.
◆ Use a constant length of blank.
◆ Place the blank near the end of the sentence.
◆ Don't overuse completion questions, as they typically test at a low level.

True–False Questions. Good true–false questions can be difficult to construct because it is often difficult to construct statements that are completely true or false. However, this is less of a problem in the primary and elementary grades as children at this level usually don't yet know enough to be concerned about qualifying statements. For example, the statement "The boiling point of water is 100°C" would probably be considered correct by an elementary school child, but would need qualifications relating to purity and atmospheric pressure to be acceptable to a high-school science student. The following guidelines should be considered for development of true–false test questions:

◆ Include only one central idea in each statement.
◆ State the question unambiguously.
◆ Place the main point of the question in a prominent position.
◆ Avoid cueing the child to the correct answer, or to an incorrect answer.
◆ Do not bias toward true or false statements.
◆ Use simple vocabulary and sentence structure.
◆ Avoid double negatives.

Like completion questions, true–false questions generally test at the knowledge level and are not suited to testing at levels of Bloom's taxonomy above this. They also suffer from the drawback that, on average, an individual without knowledge of what is being tested could be expected to guess the right answer 50 percent of the time.

Matching Questions. Matching test questions involve relating the members of two groups of objects, events, or statements, such that each member of the first group has only one match in the second group. For example, consider the following question:

Look at the two lists below. For each example in the first list, draw a line connecting it to the family to which it belongs in the second list.

dog	fish
trout	reptile
eagle	insect
ant	mammal
snake	bird
hamster	

With matching test questions, guessing is not a major factor. However, this kind of question lends itself more to testing knowledge and comprehension than to testing higher-order skills. In developing matching questions, the following points are worth noting:

◆ Present the whole question on one page.
◆ Use an unequal number of items in the two lists.
◆ Use between five and ten items in each list. More than that become too difficult to keep in mind, especially for younger children.
◆ Where possible, emphasize the matching criteria.
◆ If the statements in the two lists are of different length, place the list with the longer statements first, thus minimizing reading time.

Some teachers arrange the matching clues in the form of a crossword or a cryptogram. Although mainly motivational, such strategies may also be used for evaluation.

Multiple-Choice Questions. Consider the following question:

Which of the following would *not* be correct as a food chain?

(a) grain → mouse → snake
(b) grass → rabbit → fox
(c) hawk → rabbit → fox
(d) grain → rat → hawk

This question is typical of the construction of multiple-choice test questions in general. A stem is presented, followed by a number of alternative responses. One of these is correct, and the others are incorrect. The latter are usually called distractors. The information in the stem as well as in the distractors may be written, but alternatively may be diagrammatic, photographic, graphic, and so on. Nonwritten information is particularly useful for primary children and, to a lesser extent, for elementary children. Other variations of the multiple-choice format include multiple-completion questions and assertion–reason questions.

However, it is difficult enough for primary and elementary children to wrestle with the conventional multiple-choice format, so use these methods sparingly, if at all. Provided they are well constructed, guessing is a limited option in multiple-choice questions. Further, although it is easier to construct questions testing at the knowledge level, it is quite possible to construct multiple-choice items representing different levels of Bloom's taxonomy. Good multiple-choice questions are not easy to construct, but once constructed they offer the advantage of being able to test a range of content in a short time. It is normally possible to reuse the same questions on a number of occasions. The following suggestions are of use in the construction of multiple-choice questions:

◆ Use language that is appropriate to the level of the student and grammatically correct.
◆ For primary children and children with reading problems, a simplified diagrammatic format may be helpful.
◆ Avoid negatively worded statements whenever possible. If they have to be used, emphasize the negative by underlining or bolding.
◆ Make distractors and correct answers as similar in appearance and length as possible.
◆ Avoid consistent placement of the correct answer within the questions.
◆ Distractors should be plausible. It is most useful to construct them from typical errors and misconceptions.
◆ Put as much of the wording as possible in the stem, thereby avoiding unnecessary repetition in each alternative answer.
◆ Avoid "all of the above" and "none of the above."

◆ ◆ ◆ ◆ ◆

VALIDITY AND RELIABILITY

Authors of published tests, questionnaires, rating scales, and so on normally attempt to ensure that the *validity* and *reliability* of their instruments are both high, and they publish evidence of this together with publication of the instrument. Why do they take the trouble to do this when it is usually an expensive and time-consuming procedure? Consider some examples.

Suppose that you decide to monitor your weight on a regular basis. You would not purchase a thermometer to do this. Nor would you use a kitchen scale to determine your weight. Neither instrument would be valid, the first because it does not measure weight, and the second because it does not measure weight within the right range. Validity of measurement refers to actually measuring what we intend to measure. Without validity, any measurement is likely to be meaningless.

The same is true when teachers attempt to determine the extent of children's learning. It does not make sense, for example, to determine a child's ability to use a scientific instrument, such as a microscope, by asking for a description of the use of a thermometer. Less trivially, and more realistically in terms of actual practice, it also does not make sense to determine a child's ability to use a microscope simply by asking for a description of how to do it. For the observation to be valid, determination of a child's ability to use a microscope must be based on the child's actual use of a microscope, or at least on observation of the results of the child's use.

At a more general level, teachers cannot measure children's ability to apply by requiring only comprehension, or comprehension by requiring simply a statement of knowledge of some event or procedure. Similarly, a teacher cannot determine a child's attitude to a subject just by asking; a way is needed to observe that attitude in action. The same is true for the evaluation of children's learning of psychomotor skills; evidence of successful practice of the skill is required. With respect to validity, the essential question to ask is, "Is this procedure measuring what it is supposed to be measuring?"

A second consideration relates to reliability. Reliability refers to consistency of measurement. Suppose that the weight registered on a bathroom scale varies with factors unrelated to weight, such as temperature, humidity, or how the person steps on the scale. If this is so, then the observed weight of an individual will vary for reasons other than that the individual's weight really is varying. Such a measurement is unreliable.

As a teacher, you need to be concerned about the reliability of your evaluation techniques. You need to ask questions such as, "Is there any reason why administering a particular method of evaluation in a particular way, or at a particular time or place for some or all of a group of children, may yield a different result?" If so, the instrument is unreliable. Such questions should concern the teacher as well as the evaluation expert.

Finally, it is worth drawing attention to the fact that all measurements are subject to error. Testing specialists, like pollsters, refer to their measurement being accurate within a certain tolerance. Sometimes, also, the act of measurement itself adds to the uncertainty, in that the act of observation interferes with what happens. It is worthwhile for the teacher to reflect upon the uncertainty of measurement, especially when the results of evaluation of children are to be translated into further action.

activity 8.4 — PREPARING EVALUATION TOOLS

Choose a unit or a group of related units, representing about a month of classroom instruction, in a grade of your choice. Read the content carefully and then list all of the important outcomes that you hope children will gain as a result of this instruction. Be sure to consider each domain of learning, as well as links to other subjects. Prepare a detailed plan to evaluate children's learning of these anticipated outcomes. In your preparation of specific questions, include as many as possible of the different approaches to evaluation that are described in this chapter. Ask another student or a teacher to examine critically what you produce.

◆ ◆ ◆ ◆ ◆

LOOKING BACK AND LOOKING FORWARD

In this chapter, you have considered the theory and practice of the evaluation of children's learning in science. A number of approaches to this were illustrated, including the use of checklists, rating scales, anecdotal records, portfolios, and objective and free-response tests.

Good teaching requires good means to evaluate children's progress. Without effective means to determine the progress of children's learning, management of that learning and the planning of future learning are certain to be compromised. It is important to ensure the validity and reliability of whatever means are used to evaluate children's progress, whether that evaluation is intended to be used formatively, summatively, or diagnostically.

In the next chapter, the focus moves from evaluation of sciencing to the evaluation and selection of resources to help you with your day-to-day planning of science experiences for children.

CANADIAN ACHIEVEMENTS IN SCIENCE

RICHARD TAYLOR (B. 1930)

Richard Taylor never received a high-school diploma because he failed Latin, a required course in Alberta at that time. After a plea from his high-school principal, Taylor was admitted conditionally to the University of Alberta. His former dean of science at the University of Alberta described him as a moderately good student. Yet Richard Taylor, a native of Medicine Hat, Alberta, shared the 1990 Nobel Prize for physics with two American colleagues for "fundamental discoveries which showed the innermost structure of matter."

After completing his M.Sc. degree in physics at the University of Alberta, Dr. Taylor completed a Ph.D. at Stanford University in California, and has been there ever since. His work involves the use of a massive linear accelerator, an apparatus best described as a two-mile tunnel designed to accelerate electrons and other small particles to very high speeds through the use of very strong magnetic fields. When these electrons are made to collide with other fundamental particles, the energy of the collision, according to Dr. Taylor and his co-Nobel laureates Jerome Friedman and Henry Kendall, produces even smaller particles called quarks. Demonstrating this phenomenon demanded energy and insight worthy of a Nobel Prize.

How did Richard Taylor progress from being an apparently ordinary student to becoming one of the world's most eminent scientists? Perhaps because of his ability to persevere, his voracious appetite for reading as a child, his ability to "drive his teachers up the wall" with his constant questions, or his ability to be in the right place with the right questions at the right time. Whatever the reason, Richard Taylor became the first Canadian to win the Nobel Prize for physics.

REFERENCES

Abruscato, J. (1982). *Teaching children science*. Englewood Cliffs, NJ: Prentice-Hall.

Bloom, B.S., J.T. Hastings, and G.F. Madaus (1971). *Handbook on formative and summative evaluation*. New York: McGraw-Hill.

Bonisteel, R. (1983). *Man alive: The human journey,* 17. Toronto: Collins.

Doran, R.L. (1980). *Basic measurement and evaluation of science instruction*. Washington, DC: National Science Teachers Association.

Eisner, E.W. (1967). Educational objectives: Help or hindrance? *School Review* 75(3):250–60.

Griffiths, A.K. (1987). *The evaluation of science processes*. Toronto: Holt, Rinehart and Winston.

Gronlund, N. (1985). *Measurement and evaluation in teaching*. 5th ed. New York: Macmillan.

———. (1988). *How to construct achievement tests*. 4th ed. Englewood Cliffs, NJ: Prentice-Hall.

Krathwohl, D.R., B.S. Bloom, and B.B. Masia (1964). *Taxonomy of educational objectives: Handbook II, the affective domain*. New York: David McKay.

Mager, R.F. (1962). *Preparing instructional objectives*. Palo Alto, CA: Fearon.

North York Board of Education (1983). *Look hear: Developing programs for primary children based on observation of learning needs*. North York, ON: Board of Education.

Simpson, E. (1972). *The classification of objectives in the psychomotor domain*. Washington: Gryphon House.

Wortham, S.C. (1990). *Tests and measurements in early childhood education*. Toronto: Merrill.

CHAPTER 9

Selecting Curriculum Resources

THE TEACHER
has a crucial role in
SELECTING RESOURCES
to bridge the gap between

THEORY	**PRACTICE**
as expressed in	*using*
INTENT OF	**CONTENT OF**
THE CURRICULUM	**THE CURRICULUM**
(Aims and Philosophy)	*(Curriculum Materials)*

as recommended in
PROVINCIAL CURRICULUM GUIDES
which reflect
TRENDS IN SCIENCE EDUCATION

PROVINCIALLY	**NATIONALLY**	**GLOBALLY**

and suggest
choices from

NSF PROGRAMS 1960s	**TEXTBOOK-BASED PROGRAMS**	**PROGRAMS OF THE 1970s AND 1980s**	**PROGRAMS OF THE 1990s**	**OTHER RESOURCES**

to implement
THE EXPERIENCED CURRICULUM

◆ ◆ ◆ ◆ ◆

Scientific literacy is most likely to result from

the integration of good curricular materials and

good transformations made by good teachers.

ANGELO COLLINS (1989)

You are now at a point in your journey where you can draw on the knowledge and skills you have acquired to help you to develop units and plan daily learning experiences for your students. You have built a strong foundation for the choices you will make, starting with the framework of ideas in the beginning chapter — the directions and orientations for science in the elementary grades — and extending that framework by using solid building blocks: processes, concepts, attitudes, and interests.

The past four chapters have encouraged you to transfer these ideas to the practical setting of your own classroom, suggesting ways you can create a positive environment for learning and introducing you to science teaching strategies, skills, and evaluation techniques you'll use as you make the transition from theory to practice.

To help you make this transition successfully you'll need to become familiar with the curriculum resources that are immediately available to you, including the curriculum guides and policy statements of the ministries (departments) of education of the Canadian provinces and territories. This chapter will introduce you to these resources, as well as a whole range of other curriculum materials you can select from to supplement and enrich the school program. It will also prepare you to make wise selections from what is available.

◆ ◆ ◆ ◆ ◆

GETTING STARTED

As you begin to plan to include science in the busy life of your classroom, you will find yourself continually on the lookout for new ways to interest and engage children in learning. This chapter will widen your options by familiarizing you with a variety of materials for teaching/learning. Some will be new and some not so new, but as you begin your professional career it will be important for you to be aware of both. You should be conversant with new developments in primary and elementary science curricula, as well as outstanding materials from the past that have stood the test of time and are well worth retaining in your file of "Activities the Children and I Must Try." There will be lots of help at the school level from experienced teachers who are familiar with these curricula; but, as you grow professionally, you will be continually making your own decisions about the potential usefulness of many types of resources and their promise for fulfilling the goals you set for yourself as a teacher. To help you with your selection, Mahung (1980) suggests a method for evaluating curriculum materials.

◆ ◆ ◆ ◆ ◆

EVOLVING CRITERIA FOR SELECTING RESOURCES

Mahung (1980) warns that evaluation of curriculum materials is not an easy and straightforward task, and involves weighing many different factors, both theoretical and practical. *Explicit features* can be assessed through a cursory examination of the materials for inherent features such as the content or subject matter, the stated aims of the materials, the way the components are organized and the activities sequenced, and other features such as readability, motivating qualities, and design. *Implicit features,* such as the curriculum rationale, the way the materials provide for the needs of learners, and the nature of the subject matter, require more sophisticated analysis. Mahung criticizes many of the instruments that have been developed for evaluating curriculum materials, suggesting that they are little more than checklists of explicit features that could be just as easily identified by a cursory look at the materials. While these criteria are important, the instruments often overlook implicit features that contribute greatly to the quality of students' learning.

Mahung proposes a method of conceptual analysis that takes into account the four "commonplaces" (Schwab 1964) — the *subject matter,* the *learner,* the *teacher,* and the *milieu* — which are generally recognized in any curriculum materials conceptualized by a developer and offered to teachers to implement a plan for curriculum and instruction.

Conceptual Analysis

Conceptual analysis involves three steps that you can adapt for your own use quite easily by thinking of what you are trying to accomplish through the curriculum materials available to you and then by judging the potential of specific materials to fulfil these goals.

The following steps are involved in this methodology:

Step 1: The Theoretical Perspective Is Identified. In science curriculum materials, the theoretical perspective is based on the foundations of science education, such as conceptions of the nature of science, the structure of knowledge, and the nature of scientific inquiry and science processes, as well as conceptions of the nature of the learner and how children learn science. The theoretical perspective of science curriculum also includes conceptions of the teacher and strategies for teaching and evaluation that are implicit in the materials.

Step 2: An Analytical Framework Is Developed. This framework becomes the basis for evaluating the curriculum materials, or specific sections or aspects of the materials. To develop the framework, a series of questions or statements are abstracted from the theoretical perspective. These are used to ascertain the extent to which these features are displayed or included in the materials.

Step 3: Analysis Is Guided by the Framework. The evaluation of the materials or specific sections of the materials is guided by the relevant questions or statements of the analytical framework to determine whether certain features of the analytical framework are present and, if present, to what extent.

Four kinds of judgements are derived:

1. The adequacy of the curriculum as conceptualized by the developer — its consistency with the rationale and how well it provides for students to achieve the desired aims.
2. The adequacy of the instructional plan — whether the learning activities make it possible for the learner to achieve the desired aims.
3. The potential for judgements on unintended learning outcomes that may result from the use of the materials. (Note that this feature is an important one, in that it allows for openness in the use of the materials and unanticipated outcomes as children work with the materials in the classroom.)
4. The possibility of modifications, if necessary, for specific instructional purposes.

activity 9.1 EVALUATING CURRICULUM MATERIALS

◆ Imagine that you are a new Grade 4 teacher in a large elementary school. You have talked to other teachers about the elementary science program and have been shown the teacher and pupil materials that will be available to you for teaching and learning. As a beginning teacher, you have read the curriculum guidelines and are looking through the suggested materials.

◆ With the ideas from your science methods course and other courses fresh in your mind, make a list of questions or statements that would be suitable for use in judging the potential of the program.

❏ Reflecting and Sharing

This activity may have been difficult for you at this stage, because you are as yet unfamiliar with the curriculum materials and may not have had an opportunity to experience their use in the classroom. If your questions relate to the subject matter, the student, the teacher, and the environment for learning — the four "commonplaces" — you have made a good beginning.

Later in the chapter, you will be introduced to a variety of curriculum materials that will be available to you as you begin to teach. But first, start at the beginning by looking at a number of curriculum guides and policy statements for the provinces and territories, to see what their expectations are for science in the primary and elementary grades and whether there are commonalities in the statements of goals and the resources now being used throughout Canada.

Usually these publications are produced by ministries or departments of education following a consultative process in which science consultants and primary/elementary consultants at that level are part of a committee of teachers, science program co-ordinators, and other science educators. In addition to establishing goals for science education, the guides often include sections on child psychology, the philosophy of instruction, a variety of teaching strategies, and suggestions for evaluation. They sometimes suggest ways of selecting and organizing content, and recommend curriculum resources (which may include commercially developed modules, textbook series, children's trade books, locally produced materials, and audiovisual resources for use in curriculum implementation).

◆ ◆ ◆ ◆ ◆

CURRICULUM GUIDES: SOME INFLUENCES

Curriculum guides and policy statements for each Canadian province are usually compiled by committees of local educators working in co-operation with ministries of education. However, the statements of aims and the psychological and philosophical underpinnings expressed in the guides reflect trends in science education that are at work globally, nationally, and sometimes regionally.

Worldwide Trends in Science Education

Developments in science education in Canada have been influenced in the past and continue to be influenced by worldwide developments. Over the years, significant, trendsetting reports such as the Plowden Report in Britain (1967), the report of the Project Synthesis team in the United States (Harms et al. 1980), and the National Science Board (1983) report *Educating Americans for the 21st Century* have all influenced trends in this country.

Wherever new programs are produced and evaluated there is interest in Canada, and a number of provinces have adopted textbook-based series written by American authors and at times released simultaneously in the United States and Canada. An in-service manual for workshop leaders (Gough 1977) was developed in Canada to facilitate the implementation of the widely used *STEM Science* program (Rockcastle et al. 1976, 1980). Canadian input on a consultative basis was continued throughout the development phase of the next revision — *Addison-Wesley Science* (Rockcastle et al. 1984).

Science education in Canada is greatly influenced also by the affiliation of Canadian teachers and science educators with professional associations in the United States such as the National Science Teachers Association (NSTA), the American Educational Research Association (AERA), and the National Association of Research in Science Teaching (NARST). Canadian educators participate in international conferences on science education held in Canada and elsewhere, and contribute significantly to the growing body of research on science education. The result is that worldwide trends in science education are mirrored in revisions of policy statements, curriculum guides, and handbooks for each of the provinces and territories.

National and Regional Influences

Two influences that have been at work in the 1980s and 1990s are the tendency to share ideas from province to province, and between provinces and territories, and the findings of the large-scale study of science education by the Science Council of Canada in the early 1980s.

THE SHARING OF IDEAS

The content of policy statements and curriculum guides of provinces and territories is influenced locally by provincial science teachers' associations, as well as by committees of teachers, science educators, and scientists within provinces. Regionally and nationally, there is an ongoing sharing of ideas through annual conferences.

At times, provincial documents acknowledge the advantage of sharing rather than having every provincial curriculum committee duplicate much of the work that others are doing. In preparing the Prince Edward Island guide in the late

1970s, for example, the committee produced a modified version of the Saskatchewan Division One guide and also acknowledged the use of excerpts on philosophy of instruction, teaching techniques, and classroom organization from Newfoundland's *Elementary Science Course Description* (1978). The Northwest Territories acknowledges the help of Alberta, Manitoba, and British Columbia with certain sections of its comprehensive curriculum guides. There have to be differences, of course, for there are goals that are unique to the culture of each province and units that are most relevant to a certain way of life. The Prince Edward Island guide and others now in development there reflect the agricultural economy of the island. The Northwest Territories has incorporated a number of quite different language development/inquiry units on bears, polar bears, marine mammals, and some physical science topics as well.

As guides are revised and resource lists of teacher-produced and commercially produced curriculum materials grow, the number and quality of provincial publications will continue to increase. The common threads will run visibly through them, but new ideas will constantly add colour and new and interesting patterns. All guides might benefit in the future from increased sharing of ideas. There will always be much to be learned from the combined thinking of educators throughout Canada.

THE SCIENCE COUNCIL OF CANADA STUDY

The four-year study of science education by the Science Council of Canada has had a significant impact on the goals and philosophy of science education expressed in the provincial documents at all levels of elementary and secondary education. Chapter 1 introduced you to the goals and recommendations of the Science Council of Canada study, and it would be worthwhile to review these goals now, along with the Council's recommendations for renewal of science education, and to assess their impact on provincial policies.

As you reread the summary report *Science for Every Student: Educating Canadians for Tomorrow's World* (1984), try to set it in the context of the need that was apparent at that time for a rethinking of science education throughout Canada. The study had been prompted in part by criticism of science education from a number of quarters. Orpwood (1981) cites examples of criticism such as Suzuki's (1977) concern that school science was failing to prepare young people to deal with science-based problems they would face as members of society, and Symons's (1975) similar concern that the schools were failing to see the potential of science as an instrument of national awareness. The Commission on Canadian Studies, which had been chaired by Symons, maintained that Canadian schoolchildren learned about accomplishments in science in other countries, but were taught nothing about Canadian achievements in science and technology or about the impact of science in their own country. In papers presented to the Science Council there were more pleas to place science education in a Canadian context (Page 1979) and to emphasize the science–technology–society connection (Aikenhead 1980) so that students might be given some sense of how science is integrated with other disciplines in decision making in everyday life.

Curriculum Guides: A Comparative Analysis. The study included a comparative analysis of science curriculum policies, a review of textbooks used in each of the provinces and territories, a survey of science teachers, and a number of case studies of science in Canadian schools. Following the research phase of the project, eleven "deliberative conferences" were held, one in each province and territory, with representation from teachers, students, scientists, school principals, parents, and other stakeholders in education.

In the Science Council of Canada study, the science curriculum policy documents for each of the provinces and territories were analyzed and many similarities were found in the expressed goals for primary and elementary science. It was found that the aims could be broken down into nine categories: Science Content, Scientific Skills, Scientific Processes, Science and Society, Nature of Science, Personal Growth, Attitudes to Science, Applied Science/Technology, and Career Opportunities. These correspond with categories used by other researchers in the field such as Gabel's "dimensions of scientific literacy" (1976) and Roberts's "curriculum emphases" (1981). When you examine the provincial documents, you will see that they also correspond with the seven dimensions of scientific literacy that form an organizing framework for the philosophy expressed in the policy statements of Saskatchewan (Hart 1987).

Orpwood (1981) notes that the three categories that appeared in all curriculum guidelines in 1980 were Science Content, Scientific Skills/Processes, and Science and Society. Table 9.1 shows the frequency of occurrence reported by the Science Council for the middle school years for each of the nine categories of aims.

The Council's report brought science to the attention of the nation. In some provinces there was a flurry of activity as policy statements were revised and there were grants for the development of new programs. In all provinces, even in those where financial resources may have been insufficient to translate needed reforms into action, there has been increased awareness of the need for new approaches to learning science, for example, new strategies for instruction in which teachers free themselves from a directive role and instead create opportunities for children to construct their own learning through active involvement with materials.

TABLE 9.1

Incidence of Categories of Aims for Science Education in Curriculum Policy Guidelines

Category	Illustrative Example	Frequency of Occurrence (Maximum 11)
1. Science content	"To increase the student's knowledge of basic concepts in life, earth, and physical sciences." (Manitoba)	11
2. Scientific skills/processes	"To develop facility in using the methods and tools of science." (New Brunswick)	11
3. Science and society	"To promote an understanding of the role that science has in the development of societies and the impact of society upon science." (Alberta)	11
4. Nature of science	"To develop student appreciation of science as a way of learning and communicating about the self, the environment, and the universe." (Saskatchewan)	7
5. Personal growth	"Le présent programme considère le développement des attitudes suivantes comme un minimum: 1. La coopération: l'esprit d'équipe, l'entraide, l'aptitude à travailler en équipe; 2. l'ouverture d'esprit; 3. le sens des responsabilités; 4. le goût du patrimoine." (Québec)	6
6. Attitudes to science	"Create an enthusiasm for the method of thinking that uses observed facts as data in a logical method of solving problems." (British Columbia)	4
7. Applied science/ technology	"Students should be exposed to a representative sample of the technological applications of science — communications, transportation, scientific research, medicine, architecture, computers, household appliances, energy." (Newfoundland and Labrador)	3

(continued)

Table 9.1 (continued)

Category	Illustrative Example	Frequency of Occurrence (Maximum 11)
8. Career opportunities	"To relate science to career opportunities in technology, industry, commerce, business, medicine, engineering, education, research, and other areas in which science plays a role." (Ontario)	4

Source: G. Orpwood (1981). Science in the Canadian curriculum. In J. Donald Wilson, ed., *Canadian Education in the 1980s,* 169–70. Calgary, AB: Detselig.

It is beyond the scope of this chapter to examine the influence of the Council's recommendations on all provincial policy statements. Some examples, however, may encourage you to look further.

◆ ◆ ◆ ◆ ◆
CURRICULUM GUIDES AND POLICY STATEMENTS

Since the curriculum in each of the provinces and territories is prescribed, the curriculum guides "prescribe" guidelines to be followed by schools offering science at the primary and elementary levels.

The curriculum guides currently in use across Canada include statements of aims, which are followed by suggestions for the selection and organization of content, and a listing of authorized or recommended resources that are available to teachers for use in implementing the curriculum. This makes the guides fairly easy to review and to identify in them common goals and most frequently recommended resources. An examination of the relevant publications for your province or territory will bring you closer to the curriculum that will be experienced by children in your classroom. You can think of the aims as the *intent* of the curriculum, and the selection and organization of content and accompanying resources as the *content* of the curriculum. The environment you create for children's learning, together with the teaching strategies and specific techniques you use and the resources you select, will determine the *experienced curriculum*.

Intent of the Curriculum

A review of the ministry (department) of education curriculum documents across Canada reveals that a number of them acknowledge the influence of the Science Council report and its statement of goals in stimulating the revision of the documents and the rethinking of methods of teaching science. An examination of the "statements of intent" expressed in these documents is a fruitful exercise. The following review is designed to encourage you to look for similarities in them, while at the same time identifying the uniqueness that characterizes each of the Canadian provinces and territories.

NEWFOUNDLAND AND LABRADOR

The province of Newfoundland and Labrador published in 1988–89 separate curriculum guides for K–3, the *Primary Science Curriculum Guide* (1988), and 4–6, the *Elementary Science Curriculum Guide* (1989). Included in the rationale and philosophy is the Science Council's recommendation that the science program help students to understand natural phenomena and the interrelationships among science, technology, and society. Program objectives focus on cognitive, psychomotor, affective, and social outcomes, as illustrated in Table 9.2.

TABLE 9.2

Newfoundland and Labrador: Program Objectives, K–6 Science

There are four kinds of objectives in the Primary Science Program: cognitive, psychomotor, affective, and social. The general aims of the program are to develop students' ability to think creatively, innovatively, and independently; to help students acquire a taste for learning; and to motivate them to continue to learn.

Cognitive Objectives
◆ To encourage students to examine, analyze, and understand the world around them and to stimulate the desire to continue to do so.
◆ To promote intellectual curiosity.
◆ To provide students with a rich background of experiences and to build concepts through concrete experiences.
◆ To enable students to use the processes of science to approach problems intelligently.
◆ To develop students' ability to organize their findings and to communicate them using precise language.
◆ To encourage the critical interpretation of findings.
◆ To encourage creativity by stimulating divergent thinking.   *(continued)*

Table 9.2 (continued)

Psychomotor Objectives

◆ To teach students to construct, or assemble, and use appropriate tools and simple apparatus.
◆ To teach students to use scientific equipment and instruments to extend the senses.
◆ To teach students how to handle and care for living things.
◆ To teach students the skills of data collection, such as taking samples, observing accurately, and measuring.
◆ To teach students to keep simple records, through the use of diagrams and pictures.

Affective Objectives

◆ To help students develop a strong interest in science.
◆ To develop scientific attitudes: intellectual honesty, humility, openmindedness, a willingness to investigate, a desire for accurate knowledge.
◆ To cultivate aesthetic appreciation of patterns and relations in nature.
◆ To help students acquire a reverence for life — an appreciation of living things and a concern for their well-being.

Social Objectives

◆ To develop students' sense of responsibility for their own learning and that of others.
◆ To have students participate effectively in science learning — in small groups, large groups, and individually.
◆ To have students co-operate with teachers and classmates and abide by the rules; for example, those governing safety and care of materials.

Source: Primary Science Curriculum Guide (1988). Newfoundland and Labrador: Department of Education, 2.

NOVA SCOTIA

The *Public School Programs* guide (1988–89 and 1989–90) for Nova Scotia suggests that the elementary science program should provide "experiences which encourage positive attitudes to science and develop science skills which will serve as a basis for scientific concept development in later years" (100). Plans for a major restructuring of the Nova Scotia elementary science curriculum are reflected in the 1992 *Proposed Framework for the Elementary Science Program*. The new curriculum is designed to focus on science, environment, and technology (SET). Unifying concepts are suggested for each level from primary (Kindergarten) to Grade 6. These are embedded in the traditional strands of the life, physical and earth/space sciences, and the added strands of technology studies and environmental science.

PRINCE EDWARD ISLAND

The Prince Edward Island publication *Science Activities in the Elementary School* (1980) was prepared in the late 1970s after a survey of the province's teachers had indicated the need for more adequate guidelines for K–6 science. The guide presents a program based on active participation in science activities. Figure 9.1 represents the potential outcomes of such participation.

At the primary level (Grades 1–3), the science curriculum has been designed to complement the themes in the Language Arts program, *Expressways*. A cross-referencing in the teaching guide, *Science through Expressways* (1987), also assists teachers in following a thematic approach in their programs.

NEW BRUNSWICK

The advisory committee that developed New Brunswick's *Elementary Science: A Resource Guide* (1984) acknowledges on the cover page that the guide was developed "in conjunction with the Science Council of Canada Report establishing new trends in science." The New Brunswick curriculum guide proposes a K–6 science curriculum spanning the four major science areas, and methods that encourage autonomous, often spontaneous, learning and focus on the holistic

FIGURE 9.1

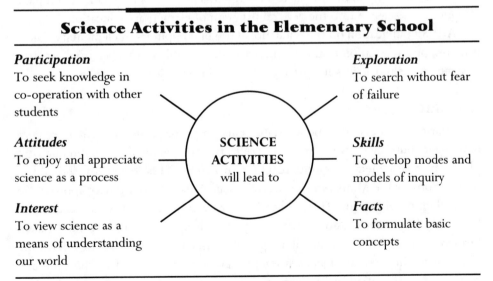

Science Activities in the Elementary School

Participation
To seek knowledge in
co-operation with other
students

Exploration
To search without fear
of failure

Attitudes
To enjoy and appreciate
science as a process

SCIENCE
ACTIVITIES
will lead to

Skills
To develop modes and
models of inquiry

Interest
To view science as a
means of understanding
our world

Facts
To formulate basic
concepts

Source: *Science Activities in the Elementary School* (1980). Prince Edward Island: Department of Education, 4.

development of the child. The point of view expressed is that "integrating science with the other courses of study will help students apply themselves to real-life situations regardless of their future plans" (1).

The document for the primary grades, *Elementary School Science Curriculum Guide Grades One–Three* (1992), emphasizes the importance of "teaching children how to learn and to express and apply knowledge ... [and], using the most relevant ideas and multiple resources in practicing how to learn" (1). Desired outcomes include the development in the primary grades of a questioning attitude that will lead to skills in critical thinking and problem solving.

Quebec

Quebec's approach to renewal of science curriculum for the early years of school science is marked by an emphasis on "scientific humanism" and "natural science." Natural science is defined in the broad sense as the study of the biological, physical, and technological dimensions of the natural environment. Figure 9.2 is a reproduction of the summary chart for the program.

An examination of the chart reveals concern throughout the program for the development of responsible attitudes and behaviour that together lead to an "environmental ethic." The follow-up publications, *Elementary School: Natural Science, First Cycle* (1985) and *Elementary School: Natural Science, Second Cycle* (1986), provide help for the teacher with classroom and out-of-classroom activities and other aspects of the curriculum. Efforts toward renewal are focussing on more complete integration of science into the general program of elementary education.

A 1989 publication on the educational use of computers in elementary school is an important addition to the resources made available to Quebec teachers. It is designed to help teachers integrate computers into the learning process.

Ontario

In Ontario, a succession of policy statements on primary and elementary science have been published over the years, reflecting the gradual development of a philosophy designed to guide teaching practice. This series of thoughtful publications by the Ministry of Education represents an evolutionary approach to curriculum development. The publication *Science in Primary and Junior Education: A Statement of Direction* (1986) is the result of a co-operative study, with Graham Orpwood of the Science Council as special adviser to the Minister of Education. This document sets out objectives for primary and junior science education and recommends 24 initiatives for renewal. The essence of effective science programs at these levels is represented in the document in the form of a triangle, as shown in Figure 9.3.

FIGURE 9.2

Quebec: Overall Objectives of the Natural Science Program

To Enable Pupils:

i   To develop as autonomous and creative individuals in a scientific and technological society.

ii   To develop a spirit of scientific inquiry.

iii   To gradually develop an understanding of the realities of their natural and technological environment.

iv   To become familiar with existing environmental problems.

v   To develop responsible attitudes and behaviour conducive to conservation of environmental resources.

───── *General Objectives* ─────

───────▶ *(Knowledge)*

7.   To become familiar with the *Plant World* and its interrelationships with other living things and the physical environment; to develop responsible attitudes and behaviour toward this resource.

8.   To become familiar with the *Animal World* and its interrelationships with other living things and the physical environment; to develop responsible attitudes and behaviour toward this resource.

9.   To become familiar with *Water* and its interrelationships with the other elements of the environment; to develop responsible attitudes and behaviour conducive to rational use of this resource and the benefits man gains from it.

10.   To become familiar with *Air* and its interrelationships with other elements of the environment; to develop responsible attitudes and behaviour conducive to rational use of this resource.

11.   To become familiar with *Soil* and its interrelationships with the other elements of the environment; to develop responsible attitudes and behaviour conducive to rational use of this resource and the benefits man gains from it.

12.   To become familiar with *Manufactured Goods*; to develop responsible attitudes and behaviour conducive to rational use of manufactured goods.

Experimental Approach
(Procedure, Skills, and Attitudes)

1.   To develop his personal potential in a harmonious manner.

2.   To learn about group life and team work within a democratic setting.

3.   To appreciate the richness and the beauty of nature.

4.   To develop attitudes which will aid him in becoming familiar with the experimental approach and in building and structuring his knowledge.

5.   To develop skills and competence in the use of the experimental approach.

6.   To become familiar with the use of certain tools which will help him to explore the environment.

Source: *Elementary School Curriculum: Natural Science* (1984). Québec: Ministère de l'Éducation, 8.

FIGURE 9.3

The Essence of Primary and Junior Science Education

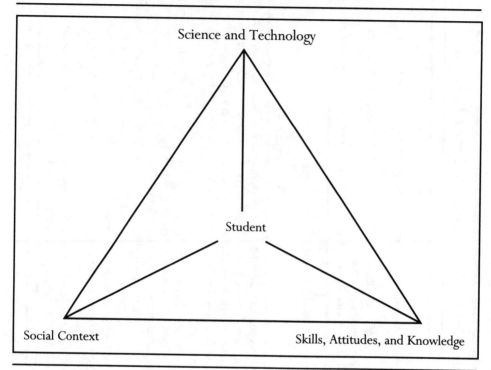

Science and Technology

Student

Social Context

Skills, Attitudes, and Knowledge

Source: *Science in Primary and Junior Education: A Statement of Direction* (1986). Ontario Ministry of Education, 8. © Reproduced with permission from the Queen's Printer for Ontario.

At the centre of the triangle is the student, "with his or her interests, aptitudes, values, preconceptions, and beliefs about the world. Three other components form the triangle: science and technology, including the content and processes of both; the skills, attitudes and knowledge that are the desired educational outcomes; and the social context, in which the student and science and technology coexist and interact" (8). The title of a later publication, *Science Is Happening Here* (1988), speaks for itself and further elaborates the philosophy represented by the triangle.

A new working document, *The Common Curriculum,* was released in February 1993 by the Ontario Ministry of Education and Training. This document reflects the need for curriculum to respond to changes in schools, society, and the world. Subject matter and outcomes are organized into four broad program areas, one of which is Mathematics, Science, and Technology. The shift in curriculum emphasis is toward more integrated programming and active, inquiry-oriented learning.

SASKATCHEWAN

The Saskatchewan publications stress the need for preparing students for lifetime learning. Saskatchewan has based its approach to curriculum development on a solid foundation of research, beginning with a careful analysis of common essential learnings in all of education (Hart 1987). The vertical framework suggests a progression in the science curriculum along seven dimensions, all under the umbrella of scientific literacy. The six common essential learnings proposed for the core curriculum are: communication, critical and creative thinking, independent learning, numeracy, personal skills and values, and technological literacy. Science K–12 is one of seven required areas of study, and the dimensions of scientific literacy identified are key science concepts, values underlying science, processes of science, science–technology–society–environment interrelationships, scientific and technical skills, science-related interests and attitudes, and the nature of science. The grade level at which these are introduced depends on the level of complexity of the topic and the developmental readiness of the children. Figure 9.4, which illustrates the umbrella analogy, is extracted from the 1989 publication of Saskatchewan Education, *Science: Program Overview and Connections (K) 1–12.*

This document sets the tone for a comprehensive elementary science curriculum guide and an information bulletin, published the following year. These documents, in common with the New Brunswick publication, emphasize the interconnections of science with the whole of learning.

MANITOBA

Manitoba revised earlier guides in 1992. Guides were produced for each grade level from kindergarten to Grade 6, articulating with new K–2 and 3–9 science curriculum publications. Each grade-level guide is organized under the following headings: Objectives, The Learner, The Teaching Environment, Evaluation, Attitudes and Skills, Scope and Sequence, Materials List, and Core Topics. The content of the guides reflects current thinking in science education, on topics such as the role of science in general education, how children learn, misconceptions in science, girls in science, science/technology/society and computers as a "way of life" for children in the future.

The evolutionary nature of the curriculum-development process is evidenced by the inclusion of a questionnaire in the teacher's guide for each grade

FIGURE 9.4

Saskatchewan Science Program "Connections": Umbrella Analogy

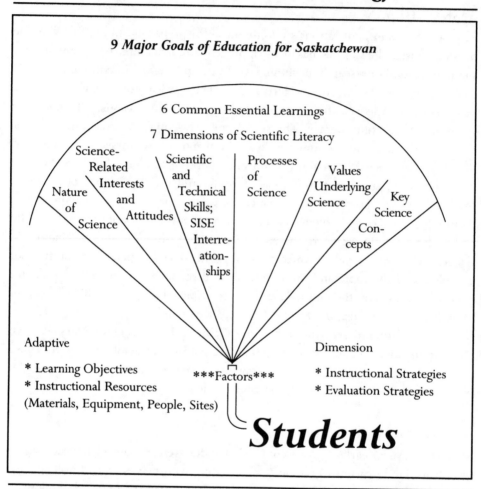

9 Major Goals of Education for Saskatchewan

6 Common Essential Learnings

7 Dimensions of Scientific Literacy

Nature of Science

Science-Related Interests and Attitudes

Scientific and Technical Skills; SISE Interre-ation-ships

Processes of Science

Values Underlying Science

Key Science Con-cepts

Adaptive

* Learning Objectives
* Instructional Resources
(Materials, Equipment, People, Sites)

Factors

Dimension

* Instructional Strategies
* Evaluation Strategies

Students

Source: Science: Program Overview and Connections (K)1–12 (1989).
Draft copy, Saskatchewan Education, 5.

level. In the questionnaire, teachers are asked to assess the adequacy of the suggested activities in realizing expected outcomes, and to make suggestions for improvement.

ALBERTA

Alberta's *Elementary Science Curriculum Guide* (1983) advocates "personal rather than vicarious learning" and an emphasis on "ways of gaining and processing information rather than learning information itself" (1). In common with other provincial guides, the Alberta guide includes introductory sections on the development of attitudes, psychomotor skills, science concepts, and process skills. At the primary level (Division One), four basic skills — observing, classifying, measuring, and communicating — are introduced in Grade 1 and sequentially developed as preparation for the use of more complex processes in later grades.

The "general objectives" for elementary science (2) are complemented by a listing of "desirable characteristics of an elementary program" (3). These guidelines suggest that the program should be activity- and success-oriented; interesting, diversified, and relevant to the child's natural world; appropriate to the psychomotor and intellectual levels of the child; and that it should allow for the co-operative development of inquiry or process skills and science concepts. A further objective is to develop awareness of the humanistic implications of science and its "role in the causes and resolution of some current social problems" (2).

As in other provinces, revision of curriculum guides in Alberta is a continuing process. It will be of interest to you to update information on curriculum development in Alberta by referring to the new documents released in 1992–93.

BRITISH COLUMBIA

The British Columbia guide, *Elementary Science: Grades 1–7* (1987), presents a rationale for elementary science education that includes four groups of goals: attitudes and appreciations; processes and skills; scientific knowledge; and creative and critical thinking. More specific learning outcomes are identified for each level of elementary school, and teachers are given a choice among three sets of resources for use in implementing the program.

Four exciting developments have been underway in British Columbia. Developments include the publication of a primary program foundations document, a primary program resource document, a curriculum assessment document for science, and a curriculum support document for the early intermediate grades. The new primary program suggests a curriculum balance between science, technology, and sustainable development emphases.

The document *Primary through Graduation Curriculum/Assessment Framework* (1992) is designed to explain the unique contribution that science makes to the overall education of students; to identify the knowledge, skills, and attitudes that are essential to this subject area; and to give teachers and students flexibility in sequencing learning opportunities.

THE NORTHWEST TERRITORIES

The Department of Education in the Northwest Territories has produced two comprehensive curriculum guides, *Elementary Science: Primary Program Guide* (1985a) and *Elementary Science: Intermediate Program Guide* (1986). For teachers in the Northwest Territories, the two documents present introductory sections on the foundations of science education, together with complete program guidelines, teaching approaches, and suggestions for an assortment of curriculum materials to use to implement the program. Separate sections are included on the four basic components of the program: process skills, psychomotor skills, attitudes, and science concepts. Table 9.3 gives specific examples of some of the overall aims of the program.

TABLE 9.3

Northwest Territories: Goals of the Elementary Science Program

The Program Advocates

1. The development of appropriate science attitudes: curiosity, objectivity and a willingness to suspend judgement.
2. The development of process skills appropriate to the level of the learner.
3. A sequential development of content (scientific knowledge) within the following conceptual framework.
   a. Life and Environment
   b. Matter and Energy
   c. Earth, Space, and Time
4. The development of effective communication skills — questioning, discussing, reading, writing and researching through science activities.
5. The acquisition of manipulative skills necessary for the safe handling of organisms, materials, and apparatus used in the development of process skills.
6. The promotion of a continuing interest in science and a continuing awareness of and understanding for one's environment with positive user attitudes.
7. The development of an appreciation for the interdependence of the scientific and humanistic streams of learning.
8. The development of skills necessary for social interaction.
9. The development of an understanding of the interplay between (1) science and technology and (2) vocational knowledge and skill.

Source: Elementary Science: Intermediate Program Guide (1986). Northwest Territories: Department of Education, 5.

THE YUKON

The Yukon follows the British Columbia curriculum guidelines for the elementary science program.

---

activity 9.2 **YOUR OWN COMPARATIVE ANALYSIS**

- ◆ Review the brief summaries of the statements of intent in each of the Canadian curriculum guides and list the expected outcomes that are common to all. It will be helpful to have the guides on hand to supplement the descriptions where necessary.
- ◆ Think about statements and/or schematic representations in certain guides that are unique. Discuss ways in which these enrich your own conceptions of the intent of the elementary science curriculum.
- ◆ Look most closely at the curriculum guide for your own province, and think about how well the goals for elementary science parallel those of other provinces.
- ◆ Make your own statement of goals, drawing from your study of curriculum guides across Canada.

How well do the goals represented in the provincial documents fit into the outcomes for children's learning in science that are discussed in Chapter 1 and elaborated on in subsequent chapters?

☐ Reflecting and Sharing

Did you find that this activity helped you to define goals more clearly and to enrich your own conceptions by adding a phrase here, a sentence there, from among the interpretations of expected outcomes that were portrayed in the curriculum guides? If the uniqueness of different provinces came through, this is as it should be. Emphases differ from province to province and change over time, because curriculum development is a dynamic enterprise, evolving as more is learned from research and especially from reflections on what works best in classrooms.

A number of provinces are in the process of revising guides, continuing this evolutionary process. Changes in emphasis over time result in the retention of some goals and the modification of others. New trends are evident in the emphasis on co-operative learning in groups (with children acquiring skills as productive members of groups and learning from one another) and on the constructivist theory of knowledge (the active involvement of children in constructing meaning from experience). There is a growing movement toward making science more relevant to the lives of students, stressing the interconnections of science and technology with the world in which they live, and developing attitudes of appreciation, aesthetic awareness, and responsibility for the environment. These will be strong emphases as new guides are written. The Earth Summit in 1992 focussed on the potential degradation of the environment as a worldwide problem — one that cannot be ignored in the school curriculum. At the primary and elementary levels, the response to these goals may be the interweaving of a big "E for Environment" with STS (Science, Technology, Society) emphases in the curriculum. Perhaps the acronym for the 1990s will be SETS.

In the next section, you'll consider how the curriculum guides help you to plan curriculum and instruction and suggest resources you may use to fulfil the goals that you now see as important to successful "sciencing" with children.

Content of the Curriculum

You have seen in earlier chapters, and also in your examination of the guides, that broad aims (along with specific objectives for each grade level) determine the *scope* and *sequence* for elementary science. The scope or breadth is the horizontal organization of the program, which may span the major science areas — the life sciences, physical sciences, and earth/space sciences — or, alternatively, a number of "big ideas" of science — conceptual themes. Recall from Chapter 4 that within this horizontal framework there is a vertical arrangement or sequence of concepts and skills that, when linked, leads to familiarity with the main concepts of each of the disciplines and/or understanding of these conceptual themes. There are also lists of objectives for each grade level, and care is taken to select developmentally appropriate learning tasks as children progress through the grades.

To facilitate this process, a variety of curriculum resources are made available to teachers. Your next step is to return to the curriculum guides, this time to answer questions such as these: What curriculum resources are being recommended by ministries of education for children learning science? Are there some that are recommended more frequently than others? Are the materials all new, or are there some that have been around for a while but are still considered to have good potential for children's learning? Are the resources American in origin? British? Canadian? Provincial? What types of resources are being used? Textbook-based programs? Commercially produced modules? Teacher-produced units? One way to find answers fairly quickly is to do Activity 9.3.

activity 9.3 CURRICULUM GUIDES: RESOURCES AT A GLANCE

Gather in one central location the most recent revisions of the curriculum guides and/or science curriculum policy statements for the provinces and territories. You may start your search with print materials and disregard for now any audiovisual resources that may be listed. Each group can work with two or three of the provincial curriculum guides and/or the resource catalogues.

Start with any guide and list the recommended resources, either in the guides or in the resource catalogues or computerized databases developed by some provinces, such as Alberta's ACCESS Network, Ontario's ONTERIS database, or British Columbia's 1990–91 *Catalogue of Learning Resources: Primary to Gradua-tion*. By sharing all the curriculum guides and resource catalogues, each group could make one entire list of the groups of resources available for implementing the elementary science curriculum.

As you go through the recommended resources, note the titles of the programs from which the resources are drawn, and indicate as well as you can at this time, in brackets after each title, whether it is a textbook series or a program made up of a number of modules or units on assorted science topics. To keep the list from being too cumbersome, list only the title of the whole program or series of books or modules, and note the number of modules or levels recommended. For example, among the resources for K–3 in British Columbia's *Catalogue of Learning Resources: Primary to Graduation* (1990–91) are *Innovations in Science* (3 levels); the *Looking at ...* series (6 titles); *Science 5/13* (10 units); *Windows on Science* (6 titles); and SEEDS (3 levels). For Grades 4 to 6, two textbook series are recommended: *Addison-Wesley Science* and *Collier Macmillan Science*. Also available is the first edition of the activities collection, *Science Is ...* (Bosak 1986).

Once each group has a listing of the major resources for each province and territory, prepare a class chart displaying them according to the type of resource they represent. Divide a large piece of cardboard into about fifteen columns, with one column for each type of resource. Develop a code to represent each new program that you find listed among the recommended resources. For example, if twelve Elementary Science Study units are listed, code this as ESS (12) or use the designation CMS (TBS) to denote *Collier Macmillan Science* (textbook series).

Enter all the data on your chart, with textbook series in one column, ESS units in another, EYE in another, the Energy Literacy Series (SEEDS) in another, government publications on the environment in another, and so on. A class chart of the data will give you the relative frequencies of different types of resources for the provinces and territories.

❑ Reflecting and Sharing

You are probably left with the impression that a great many resources are recommended for elementary science, although the range of resources varies in different provinces. In provinces and territories where the curriculum is centralized, the same basic program is used by all schools in a province, supplemented by teacher-produced and other resources. In others where the curriculum is not centralized, a selection is made, at the school level, from a variety of resources, and individual teachers can follow the appropriate guidelines and select various materials that suit their individual teaching styles.

You'll find many of these curriculum materials in schools and in your library. The overview that follows is meant to introduce some of the materials, so that you get to know them as living resources you can draw upon in your teaching.

They fall naturally into four groups, beginning with the National Science Foundation (NSF) programs, developed by the National Science Foundation in the 1960s, and followed by two groups of programs from the 1970s and 1980s — a "new generation" of textbook-based programs and a variety of innovative curriculum projects in the United States, Britain, and Canada. The fourth group — programs developed in the 1990s — will bring you up to the present and into the future, since many of the newer programs are still under development and could continue to be for some years to come.

◆ ◆ ◆ ◆ ◆

CURRICULUM RESOURCES: A HISTORICAL OVERVIEW

National Science Foundation Programs

The *Science Curriculum Improvement Study* (SCIS), *Science: A Process Approach* (SAPA), and *Elementary Science Study* (ESS) were among the programs produced in the United States in the post-*Sputnik* wave of curriculum reform in school science, with generous funding from the National Science Foundation (NSF).

Although the programs had a lot in common, they assumed different positions on a process–content continuum and, as mentioned in Chapter 2, in the learning theories on which they were based. Some similarities and differences are noted in Table 9.4.

TABLE 9.4

National Science Foundation Programs: Similarities and Differences

Similarities	Differences
Developed by teams of scientists, educators, and psychologists.	**SCIS**
	Primary emphasis concept development. Organized to develop major ideas in the life sciences, physical sciences.
Stressed importance of science in the early school years.	
Extensively trial-tested, revised on basis of feedback from teachers, students.	Attempt to match concepts to developmental levels posed by Piaget.
Less emphasis on reading about science, more on acquiring knowledge through direct experience.	Instructional sequence: exploration, invention, and discovery.
	Overriding goal scientific literacy.
Emphasis on hands-on activities, active involvement in learning.	**SAPA**
	Heavily process-oriented. No attempt to develop concepts.
Teacher's role facilitative, a partner in discovery.	Focus on two lists of processes — basic (simple) and integrated.
Emphasis on positive attitudes toward science.	Step-by-step sequential organization based on Gagné's hierarchy of learning.
Spanned major sciences. Concern for accuracy of science concepts.	Evaluation based on mastery of prerequisite skills, before moving on to next step in learning.
Kits of specially designed equipment and materials.	**ESS**
	No systematic attempt to develop concepts or processes.
	Based on Piaget and Bruner. Belief in potential for learning in all domains through free exploration.
	Initial playlike phase, referred to as "messing about in science."

All of these programs were designed to give children the opportunity to be involved in investigative and exploratory activities akin to those that scientists use to investigate the natural world. In 1989, Shymansky used a meta-analysis technique to re-examine the effectiveness of the NSF programs, and found that students in these programs outperformed by nine percentile points those in traditional elementary science programs on such measures as achievement, perceptions of science, and problem-solving skills. When performance on process skills and positive perception of science were compared, the three programs outperformed other programs featured in the studies by seventeen and nineteen percentile points. Shymansky believes that the collective evidence from the research has numerous implications for the design of elementary science curricula in the future.

In view of these research findings, and also because of the comprehensive nature of these classroom-tested units, it would be worthwhile to familiarize yourself with some of the teachers' guides that were produced by ESS, as well as the revised SCIS and SAPA materials.

The Self-Help Elementary Level Science (SHELLS) project (Rowe 1988) is a tribute to the timelessness of the programs developed in the 1960s. Mary Budd Rowe's work at the University of Florida involves collecting, indexing, and capturing on the CD-ROM Science Helper activities from SCIS and ESS, as well as from other NSF-funded programs over the past two decades, so that they provide an activities bank for teachers to use in curriculum implementation.

Textbook-based Programs

You have probably heard many negative comments about textbooks in elementary science, and the phrase "read about–tell about" science may be an immediate association as you consider this source of ideas. A closer examination, however, may reveal that in many textbook programs there is an honest attempt to base the organization and the nature of the learning experiences on the generally accepted goals of primary and elementary science. In fact, the influence of the NSF curricula is evident in the child-centred, activity-oriented approach of the textbook programs that have been developed in the past two decades.

In your examination of the curriculum guides, you found that textbook programs are among the recommended resources in many of the provinces and territories. You probably noticed as well that the broad guidelines for the curriculum, as well as the specific topics for certain grade levels, are usually referenced to sections in these texts. For novice teachers, textbook-based programs provide a sense of structure within which they can feel comfortable as they use the teachers' guides and student materials, together with whatever supplementary material is supplied with the program, to implement the curriculum guidelines. To become familiar with some of the available programs and to judge their usefulness, form a small group and work through the next activity.

A child-centred, activity-oriented approach to textbook programs has developed in the past two decades. A textbook becomes a co-operative learning tool as these children work together to understand concepts.

activity 9.4   EXAMINING AND COMPARING TEXTBOOK-BASED PROGRAMS

Begin by dividing up as many textbook-based programs as you can find, preferably the teachers' guides, which usually contain reproductions of the corresponding page of the student text. Work co-operatively in small groups, with one program per group.

In Table 9.5, nine criteria are presented that you can use to judge the potential effectiveness of a textbook-based program. To help with this process, sample questions are included for each of the criteria. Think of additional questions you might ask to complete your analysis, and use Table 9.5 as a checklist for evaluating the programs you examine.

TABLE 9.5

Examining and Comparing Textbook-based Programs

Criteria	Related Questions
Expected outcomes	Are overall goals presented clearly? Are concepts clearly stated and learner objectives specified? Is there evidence of attention to affective outcomes?
Organization	Is there a balance among the major sciences? Is the sequence of topics logical and hierarchical? What is the balance of content and process?
Nature of children	Are concept and process development based on how children learn? Is there an emphasis on the child's construction of meaning? Is there provision for individual differences?
Nature of science	Are inquiry/discovery teaching strategies called for? Is there reference to the tentative nature of knowledge? Is the information presented scientifically accurate?
Process/inquiry skills	Is there ample opportunity for process development? Are activities open-ended and investigative? Are opportunities provided to pursue children's questions?
Concept development	Is the conceptual structure well defined? Is concept development compatible with Piagetian research? Are opportunities provided for talking through ideas?
Meaningfulness	Is the program success-oriented and interesting to children? Are there frequent attempts to relate learning to everyday life? Are environmental concerns, STS issues included?
Evaluation	How closely does evaluation parallel expected outcomes? Are a variety of assessment techniques suggested? Where in Bloom's taxonomy do assessment items fit?
Teachability	Are clear directions, adequate science background provided? Are related resources suggested? Learning centre ideas? Is the program easily implemented, equipment inexpensive?

❏ Reflecting and Sharing

Your group may have begun this analysis by sampling teachers' guides at several grade levels to get an overall impression of the program — its goals, scope, and sequence; the number and placement of activities throughout lessons and units; the suggestions for enrichment that are built into the program; the bibliography of supplementary resources. To answer more specific questions such as the nature of the investigations or the open-endedness of the discussion requires a closer look at selected units and lessons within units. Some of the questions you've added may have led you to this kind of examination of the materials.

A final question you may wish to include is whether the program is comprehensive enough to be used as a major resource, yet open enough to allow you to make selections from it, add your favourite activities and ways of teaching, and "make it your own." For it will be at the level of the teacher in the classroom — the interface between theory and practice, between goals and reality — that the real test of curriculum materials will be made. You will be the final arbiter of how successfully the *intended* and *planned* curriculum becomes the *experienced* and *learned* curriculum. Whatever the drawbacks and restrictions of textbook-based programs, the organizational frameworks they provide can be helpful to a beginning teacher. The framework and the suggested activities will show how the grade level you teach fits into a broader scheme. Once you are familiar with the structure, you can adapt, supplement, enrich, and modify the curriculum so that it reflects your teaching style and provides for the diverse needs of your students.

Programs of the 1970s and 1980s

In the 1970s and 1980s, important curriculum materials were produced for use in British schools and innovative resources were developed in Canada and the United States. These resources were similar in that all reflected the influence of Piagetian theory and the ideology of child-centred learning. Each of the programs was designed to involve students in investigative activities, in small groups and individually. Some produced student materials as well as teachers' guides; others produced only teacher materials. Some involved teachers in the development of the units; others did not. In contrast with the SCIS and SAPA materials and the textbook programs, there was no systematic attempt to cover the spectrum of science or to arrange the units hierarchically. The result of the flurry of curriculum development in this period was an increase in the variety of teachers' guides and student materials from which teachers could draw to implement curriculum guidelines.

BRITISH PROGRAMS

The materials developed in Britain were produced mainly for teachers, and were designed to stimulate and support their efforts to involve children in scientific activities and experiences. Teachers throughout the United Kingdom were heavily involved in trial testing the activities suggested in the teachers' guides and in developing, on their own, new starting points for science explorations and interdisciplinary units.

Nuffield Junior Science. Although this program was developed in the late 1960s, it is important as a prototype for the innovative British curricula that followed. It was a free, unstructured program that put children at the centre of learning, encouraging them to pose questions of interest and significance to them, and integrating science with the whole of the primary school curriculum. Process and attitude objectives were stressed, with children choosing what to investigate, developing process skills, and extending science learnings across the curriculum. No specific guidelines for concept development are included in the *Nuffield Teacher's Guide 1* and *Teacher's Guide 2*. In practice, however, the "starting points for learning" covered a diversity of activities and a wide range of content.

Science 5/13. These curriculum materials consist of 24 teaching units published between 1972 and 1979, with continued emphasis on process, the use of the environment, the need for concrete materials, and starting from children's questions. *Science 5/13* begins by setting out the goals of the program and defining objectives along three Piagetian levels, in a teacher's guide titled *With Objectives in Mind*. The books give guidance and examples of students' work on specific themes, and have titles such as "Science from Toys," "Change," "Metals," and "Minibeasts." Modes of learning are inquiry and guided discovery. The teacher has a great deal of flexibility in the way the units develop with different classes.

Learning through Science. This project was jointly sponsored by the Schools Council in Great Britain and the Scottish Education Department. Thirteen modules were produced using themes considered appropriate for primary science, such as "Ourselves," "Sky and Space," "Materials," and "Out of Doors." For each of the units, a series of 24 activity cards present problems to solve or mini-topics in which children can become involved, either individually or in small groups. The cards suggest tasks of different levels of difficulty and encourage children's questions. Topics are relevant to life, and the emphasis is on developing the processes of science and using them to solve problems.

Science Horizons. This is a series of units written and tested by teachers in West Sussex for incorporation into the *Science 5/13* framework. They provide background information for the teacher and suggest resources, core and optional activities, integration with other areas, and tips on assessment. Activity sheets guide the children through observing, recording, and interpreting the results of their observations and experiments. Some topics are "Planet Earth," "Floating and Sinking," and "Flying Starts Here."

A National Curriculum. Britain now has a national curriculum with well-defined science curriculum guidelines. The document is a comprehensive one, including goals (attainment targets) in the cognitive, affective, and psychomotor domains, and suggesting the scope and sequence of the curriculum at different levels, as well as evaluation guidelines.

CANADIAN PROGRAMS

The Canadian resources developed in the 1970s included an assortment of environmentally oriented materials: modular units with accompanying teachers' guides, activities books, science trade books, and other instructional resources.

Examining Your Environment (EYE). The EYE materials (Couchman et al. 1971–77) consist of separate modules with an emphasis on the environment and out-of-school investigative experiences with "Snow and Ice," "Dandelions," "Mapping Small Places," "Miniclimates," and other topics related to the everyday lives of the students. Children work in groups, planning experiments (often constructing their own equipment); gathering, recording, and interpreting data; and learning about the natural world. These modular units are now out of print, but, fortunately, are still available in many schools and libraries.

Western Educational Development Group (WEDGE). The WEDGE materials (1978) invite explorations of the natural environment with titles such as "There's Dirt in the Forest," "The Pond Book," "The Creek Book," "Grounds for Erosion," "The Jolly Green Classroom," and "Science on a Kite String." They include a wealth of background information for the teacher and ideas for field trips and outdoor activities, with sketches and line drawings to help with identification of living things.

Society, Environment and Energy Development Studies (SEEDS). The (SEEDS 1974) series includes for each level a teacher's guide, student text, activity sheets, and audiovisual package. The topics for the primary level are "The Sun,"

"Wind, Water and Wood," and "Fossil Fuels." At the elementary level, the concepts of renewable and nonrenewable resources are developed, along with the good and bad effects of fossil fuel extraction. Students explore forms of energy and the effects of energy conversion into electricity, and think of ways of using energy more wisely. Process skills are enhanced through additional short investigations that are correlated with the core curriculum.

Project Wild in Canada. *Project Wild: Elementary Activity Guide* (1987) was introduced in Canada by the Canadian Wildlife Federation, with the goal of encouraging "responsible environmental citizenship among young Canadians" (iii). Instructional activities are easily integrated into the existing curriculum, and the conceptual framework is organized in seven major sections, which begin with awareness and appreciation that the earth is home for wildlife and people. Activities provide a good foundation for students' understanding of the diversity of wildlife, ecological principles, and the need for management, conservation, and responsible human action.

Science Is ... The first edition of *Science Is ...* (Bosak 1986) is a well-organized collection of science investigations sponsored by the Youth Science Foundation, a nonprofit organization involved in promoting appreciation and understanding of science among young Canadians. The expanded revised edition (Bosak, Bosak, and Puppa 1991) continues the tradition of "every child a scientist" and offers a similar collection of hands-on activities, experiments, and projects that can be used to supplement teacher or commercially produced programs. Activities are open-ended and investigative, and science background for each lesson is provided for the teacher. One of the introductory pages from the second edition of *Science Is ...*, reproduced in Figure 9.5, sets the tone for this compendium of activities.

Looking at ... Series. These books include titles such as the award-winning *Looking at Insects* (Suzuki and Hehner 1986) and *Looking at the Environment* (Suzuki and Hehner 1989). Interesting content is interspersed with "Something to Do" and "Amazing Facts" sections, together with excellent line drawings to illustrate the narrative sections and guide children through the activities.

Programs under Development in the 1990s

Innovative programs have been developed in the period from the late 1980s to the present in response to a second wave of curriculum reform in science education similar to the impetus for reform that resulted in the nationally funded programs in the United States in the 1960s. The impetus for change in Canada, the United

FIGURE 9.5

Science Is ...

A newborn infant babbles, gurgles, wriggles, and reaches out to touch the world.
Each day of life commemorates that very first day.
Each day you and I reach out to our surroundings a wonder. We are human and we are wonderers.
(Joe Abruscato)

WOW!

The formulation of a problem is often more essential than its solution, which may be merely a matter of mathematical or experimental skill. To raise new questions, new possibilities, to regard old problems from a new angle, requires creative imagination and marks real advances in science.
(Albert Einstein)

People learn nothing unless they proceed from the known to the unknown.
(Claude Bernard)

To myself I seem to have been only like a boy playing on the seashore, and diverting myself in now and then finding a smoother pebble or a prettier shell than ordinary, while the great ocean of truth lay all undiscovered before me.
(Isaac Newton)

Science is not a list of facts and principles to learn by rote; it is a way of looking at the world and asking questions. (F. James Rutherford)

If science is a topic of general interest and concern — if both its delights and its social consequences are discussed regularly and competently in the schools, the press, and at the dinner table — we have greatly improved our prospects for learning how the world really is and for improving both it and us.
(Carl Sagan)

Source: S.V. Bosak, with D.A. Bosak and B.A. Puppa (1991). *Science Is ...*, second edition, 1. Richmond Hill, ON: Scholastic Canada and Markham, ON: The Communication Project.

> ✍ **From a Teacher's Journal**
>
> In my first year of teaching, I relied heavily on the textbooks and materials left by previous teachers, and, with great anxiety, began my teaching career without the benefit of any classroom orientation, observation sessions, student teaching, or internship placement. It was really a day-to-day, hit-or-miss program that I offered over that first year; but, at the same time, there were the beginnings of growth with the experience of having a class of my own. My development as a teacher has come from experience, reflecting on that experience, and talking with other teachers.
>
> After nineteen years of teaching, I have evolved a style of my own. My present form of instruction is oriented toward a resource-based approach, with considerable subject overlap, teaching in themes where possible, and encouraging student exploration. It is important for beginning teachers to be knowledgeable about world issues and comfortable with the technologies of today. The beginning teacher should specialize, but at the same time be a generalist, in the sense of being able to adapt, to be flexible in programming and very aware of the social issues that impinge on education.
>
> *Wallace Denny*
> *St. John's, NF*

States, and other countries has been manifested in research at the classroom level, in interchange of ideas at conferences, and in a flurry of curriculum development in elementary science.

The fourth group of resources, the programs of the 1990s, brings you up to the present and into the future, since many of the newer programs are still under development and could continue to be for some years to come. The initiative on a national scale has been taken by the United States, where, again with massive funding, a number of curriculum resources are in various stages of production and testing. These will be reviewed in this section, followed by some exciting new developments in Canada.

THE UNITED STATES IN THE 1990S: NEW CURRICULA IN K–6 SCIENCE

In the United States, national concerns have been expressed and recommendations for action have been made. The result has been a proliferation of new programs, some of which you might like to investigate further because of their innovative nature and their potential for adding to the storehouse of ideas you will continue to build throughout your teaching career.

Recommendations for Renewal. The recommendations for action by influential bodies in the United States were strikingly similar to the recommendations for renewal of science education that were advanced by the Science Council of Canada.

The National Science Teachers Association's position statement *Science-Technology-Society: Science Education for the 1980s* (1982) underscored the broad objectives of appreciation and understanding of science and technology, and the interaction of these with society, using these goals to define a scientifically literate person. There was an emphasis on integrating science with other basic curriculum areas.

The National Science Board (NSB) (1983) report *Educating Americans for the 21st Century* focussed on the need for scientific and technological literacy for all students, and stressed the need for process and problem-solving skills. Again, the potential for integration of science with other areas was mentioned. The working group felt that teachers should take advantage of high student interest in science and use it as a vehicle for enhancing skills in reading, language arts, and communication.

Project 2061 brought together working groups, consultants, the American Association for the Advancement of Science (AAAS), and the National Council on Science and Technology Education in a collaborative effort to identify science and technology learning goals for high-school graduates, and to recommend knowledge and skills that students will need to function well in the world of the future. James Rutherford (1986), the director of the AAAS educational programs, sees childhood as "a time of life that is important for its own sake, for the value of what happens then, and not solely for what it may lead to later in life" (65). The long-range plan is to develop guidelines that state and local districts can use for generating their own curricula.

The first report of Project 2061, *Science for All Americans* (1989), sponsored by the AAAS, received enthusiastic support as it delineated goals for science education K–12 and made specific recommendations that also helped greatly to lay the foundation for the reform of science education.

The National Science Resource Center (NSRC) was established in 1985 under the sponsorship of the National Academy of Sciences and the Smithsonian Institution in Washington, D.C. The NSRC, with two former members of the ESS team among the consultants, began a four-year elementary science curriculum development project. Science and Technology for Children (STC 1990) consists of 24 hands-on science teaching units in the areas of physical science, life science, earth science, and technology, which are designed to develop skills in problem solving and critical thinking that students can use throughout their lives.

The National Science Foundation has once again funded initiatives in elementary science. Among the programs under development are the Triad projects, so called because of joint development by a triangle coalition consisting of a team of scientists and science educators who control the pedagogy, a publisher to supply matching financial support for materials development and teacher in-service over the development phase, and a school where trial testing of the programs takes place. The Triad projects include the following programs.

Science for Life and Living (K–6).
This program was developed by the Biological Sciences Curriculum Study (BSCS) in 1989. It attempts to develop scientific literacy through in-depth integrative activities in science, technology, and health. The emphasis is on developing personal and social goals, co-operative learning, problem solving, and decision making. Program management software, implementation guides, and supplementary activites enhance the program.

National Geographic Kids Network Project (4–6).
This environmental education program was developed in co-operation with the National Geographic Society (1989). It is designed to supplement existing programs through developing skills in collecting, sharing, and organizing data nationwide through a telecommunications system linked by personal computer. The emphasis is on skills that foster scientific, literacy by involving students in issues that have social, scientific, and geographic significance. The program is intended to provide the structure for year-long courses or to be used to supplement existing curricula.

Full Option Science System (3–6) *(FOSS)*. FOSS (1989) is a joint effort between the Lawrence Hall of Science and the Encyclopedia Britannica Educational Corporation. It is designed to increase flexibility of use through a set of correlation tables that help integrate FOSS activities with texts and/or district curriculum guidelines. Multisensory activities are organized around one theme in each of four areas — physical science, life science, earth science, and scientific reasoning and technology. There is much support for teachers on how to organize and monitor small co-operative groups. Materials kits accompany the program.

Altogether, there are eight Triad programs that offer a variety of options. Some can stand on their own; most offer a selection of units and materials that can be combined with, or used to supplement, existing programs. They are all hands-on, inquiry-based programs, emphasizing co-operative learning and science that is relevant and meaningful to the everyday lives of children. In all of these programs, there is an attempt to reduce the number of concepts but to cover them in greater depth. Wherever possible, content is integrated with other areas of the primary and elementary curriculum. If you would like information on other Triad programs, it is available in a comprehensive publication by the National Science Resources Center, *Science for Children: Resources for Teachers* (1992), which is updated periodically and will include in future editions information on materials for computer-assisted instruction.

Roger Bybee (1988) identifies some features of the new curricula that distinguish them from current programs:

◆ While current programs are organized around topics, such as plants, animals, rocks, and minerals, the newer programs tend to be organized around themes, such as cause and effect, structure and function, etc.
◆ Technology, both as content and a tool, is an innovation in the new curricula.
◆ Fewer concepts are studied in greater depth.
◆ There is more opportunity to study science and technology in a socially significant context.
◆ The theoretical base is that children are active, motivated to learn about the natural world.
◆ The hands-on approach is once more stressed, and is shown to be effective.
◆ Co-operative learning, in the sense of the social psychology of working in groups, is a new feature.
◆ Teaching models are designed to facilitate students' construction of knowledge.

CANADA IN THE 1990S: INITIATIVES TOWARD RENEWAL

In Canada, financial support and stimulation for improvement of science education are not available through national boards and agencies such as the National

Science Foundation or the American Association for the Advancement of Science. There is nevertheless a great diversity in the Canadian curriculum materials in use throughout the country.

In spite of the co-ordinating influences described earlier there is uniqueness from province to province in the resources available to teachers and in the responses to changing needs. Within the scope of this chapter, it is possible to review only a few examples of exciting curriculum developments and to suggest that through your library and other sources you may familiarize yourself with curriculum innovations in your own province.

Innovations in Science. *Innovations in Science* (Peturson 1990) consists of many interrelated components such as student books, teacher resource guides, and activity cards. The program is based on the premise that science and language arts are natural partners in education, and topics are developed through integrated themes. Language strategies used are science-related literature, reading aloud, keeping journals, and recording information. A strong environmental component is woven throughout the program.

The "Innovations in Science" program is based on the premise that science and language arts are natural partners in education, and topics are developed through integrated themes.

Explorations in Science. *Explorations in Science* (Harcourt and Wortzman 1992) is a textbook-based elementary science program that reflects the experience of a team of authors from British Columbia, Alberta, Ontario, and Nova Scotia. It uses a thematic approach to curriculum organization, focussing on the themes Form and Function, Patterns and Cycles, Systems and Interactions, Energy, and Change through Time. The program uses an inquiry–discovery approach to teaching/learning, with emphasis on using process skills to solve problems. There is an integrated approach to units on the environment and science–technology–society issues.

Know Your World. Another example of a new program is *Know Your World* (1982), an eight-part series produced in Alberta. Materials consist of fifteen-minute videotapes with accompanying teachers' guides and innovative features such as instructions for make-ahead equipment and curriculum-related projects. Some of the *Know Your World* titles are "Wind Gauge," "Mini Terrariums," "Grid Maps," and "Pour a Pond."

Let's Find Out ... Manitoba has produced a textbook-based program, *Let's Find Out ...* (1992). This program follows closely the 1992 curriculum documents, including the new overall framework for elementary science and the curriculum guidelines developed for each grade level. This is a provincially oriented program, with an emphasis on the local environment.

Ontario: School Board Initiatives. Ontario provides an example of how initiatives toward renewal can spark the production of a variety of new curriculum materials. Among the initiatives proposed by the Ministry of Education in the document *Science in Primary and Junior Education: A Statement of Direction* (1986) was that a science unit purchase plan be developed to enable school boards to purchase curriculum support units and to encourage boards to develop additional units. All teacher-produced units have been listed in the ONTERIS database and made available to boards throughout the province.

Units for various levels from junior kindergarten to Grade 6, with titles such as "Science and Magic," "Blocks," and "Changes," have been produced by the North York Board of Education. The Scarborough Board has developed a series of comprehensive units known as the *Take a Closer Look At ...* series, which includes units on "Weather," "Rocks and Minerals," and others.

Science Kit/Loan Program. Another initiative through the science unit purchase plan was the development of a science kit loan program, with kits and print materials produced for specific units of study. The Ontario Science Centre, in co-operation with the Ontario Ministry of Education, has developed *Science-in-*

a-Box kits (1988b) consisting of equipment, materials, and printed teachers' guides to the activities. These are distributed throughout the province. Some titles for the *Science-in-a-Box* program are "Kitchen Scientist," "Weather," and "Batteries and Bulbs." Teacher directions for the activities and related reading material are included with the kit. It is suggested that the kit can be easily integrated with other curriculum materials. The Science Kit Steering Committee suggests that displaying the materials in a learning centre is often the best way to encourage open-ended inquiry.

Science Activity Books. The staff of the Ontario Science Centre have also produced inviting collections of information, activities, and games that are suitable for independent involvement or with adult supervision. *Scienceworks* (1984) introduces children to the excitement and wonder of science through 65 experiments compiled by Ontario Science Centre staff. Activities focus on making low-calorie breakfasts, ice fishing, making butter, flying airplanes, and many other real-life issues. *Foodworks* (1986) invites children to grow a hydroponic garden, make ice cream, and learn about the history and cultural aspects of food. Other Ontario Science Centre trade books are *Have Fun with Magnifying* (1987); *How Sport Works* (1988); *Science Express* (1991); and *Toying with Science,* to be published in 1994. In a similar vein, the Royal Ontario Museum has produced resources that can extend learning for children on topics such as *Discover: Mysteries of the Past* and *Bones*.

Another exciting series, which includes titles such as *The Amazing Apple Book* (Bourgeois 1987) and *The Amazing Egg Book* (Griffin and Seed 1989), has been developed with funding from the Canada Council and the Ontario Arts Council, and the co-operation of Agriculture Canada and ministries of agriculture in New Brunswick, Nova Scotia, British Columbia, and Ontario and other farm-related agencies. A 1991 publication, *The Amazing Milk Book* (Ross and Wallace 1991), continues this series, which is published by the Kids Can Press of Toronto.

The above listings are not intended to be exhaustive, but merely to open doors to the Canadian resources that are being made available to teachers. They aim to help you add to the storehouse of ideas and resources that will make your classroom experiences in science rewarding for you as teachers and memorable and productive for your students.

TEACHER-PRODUCED MATERIALS: THE POTENTIAL FOR SHARING

The great potential for sharing of teacher-produced materials has not been tapped to the extent that it might be. Canadian teachers in all provinces, either on their own or in co-operation with their colleagues, are constantly developing integrated themes, evolving new approaches to instruction, planning learning centre tasks, and developing interdisciplinary units that can be fruitfully used in other class settings. The materials developed in any one province could be shared profitably with provinces that may not have the resources to develop such materials.

The language development units in use in the Northwest Territories, such as environmentally based primary units "Bears/Polar Bears," "Birds," and "Land Animals" or units with more general topics such as "Popcorn" or "Magnets," would surely be useful wherever there are Native children for whom English is a second language. A Grade 5 unit such as "Getting Along: Fish, Whales and Fishermen" (Whale Research Group 1984) would surely be as interesting and productive elsewhere in Canada as it is to the children of Newfoundland and Labrador. Lessons and units developed at the Huntsman Marine Education Centre or copies of *Eau Canada*, their quarterly newsletter, would surely be valuable wherever there are schools and Canadian schoolchildren close to the ocean.

There *is* sharing, of course, as in the case of a beautiful integrated unit, "Rainy Days" (1988) — by V. McConnell and L. Whiles, two teachers from a Vancouver school board — which somehow found its way across Canada recently to a student teacher in St. John's! The technology exists for much more intercommunication as databanks such as Alberta's ACCESS, Ontario's ONTERIS, and British Columbia's Clearinghouse for Locally Developed Materials continue to grow and other similar networks are added. Consider for a moment the effects of a much greater sharing in the future, a sharing that will enrich children's experiences in science and perhaps become part of the "national vision" for science that will be discussed in the final chapter of this book.

There is a need, as James Page (1979) pointed out to the Science Council, for the science curriculum to have a Canadian context, and for drawing students' attention, as Symons (1975) suggested, to Canada's achievements in science and engendering a sense of national awareness and pride in such accomplishments. There is a need for more locally produced materials that focus on the relevance of science to everyday lives, its interconnections with the unique cultures of each of the Canadian provinces, and the potential of science to both create problems and work toward their solution.

◆ ◆ ◆ ◆ ◆

OTHER RESOURCES

Government Publications

Many free or inexpensive supplementary materials are obtainable on request from provincial and national government departments related to the environment. Some of these are discussed in Chapter 13, where it is suggested that the best way to find out about them is by writing for information on specific topics. Complete resource lists are available that can lead to a wealth of information for both teachers and students.

Science Trade Books and Magazines

SCIENCE TRADE BOOKS

Another group of print resources that has tremendous potential for children's learning in science consists of science-related children's literature, commonly referred to as "science trade books." These range from descriptive books on an assortment of life science, physical science, and earth/space science and interdisciplinary topics, to science activity books for various levels, and science series built on a succession of topics for a specific age group. Some of the Canadian resources have already been mentioned, such as the *Looking at ...* books, the Kids Can Press material, and the activity books developed by the Ontario Science Centre and the Royal Ontario Museum. Fortunately for children and for school resource centres, there are many, many more.

Annotated Book Lists. To keep up-to-date on new releases, read the annual reviews of "Outstanding Science Trade Books" as well as annotated listings in all editions of *Science and Children*. The American Association for the Advancement of

An exciting variety of Canadian "science trade books" are available to school resource centres.

Science (AAAS) publishes five times yearly *Science Books and Films*, which reviews textbooks, trade books, and audiovisual resources for all levels. The AAAS has also compiled several bibliographies, such as *The Best Science Books for Children* (1983).

There is an abundance of high-quality, well-illustrated children's books on science and science-related topics. Some publishers of textbook-based series are also publishing small books on science and other topics to supplement the programs.

SCIENCE MAGAZINES

Chickadee, for Grades K–4, and *Owl,* for Grades 2–9, are popular children's magazines published by the Young Naturalist Foundation. Others to be found in school resource centres are *Ranger Rick* (1–6) and *Your Big Backyard,* both from the National Wildlife Federation, and *National Geographic World* (National Geographic Society). Another colourful publication for the primary level is *Scienceland,* which focusses on one scientific topic per issue and has an accompanying teacher's guide.

For teachers, a valuable resource is *Science and Children,* a publication of the National Science Teachers Association (NSTA). It is packed with ideas for stimulating and sustaining children's interest in science, and also has features such as "What Research Says," which will help to keep you current on developments in science education at the K–6 level. Another NSTA publication, *Science Scope,* extends the range of teacher resource material to the middle school level.

The Youth Science Foundation and the SEEDS Foundation have each published newsletters that are very informative for both students and teachers, and that contain ideas for activities, games, and projects to enliven the curriculum.

Nonprint Resources

Resources for teaching are not confined to printed materials, of course. Listings of nonprint resources are often found in teachers' guides for specific units, and are available in media and instructional materials centres in your own provinces and at the national level. In 1985, the Council of Ministers of Education, Canada (CMEC), began a project to facilitate the evaluation and selection of educational software for use in Canadian schools. All provinces and the territories were to participate in a review of instructional materials accompanying the software, try out the materials, and evaluate them according to established criteria, such as objectives, pedagogical content, instructional format, and technical design. The importance of such data in helping teachers make wise selections from the educational software that is flooding the market is discussed in Chapter 11.

◆ ◆ ◆ ◆ ◆

LOOKING BACK AND LOOKING FORWARD

Just as the Science Council of Canada study revealed many commonalities in the statements of aims of each of the provinces and territories, your own research has also revealed common threads, as well as some interesting new ways of defining goals, such as the umbrella analogy in the Saskatchewan documents, the student-centred triangular schema proposed by Ontario, and Quebec's summary chart of overall science objectives.

You have looked at curriculum development over a 30-year period, from the reforms of the 1960s to the efforts toward renewal that are underway in the 1990s. The review of curriculum guides, position statements on science education, and the aims and objectives of a variety of elementary science programs has revealed some goals that have remained unchanged and others that have changed in response to new theories of how children learn and to national concerns and societal demands for improvement of science education.

You have seen that the selection of curriculum resources and, ultimately, the selection of learning experiences for children are linked to the expected outcomes for children's learning in science, and to the influences on the curriculum and its organization.

An observer coming into your classroom some day in the future will see all of these underpinnings coming to life, as it were, in the context that you create. Remember that you will be the most important determinant of how successfully theory is interwoven with practice; how well dreams are translated into reality and expected outcomes realized through the experiences provided; and how your classroom will look and sound and feel to the boys and girls who will be your students.

As a teacher, you will have intuitive knowledge about what works best with children, and will be conscious of the need for a variety of resources to help you provide for the diverse needs of your students. The next chapter begins a focus on the broad goal of "science for all children." It emphasizes the importance of the early school years in beginning the realization of that goal by providing for the diverse needs of the children in your care.

CANADIAN ACHIEVEMENTS IN SCIENCE

NEIL BARTLETT (B. 1932)

Historians have documented many chance discoveries in the history of science. For example, Louis Pasteur developed the principle of vaccination from a "chance" event, Wilhelm Röntgen discovered X rays when he accidentally put his hand between a discharge tube and a screen, and Alexander Fleming discovered penicillin when spores entered his laboratory through an open window and fell on a bacterial culture he was working with. Yet these, and many other apparently chance discoveries in science, probably reflect scientists with minds prepared to take advantage of chance events. Neil Bartlett, working at the University of British Columbia in 1962, provides another example.

Bartlett came to Canada from England in 1957 and left nine years later to move to the United States. He is best known for a discovery that achieved the seemingly impossible — the first preparation of a compound between an "inert" gas and another chemical element. Although an element of the accidental was involved, Bartlett was alert and prepared enough to take advantage of this chance.

For 50 years before Bartlett's discovery, the explanation for how chemical elements form compounds was that atoms combine in ways that result in the perfectly stable electron arrangements of the inert gases. Bartlett had no thought of changing this view when he made his chance discovery. He was not even experimenting with inert gases — he was trying to make a new compound between platinum and fluorine. Unexpectedly, some oxygen was present as impurity. This oxygen produced a red powder, which Bartlett showed to be a brand-new chemical compound of platinum, oxygen, and fluorine. This was an exciting discovery, but the real excitement was to follow. Bartlett reasoned, on theoretical grounds, that if this substance could exist then so could a chemical compound between the inert gas xenon and fluorine. Putting his idea to the test, xenon and fluorine were heated together to form a red powder. The red powder was xenon tetrafluoride. Suddenly, the "impossible" was possible, and within a few years a number of additional compounds of the inert gases were produced. It happened first in Canada!

☐ REFERENCES

Aikenhead, G.S. (1980). *Science in social issues: Implications for teaching.* Ottawa: Science Council of Canada.

Alberta (1983). *Elementary Science Curriculum Guide.* Alberta: Alberta Education.

American Association for the Advancement of Science (AAAS) (1983). *The best science books for children.* Washington, DC: AAAS.

————. (1989). *Science for All Americans: A Project 2061 report on literacy goals in science, mathematics and technology.* Washington, DC: AAAS.

————. *Science books and films.* Washington, DC: AAAS.

Bosak, S.V. (1986). *Science is ...* Ottawa: Youth Science Foundation.

Bosak, S.V., D.A. Bosak, and B.A. Puppa (1991). *Science is ...* 2d ed. Richmond Hill, ON: Scholastic Canada; Markham, ON: The Communication Project.

Bourgeois, P. (1987). *The amazing apple book.* Toronto: Kids Can Press.

British Columbia (1987). *Elementary Science Grades 1–7.* British Columbia: Ministry of Education.

————. (1989). *Year 2000: A Curriculum and Assessment Framework for the Future.* Draft. British Columbia: Ministry of Education.

————. (1989–90). *K–12 Clearing House Catalogue for Locally Developed Materials.* 7th ed. British Columbia: Ministry of Education.

————. (1990–91). *Catalogue of Learning Resources: Primary to Graduation.* British Columbia: Ministry of Education.

————. (1992). *Primary through Graduation Curriculum/Assessment Framework: Sciences Strand, Science.* Draft. British Columbia: Ministry of Education.

Brummett, M.R. (1988). *Windows on Science: Management guide.* Sunnyvale, CA: Creative Publications.

Bybee, R.W. (1988). Contemporary elementary school science: The evolution of teachers and teaching. In *This year in school science 1988. Science teaching: Making the system work,* 193–71. Washington, DC: AAAS.

Collier Macmillan Science. Don Mills, ON: Macmillan Canada.

Collins, A. (1989). Elementary school science curricula that have potential to promote scientific literacy (and how to recognize one when you see one). In *This year in school science 1989. Scientific literacy,* 129–55. Washington, DC: AAAS.

Computers in Education. Don Mills, ON: Moorshead Publications.

Couchman, J.H., J.C. MacBean, A. Stecher, and D.F. Wentworth (1971–77). *Examining your environment.* Toronto: Holt, Rinehart and Winston.

Council of Ministers of Education (1985). *Software evaluation: Criteria for educational computer software evaluation.* Toronto: Council of Ministers of Education.

Elementary Science Study (1966–74). Newton, MA: Educational Development Center.

Foodworks: An Ontario Science Centre book (1986). Toronto: Kids Can Press.

Full Option Science System 3–6 (1989). Berkeley, CA: Lawrence Hall of Science.

Gabel, L.L. (1976). The development of a model to determine perceptions of scientific literacy. Ph.D. thesis. Columbus, OH: Ohio State University.

Gough, R.L. (1977). *STEM Science in-service: Manual for workshop leaders.* Don Mills, ON: Addison-Wesley.

Griffin, M., and D. Seed (1989). *The amazing egg book.* Toronto: Kids Can Press.

Harcourt, L., and R. Wortzman (1992). *Explorations in science.* Don Mills, ON: Addison-Wesley.

Harms, N., and S. Kahl et al. (1980). *Project Synthesis final report.* Washington, DC: National Science Foundation.

Hart, E.P. (1987). *Science for Saskatchewan schools: A review of research literature, analysis and recommendations.* Report #6. Saskatchewan: University of Regina, Instructional Development and Research Unit.

Hawkins, D. (1965). Messing about in science. *Science and Children* 2(5):5–9.

International assessment of mathematics and science. IEA science achievement in seventeen countries: A preliminary report (1988). Oxford: Pergamon Press.

Kahl, S., and N. Harms (1981). Project Synthesis: Purpose, organization and procedures. In N.C. Harms and R.E. Yager, eds., *What research says to the science teacher,* vol. 3. Washington, DC: National Science Teachers Association.

Know your world. Teacher's guide (1982). Alberta Educational Communications.

Learning through science (1981–85). London: Macdonald Educational.

Let's find out ... (1992). Toronto: D.C. Heath.

McConnell, V., and L. Whiles (1988). *Rainy days*. Typescript. Vancouver: Vancouver School Board.

Mahung, S. (1980). Evaluating curriculum materials using conceptual analysis. In H. Munby, G. Orpwood, and T. Russell, eds., *Seeing curriculum in a new light: Essays from science education,* 100–110. Toronto: OISE Press.

Manitoba (1991). *Science: Kindergarten, Grades 1–6, Interim Guides*. Manitoba Education and Training.

National Geographic Kids Network Project 4–6 (1989). Cambridge, MA: Technical Education Research Center and National Geographic Society.

National Geographic World. Washington, DC: National Geographic Society.

National Science Board (1983). *Educating Americans for the 21st century*. Washington, DC: National Science Foundation.

National Science Resources Center (1989). *Annual report*. Washington, DC: Smithsonian Institution, National Academy of Sciences.

————. (1990). *Science and technology for children*. Washington, DC: NSRC.

————. (1992). *Science for children: Resources for teachers*. Washington, DC: NSRC.

National Science Teachers Association (1982). A NSTA position statement. *Science-Technology-Society: Science education for the 1980s* (November). Washington, DC: NSTA.

————. *Science and children*. Washington, DC: NSTA.

————. *Science scope*. Washington, DC: NSTA.

National Wildlife Federation. *Ranger Rick*. Washington, DC: National Wildlife Federation.

————. *Your Big Backyard*. Washington, DC: NWF.

New Brunswick (1984). *Elementary Science: A Resource Guide*. New Brunswick: Department of Education.

————. (1992). *Elementary School Science Curriculum Guide: Grades One–Three*. New Brunswick: Department of Education.

Newfoundland and Labrador (1978). *Elementary Science Course Description*. Newfoundland and Labrador: Department of Education.

————. (1988). *Primary Science Curriculum Guide* (1988). Newfoundland and Labrador: Department of Education.

————. (1989). *Elementary Science Curriculum Guide*. Newfoundland and Labrador: Department of Education.

Northwest Territories (1985a). *Elementary Science: Primary Program Guide*. Northwest Territories: Department of Education.

————. (1985b). *Language Development Units Grades 1–3*. Northwest Territories: Department of Education.

————. (1986). *Elementary Science: Intermediate Program Guide*. Northwest Territories: Department of Education.

North York (1983). *North York Science Units*. North York, ON: North York Board of Education, Materials Resource Centre.

Nova Scotia (1988–89, 1989–90). *Public School Programs*. Nova Scotia: Department of Education.

————. (1992). *Proposed Framework for the Elementary Science Program*. Nova Scotia: Department of Education.

Nuffield Junior Science (1963). London: Collins.

Ontario (1986). *Science in Primary and Junior Education: A Statement of Direction*. Ontario Ministry of Education.

————. (1988a). *Science Is Happening Here: A Policy Statement for Science in the Primary and Junior Divisions*. Ontario Ministry of Education.

————. (1988b). *Science-in-a-Box* kits. Ontario Ministry of Education and Ontario Science Centre.

————. (1993). *The Common Curriculum. Grades 1–9*. Working document. Ontario: Ministry of Education and Training.

Ontario Science Centre (1984). *Scienceworks: An Ontario Science Centre book of experiments*. Toronto: Kids Can Press.

Orpwood, G. (1981). Science in the Canadian curriculum. In J.D. Wilson, ed., *Canadian education in the 1980s,* 159–72. Calgary: Detselig.

Owl and *Chickadee*. Des Moines, IA: Young Naturalist Foundation.

Page, J.E. (1979). *A Canadian context for science education*. Ottawa: Science Council of Canada.

Peturson, R., ed. (1990). *Innovations in science: One to six*. Toronto: HBJ-Holt.

Plowden Report (1967). *Children and their primary schools*. A report of the Central Advisory Council for Education. London: Her Majesty's Stationery Office.

Prince Edward Island (1980). *Science Activities in the Elementary School*. Prince Edward Island: Department of Education.

———. (1987). *Science through Expressways: A Teaching Guide*. Prince Edward Island: Department of Education.

Project Wild (1987). *Elementary Activity Guide*. Ottawa: Canadian Wildlife Federation.

Québec (1984). *Elementary School Curriculum: Natural Science*. Québec: Ministère de l'Éducation.

———. (1985). *Natural Science, First Cycle*. Québec: Ministère de l'Éducation.

———. (1986). *Natural Science, Second Cycle*. Québec: Ministère de l'Éducation.

———. (1989). *Practical Guide on the Educational Use of Computers in Elementary School* (1989). Québec: Ministère de l'Éducation.

Roberts, D.A. (1981). Developing the concept of curriculum emphases in science education. Paper presented at the annual meeting of the American Association for the Advancement of Science.

Rockcastle, V.N., B.J. McKnight, F.R. Salamon, and V.E. Schmidt (1976, 1980). *STEM Science*. Don Mills, ON: Addison-Wesley.

———. (1984). *Addison-Wesley science*. Don Mills, ON: Addison-Wesley.

Ross, C., and S. Wallace (1991). *The amazing milk book*. Toronto: Kids Can Press.

Rowe, M.B. (1988). *Self-Help Elementary Level Science (SHELLS)*. Gainesville, FL: Florida State University and Association of Supervision and Curriculum Development.

Rutherford, F.J., et al. (1986). Project 2061: Education for a changing future. In *This Year in school science 1986: The science curriculum*. Washington, DC: AAAS.

Saskatchewan (1989). *Science: Program Overview and Connections (Kindergarten) 1–12*. Draft. Saskatchewan Education.

———. (1990). *Science: A Curriculum Guide for the Elementary Level*. Saskatchewan Education.

Scarborough Board of Education (1990). *Take a closer look at …* series. Scarborough, ON: Scarborough Board of Education.

Schwab, J.J. (1964). Problems, topics and issues. In S. Elam, ed., *Education and the structure of knowledge*. Chicago: Rand McNally.

Science: A Process Approach (SAPA/SAPA II) (1967, 1974). Washington, DC: AAAS.

Science Council of Canada (1984). *Science for every student: Educating Canadians for tomorrow's world*. Report 36. Science Council of Canada.

Science Curriculum Improvement Study (SCIS/SCIS II) (1970–74). Berkeley, CA: Lawrence Hall of Science.

Science 5/13 (1972–79). London: Macdonald Educational.

Science for Life and Living, K–6 (1989). Boulder, CO: Biological Sciences Curriculum Study and Kendall Hunt Publishing.

Science Horizons (1986). West Sussex County Council. London: Macmillan Education.

Science in the National Curriculum (1989). Department of Education and Science and the Welsh Office. London: Her Majesty's Stationery Office.

Scienceland. New York: Scienceland Inc.

SEEDS *Foundation Newsletter* (1990). No. 1. The Energy Literacy Series.

SEEDS: The Energy Literacy Series (1974). Levels 1–6. Society, Environment and Energy Development Foundation.

Shymansky, J.A. (1989). What research says … about ESS, SCIS, and SAPA. *Science and Children* (April):33–35.

Stecher, A., J. Wentworth, J.R. Couchman, and J.C. MacBean (1974). *Examining your environment*. Toronto: Holt, Rinehart and Winston.

Suzuki, D. (1977). Science and society: The missing dialogue. *Perception* 1(1).

Suzuki, D., and B. Hehner (1986). *Looking at insects*. Toronto: Stoddart.

————. (1989). *Looking at the environment*. Toronto: Stoddart.

Symons, T.H. (1975). *To know ourselves*. Report of the Commission on Canadian Studies of Universities and Colleges of Canada. Ottawa.

Western Educational Development Group (1978). WEDGE *Teachers' guides*. University of British Columbia: WEDGE.

Whale Research Group (1984). *Getting along: Fish, whales and fishermen.* The Whale Research Group, Memorial University of Newfoundland. St. John's: Breakwater.

Wilson, J.D., ed. (1981). *Canadian education in the 1980s.* Calgary: Detselig.

PART 3

Science for All Children

■ ■ ■ ■ ■ ■

CHAPTER 10 *The Beginning Years*

CHAPTER 11 *Meeting Individual Needs*

CHAPTER 12 *Teaching Exceptional Children*

The theme of "science for all children" begins with an emphasis on the importance of science education in the early school years and the need to continue child-centred approaches in subsequent years to provide for individual differences among children in interests, abilities, learning styles, and cultural backgrounds. In this way, the stage is set for providing for an even wider spectrum of differences when intellectually, physically, or emotionally challenged children are welcomed into the mainstream. Suggested teaching strategies include a number of models for teaching the gifted and talented.

CHAPTER 10

The Beginning Years

The goal of
SCIENCE FOR ALL CHILDREN
can begin by
extending
**CHILDREN'S
PRESCHOOL SCIENCE**
into
KINDERGARTEN
and the
EARLY SCHOOL YEARS
by building on the spirit and ideas of

FROEBEL	MONTESSORI	PIAGET	BRUNER

to create
A SPECIAL TIME AND PLACE
for

CHILD CENTRED
LEARNING
based on
DEVELOPMENTALLY
APPROPRIATE
PRACTICE

EARLY EXPERIENCES

AN INTEGRATIVE
APPROACH

DEVELOPING BASIC
LEARNING SKILLS
such as
OBSERVING
CLASSIFYING
ORDERING
NUMBER / TIME / SPACE RELATIONS
MOTOR SKILLS
COMMUNICATION SKILLS

and
LEARNING THROUGH PLAY

◆ ◆ ◆ ◆ ◆

We can turn (the primary school years)

into progressive approaches towards science

which will greatly help both the majority

of eventual non-scientists and the minority of

future scientists.

NATHAN ISAACS (1983)

A recurring theme in the writings of those who have been involved with children and science is the importance of early "beginnings." This has been supported by the awareness that children's interest in science and aptitude for science have begun long before they come to school, long before teachers have an opportunity to nurture their students' natural inclinations to explore and discover. This chapter highlights the importance of these beginnings and invites you to experience the excitement and challenge of science with young children.

In Part 2, you considered ways of creating a positive environment for children's learning, and within this setting explored a variety of teaching strategies, evaluative techniques, and curriculum resources that will help you to translate curriculum goals into classroom practice. This chapter begins a new section that emphasizes the importance of the overall goal of *science for all children*.

The goal of "science for all children" includes two major components. One is a commitment to *beginning science early* so that interests will be kindled and attitudes formed that will lead to lifelong learning — to science for life. Support for the need to provide stimulating and satisfying experiences for children in the early grades comes from studies indicating that attitudes formed in the primary school are stable and have an effect on the kinds of subjects students choose to study in later life (Harlen 1987). This research, along with the finding that attitude formation happens earlier for girls than for boys, makes it even more important to begin science early and to make the experience exciting and challenging for children.

The goal of "science for all children" also involves *providing for individual differences* among the children in your classroom. This will be the topic of Chapters 11 and 12, but, because this task permeates the whole of education, it will be one of the themes in this chapter as well. In kindergarten and the primary years, providing for individual differences translates into putting children at the centre of what happens in classrooms and recognizing them from the start as agents of their own learning. Nowhere is the task of providing for uniqueness more challenging or more rewarding than in the early school years. Teachers of young children have always accepted the need to provide for individual differences. Their experience, their observational skills, and their ongoing dialogue with their young students help them to get to know a child's interests, aptitudes, strengths, and weaknesses at a personal, almost intuitive level. The primary teacher's response to the challenge to provide for uniqueness is to ensure that the classroom environment and ways of teaching/learning are truly child-centred, fostering the maximum and continuous development of children in all areas of growth, and continuing the no-risk ways of learning that have characterized the preschool years.

◆ ◆ ◆ ◆ ◆

CHILDREN AS PRESCHOOL SCIENTISTS

Teachers who have worked with very young children have found that science is a logical starting point for learning because it is a natural part of children's lives. Their endless curiosity and fascination with "things," both living and nonliving, have led them to explore every nook and cranny of their surroundings. They have learned before they come to school that wet sand can be shaped; that dry sand is harder to make into piles; that damp snow is better for snowballs; that puddles disappear on a sunny day; that there are different ways of moving things; that things fall off wagons when they are piled too high or pulled too fast; that some stones are rounded and smooth and others are not, depending on where you find them; that flat stones make the best "skimmers"; that there are creatures to be watched in the cracks in the sidewalk, near the edges of houses, in the grass, and in tidal pools by the seashore.

They have learned a great deal about themselves, and some things are puzzling and lead to further questions. They have learned language before they come to school by playing with the world and one another, and by interacting with significant adults in their lives.

As a teacher of young children in those first years of school, you will be one of those "significant adults." You will have the privilege and the challenge of keeping alive children's wondering and their fascination with the world, and of fostering the growth of language by providing them with new ways to learn more about themselves and the phenomena that have captured their interest. You will set up the conditions and provide the experiences that will encourage children to continue their voyage of discovery.

These experiences will not always be called "science," although the processes of science will be there, because these are some of the ways a young child learns. The school environment must encourage children to continue their "play" if they are to continue in school their earlier ways of learning. Choices will be provided within a structure that you have devised, so that expected outcomes are realized for each child, at his or her own pace and according to his or her own abilities and aptitudes.

This chapter is for those of you who will teach children in the early years of school. Some of you will be *kindergarten* teachers; others will teach children in Grades 1, 2, or 3, the levels that are sometimes known as the *primary years* (and, for simplicity, will be referred to here in this way). Table 10.1 indicates that, although there are some differences from province to province in the curriculum arrangements for the early years, the kindergarten year is the first year of school in most provinces in Canada.

TABLE 10.1

Provincial Kindergarten Curriculum Arrangements

Newfoundland and Labrador	Children enter kindergarten at age 5. First year of school.
Nova Scotia	Children enter kindergarten at age 5. Kindergarten referred to as Primary.
Prince Edward Island	School begins in Grade 1. Private kindergartens only. Public funding planned.
New Brunswick	Children enter kindergarten at age 5. First year of school.
Quebec	Kindergarten is part of preschool. School starts in Grade 1.
Ontario	Junior kindergarten for 4-year-olds. Senior kindergarten for 5-year-olds.
Saskatchewan	Children enter kindergarten at age 5. First year of school. *(continued)*

Table 10.1 (continued)

Manitoba	Kindergarten entrance at 5. Kindergarten to Grade 2 curriculum called The Early Years.
Alberta	Kindergarten is preschool level. Considered part of Early Childhood Services.
British Columbia	Kindergarten is Year One of a nongraded integrated K–2 curriculum called The Primary Years.
Northwest Territories and Yukon	Same as British Columbia.

This chapter will focus first of all on the beginning year, and suggest that the qualities that make kindergarten a "special experience" can set the tone for the primary years that follow. A good way to begin to capture the spirit of kindergarten is to examine the history of the founding of the first kindergarten and the thinking of the educators who long ago established guidelines for early childhood education.

activity 10.1 ◆ **A CHILD'S GARDEN**
- ◆ Read the following notes on the views of Froebel, Comenius, Rousseau, and Montessori on childhood and teaching the young child.
- ◆ Compare the views of these early educators with any of the twentieth-century psychologists with whom you are familiar.
- ◆ Compare their views with your own.

◆ ◆ ◆ ◆ ◆

A BRIEF HISTORY OF THE KINDERGARTEN

Froebel's Kindergarten

Although Friedrich Froebel founded the kindergarten in Germany in 1837, the principles on which it was established had been enunciated much earlier in his "educational laws." Through his writings, as translated by Hughes (1897), run the beliefs that were the foundations of practice in the first kindergarten — his respect for childhood, his belief that children should be actively involved in their own learning, and his perception of nature as "the child's universal sphere of greatest interest" (209).

Almost two centuries earlier, John Amos Comenius (1907) had written in a similar vein about how one should go about the study of nature: "Men must, as far as possible, be taught to become wise by studying the heavens, the earth, oaks and beeches ... that is to say, they must learn to know and investigate these things and not the observations that other people have made about them."

The importance of childhood and appreciation for a child's natural activities had also been expressed in the writings of Jean-Jacques Rousseau, who wrote in *Emile* (1911) that "childhood has its own ways of thinking and feeling, and nothing is more foolish than to try to substitute ours for them."

It is interesting in the light of current views on the potential of science experiences for the development of language that Froebel saw nature (the sciences) as "the connecting centre through which the child could be most easily led to study other subjects" (Hughes 1897, 209). In Froebel's kindergarten, storytelling, songs, poems, and discussion were an important part of the program, just as they

Friedrich Froebel believed that storytelling, songs, poems, and discussion were important parts of the kindergarten program. Froebel's ideas are still vital features of kindergarten classes today.

are part of the early childhood programs of today. The teacher's role was to initiate learning by supplying young pupils with manipulative materials to stimulate creative self-activity. Hughes refers many times to Froebel's belief in the uniqueness of each child and the importance of attending to individual needs and encouraging young children to learn how to learn. "Other educators," he writes, "saw the necessity for training the child to act. Froebel saw that the child should be trained to act independently" (201).

Maria Montessori

Other ideas that have found their way into today's early childhood programs came from Italy where Maria Montessori, a doctor and pioneer in education, was awed, as Froebel was, by the strength of the child's inner urge to learn. In her tenement schools in Rome, Montessori emphasized self-activity and self-discipline, with children acquiring competency in eye–hand co-ordination, small muscle control, and practical, everyday life skills through playlike "learning-by-doing" activities (Orem 1974). Among the characteristics that impress a visitor to modern schools and preschools modelled after Montessori is the capacity for organization and independence that is evident even in very young children. In a Montessori school, children know where materials are located for each task. Each day they choose where they would like to begin, pick up the materials, and begin the task on their own, bringing their work to the teacher for checking as needed. Children carefully put back all materials from the previous activity before starting another task, whether it involves working on prereading skills, going to the art centre to put on an apron and begin painting, or using the manipulatives to help with numbers. From time to time, the class comes together for "whole class" activities, such as action songs (perhaps with a visiting music teacher), or a relaxed get-together in groups with the teacher or for snack or lunch breaks. But, in keeping with Montessori's belief that "the best teachers of children are children themselves" (Orem 1974, 25), the larger part of the day finds the children working on their own, with a great degree of choice in the order in which they do things. There is a climate of "busyness," but there is no chaos, and there is a great sense that children thrive on and enjoy this independence.

A common thread that runs through the writings of these educators of the past — Comenius, Rousseau, Froebel, and Montessori — is their respect for children and all they are capable of learning. Theory and practice are interwoven throughout their writings, with practical suggestions to teachers on how to stimulate children's interests through sensory experiences and the study of nature; on how to stand back and listen and facilitate rather than be too directive; and on how to allow children to become actively involved in their own learning.

❑ Reflecting and Sharing

You probably recognized the similarities in Froebel's philosophy and what Piagetian and neo-Piagetian research has revealed about how children learn — through developmentally appropriate activities, with opportunities to construct their own knowledge from raw experience. Piaget's goal for education, as cited by Duckworth (1970) was "not to increase the amount of knowledge, but to create the possibilities for a child to invent and discover" (137). Think back to Bruner and what he says about the intrinsic rewards that come from the act of discovery, or think back to Dewey and his emphasis on a rich environment in which children learn by doing. The terms change, with the literature of today referring to facilitative environments, constructivist views of learning, open education, developmentally appropriate practice, and learning through play. But all of these, like the tenets expressed in Froebel's educational laws, place the child at the centre of what happens in classrooms and can be included under the concept of *child-centredness*. Child-centred instruction seems singularly appropriate in kindergarten, where the name sets the tone for a place that is truly a child's garden, with all that this implies for planting, nurturing, blossoming, and the promise of fruitful growth.

As a kindergarten teacher, you will need to plan experiences for all children that

◆ are developmentally appropriate,
◆ continue an integrative, holistic approach to learning, and
◆ recognize the importance of learning through play.

Your role will be that of a participant observer as children practise and refine the skills that are prerequisite to all learning, and a facilitator of learning as children begin developing concepts and attitudes that will help them make the transition into the intermediate grades and begin the task of lifelong learning. It is a process in which children are actively involved as they construct their own knowledge. It is a process they would have difficulty managing without your help. It is a process that can be infinitely better because of your input, feedback, and guidance.

◆ ◆ ◆ ◆ ◆

SETTING THE TONE: THE BEGINNING YEARS

Ideally, the environment and activities provided in the early school years must:

◆ provide in the beginning years a *special experience,* extending the spirit of preschool learning into the kindergarten and primary grades;

- be truly *child-centred,* promoting activity-based learning and encouraging children to pursue interests and make choices;
- *develop basic skills,* which are prerequisite to all of learning;
- continue the *playful, playlike* ways of preschool learning; and
- encourage an *integrative approach* to teaching/learning.

◆ ◆ ◆ ◆ ◆

KINDERGARTEN: A SPECIAL EXPERIENCE

Envision a kindergarten classroom you have visited. Maybe you have memories of your own kindergarten. Memories of schooldays are often rather erratic — some good ones, some bad. Why is it that even though kindergarten was the earliest school experience it is often the one that can be brought to mind? Among the remembered images there may be general impressions of colour and sound; of children's drawings pasted on walls; of books with large printing; of games and singing, blocks, a sand play area with scoops and containers; of other children; and of a teacher's face — a special place indeed, with special experiences to remember.

Those of you who will one day be kindergarten teachers may be already planning experiences for children that will also build memories. Think for a while of what you will do to make these memories special, how you will get to know each child, how you will allow for individual variations in the depth and pace of the learning experiences. Imagine how your classroom will look, the centres that will be set up, the equipment and materials that may be there, the kinds of activities that are likely to be in progress, and what the children may be doing — alone, in pairs, in small groups, with or without you nearby.

To individualize learning in the kindergarten is to centre on the child, his or her needs and interests, his or her ways of learning. The teacher becomes a partner in that learning, and accordingly a partner in the explorations that develop skills and concepts and attitudes. By becoming a partner, the teacher learns more about what it is to discover new things, and more about the cognitive, psychomotor, and affective possibilities in each new experience.

Your role in starting children on the journey toward "science for life" is an important one indeed. The attitudes and interests you encourage, the opportunities you provide for children to make decisions about their own learning, and the enthusiasm for science that you model in your teaching will all have a profound impact on the course of this journey.

From a Teacher's Journal

The kindergarten classroom should be an extension of children's preschool explorations, with lots of things to feel, listen to, look at, smell, taste, explore, and discuss. It is also a place where children are given practice in pre-math and pre-reading skills that are needed for success in later grades. Development in language arts is enhanced as children discuss and record their observations. Development of pre-math skills is enhanced through sorting and classifying, as well as through graphing various things, such as birthdays, eye colour, number and kinds of pets, types of leaves, and so on.

Teaching in kindergarten means setting up conditions for children to explore things that have scientific principles built into them. Much of this occurs through play with multi-links, wooden blocks, water, and sand. Opportunities to observe and discuss occur also when children are encouraged to bring their pets to class, and to share shell, leaf, and rock collections by displaying them in the science centre.

Joyce Crim

St. John's, NF

◆ ◆ ◆ ◆ ◆

CHILD-CENTRED INSTRUCTION

What are the characteristics of child-centred instruction? You will find them in many of the curriculum documents published by ministries of education, and also in reports compiled by associations or committees of experienced and insightful early childhood educators. But first, reflect on your own ideas about a child-centred classroom.

---

activity **10.2** **CHILD-CENTREDNESS: WHAT IS IT?**

Have a brainstorming session within your group to consider the following questions:

◆ What are your ideas of what a child-centred approach to education involves? Jot them down and keep them until the end of the chapter.

◆ What would you see if you entered a child-centred classroom? Again, save your description until the end of the chapter.

NAEYC **Guidelines**

The National Association for the Education of Young Children (NAEYC 1986) suggests that, to be child-centred, instruction must be *developmentally appropriate*. The NAEYC recommendations for developmentally appropriate practice in the early years of school were derived from a review of work published by early childhood professionals. These recommendations, many of which parallel those found in provincial curriculum guides, emphasize the importance of designing curricula, classroom environments, and ways of teaching and learning that are responsive to the differing learning and developmental needs of young children.

DEVELOPMENTALLY APPROPRIATE PRACTICE

The phrase "developmentally appropriate" takes into consideration the natural order of development posed by Piagetian theory (*age appropriateness*) and also recognizes that each child brings to a learning situation a unique personality, level of functioning, and experiential background (*individual appropriateness*). To take these two dimensions into account in the classroom and to create the kind of atmosphere in which curiosity and creativity will thrive, teachers need to adopt practices that are child-centred (in the sense of being based on the needs and interests of the child), such as active involvement of children in their own learning, a continuation of the integrative approach to learning that has been characteristic of their preschool years, and learning through play. Examples of "appropriate practice" from the NAEYC criteria are:

◆ A curriculum designed to develop children's knowledge and skills in all developmental areas — physical, social, emotional, and intellectual — and to help children to establish a foundation for lifelong learning by learning how to learn.

◆ Learning occurring primarily through integrated learning in learning centres, and through projects and playful activities that reflect children's interests and challenge their thinking.

◆ Incorporation of multicultural and nonsexist activities to encourage respectful acceptance and appreciation of differences and similarities.

◆ Parent involvement as partners with teachers in home–school learning experiences.

◆ Generous amounts of time to develop language and literacy skills, improving the ability to communicate orally and to read and write about activities in all areas.

◆ Discovery science, in class and outdoors, comprising a major part of the curriculum, building on children's natural drive to make sense of the world.

FROM GUIDELINES TO PRACTICE

The Role of the Teacher. The NAEYC guidelines, in common with most curriculum guidelines for early childhood education, reflect the role of the teacher as an active participant in children's learning. Only by participating actively in the discovery experiences and thinking them through can a teacher anticipate children's questions, be ready to give help as it is needed, and encourage further explorations.

The Role of Science. The NAEYC guidelines suggest that science, because of its high intrinsic interest and its potential for providing the concrete experiences so appropriate for this level and for involving children actively in their own learning, should comprise a major part of the curriculum for young children.

Integrative Learning. Fortunately, the high intrinsic interest of science and its relevance to the lives of children, as well as its meaningful experience base, all make it an excellent starting point for integrative learning. In this way science can be a major part of the curriculum while at the same time enhancing the development of language and initiating and enhancing learning in other important areas. The skills, concepts, and attitudes developed in this way would also have an enhancing effect on children's growth in science-related outcomes.

Basic Skills. It is important that there should still be times when children sort buttons for the sake of sorting, measure for the joy of measuring, race toy cars to find out about energy in a tightened spring. There should be times when each child makes a "touch and feel" book with a different texture on each page, for the sake of gaining knowledge about a property that can then be applied to the way leaves are different — from each other, or on the top as opposed to the underside.

These skills, which you recognize as science processes, should be a major part of the kindergarten curriculum, and practice of these skills should continue through the years that follow.

Developing Basic Learning Skills

The development of basic skills can be considered a primary function of the early years of science education, or of any area of education. Such skills are transferable to the whole of learning, and children acquire additional practice of these processes in the context of the thematic approach to learning, which is popular in the early years.

IDEAS FROM SCIS: BEGINNINGS

The Science Curriculum Improvement Study (SCIS) materials recognize the potential in starting points in science for interdisciplinary inquiry and enhancement of other areas of the early childhood curriculum. The teacher's guide for "Beginnings" (1974), the kindergarten module, suggests that activities should be selected according to the individual needs of the children, and that the activities should be used as a basis for stories, art activities, and other group projects that encourage language usage.

The focus in "Beginnings" is described in the program overview in the teacher's guide:

> In Beginnings, children observe and describe a wide variety of objects and organisms in the classroom and outdoors. Through suggested games, puzzles, and other activities, you help develop the children's ability to describe and compare objects by their color, shape, size, texture, odor and sound. Ideas of number and volume are introduced in simple activities such as weighing objects, counting beads, and measuring quantities of water. Changes that occur over time are considered in a unit on organisms, where the children work with seeds, seedlings and plants. The children are introduced to spatial relationships when they describe the positions of objects in relation to other objects and when they reproduce printed patterns. The experiences in this unit contribute to the development of language and a growing understanding of science concepts (14).

Part of the rationale for the development of this unit was to give children experience and practice with processes and skills that are necessary, as they continue the science program.

Embedded in all of the curriculum materials discussed in this chapter are ways of learning that are natural to children and at the same time basically scientific. This is not surprising, because science is everywhere in a young child's world and the methods of science are the child's way of exploring it. From the beginning, children have been using all of their senses to discover the world — observing how things taste, smell, look, sound, and feel — and it is very important that these explorations continue. Observing is a vital aspect of science. Observations lead to discovering the properties of objects, and properties of objects are a basis for *grouping, comparing,* and *ordering* things and *finding patterns.* Other essential basic skills include *developing number, time, and space relations,* all of which are prerequisites to subsequent learning. Whatever the activity, there will be opportunities for *developing communication skills,* as children talk about their discoveries and the teacher records their words on experience charts or adds their drawings to the science centre. The development of other basic skills such as *eye–hand co-ordination* and the development of *fine* and *gross motor skills* are natural outcomes of activities where there are materials and equipment to use and objects to manipulate in various ways.

Let's begin by thinking of exciting ways to involve young children in sensory observations, and afterward work through some experiences that will develop other basic skills. Imagine that you are children and learners again as you participate in groups on some of the following activities.

activity 10.3 OBSERVING: FUN WITH THE FIVE SENSES

Think for a moment of how you could initiate explorations of the senses — sight, smell, touch, sound, and taste. It would be most effective if small groups concentrated on one of these senses and later pooled ideas, leaving time at the end for everyone to work on a sixth sense — the kinesthetic sense, which has to do with body awareness, with movement and balance in space.

◆ Materials for such an assignment are readily available at home, in the classroom, and out of doors. Use your ingenuity and see how many learning centre or whole-class activities you can prepare for the next class. Five stations will be set up, each based on one of the five senses, and groups will rotate to each station and try some of the activities.

◆ As you finish, focus for a while on the sixth sense — the kinesthetic sense. Ponder the meaning of the word, relate it to children, and think of some possibilities for associated activities.

◆ Finally, think of at least one activity that involves five (or even six) senses, and be ready to share your ideas.

❑ Reflecting and Sharing

Vision is usually the faculty associated with observing, a fact that is readily demonstrated when students in later grades have their first experience with writing as many observations as they can about a burning candle. Most observations describe only properties that are observed with the eyes — the colour of the candle, its cylindrical shape, the colours in the flame, the appearance of the wick at various stages, and so on. The list grows once other senses are brought into awareness — tactile observations such as the smoothness of the candle and the warmth from the flame; various olfactory sensations during the burning, the absence of sound, the taste of the wax (if such an observation is allowed).

When observations with all the senses are encouraged, children do in school what they've been doing all their lives when they have encountered new things. Children are intrigued not only by how things look but also by the kinds of noises that can be made with them, the way some materials feel to the touch, the smells and tastes of things. Language grows as they try to put into words the messages that are coming to them through their senses, as they contrast rough and smooth things, dark and light things, sweet and sour things, sweet-smelling and not-so-sweet-smelling things. The capacity to recognize and distinguish objects by their properties also grows, and becomes the basis for a number of other important skills.

How did you make out with your explorations with each of the five senses? Check your list against some of the suggestions below.

SEEING THINGS

◆ Activities could focus on eyes by looking at the eye colours of the children in the class, and, with the help of the teacher, by making a pictogram to communicate the results.
◆ Set up a tray of objects of interest to young children, and pass it around. Cover it with a cloth and have children draw the things they remember.
◆ Find spectra or "rainbows" in bubbles, or in crystals hanging in windows. Use paints to reproduce the colours.
◆ Look at an insect through the lens in the cover of a viewing box. Have children draw what they see.
◆ Be a window watcher. Draw what can be seen in the daytime sky. Look at the nighttime sky at home. Draw the Big Dipper.
◆ Go on a colour hike. Find as many different colours as you can.
◆ Make primary colours of water and food colouring. Mix to make new colours.

TOUCHING THINGS

Children "see" through their fingers. They love to experience the way animals feel in a touch tank, to stroke different fabrics, to identify and describe differently shaped blocks in a touch bag.

◆ Go on a "texture walk." Mount on cardboard interesting finds and make a "Touch Me" collage on the bulletin board.

◆ Ask children to bring from home an object in a paper bag, and then to trade with another child and play a game, guessing by touch alone what objects are inside.

◆ Children can make a "touch and feel" book in the shape of a hand, with materials of different textures pasted on the pages. They feel the materials and describe the textures.

◆ Make a "foot-feely" box with a slanted platform inside on which bare feet can experience the "feel" of different materials.

◆ Add sand, rice, or other granular materials to fingerpaint so that children can perceive the differences with their fingertips.

Children love to touch things. Adding various textured materials to fingerpaint allows children to experience the differences with their hands and, in this case, their feet.

HEARING THINGS

◆ Make "shake cans" by filling numbered film cans with rice, sand, and other materials. Check a list of numbers and samples to see whether the inferences about the contents were correct. Have students match pairs with like sounds.

◆ Go on a listening walk. Remember the sounds to talk about later.

◆ Distinguish between loud and soft sounds, high and low sounds, and sounds made by different rhythm band instruments.

◆ Tape-record household sounds and have children listen and identify the sound, e.g., the toaster popping, the vacuum running.

◆ Be really quiet and listen for quiet sounds, e.g., a clock ticking, fluorescent lights humming, an air conditioner.

◆ Make a collection of words that describe sounds — thump, whoosh, etc.

◆ Tape-record children's voices and play them back. This adds motivation and a feeling of importance as one's voice is recognized.

SMELLING THINGS

◆ Make a collection of "mystery jars," using distinctive smells like coffee, peppermint extract, a piece of orange, peanut butter, a garlic clove, cinnamon. Have children guess what's inside.

◆ Sort the smells into two groups — pleasant and unpleasant.

◆ Open a bottle of perfume and time how long it takes for the aroma to reach the other side of the room.

◆ Identify cooking smells in the school cafeteria.

TASTING THINGS

◆ Prepare a tray of food, with mixed fruit and raw vegetables cut in bite-sized pieces. Have children paste pictures of the food in a "tasting party" book and, as you visit the children, help them to associate the description with the taste by adding to each page a word that describes the taste — sweet, sour, spicy, etc.

◆ With eyes closed and nose held, have the children taste pieces of crunchy food, such as cubes of raw potato, turnip, pear, apple, and water chestnut. Have them try to identify the taste.

◆ In class, make butter with whipping cream. When the butter begins to separate, add salt and cold water and have children take turns shaking and passing the jar to the next person to shake as they sing this song:

Come, butter, come!

Come, butter, come!

(Child's name) is waiting at the gate,
Waiting for his butter cake
Come, butter, come!
(Alternatively, provide a small plastic bottle for each child to shake, with several tablespoons of cream in each.)

When the butter has been made, pour off the buttermilk, add a little salt to the pat of butter, and serve on crackers.
(Safety note: Tasting is *only* with the teacher's permission. Another safety precaution has to do with smells, which should always be "wafted" toward the nose rather than sniffed directly.)

ONE MORE — THE KINESTHETIC SENSE

Physical education teachers are aware of the kinesthetic sense, since it involves movement, body awareness, starting and stopping in space, developing balance in space, and exploring space.

- After introducing animals into an aquarium — turtles, a toad, a frog, and a salamander — the children are invited to imitate their movement.
- Children develop a sense of balance in space by imitating a car rounding a curve.
- Have the children pretend to be a plane taking off at an airport.

MIXING AND COMBINING THE SENSES

Children love to mix the senses. The caterpillar "looks soft" and has a "warm, furry smell."

And you may like to combine all of them in a cooking activity that includes tastes and smells, textures and appearance. In the activity that follows, you'll add sound as well, and a great deal of enthusiasm and excitement!

activity 10.4 — A MULTISENSORY ACTIVITY

Making popcorn in class is a multisensory experience that, like the butter-making, involves the concept of change and also provides opportunities for observing with all the senses.

How would you organize such an activity in a kindergarten class to enhance all possible outcomes for learning?

❏ Reflecting and Sharing

The five senses — perhaps even six — are brought into play in this extremely popular activity. Sight and touch are involved as children observe the corn kernels before and after popping, and note the differences. Smell and hearing are there in the tantalizing, familiar odour and in the beginning and accelerating pace of the popping sounds. The tasting is the high point, of course, as is the transformation of the texture from the smooth, brittle kernel to the rough, fluffy, uneven surface of the popcorn.

The kinesthetic sense? At a time when children have been sitting for too long, a trip to the gym and being invited to pretend they are corn kernels popping in an enclosed space might be just what is needed to work up an appetite for the popcorn treat.

Developing Other Basic Learning Skills

Early childhood is the time when the child constructs operational logic from experiences in observing and labelling the attributes of things (*observing*); sorting and matching on the basis of differences and similarities (*classifying*); comparing things and ordering them according to certain attributes (*seriation*); comparing numbers, comparing sets, and counting objects (*developing number concepts*); developing a sense of time, ordering events, comparing time periods, and observing seasonal change (*developing time relations*); and in observing positions of things in relation to each other, developing body awareness and part–whole relationships (*developing space relations*). Built into many of the activites are many opportunities for enhancing *communication skills,* as children describe in precise language the results of their observations and experiences. The more actively they are involved the more likely they are also to develop *eye–hand co-ordination,* as well as *fine* and *gross motor skills.* Using viewing boxes to look at insects, planting seeds, pouring sand and water through sieves and funnels, making a "touch and feel" book, and sorting buttons are all excellent opportunities for developing fine and gross motor skills. It is easy to think of activities associated with forces and motion, measurement, and so on that develop gross motor skills. Examples are demonstrating concepts such as push/pull or roll/slide on tumbling mats from the gymnasium; measuring the length of a broad jump; and playing shadow tag on the school playground.

- - - - - - - - - - - - - - - -

activity 10.5 DEVELOPING BASIC SKILLS

One or two activities are suggested here to help children develop each of these basic skills. See how many others you can add.

CLASSIFYING

Children arrange and group objects from nature, such as shells, leaves, cones, or seeds, and describe the basis for placing objects in a certain group.

SERIATION

Children order from rough to smooth a collection of swatches in a textures collection.

NUMBER CONCEPTS

Measuring: Measure with string the distances children can jump. Have them take the strings home to show their parents.

One-to-One Correspondence: Make garages from boxes, with a numeral on the roof of each. Paste dots with numerals on toy cars. Have children match cars with garages.

TIME RELATIONS

Sequencing of Time: Supply a long strip of paper and a number of cartoon-like sketches of children involved in events that happen in a typical day. Have children "draw their own day" as they select from the pictured scenes and make murals depicting the order in which things happen, from the time that they get up in the morning until the time they go to bed.

SPACE RELATIONS

Shapes: Make a shape book by pasting illustrations on each page, for example, a spherical balloon, a crescent moon. Have children, with your help, draw animals made of triangles, rectangles, circles, and squares. Look for symmetry in birds, butterflies, and their own bodies.

Direction of Movement: Create an obstacle course with signs for a child to follow to complete the course, such as over, into, toward, on top of, away from, and so forth.

COMMUNICATION SKILLS

Play "What Am I?" Encourage a child to pretend to be an animal and to describe accurately the animal's characteristics so that other children can guess what the animal is.

Draw a histogram showing number and kinds of leaves collected on a field trip.

MOTOR SKILLS AND EYE–HAND CO-ORDINATION

Many of the activities described so far, and those you have created on your own, have the potential for gross motor co-ordination (those that increase the proficiency of the large muscles). A well-known adage is that "children learn on their feet, not on their seat." Activities that involve sand and water play, building structures, playing with blocks, and moving things build gross motor co-ordination and frequently provide practice with fine motor co-ordination as well. Think of some of the sensory activities, where observing is extended by using hand lenses, manipulating smell jars and sound boxes, and making leaf prints, and you will quickly see the potential for enhancing fine motor and eye–hand co-ordination skills as well.

❏ Reflecting and Sharing

A developmentally valid early childhood curriculum includes all these skills, either as important aspects of an integrated unit, or just for the sake of developing and refining competencies that children need to develop for reading, mathematics, social studies, science, art ... and living. Your role as a teacher will be that of a

Activities such as building structures develop gross motor co-ordination.
This child is also enhancing eye–hand co-ordination.

supporter of development as children construct learning through active, concrete experiences that engage the senses and the motoric system, and begin the development of understandings.

You'll provide materials and an environment in which the initial discoveries will be made as children play with the materials. You'll provide long blocks of time and diverse opportunities for the explorations to continue and skills to be practised. In the context of play, the needed vocabulary will be developed. With your guidance and with improvement in motor co-ordination, practice play will give way to the constructive play that is common among young children.

◆ ◆ ◆ ◆ ◆

LEARNING THROUGH PLAY

Play is not the only way of learning in the primary years. There will be other, more structured, teacher-directed activities as well. But play will permeate aspects of whatever experiences are set up for children, because children, when free to do so, will approach learning in an atmosphere of fun and enjoyment, especially when enthusiasm for learning is modelled for them by the teacher.

In Chapter 7, play is discussed in the context of motivating beginnings, as an introductory "messing about" phase of learning in science. In kindergarten and the primary grades, it is more than this. Play is the "work" of young children. It is their way of learning and, according to Piaget, serves an assimilative function, allowing children to consolidate their experiences. Bruner (1972) sees an important function of play in minimizing the consequences of one's actions and therefore encouraging more risk taking, so that children try new things during play that would never have been tried otherwise. Positive attitudes to science are formed in an accepting atmosphere where children learn for themselves without fear of frustration or failure.

With teacher guidance and just the right amount of intervention, "ordinary" play becomes "educational" play. For this reason, the materials chosen for children's play should be rich with potential for learning. Many of them have been mentioned already — sandboxes with containers of various sizes; basins of water with floaters and sinkers; blocks and boxes for building stuctures; clay for shaping; collections of stones and shells; and magnets, mirrors, and magnifiers. Science is everywhere in a young child's world — science and air, science and water, science and soils, science and food, science and plants, science and animals, and the materials for play and for learning can come from all of these.

CHILDREN'S PLAY

Think about the learning opportunities for science, math, language development, and other areas in the following play experiences, some of which are suggested by Henniger (1987).

1. Children in the sandbox are filling and emptying containers, pouring from one to the other. One child is counting the number of spoonfuls of sand required to fill a container. Two are building a sand castle and are experiencing difficulty with collapsing walls. Finally they succeed, with a combination of sand and water, in making a durable wall.

2. A teacher and three children are digging in a garden plot in preparation for seed planting. They discover two fat earthworms. They find plants from last year's garden and remove the seeds.

3. Two children are using colourful plastic building blocks to construct a fort. They select blocks of different lengths and shapes to use for walls. The children return the blocks to the play area at the end of the activity.

4. Two children are lying on the grass, staring at the sky. They talk about the "funny shapes" they see.

5. Back inside, the children are making flavoured gelatin, and each child has a small bowl of the cooled liquid. The teacher has cut up canned pineapple, bananas, melon, strawberries, walnuts, and minimarshmallows to stir into the liquid Jello. Some pieces are floating, some are sinking. Children are wondering why. The bowls of gelatin, with name labels attached, are put into the refrigerator to set for snack time.

6. It is obvious from looking around the classroom that the class has had a "Share a Pet" week. The science centre contains fish, a gerbil, rabbits, and a cat. The book centre has several books and a video on pet care.

❑ Reflecting and Sharing

1. As children fill, empty, and pour, they are gaining experience in volume relationships. By counting spoonfuls, they are developing number concepts. Problem-solving skills important in science and math are developed in the sand play. And did you think of the potential for language development?

2. Finding the earthworms is an opportunity for observing and finding out about the life cycle of worms and the importance of worms in the soil. Seeds can be sorted and root systems can be examined to show how nutrients and water enter the plant. Sculpturing the root systems or germinating the seeds in a Ziploc bag of soil could be follow-up activities.

3. Children place blocks and compare lengths. (Two half-sized blocks can cover one long block.) They classify blocks by shape when returning them to the storage area.

4. In this activity, there is the opportunity to observe, to compare with other known objects, to imagine and create, and to communicate with each other and share impressions.

5. The children explore sinking and floating again, as well as the beginning concepts of diffusion, viscosity, change of state, density, and buoyancy, all of which will be understood much later in their school experience. At this stage, interest and curiosity may lead to experimentation to see if the results would be the same in water. Sensory experiences include taste, smell, sight, and touch.

6. Children extend the concept of "animal," learning about needs and caregiving, and seeking information to find out more.

Materials for Children's Play

Laser Goldberg (1970) suggests that the materials offered for children's play should

◆ be interesting to the child;
◆ have significant ideas built into them; and
◆ foster real solutions, i.e., the child's own solutions" (70).

Primitive materials such as sand, water, clay, blocks, and soap bubbles attract young children and stimulate creativity and inventiveness. Think first of the possibilities in sand play.

SAND PLAY

Usually there is a sand table, but if there isn't use plastic dishpans with beach sand, which will allow you to have two groups working at sandplay centres, or at times a child who wants to work alone. Stored near the centre are pails; spoons; containers of many sizes, shapes, and volumes; sieves and funnels. Only a few containers should be brought out at first so as not to confuse or overwhelm children with too great a variety of things to do. Work initially with dry sand, encouraging the children to describe what they are doing as they fill their containers. As words come up, they are printed on a large chart, along with sketches to illustrate what the words mean — big, small, deep, shallow, full, empty, few, many, straight, curved.

The children count the number of medicine cups it takes to fill the small jug, then the large jug. The list grows as comparisons are made — bigger, biggest; small, smaller than — and as wet sand is used to explore shapes, and a child has to select the containers to make a succession of three sandpies, from small to large.

Time concepts enter the conversation as sieves and funnels are used to pour sand through, and the timing begins, perhaps by counting aloud to see whether a scoopful of sand takes longer to go through the small funnel than the large one. It may be difficult to pour and count at the same time — maybe a partner would help.

The play goes on if appropriate materials are there to invite further exploration. Does bigger also mean heavier? A balance will help with that problem, and also invite a child to discover which is heavier — a cupful of dry sand or a cupful of wet sand. If the two lots of sand are left on the balance for a day or so, another surprise may be in store for children. Why is the balance now balanced? Why did the sand dry out? Where did the water go? And the play continues, opening new vistas to be explored through the science experiences in the school years that follow this important year of beginnings.

WATER PLAY

Water play is even more fascinating to young children. Again, the basin is there, or a baby's bath, and the same assortment of containers of different sizes and shapes, with some of equal volume. Add egg beaters, ladles, lengths of tubing, basters, and lots of newspapers to catch spills and aprons to protect clothing. Again, introduce just a few things to begin with, recognizing some order in which discoveries will be made and the need to intervene occasionally, but not too often. With the play will grow understanding of the properties of water, that it pours; takes the shape of its container; runs off some surfaces and is absorbed by others; is wet, cold, and slippery.

Later there will be floaters and sinkers, water drop races, bubble blowing with the soap/glycerine/water recipe that has been made up and placed in the centre beforehand, along with wire rings and pipe cleaners shaped into a square. Can bubbles be square?

A bulletin board at child's eye level is proclaiming the discoveries. "Things That Sink" and "Things That Float" are grouped on the table, along with the latest addition to the "Not Sure" items. And the play continues.

Now it's your turn, as another topic is suggested that can initiate children's play and encourage the development of skills and the building of concepts.

activity 10.7 STRUCTURES

Think of ways that children's play can lead to learning as they begin to build structures. If you like, start with primitive materials — materials that can be shaped and moulded or fastened together — or use your imagination and think of recyclable materials that may be combined in various ways into structures as children play.

☐ Reflecting and Sharing

Whether the initiating activity for a theme is a child's gift (a shell from a treasured collection or a caterpillar discovered on the way to school) or a topic chosen by the teacher for its great potential for integrating a number of subject areas, the outcomes for children's learning are substantial. When the integrative process also brings together the child's intellect, emotions, and inner drive through high-quality play experiences, the gains for children are even more substantial.

The British Columbia *Kindergarten Curriculum Guide and Resource Book* (1985) expresses this well:

> Play is the fundamental, natural, universal activity of children. Play is what children do, what they have always done, and what they must continue to do. Play is intrinsically motivated for personal satisfaction and a way of learning. It is the expressive activity from the child's desire to make sense of the world (61).

> The child's desire to make sense of the world and the teacher's respect for childhood and willingness to encourage and facilitate the wondering, searching, and exploring are the key factors in the success of science experiences in the early years. The child, in saying "I want to know," expresses a need and simultaneously an awareness that an adult can help by supplying the feedback that will enable her to go about her learning. When this happens in an atmosphere in which work and play are indistinguishable, the kindergarten classroom is indeed a special place.

An Integrative Approach

The development of basic skills begun in kindergarten will continue throughout the primary years, with children experiencing increasing confidence in their ability to use these skills to learn on their own. Similarly, the "learning through play" emphasis will certainly not end in kindergarten but will permeate the primary and intermediate years, because of its intrinsically motivating quality and its affinity with both the way children learn and the nature of science. Both basic skills and playfulness will be necessary prerequisites to successful involvement in the integrative approaches to learning recommended for the primary grades.

Recall that the NAEYC guidelines suggest that child-centred curriculum and instruction must be designed to suit the way young children learn, and emphasize that the way young children learn is not through discrete subject areas but in a way that sees knowledge as a nonfragmented whole. To translate these beliefs into practice the guidelines advocate an integrative approach to teaching/learning in the primary grades. In keeping with this approach, the curriculum would be based on a number of themes, chosen for their interest to children, that have potential for integrating most areas of learning.

IDEAS FROM SCIENCE 5/13: EARLY EXPERIENCES

Borrow from the library the *Science 5/13* module "Early Experiences." This program is based on a conception of science as a child's asking questions of the world. The aim of the teachers' guides is to help teachers to make use of what is likely to

---

From a Teacher's Journal

The kindergarten classroom is a busy, active environment, with many areas/centres for learning that children are encouraged to use, individually or in pairs or groups. There is a book/reading/language centre; a science centre with story and picture books, a felt board, a seed-planting area; plants; animals, such as guinea pig, hamster, bird, fish, turtle, newt; magnifying area; magnet centre; scales; water and sand table; a playhouse/doll area; a building/construction area with Lego and other blocks; a listening centre with record player and tape player; a sensory discrimination centre; a toy area; a gross motor area with a slide for climbing, riding toys, and a teeter-totter; a fine motor centre with puzzles and peg game; an art centre with a craft table and easels; a display centre for children's work. The room is decorated to be aesthetically pleasing and stimulating, with activities at each centre changing weekly and as themes are developed.

(continued)

✍️ **From a Teacher's Journal (continued)**

Kindergarten science in integrated in all areas of the kindergarten program — through science storybooks and chart experience storymaking, picture-card science activities (pre-reading); through measuring, pouring, sorting, counting (pre-math); through cutting and pasting story-sequence cards (e.g., planting a seed, nest building by a bird, star patterns, eye–hand co-ordination); through climbing (e.g., trees), physical exercises, simulating animals and flowers, snow angels, footprints in snow (gross motor co-ordination); and craft-making, e.g., paper-tearing leaves, making seed pictures (fine motor co-ordination).

Doreen Collins

Toronto, ON

be found in a school environment and to reveal its possibilities as material for investigation. Inviting topics such as "Sunny Day Things," "Doing Things," "Listening to Things," "Comparing Things," and "Looking After Things," complete with reproductions of the children's records in drawings, bar graphs, poems, and narrative descriptions, may suggest many starting points you may like to try out during your student teaching or in class with members of your group. The small sample below, reproduced in Figure 10.1, gives a brief glimpse into how a unit on "Rainy Day Things" was developed, and may encourage you to browse further in the teacher's guide as you work through the next activity.

activity 10.8 **FROM PRINCIPLES TO PRACTICE**

Browse through the "Early Experiences" unit for teachers, and use the children's experiences in any of the units as a basis for discussion of the following questions:

◆ Are opportunities provided in this unit for children to practise science process skills and to develop science concepts? Think of examples to support your answer.

- Do the experiences fit into the integrative approach to learning espoused by the NAEYC?
- In your opinion, can the two approaches be successfully combined?

❑ Reflecting and Sharing

You probably came to the conclusion, as you thought through this problem and browsed through the teacher's guide, that both approaches are possible in the primary years, that they can be either separate or combined. Whatever the starting point, the spinoff for all domains — cognitive, affective, psychomotor, social — and for all areas of the curriculum will be significant.

FIGURE 10.1

Rainy Day Things

Wet things

Wet materials

Begin by wetting fabrics. Try gaberdine, PVC, leather, linen, nylon, cotton, and so on. What words can children find to describe these fabrics when dry and when wet?

Words like absorbent, waterproof, soggy, and so on will probably fit well into this context. Make a list of fabrics that will absorb water easily and another list of those that will not. Which fabrics will let water through?

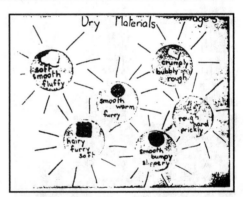

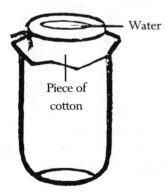

Try timing the passage of a tablespoonful of water through each fabric.

Does it make a difference if you start with the material wet?

Which fabrics do children think

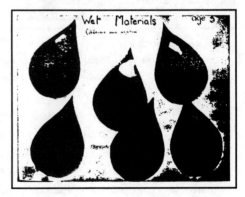

will be best for a rainy day? What sort of clothes do they wear on a rainy day? *(continued)*

Figure 10.1 (continued)

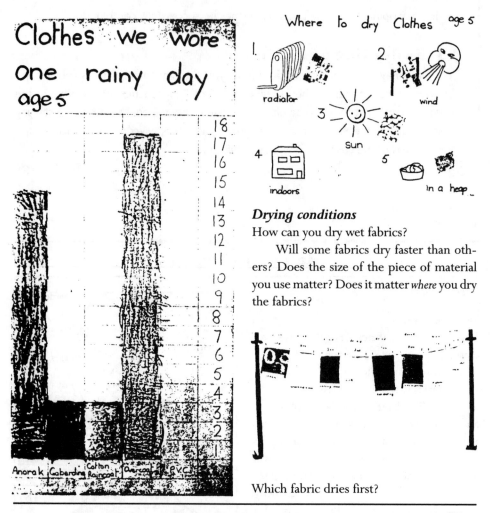

Drying conditions

How can you dry wet fabrics?

Will some fabrics dry faster than others? Does the size of the piece of material you use matter? Does it matter *where* you dry the fabrics?

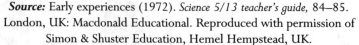

Which fabric dries first?

Source: Early experiences (1972). *Science 5/13 teacher's guide,* 84–85.
London, UK: Macdonald Educational. Reproduced with permission of
Simon & Shuster Education, Hemel Hempstead, UK.

When learning begins with an integrated theme, the learning will encompass rich, new language to describe the happenings, math skills as needed for comparing and measuring, and excursions into the social environment as topics are related to children's lives. There will be the need to express what is being learned in many ways, in paint and Plasticine, in finger plays and music, in puppetry and pantomine. There will be times you will explore a topic of high interest to children and keep on for as long as new paths of learning flow naturally from the one with which you began.

At other times, a process-oriented topic such as observing will carry you and the children fruitfully through weeks of explorations of all the senses, with ideas for extending the activities springing from the first. And along with the explorations, knowledge will grow and positive attitudes toward learning will be developed, for concept building and processes go hand in hand, and cognitive successes lead to improved self-confidence and self-concept.

The developers of *Science 5/13* discuss the philosophy of the program in the teacher's guide *With Objectives in Mind* (1972). They were convinced that a discovery approach should not be used in science alone, but should permeate all of the curriculum. "The consequences of this," the guide suggests, "are that activities recognisable as 'science' activities are likely to be pursued at various times and, conversely, that a great deal of 'science' may come out of activities not recognisable in the first instance as 'science'" (39). Think about this as you read about (or, better still, watch a film showing) the learning experiences that developed from a unit developed in California entitled "A Child's Garden."

IDEAS FROM "A CHILD'S GARDEN"

One way of capturing the flavour of a thematic unit on "growing things" is to borrow from your library a wonderful film called *Growing, Growing* (Fillinger 1972). The film is well worth the eleven minutes it takes to look and listen. A teaching guide for use with the film, along with ideas for many related activities, is included in a publication appropriately called *A Child's Garden* (Doughty et al. 1972).

- - - - - - - - - - - - - -

activity 10.9 GROWING, GROWING

If the film *Growing, Growing* is available from your library or media centre, set it up and run through it, once for the sheer enjoyment of it, and a second time to catch details that may have been missed in the first viewing of this fast-moving romp through nature.

As the film runs through for the second time, savour the adventure, enjoy the words of the song, and listen intently for snatches of conversation. As you watch and listen, think back to the outcomes for primary science, make some quick notes, and share with group members afterward your ideas on which outcomes specific to science are being realized through the experiences the children are having.

Think also of the potential for children's learning in all areas of the curriculum when they are exposed to experiences such as this. Select examples to illustrate the points you are making, and share your pooled observations and comments with the class.

(Note: If the film is not available, read the review that follows and use the description of the activities to identify potential outcomes for primary science and examples of how involvement in these experiences would enhance learning in all areas of the primary curriculum.)

❏ Reflecting and Sharing

The film *Growing, Growing* portrays the beginnings of science (and a whole host of exciting outcomes in other disciplines and in all domains of learning) when 6- to 8-year-old children plant a school garden and keep returning to the ongoing adventure through the changing seasons. There's a song that goes through it, sung by the children as they plant their seeds, savouring the rich, warm smells and textures of the earth. Judging distances and manipulating hammers and sticks and string, they stake out their plants, tend them, water them, watch them grow, measure their growth and record it on bar graphs. Recalling the story of Jack and the Beanstalk, they begin to use words like "gigantic," to recognize words like "seed" and "bean" and "autumn" on experience charts, and to use them in their conversations about what is happening.

They find insects, noting differences and similarities, make drawings to record their observations, and wonder "how it feels to be so small." They look at the flowers in the garden and are moved to reproduce their beauty with crayons and water paint, and their wonder in magical stories: "Can all the flowers talk?" In the autumn there is fruit — ears of corn and ripe pumpkins — and leaves change colour and fall, captured in movement and collage. There is the texture and crunching sound of drying grass underfoot, along with skeletal outlines of cell walls, bursting seed pods, and, finally, the hint and the promise in the hushed voices that whisper: "Wait for spring."

The verses in the children's song change with the seasons, but the chorus has a recurring theme: "I want to know — what makes them grow?" for the summer experiences; in the autumn, the time of change and decay, the song changes to "I want to know — where do they go?"

These rich, sensory experiences invite the children to talk about them, to read and record, and to share the excitement as strips of coloured paper become a record of plant growth. There is another kind of sharing, in groups ("I'll be the planter; you be the waterer"), and through it all the development of concepts (of plants and animals and how to care for them, of differences in living things, of the seasons and change) and the improvement of skills (in fine and gross motor co-ordination, time and space relations, the ability to group things on the basis of likenesses and differences, to communicate, to make predictions based on raw experience and inferences about why things sometimes go wrong).

"I want to know" is an appropriate theme for the primary years. It speaks to the high level of curiosity that children bring from their preschool and kindergarten years into the primary school. There are many ways in which the needs expressed in the "I want to know" theme are being met. But there is more than this, for the learning here is as wide and intense as the interests of young children, freely cross-ing artificial barriers created by schools and typifying a holistic way of learning that is very natural to children. At the same time, there is no loss of the integrity of the expected outcomes for science: process, content, attitudes.

It may not be possible, given the restrictions of the Canadian climate, to cultivate a school garden and watch it through the seasons, but field trips are possible, and there are farms, nurseries, parks, and botanical gardens that may be included in your planning. Flowering plants from the garden can be salvaged in the fall and their blooming extended indoors in the classroom. Young children derive immense satisfaction from just growing their own bean plants on a windowsill in the class-room, each in a styrofoam cup marked clearly to show ownership, and each with a string to climb, hopefully to the top of the window, with the appearance of flowers and pods adding to the excitement as time goes by. One group of children was very proud and excited when a pumpkin vine from a parent's garden was trans-planted in the fall into a large, hand-crafted, soil-filled planter in the school re-source centre, where it became the focus of interest for the whole school at Halloween!

The film *Growing, Growing* and its accompanying song describe a thematic unit, or "topic," that could begin in the first year of school and extend through the primary years without loss of interest because of the diversity of activities and their developmental appropriateness. Whatever theme is planned at this level, or whatever the sequence of science activities, substantial blocks of time should be set aside so that the pace is leisurely, materials can remain in the classroom, and tasks can be added to centres to provide for differences in needs and abilities.

With any group of children, the topics for integrated units will vary, depend-ing on the structure planned by the teacher and the interests of the children. There are no limits to the potential starting points in science for interdisciplinary learning. Starting points for children's learning are found in the study of plants and animals; the earth beneath their feet; everyday things and what they are made of; structures; things that move; water in its various forms; the daytime and nighttime sky; the changing seasons; and, of course, themselves.

THINKING BACK

At the beginning of the chapter, you were asked to jot down some ideas on a child-centred approach to education and what you would see if you walked into a child-centred classroom.

To answer the first question you may now be inclined to put together the examples of child-centred approaches and child-centred activities you have explored and the ideas you have gained about the nature of primary children and how they learn. Compare your notes with those that follow.

◆ In a child-centred classroom, the child's needs and interests are clearly at the centre of instructional planning and decision making.

◆ In a child-centred classroom, there is a genuine attempt to take into account the uniqueness of each child and to provide for individual differences in the style and pace of learning.

◆ In a child-centred classroom, children are viewed as individuals who construct their own knowledge of the world.

◆ In a child-centred classroom, opportunities are provided for child-selected and child-initiated activities.

◆ In a child-centred classroom, integrated units are designed that take into account the developmental level, interests, needs, learning styles, and experiential background of the children.

◆ In a child-centred classroom, children interact with their world through play, with play often originating from their own spontaneous interests.

As for your tentative responses to the second question ("What would you see if you walked into a child-centred classroom?"), the thoughts you jotted down may be interesting to compare now with the ideas gleaned in the course of this chapter, and with the summary table that follows. Table 10.2 presents a summary of a literature review of the concept "child-centred teaching/learning" under the headings curriculum, instructional strategies, the role of the teacher, and the learning environment. The summary, compiled in 1991 by Marie Wiseman, then a graduate student in primary education, lists the main ideas abstracted from curriculum documents and the literature on play, education as process, constructivism, children and change, historical views, and theory into practice. It provides an organizing framework not only for this chapter but also for your own reflections on a concept that is so important in your preparation for teaching.

Children relate to the world through play. This is an important component of a child-centred classroom. These children take play time seriously.

◆ ◆ ◆ ◆ ◆

LOOKING BACK AND LOOKING FORWARD

This chapter has served two purposes. As the opening chapter of a section focussing on science for all children, it underscored the importance of the beginning years in accomplishing this aim. If the goal of "science for all" is to be realized, science must begin early in the school experience, so that interests can be stimulated and attitudes formed that will lead to lifelong learning. To realize this goal, it is also important in the beginning years to prize uniqueness and to provide adequately for the individual differences among the children in your classroom.

The second purpose was to explore the magical world of early childhood and to focus for a while on the special nature of the kindergarten year — the year that coincides for most children in Canada with their first year of school. The concept of kindergarten as a "child's garden," where a child's needs, interests, and ways of learning determine the nature of the learning experiences, was explored through the history of its founding in the nineteenth century, and through the thinking of early childhood educators.

TABLE 10.2

Child-Centred Teaching and Learning: Summary of Literature Findings

	Curriculum	Instructional Strategies	Role of the Teacher	The Learning Environment
Curriculum documents and resources	• differential and interdisciplinary • learning must be made relevant • focus on "how to learn" • concerned with all areas of development	• active learning opportunities • resource-based teaching/learning • flexible grouping practices • individualized instruction • integration of common objectives • theme approach	• teacher as facilitator of learning • promotes positive self-concept • promotes learning by doing • regularly communicates with parents	• filled with concrete materials • includes learning centres • flexible spatial arrangements • extends beyond classroom • inviting • rich, supportive environment
Play	• promotes skill building in curriculum areas • used to promote holistic learning • meaningful	• use of play as a medium for active learning • time for unhurried learning	• provides 'messing about' times for children • recognizes and supports value of play	• encourages play • provides opportunity for social interaction • provides learning centres as starting point for play
Education as process	• determined by needs and interests of children • develop maximum potential of children	• flexible use of materials, time, and space • resource-based training • active learning • collaborative learning	• teacher as a partner in learning • teach children, not subjects • creating a child-centred environment	• activity-centred • provides for first-hand experiences • provides for play • rich in resources, toys, and materials

Table 10.2 (continued)

	Curriculum	Instructional Strategies	Role of the Teacher	The Learning Environment
Constructivism	• focus on understanding as opposed to superficial skills	• discovery learning • errors as part of learning • use of high-level questioning	• recognize children construct their own knowledge • follows, not leads • helps children move from novice to expert learner	• encourages risk taking • emphasis on meaning • ability to learn on their own
Children and change	• focus on child • process-oriented • active and experiential • interdisciplinary	• activity-based • collaborative learning • individualized learning • flexible time and curriculum	• views children as life-long learners • gives children autonomy • collaborative	• promotes active learning • provides choices • extends beyond classroom
Historical views	• must originate from child • focus on development of whole child	• play experiences • activity-based	• recognize children as agents of their own learning • consultative and guiding	• rich in sensory materials
Theory into practice	• development of basic skills • education of the whole child	• interdisciplinary learning • thematic work • learning centres • group learning	• facilitator • uses varied instructional approaches	• rich in resources • active and busy • supportive

Source: M. Wiseman (1991). Towards an understanding of child-centered instruction, 197–98. Unpublished Master's thesis. Memorial University of Newfoundland.

It was suggested that the spirit of kindergarten can be extended to the primary years. As a teacher in the early school years, you need to provide a classroom environment and teaching methods that are child-centred in nature. You can work toward this by ensuring that the experiences provided are developmentally appropriate, with children's natural curiosity and sense of wonder providing a foundation for further explorations and discoveries.

Since the methods of science are so close to the ways a young child learns, science activities such as observing with all the senses and grouping and ordering objects have the potential for developing and enhancing basic skills. Other basic skills developed through "sciencing" are number, space, and time relations and fine and gross motor skills.

You have seen that science, because it is so close to the child's natural, holistic way of learning, can be pursued through a topic or theme such as starting a school garden and watching it through the seasons.

You have explored the potential of continuing in the primary grades the playlike modes of learning that characterize the preschool years. You have reflected upon the value of learning through play, using primitive materials such as water, sand, and clay to help children acquire skills that are prerequisites to further learning, and beginning the development of concepts that will give meaning to their world.

Science, in the sense of asking and answering children's questions about the world, was considered an important component of early childhood education, both as an intrinsically interesting starting point for integrated themes and as a way of developing skills and fostering positive attitudes. The early years are special indeed and are made more special by putting the child at the centre of teaching/learning experiences, and by recognizing the uniqueness that is apparent even in very young children and that will continue to be an important factor as children progress through the grades. The challenges you will face as a teacher in accepting these differences and in trying to provide for them is the topic of the next chapter.

CANADIAN ACHIEVEMENTS IN SCIENCE

DAVID SUZUKI (B. 1936)

David Suzuki is a third-generation Japanese Canadian who has won acclaim as a geneticist, a radio and television host, a popularizer of science, and an environmentalist with a sense of mission. His autobiography, *Metamorphosis*, written in 1987, is a tribute to his father, who instilled in him his intense love of nature and his tremendous drive to succeed. His interest in genetics began while he was an honours biology student at Amherst College in Massachusetts, and continued through his doctoral program at the University of Chicago and career as a professor of zoology at the University of British Columbia. Suzuki's work at UBC in developing temperature-sensitive fruit flies (ts mutants), which are normal at 22°C but become paralyzed when the temperature is raised to 29°C, put the University of British Columbia at the forefront of genetic research aimed at relating mutational changes to their genetic base. Suzuki was awarded the Steacie Memorial Fellowship in 1969 as the best young Canadian scientist.

Other awards followed as he began his career in radio and television. His programs have included "Suzuki on Science" and "Science Magazine" in the 1970s, as well as the weekly CBC radio show "Quirks and Quarks." He became host of the popular television program "The Nature of Things" in 1979, attracting as many as one million Canadian viewers per week. The number of Canadian viewers doubled with the eight-part series "A Planet for the Taking," which traced the history of humankind's understanding and control of nature. "Amazonia," in 1989, described the clearing of the Brazilian rain forest. Suzuki's awards during this period include the Order of Canada in 1976 and the UNESCO Kalinga Prize in 1986 for his contribution to public understanding of science and technology.

For Suzuki, television is a vehicle for expressing his concerns about the world, and a powerful medium for educating the public about the importance and implications of science and technology. As a writer for newspapers and journals, his message is the same: **"The planet is in deep trouble and the reason for this crisis is us."** As a children's book author (*Looking at Insects/Looking at Plants*), he tries to instil in young people the same love of science and sense of responsibility for the natural environment that were his father's legacy to him in his childhood.

▢ REFERENCES

Beginnings. Teacher's Guide (1974). Science Curriculum Improvement Study. Chicago: Rand McNally.

British Columbia (1985). *Kindergarten Curriculum Guide and Resource Book.* British Columbia: Ministry of Education.

Bruner, J.S. (1972). The nature and uses of immaturity. *American Psychologist* 27(8):687–708.

Comenius, J.A. (1907). *The great didactic of John Amos Comenius.* Edited and translated by M.W. Keating. London: A. & C. Black.

Doughty, W., R. Hildebrand, C. Malcolm, and R. Beatty (1972). *A child's garden: A guide for parents and teachers.* San Francisco: Chevron Chemical Company.

Duckworth, E. (1970). Piaget rediscovered. *The ESS reader,* 135–39. Newton, MA: Educational Development Center.

Early experiences (1972). Science 5/13 Teacher's Guide. London: Macdonald Educational. Schools Council Publications.

Fillinger, P. (1972). *Growing, Growing.* Los Angeles: Churchill Films.

Goldberg, L. (1970). *Children and science.* New York: Charles Scribner's Sons.

Harlen, W. (1987). Primary school science: The foundation of science education. *Physical Education* (22):56–62.

Henniger, M.L. (1987). Learning mathematics and science through play. *Journal of Research in Early Childhood Education* (February):167–71.

Hughes, J.L. (1897). *Froebel's educational laws for all teachers.* London: D. Appleton & Co.

Isaacs, N. (1983). The case for bringing science into the primary school. In C. Richards and D. Holford, eds. *The teaching of primary science: Policy and practice,* 105–12, 111. Sussex: Falmer Press.

National Association for the Education of Young Children (1986). Position statement on developmentally appropriate practice in early childhood programs serving children from birth through age eight. *Young Children* (September):4–24.

Ontario Teachers' Federation (1973). *Curriculum guidelines for junior kindergartens.* Toronto: Ontario Teachers' Federation.

Orem, R.C., ed. (1974). *Montessori: Her method and her movement*. New York: G.B. Putnam's Sons.

Rousseau, J.J. (1911) *Emile*. Translated by B. Foxley. London: Dent.

Wiseman, M. (1991). *Towards an understanding of child-centered instruction*. Unpublished Master's thesis. St. John's, NF: Memorial University of Newfoundland.

With objectives in mind: Guide to Science 5–13 (1972). London: Macdonald Educational. Schools Council Publication.

CHAPTER 11

Meeting Individual Needs

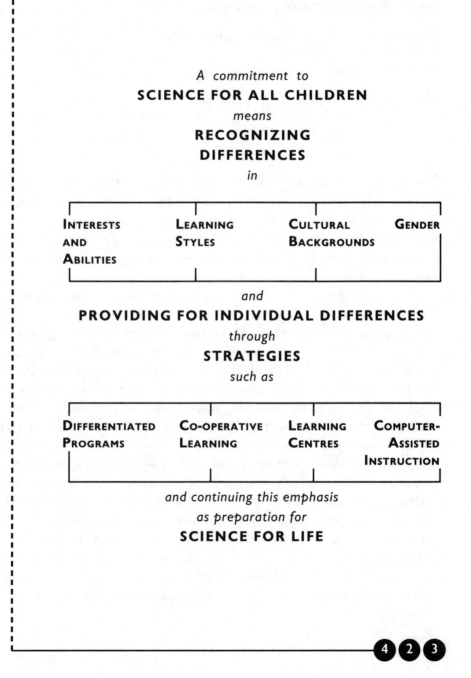

A *commitment* to
SCIENCE FOR ALL CHILDREN
means
**RECOGNIZING
DIFFERENCES**
in

INTERESTS AND ABILITIES	LEARNING STYLES	CULTURAL BACKGROUNDS	GENDER

and
PROVIDING FOR INDIVIDUAL DIFFERENCES
through
STRATEGIES
such as

DIFFERENTIATED PROGRAMS	CO-OPERATIVE LEARNING	LEARNING CENTRES	COMPUTER-ASSISTED INSTRUCTION

*and continuing this emphasis
as preparation for*
SCIENCE FOR LIFE

◆ ◆ ◆ ◆ ◆

Individualizing learning comes about by

varying the teaching and learning processes

according to the interests, preferences,

sociometrics, learning styles, and abilities

and achievements of the students.

SANDRA NINA KAPLAN ET AL. (1973)

Implicit in the goal of "science for all children" is the challenge of finding ways to provide for the wide spectrum of individual differences among students. The first step for you as a teacher is to recognize, accept, and respect these differences, and then to use your creative imagination to work toward establishing a positive, encouraging climate for learning and exposing your students to a wide variety of teaching approaches and strategies.

In the last chapter, you explored ways in which teachers provide for individual differences in the beginning years of school through child-centred methods of teaching/learning. In child-centred instruction, children are active agents of their own learning. They are given practice in the development of basic skills and are involved in open-ended explorations, with opportunities to make choices based on interests and needs. Child-centred instruction is individualized instruction, and is not confined to the beginning years but should permeate the years that follow as children progress through the elementary grades into the more specialized sciences at the secondary level.

This chapter lays the groundwork for the concluding chapter in this section, which deals specifically with how you will meet the needs of exceptional children — the intellectually, physically, and emotionally challenged children who may be mainstreamed into your classroom, as well as the gifted and talented, also in the mainstream. The present chapter suggests that the more successful you are in identifying and providing for individual differences among *all* children, the more prepared you will be to provide for children with special challenges. It encourages you to welcome diversity and seek ways to deal with it successfully.

◆ ◆ ◆ ◆ ◆

RECOGNIZING UNIQUENESS

Why is it so important to individualize instruction? Perhaps the best answer to this question is that the very process of individualization recognizes the uniqueness of students and the desire to place their interests and needs ahead of subject matter, to realize that the school exists for students, not students for the school. The aim of *individualization,* therefore, is to maximize the learning potential of each child by modifying and adapting curriculum materials and instructional practices to suit the needs of the students. When instruction is maintained at approximately the same level with a class of students, some students are frustrated and turned off by lack of understanding. Others are bored because the material is not sufficiently challenging. Individualization can be an empowering force, resulting in students who are becoming *active learners,* taking responsibility for their own progress and gaining intrinsic rewards through successful completion of appropriate tasks.

Begin by imagining your first class and the individual differences you may find among your students.

activity 11.1 YOUR FIRST CLASS: IDENTIFYING INDIVIDUAL DIFFERENCES

Think of ways in which the students in your first class may differ from one another — for example, in interests, abilities, and so on.

Share your thoughts with other group members and make a composite list.

☐ Reflecting and Sharing

As teachers meet a new group of students each September, they know that the new class will present different joys, different problems, and different challenges. They know that each of the students in the new class, like others before them, will be unique, and that their uniqueness will unfold during the school year they spend together. It will be the same for you when you begin your internship and when you have a class of your own. The challenges you face as a teacher because of this will be great, but they are not insurmountable, and the more thought and preparation you put into getting to know your students and providing for these differences, the more successful and satisfying your teaching will be.

In your group discussion, you probably began your list of individual differences with "interests and abilities." Perhaps you added aptitudes to this group, and illustrated your answers with examples of each.

Included under this broad group of *differences in interests, abilities, and aptitudes* are *developmental differences*, which you will have to take into account in your instructional planning, and *differences in prior learning, understandings, and experience* that children bring to school. In your first class, there will be children with *different learning styles and personalities*. Your students will come from *different home environments* — some from affluent families, some from families low on the socioeconomic scale — and, given Canada's multicultural society, the boys and girls in your class will represent a number of *different racial and ethnic origins*. There will be *gender differences*, and you will be concerned with removing stereotypes that exist and providing equality of opportunity for both boys and girls.

Let's begin with the most obvious group of individual differences — interests and abilities — and consider how your repertoire of teaching strategies and approaches and the variety of curriculum resources available to you can help you to plan instruction to meet these needs.

◆ ◆ ◆ ◆ ◆

DIFFERENCES IN INTERESTS AND ABILITIES

Many of the methods of science teaching that you have been considering lend themselves to individualization, with the teacher playing a facilitative rather than a directive role. Children are provided with meaningful and personalized experiences, with autonomy to learn on their own through their own observations and investigations.

Within the framework of a broad curriculum plan for elementary science, it is often possible to select learning experiences from existing programs that include core and extension or enrichment activities. The potential for providing for differences in this way is enhanced when you organize your classroom so that children at any one time are learning in a variety of ways. With the combination of diverse activities and different ways of learning, it is possible to accommodate children of different levels of ability and different aptitudes. There can be tasks for children who need remediation or extra practice, as well as tasks for those who have mastered core material and need challenging tasks at a more demanding level, or the incentive to begin independent projects. If activities are intrinsically interesting and open-ended, and you provide a low-risk environment and many opportunities for choice, creativity is encouraged and interests are enhanced as well.

DEVELOPMENTAL DIFFERENCES

It is important to ascertain what children already know and at what level they are in developing certain skills. You are already aware of the importance of knowing the limits of children's understanding at various developmental levels, and the diagnostic value of administering Piagetian tasks to children you are concerned about. The policy of matching tasks to stages of development has been seen to be important in the beginning years. The concept of developmental appropriateness as applied to child-centred teaching/learning is no less important in subsequent school years.

DIFFERENCES IN UNDERSTANDINGS

You have been introduced in a previous chapter to some of the alternative conceptions that children bring to the learning situation, and know something of the interfering role these differences in understandings can play in their learning of science. You also know now how necessary it is to recognize, challenge, and test such alternative conceptions if your pupils are to develop more accurate science concepts. Once you begin to take all this into account and try to ascertain which children need help in certain areas and which children can benefit from enrichment, you will have already begun to individualize your classroom. The next step is to respond diagnostically to needs and to make available learning tasks that will take each of your students a step closer to understanding a concept, a step closer to mastery of a skill, and a step closer to a feeling of self-confidence.

Differences in Interests and Abilities: Possible Strategies

DIFFERENTIATED INSTRUCTION

The best of the modular programs and textbook series are designed to include core activities that are seen as essential to concept building, skill development, and attitude change. As mentioned earlier, there are usually optional activities within units that extend the learning horizontally, giving further practice at about the same level of difficulty, or challenging activities and problems that go beyond the core and provide vertical enrichment. Such programs sometimes provide for delayed readers by including pictured directions with verbal directions for activities, labelled illustrations to help with vocabulary, and other features such as glossaries and bulletin board and learning centre ideas. All of these have the goal of providing for individual differences.

Some modular programs include, along with core and optional activities, take-home ideas for science, with everyday things and suggestions for interest activities that motivate children to start new investigations and pursue paths of learning that are novel and interesting to them. Figure 11.1 shows how an activity — in this case, building a bridge — can begin with the whole class working in groups of three on the same activity, and can be extended in the "More to Explore" section to provide enrichment for children who want to go further.

FIGURE 11.1

Building Bridges: From "Challenge" to "More to Explore"

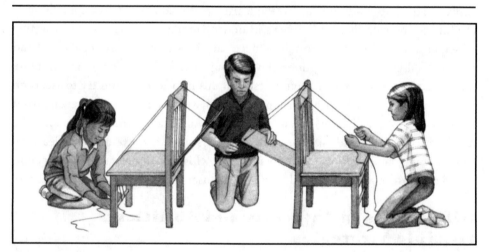

Challenge

Build a bridge that will span a gap, support an object, and open up to allow ships to pass.

You Will Need

- materials such as toothpicks, straws, wooden splints, string, paper clips, glue, spools, and so on
- your choice of toy cars, trucks, boats, or ships

In Action

1. Look carefully at the pictures of bridges with movable sections to help you decide which part of your bridge will move.

2. Design and build your bridge using the materials you think will work best.

3. Record the successes and failures that occur while you are building and while you test your bridge. Give reasons why you think they happened. *(continued)*

Figure 11.1 (continued)

Sharing

When the bridges are complete, show other groups how they work. Then invite another class to a demonstration. Use your toy cars and boats to show how the bridges work. Be ready to answer questions about the construction of your bridge.

Write a story about your bridge and how it plays an important part in an exciting event in the history of the town.

More to Explore

◆ Build another type of movable bridge of a different design.

◆ Why were drawbridges important in the days of castles and knights in armour? Find out how they were made and how they worked. Write a story of romance and adventure in which a drawbridge is raised in the nick of time. You may want to illustrate your story.

Source: V. Stief and P. Williams (1991). *Innovations in Science, Level 4,* 159. Toronto, Ontario: Holt, Rinehart and Winston of Canada. Copyright © 1991 Holt; Rinehart and Winston of Canada, Ltd. Reproduced by kind permission.

At most levels of schooling, programs have been developed with the goal of providing for individual differences in mind. In the 1960s, Science: A Process Approach (SAPA) recognized individual differences by emphasizing mastery learning and using "tracking cards" to keep records of each child's progress. The *Examining Your Environment* (EYE) materials (Couchman et al. 1971) consisted of high-interest modules, among them "Snow and Ice," "Miniclimates," and "Dandelions." In addition to the core investigations for all students, there were "Branching Out" activities for further practice and "Digging Deeper" sections for enrichment. In *Explorations in Science* (Campbell et al. 1992), a section titled "Extending the Activity" suggests additional related activities. *Innovations in Science* (Stief and Williams 1991), as illustrated in Figure 11.1, has "Challenges" for all students, an "In Action" section that encourages individual projects, and a "More to Explore" invitation to students to become involved in research, group games, and additional experiments.

activity 11.2 **GOING FURTHER**

Select a science unit for any level from Grade 4 to Grade 7. Identify the ways in which the unit provides for individual interests and abilities.

Think of ways you might adapt lessons to accommodate individual differences still further.

❑ Reflecting and Sharing

Providing for differences in interests and abilities requires thoughtful, creative planning and adaptation of the learning environment so that each child is empowered to learn in his or her own way and at his or her own pace.

Programs with "built in" components for individualizing instruction make it easier for you to take into account the diversity that exists among students, the "different pairs of eyes," as Abruscato and Hassard (1976) wrote, through which "they look at themselves and their world" (118).

Over time, build up files of optional activities to create new approaches to instruction for particular students as the need becomes apparent. Provide opportunities for children to work on their own, to choose what they wish to investigate, to learn from successes and failures, and to develop a sense of self-worth.

◆ ◆ ◆ ◆ ◆

DIFFERENCES IN LEARNING STYLES

A *learning style* is the specific manner in which a student learns. Some examples of differences in the ways students learn are as follows:

- There are children who work well in groups, and others who function best on their own. Both kinds of students often benefit from working in pairs in a peer tutoring arrangement — the "teacher" and the "learner."
- Some children learn best in a divergent mode; others are more comfortable with a convergent, linear approach to learning.
- Some children have one or more preferred learning modalities — visual, auditory, or tactile/kinesthetic. If much of what happens in classrooms is focussed on auditory and visual modes, those who prefer tactile and kinesthetic modes are at a disadvantage.
- Children of different cultural backgrounds view the world differently. They bring to school differences in family backgrounds and value systems that should be recognized and respected.
- Differences in learning style have been associated with left- versus right-brain hemispheric function. Although interpretations of brain research have often been oversimplified, there *are* differences in the way children perceive and process learning. Some perceive actively, some reflectively. Some process information holistically (right hemispheric thinking) and some analytically (left hemispheric thinking).

Differences in Learning Styles: Possible Strategies

In the discussion of differences and abilities, it was suggested that a variety of individual differences can be accommodated through a variety of approaches to instruction. The same applies to differences in learning styles. Since in any one classroom there are students with many different learning styles, one teaching approach will not be effective with all students. The broader the repertoire of teaching methods you have mastered, and the more you vary your approach within lessons, the more likely it is that different learning styles will be accommodated.

By the same token, if some children in your class have preferred learning modalities, using primarily visual approaches will not be effective with all students. Fortunately, science activities lend themselves easily to a multisensory approach. When teaching elementary science, it is not difficult to provide for children who prefer particular learning modalities. Most activities combine all modalities: *visual modes* (watching a demonstration, recording observations); *auditory modes* (listening to and discussing instructions, talking through the results of experiments); *tactile/kinesthetic modes* (manipulating apparatus, moving around, touching things). It is relatively easy to work toward a multisensory approach by using an overhead projector while giving instructions (including tape-recorded directions with learning centre activities), encouraging tactile observations, and so on.

Because science instruction has physical (concrete) components, as well as reflective (abstract) components, almost any science investigation simultaneously provides for students with a variety of learning styles. An activity may be introduced with an oral presentation (accompanied by a demonstration of equipment to be used or procedures to be followed, and perhaps written directions), along with a data chart to facilitate the recording of observations. Children work in groups, manipulating materials and talking together about their observations, and later share their data with other groups. They are encouraged to generalize from the experiences and to identify further questions to investigate.

The variety inherent in any one experience in science has great potential for accommodating diverse learning styles and learning modalities. Science activities meet the needs of children with a specific learning style *some* of the time, while tempting them as well to learn in other modes.

◆ ◆ ◆ ◆ ◆

CULTURAL DIFFERENCES

The population of Canada is made up of people from many cultural backgrounds, and multicultural differences are found in most school populations. In addition to the English- and French-Canadian populations, there are Native groups — for example, Inuit and Métis peoples — as well as immigrants, from many lands, who have made a new home in Canada.

An item on CBC's "Prime Time News" in April 1993 focussed on the multicultural mix in Canada's largest city, Toronto. It showed scenes along a 15 km streetcar route through the heart of the city. Very little English was being spoken, and very little of what people were reading was in English. The streetcar passed through a number of neighbourhoods: "Little India," Chinatown, and Italian and Portuguese areas. The report stated that 31 percent of the population in the Toronto area is of neither British nor French ancestry, and that many different nationalities are represented in a cross-section of the city's population.

Although the multicultural mix in the whole of Canada is nowhere as diverse as in the Toronto area, multiculturalism is a characteristic of Canadian life in the provinces and territories, and is also reflected in the nation's schools. Teachers all over Canada are being challenged to provide for children for whom English is a second language, and for whom cultural backgrounds are extremely diverse.

There are problems in cross-cultural education other than those related to language. Native groups throughout Canada are often economically disadvantaged, as are other sectors of our society such as low-income families, single-parent families, and those whose geographical location confers certain disadvantages. There is often lack of understanding of ethnic and racial groups, and discrimination is evident at school. Teachers have a role to play in fighting prejudice and teaching children to accept and respect cultural differences.

A multicultural country such as Canada presents many challenges to teachers, who must attempt to meet the needs of students with different cultural backgrounds.

Regional Concerns and Recommendations

Ministries of education include in their curriculum documents recommendations for accommodating cross-cultural differences at the school level. Some examples follow.

The British Columbia curriculum document *Year 2000: A Curriculum and Assessment Framework for the Future* (1989) stresses the need to "encourage awareness and respect for the similarities and differences among the cultures which comprise British Columbia, Canadian and other cultures" (12). It suggests that curriculum content reflecting First Nations' history and culture can benefit all students.

A second example of the commitment to cross-cultural education is found in the Saskatchewan Education document *Science: A Curriculum Guide for the Elementary Level* (1990). This document describes curriculum initiatives designed to foster positive images of Native peoples; to reinforce and complement their beliefs and values; and to reflect their social, linguistic, political, and regional diversity.

In the Northwest Territories, students come to school understanding and speaking a number of different languages. The curriculum documents for elementary science recommend that, where possible, young children should be instructed in the language in which they are most proficient. Language fluency is an important component of success in school, and language problems present special challenges to all children for whom English is a second language. Various strategies can be used to build confidence and self-esteem through the science program.

LANGUAGE DEVELOPMENT APPROACH

When students are not proficient in standard English, Northwest Territories teachers are asked to take the time to teach them the language they need in order to talk, read, and write about science concepts and to develop thinking skills. A *language development approach* to science teaching is recommended when the language of instruction is not the first language of the student. Language development/science units have been developed, for example, on arctic and subarctic land animals and other topics of relevance to students' lives. Weather is the topic of an integrated science/social studies/math unit.

PEER TUTORING

Peer tutoring — in which students teach other students, either in pairs or as members of co-operative learning groups — is especially effective for language development, particularly when the "teacher" is bilingual. In co-operative groups, the technique is used to raise the standard of the whole group.

USING VISUALS

Science activities can be introduced by using visuals, models, and demonstrations. Labels can be affixed to concrete materials in a learning centre. Vocabulary can be developed through word selection and experience charts such as the one illustrated in Figure 11.2.

LANGUAGE AS AN OUTGROWTH OF SCIENCE EXPERIENCES

Successful science experiences can be the starting point for language development. Because of the concrete nature of science activities and the need to talk

FIGURE 11.2

Meeting Language Needs

Source: *Elementary Science Primary Program Guide* (1986).
Northwest Territories: Department of Education, Culture and Employment, 27.

about observations and to write about them, students communicate more freely. With successful experiences, there is growth in self esteem — another important outcome.

Cultural Differences: Possible Strategies

It is very important to recognize differences in the learning styles of children of different cultures, to take these into account in your teaching, and to help students acquire alternative ways of learning.

As the cultural mix becomes more diverse, teachers can take advantage of the varied experiences that children from different cultures bring to the classroom. Here are some ideas, to which you can add some of your own.

EXPANDING AWARENESS

In regularly scheduled visitors' programs include people from different racial groups who are involved in science-related careers. Highlight the concerns of Native people about the impact of new technologies on their way of life, and about the preservation of the natural environment.

POSITIVE SELF-CONCEPT

Encourage the growth of positive self-concept in children from minority groups by capitalizing on strengths and emphasizing the need for understanding the history and beliefs of people of different cultures.

INTERETHNIC FRIENDSHIPS

Encourage the growth of interpersonal relationships through interaction in small groups mixed by age, race, religion, and gender. Co-operative learning groups are especially effective in building positive attitudes and eliminating prejudice. As children interact in peer tutoring situations or as members of co-operative learning groups, barriers are broken down and interethnic friendships are formed.

CULTURAL RELEVANCE

It is important in the early years of school to stimulate interest in science, and nowhere is this more essential than for minority students, who often fail to find in science- and technology-related experiences any relevance to their culture. To counteract these attitudes and to capture interest in the elementary school, issues should be drawn from within their culture and interest generated through examples with which they are familiar. One way to extend the perceived relevance of science is to extend it to other curriculum areas with themes that cross interdisciplinary barriers.

INVOLVING PARENTS IN SCIENCE

Invite parents of minority children to come to the classroom as helpers. They have language skills that can be used to help children who are learning English. Invite them to participate in units on topics such as nutrition and weather, to teach children to appreciate and value diversity in the population of Canada and in Canadian schools.

RESOURCE-BASED LEARNING

The unit approach is even more effective when combined with resource-based learning, which not only teaches skills in finding information, but offers students many opportunities for choice. The child-centred nature of this way of organizing learning is espoused by the Saskatchewan Education (1990) curriculum guide for elementary science:

> Resource-based instruction is student-centered. It offers students opportunities to choose, to explore, and to discover. The opportunity to make choices, in an environment rich in resources where the thoughts and feelings of students are respected, is vital to the development of autonomous learners (27).

From a Teacher's Journal

As teachers, we must try to provide as many opportunities as possible for children to discover for themselves by exploring their environment. After teaching for many years, it's my firm belief that science lessons are most meaningful to children when they learn from one another through interaction in mixed groups and a hands-on approach to learning.   (continued)

✍ From a Teacher's Journal (continued)

To provide for individual differences, I use a variety of approaches. Some include whole-class discussion where I use visual stimulation such as pictures, videos, slides, and filmstrips as a basis for observing, predicting, and so on. Children work in small groups, manipulating materials, experimenting, talking, and interpreting their findings. In our unit, we had live lobsters that we handled and watched being "put to sleep," and snails that we observed and wrote journal articles about. A learning centre on measurement worked very well in providing for individual differences. A variety of task cards led children to measure objects in the classroom, using arbitrary and standard units, and to record results. By using a wide range of approaches and making available a variety of different experiences, I have successfully catered to individual personalities and encouraged children to use science processes to become more aware of the world around them.

Betty Cooper

St. John's, NF

Another advantage of resource-based learning is that alternative materials with a range of readability levels are available to students who are having difficulty with the level of difficulty of the regular course material. Ensure that the resource materials cover a wide range of interests and a variety of different formats so that they reach as many students as possible. Include resources specific to various ethnic and cultural groups, so that all students learn more and come to appreciate the customs and values of other countries.

activity 11.3

LOOKING AHEAD

◆ Do some research to find out about the cultural mix in the province or territory where you hope to teach. Compare rural and urban schools, and schools in different geographical areas to ascertain the proportion of minority children in the school populations in each location.

◆ Review the suggestions in this chapter and plan one or two ways you will try to deal with cultural diversity.

◆ ◆ ◆ ◆ ◆

OVERCOMING GENDER BIAS IN SCIENCE EDUCATION

You may be surprised to find gender included in a discussion of individual differences among your students in the primary and elementary grades. Intensive investigations of the cognitive abilities of boys and girls have found few differences. However, in spite of the need for a scientifically literate society and an equal need for men and women to be scientists and technologists, differences do exist in the representation of girls and boys in secondary and postsecondary science and of women in careers related to science. Shepardson and Pizzini (1991) refer to the underrepresentation of females in school science and science-related careers as a function of our culture, educational system, and attitudes.

Although we aspire to "science for all," it is well known that some young people do not get an ideal science education, that in many cases the attribute that causes this is their gender. Differences in attitude toward science appear very early, as evidenced by studies in a number of countries. Wynne Harlen (1985), reviewing reasons for this, suggests that sex-role stereotyping in home and school has begun to create inequality of opportunity for learning science long before the end of elementary school. This was one of the concerns addressed in the early 1980s by the Science Council of Canada. In the conference report *Who Turns the Wheel?* (Science Council of Canada 1982), it was noted that enrolment in high-school physics was two to three times higher for boys than for girls, and that the percentage of girls studying chemistry was significantly less than for boys. Only in biology were there greater numbers of girls. Another Science Council of Canada (1984) document, *Science for Every Student: Educating Canadians for Tomorrow's World,* recommended that the imbalance be addressed so that the participation of girls in science would be increased. It was suggested that schools should avoid practices that reinforce male stereotypes, emphasize the human dimension of science, and try to change the masculine image of science by exposing both sexes to role models of women scientists and inventors.

FIGURE 11.3

Draw a Scientist: Typical Response

Source: Sandi Sanders, Rainier Middle School, Rainier, Oregon.

Chapter 2 discussed the stereotypic image of a scientist. Figure 11.3 shows a typical response when children of any age are asked to "draw a scientist" or "draw a scientist at work." In addition to the wild hair and glasses and the lab bench with smoking test tubes, another stereotype is that the scientist is almost always a *man* in a white coat.

The masculine image of science is perpetuated in many student texts and in the way teachers unconsciously respond differently to boys and girls. It is recognized that through their expectations and verbal behaviour teachers may unconsciously influence what boys and girls believe they can achieve in science and mathematics. There is evidence from classroom observations that boys get most of teachers' attention and are given more time to respond to questions (Tobin and Garnett 1987). Awareness of these subtle, subconscious gender biases in teaching styles is the first step toward improving the situation and increasing the likelihood of effective participation of both sexes in high-school and college science and in the choice of careers in science. Activity 11.4 invites you to recall your own school experience to see what influenced your choice of high-school and university science courses, and how successful the experiences were for you.

FIGURE 11.4

Thoughts on Gender Biases

The cultural influences and biases that channel girls away from nontraditional careers in the preschool years start with parents and other caregivers. Once in school, many girls and young women continue to be discouraged from pursuing interests and careers in mathematics, science, technology, and engineering by those teachers and guidance counsellors who are not sensitive to gender stereotyping.

To ensure equal participation of girls and boys in science and mathematics, there must be more women in the classrooms teaching these subjects and interacting with the students. Textbooks should portray the achievements of women scientists and engineers, and should use examples that are of interest to young women. The most important factor, however, remains in the development of the self-esteem and self-confidence of the young women, especially between the ages of 13 and 17.

To ensure an increased participation from both genders, it is vital to make science a "fun" subject and to narrow the gap between the science taught in the schools and the current scientific research and development in the real world, especially in fields where developments have led to some controversy and public debate. Discussing the controversial aspects of science and the societal relevance of scientific development should stimulate the desire of young people to participate in activities that design tomorrow's world.

Monique Frize

Source: M. Frize. (1993). Thoughts on gender biases. Personal communication.

activity 11.4 GENDER EQUITY

In a co-operative learning group, mixed by gender, recall together your high-school science classes. Do you recall any hidden or overt messages that either encouraged you to take, or discouraged you from taking, additional science courses and considering a science-related career as an option?

Have a frank discussion, focussing on how you might change negative messages and substitute positive ones for all children in your classooms.

❏ Reflecting and Sharing

Answers are still being sought to many of the questions about gender equity. Read Dr. Monique Frize's reflections on gender biases in Figure 11.4, especially the sentence "The most important factor, however, remains in the development of the self-esteem and self-confidence of the young women, especially between the ages of 13 and 17." A CBC Newsworld television interview (April 1993) with young women studying physics in "all girl" classes raises the question of whether myths about girls and science are perpetuated not only by parents and teachers but also by the peer culture in the classes where boys and girls study together. The television interview indicated that the majority of the young women in the single-sex class achieved more, enjoyed science more, and were more confident in their ability and less intimidated than they had been in a mixed class.

The Girls into Science and Technology (GIST) project (Kelly, Whyte, and Small 1984) is an example of an action research project in which teachers became involved in looking for the reasons for girls' underachievement in science in the early junior-high years and in exploring the feasibility of certain interventions. Teachers were asked to reflect on their attitudes and behaviour and to try to change. Components of the intervention were "girl-friendly" curriculum materials, discussions of the relationship of science to everyday life, linking of science to creative writing, and school visits of women in "masculine" occupations.

The evidence is accumulating that awareness of the need to reduce gender biases, coupled with curriculum interventions aimed at reducing such biases and stereotypes, can increase the likelihood of effective participation of girls in high-school and college science. However, the inequalities are still a concern in the 1990s. Geraldine Kenney-Wallace, while chair of the Science Council of Canada, highlighted in the introduction to a (1988) WISH (Women In Science, Hopefully) publication the problems that still exist, suggesting that a "fundamental fear and lack of inner confidence" has to be overcome before women will tackle the so-called "hard sciences" of physics, chemistry, and computer and engineering sciences. She maintained that a "persistent yet patient effort is required to re-educate young women to the broader horizons of their own potentials" (Introduction).

This re-education may not be necessary if the education of both boys and girls in the primary and elementary grades already encourages and reflects the potential of both sexes for learning science. The argument usually given for encouraging girls to achieve in science is the avoidance of an impending shortfall of highly qualified engineers and scientists. However, an equally good reason is that their lives will be richer with the attitudes of inquiry and the appreciations and aesthetic awareness that exposure to science inspires.

Gender Equity: Possible Strategies

Clearly there is a need to improve opportunities for girls in science. It is important for you as beginning teachers to be conscious that your style of teaching, your verbal behaviour, and the way you give praise, criticism, or encouragement may express gender bias, however slightly. Remember that your expectations can

In the 1990s, the inequalities of women in the "hard sciences" are still a concern. Awareness of subconscious biases and the deliberate encouragement of the potential of girls in primary science may change this.

encourage or discourage your female students' desire to participate more fully in science and to continue to build on the foundation you have provided for them in the early years.

Some positive suggestions are:

◆ Emphasize the practical and social implications of science, reflecting the interests of girls as well as boys.
◆ Be conscious of the need to direct challenging questions to both sexes and to take note of the way students respond.
◆ Encourage "tinkering" in girls as well as boys.
◆ Avoid sexist language.
◆ Include in your lessons information on female scientists and/or invite them to your classes to talk about their work, so that girls have role models to emulate and are encouraged to continue their interest in science as they enter the next level of education.
◆ Arrange full participation of girls in co-operative learning groups.

◆ ◆ ◆ ◆ ◆
SCIENCE FOR ALL: SOME PRACTICAL SUGGESTIONS

You have identified many of the individual differences you will encounter among the children in your classroom — differences in interests, abilities, and learning styles, as well as cultural and gender differences. What follows are suggestions for organizing your classroom and planning instruction to provide for *all* of these differences by truly individualizing your approach to teaching.

An exciting and rewarding aspect of providing for individual differences is that as you add to your storehouse of ideas, you will be creating a positive, encouraging classroom environment in which diversity is valued and children are actively involved, sometimes in *co-operative learning groups,* sometimes in individual projects in *learning centres,* with many opportunities for choice and self-evaluation of progress. To these may be added a third strategy for providing for individual differences — the use of *computer technology.* These techniques are not new to you. You have encountered them briefly in various contexts throughout the book, but will consider them now because of their great potential for providing for the uniqueness of every child in your classroom.

Co-operative Learning in Science

Groups are natural to science learning — just as natural as the hands-on learning that goes on in them. However, the emphasis in science education has been largely on the physical arrangement of children in groups as they interact with materials rather than on the interaction of students with one another in groups. Piagetian theory stresses the importance of both kinds of interaction in child development and learning. Children acquire knowledge through physical experience — through active involvement in their own learning — and they also learn through social interaction, through talking to one another in groups and becoming less egocentric as they learn that others sometimes hold viewpoints different from their own.

The research of Johnson et al. (1984) and Johnson and Johnson (1986, 1990) has focussed attention in the past two decades on the potential for children to learn from each other and to develop both academic and social skills as they interact in groups.

Co-operative Learning Groups

The Johnsons and their colleagues have been looking for ways to facilitate group learning, to make the roles of group members more effective, and to improve the quality of the interaction. Johnson et al. (1984) suggest that there are several patterns of interaction — competitive, individualistic, and co-operative — that emerge as children work together, and that each is useful. However, their research indicates that both individual growth and group goals can be fostered through co-operative learning in groups.

Patterns of Interaction

When students obtain their goals only when others fail to obtain theirs, the pattern is a *competitive* one. When achievement of students' goals is unrelated to achievement of others, the pattern is *individualistic*. The third pattern, that of *co-operative* interaction, exists when students perceive that they can obtain their goal only when other members of their group obtain theirs.

In their book *Circles of Learning: Cooperation in the Classroom,* Johnson et al. (1984) recommend the use of all three patterns, so that students learn to enjoy healthy competition, learn how to work independently and complete tasks on their own, and also learn how to work co-operatively with each other as effective group members.

According to Johnson and Johnson (1990), the results of studies comparing the three patterns of interaction show more positive cognitive, affective, and social gains for co-operative learning. These gains include:

1. higher achievement and longer retention of the material learned;
2. more positive attitudes about the subject matter and the teacher;

3. higher self-esteem;

4. more effective use of social skills; and

5. more positive feelings about each other. (This "positive cathexis" works regardless of differences between students and has implications for the integration of different ethnic groups, mainstreaming of challenged students into regular classroom settings, and managing the heterogeneity present in every classroom.) (87)

Since most of the research on co-operative learning has been in science classes, the results have direct relevance to your teaching of science and science-related themes.

CHARACTERISTICS OF CO-OPERATIVE LEARNING GROUPS

Face-to-Face Interaction. Since the emphasis is on face-to-face interaction, the preferred seating arrangement is in circles, so that children can communicate effectively with each other. There should be a great deal of conversation and debate. Students explain to each other what they are learning and help each other to understand what they are studying or observing.

Co-operative learning allows students to collaborate on ideas, yielding positive, cognitive, affective, and social outcomes.

Positive Interdependence. The Johnsons (1986) suggest that "there's a considerable difference between putting students physically into groups (merely rearranging desks) and structuring groups for cooperative learning (promoting positive interdependence and collaborative skills)" (32). Group skills grow with practice, and as you experiment with co-operative learning you and your students will make more and more effective use of a way of learning that, as research indicates, will yield positive cognitive, affective, and social outcomes.

Individual Accountability. Although the interaction takes place in groups, there is individual growth, as well as growth in group skills, because each group member is responsible for learning the assigned material, and each member is assigned a specific role.

activity 11.5 DEVELOPING AN INTEGRATED UNIT

- ◆ Choose a topic for an integrated unit for a Grade 7 class in a departmentalized middle school.
- ◆ Form groups of five. One group will assume the role of "workshop leaders," and the remaining groups will be co-operative learning groups. Each workshop leader will arrange for space in the classroom for one of the groups, introduce the activity, discuss group skills, assign roles to group members, and monitor their progress, giving feedback as needed.
- ◆ In each group, the roles to be assigned to group members are the roles of department heads in the middle school — one for each of five departments that are collaborating in the production of the unit. In this case, the departments are science, social studies, art, language arts, and mathematics.
- ◆ The task is to prepare for the unit a framework that will integrate all five subject areas by making appropriate use of the expertise of each group member, while reaching a group consensus on the nature of the unit.
- ◆ Finish with a whole-class discussion and evaluation of the results.

☐ Reflecting and Sharing

The situation in Activity 11.5 is a contrived one, of course, intended to give you some idea of the thought processes that children go through as they work co-operatively in groups for a common goal. The activity also focussed on the role of the teacher in facilitating the interaction among students and their growth, both individually and as group members.

THE ROLE OF THE TEACHER

The Johnsons (1986) suggest that "changing science instruction to create a cooperatively structured classroom need not be difficult, but it probably won't be simple" (32). As you play a facilitative rather than a directive role in children's learning, you will become very conscious of group dynamics — how students function as group members and how their interaction with one another as group members can become more focussed and productive. With practice and your guidance, children within groups involved in sciencing can develop skills in co-operative learning.

Your role as a teacher is described below.

Set Up Heterogeneous Groups. Form groups of five students, mixed by age, ability, gender, personality, and ethnic and racial origins. Arrange each group in a circle, so that group members can communicate effectively with one another. Separate the groups as much as possible, so that they will not disturb each other as they talk. Have all needed materials (books, concrete materials, writing supplies, and so on) within easy reach of each group.

Assign Roles. Roles should rotate with each new activity. If there is to be peer tutoring within the groups, pair high achievers with low achievers or, as previously suggested, bilingual students with students for whom English is a second language. Assign to each group member a specific role, such as gathering information, recording data, collecting materials for the group, summarizing the activities of the group, or reporting on the conclusions. The teacher should encourage mutual respect for the contributions of group members, with no criticism or "put-downs."

Introduce Objectives. Spend adequate time to ensure that the steps in the investigation are understood, as well as the roles of each group member. A chart is useful for this purpose. Teach group skills, such as how children can be responsible for the group's learning as well as for their own.

Monitor Groups. Circulate among groups, listening, observing (intervening only to support the learning process), and checking the noise level. Model respect for and acceptance of the ideas of individual group members, and encourage the same respect among group members. As you circulate from group to group, encourage quiet members to share their ideas, and if you notice strong members of the group are already doing this, support their efforts.

A Final Synthesis. Have the group members contribute to a final synthesis of what they have learned, with all members in agreement with the statement. These syntheses are the basis for the whole-class discussion that follows the group work.

In the context of this chapter, the importance of co-operative learning in groups lies in its great potential for promoting interethnic friendships, and for reducing stereotypes and prejudice. This happens because of growing respect and liking for one another that develops as children with a wide variety of individual differences learn together and contribute to the goals of the group.

Learning Centres

If children are to be encouraged to work independently, there must be a place within the classroom for them to carry out such tasks and projects. One way to arrange this is by setting up with each new unit an interest corner or learning centre that will provide a highly motivating set of learning experiences related to the expected outcomes for that unit — the concepts, skills, and attitudes you hope will be developed.

In Chapter 5, you considered the preparation and organization of learning centres. This section extends the discussion of learning centres by focussing on the great potential of centre activities for providing for individualization of learning and other important outcomes.

LEARNING CENTRES: GOALS AND GUIDELINES

Goals. Learning centres are designed to introduce new material; to reinforce or enhance the development of specific concepts; to give practice in the development of psychomotor skills; and to teach, reinforce, or enrich process and problem-solving skills. By giving children autonomy of learning and frequent opportunities for choice, the potential for creative responses is increased. The motivating quality of the tasks and the incentive for children to add to the centre their own collections and their own questions also lead to important affective outcomes such as interests and positive attitudes toward science.

Guidelines. Both thematic units and science-based units lend themselves to the creation of interest centres in a self-contained area of the classroom, with an attractive backdrop highlighting the topic under consideration and as much counter space as can be managed for a collection of specific learning activities.

The centre should change with each new unit. It is meant to focus attention on the theme and provide a location for teacher-produced activities and related projects and ideas for further investigations, either generated or selected by students. Science interest centres can be located near a window to accommodate growing things, and preferably near the language arts centre so that related science trade books and reference materials can be shared.

If the whole class is working within the same topic or theme, it's advisable to begin with common activities, with children working in groups, and to provide for diversity as the unit progresses through a variety of learning centre tasks that vary in difficulty (from simple to complex) and concreteness (from concrete to abstract). Within a science topic or integrated theme, it is possible to spread out in a number of directions, to challenge the most gifted students and find alternative paths of learning for those who need extra help with skill or concept development. Think of a learning centre as a collection of related task cards, games, puzzles, project ideas, challenges, opportunities for further practice — all of which motivate children and "trick them into learning."

This is by no means haphazard or unstructured, but rather a carefully planned way of teaching and learning that demands a significant investment in time at the beginning, especially when you are planning instruction for a whole unit and selecting core and optional activities, some for whole-class activities and others as learning centre tasks. It is important not to try to develop too many activities all at once. Start instead with *one* set of task cards, or *one* game or puzzle, for *one* child and then add new activities as needed each time the unit is retaught. Remember that each time you add a task to meet some specific need, you will have it to use in a centre another year for another child or group of children. For true individualization you will need a variety of multilevel, multisensory activities for children to choose from, according to their interests and abilities.

----

activity 11.6 — DESIGNING A LEARNING CENTRE

Working with a partner, choose a unit from an activity-oriented module or textbook series. Using the ideas discussed and other ideas that you may have, design a learning centre to be used to accompany the unit. The learning centre should stimulate the interest of all of the children in the topic and provide a variety of learning tasks for children at several individualized levels.

Use the following guidelines in developing the centre:

◆ Start by sketching an attractive backdrop or bulletin board, focussing on the unit or topic. Think about how to display safety rules, directions, labelled diagrams, charts, and children's contributions.
◆ Read through the unit and define the objectives to be accomplished, focussing on the directions children's learning can take.

- Develop a number of activities, varying the nature of the tasks, e.g., boxes of task cards, games, puzzles, questions, manipulative materials for exploration and discovery, and for skill and concept development.
- Develop some activities to be done individually, in pairs, and in small and large groups.
- Make lists of materials needed and identify the location of other resources.
- Provide for individual differences by having tasks at varying levels of difficulty, and by catering to varied interests.
- Decide how you will introduce the centre to the children and organize its use.
- Allow for choices, sharing, and "just for fun" activities.
- Plan ways to evaluate children's progress, based on the unit and lesson objectives. Allow children in pairs to check each other's responses, and provide opportunities for self-evaluation.
- Plan where to store unfinished work so that it can be resumed later. Prepare individual folders for finished work.

Perhaps you would like to go beyond planning the design of the centre and actually prepare a backdrop, along with a number of learning centre activities for "imagined" children. Think of the varying needs of the children as you prepare the items and also build into your centre as many different kinds of tasks as you have time for. Shoebox kits are easy to assemble and easy to store until all centres are ready. Clear instructions should be included and there should be some means of evaluating whether the child has indeed accomplished the task.

If other student teachers become involved with this project, you could set up a series of centres, week by week, toward the end of the semester, transforming the area where you are working and getting a real feeling for how your classroom will one day be transformed as you create learning centres to meet the needs of your students. The finished products will be even more effective if the centres sample a variety of topics and a number of different grade levels.

❏ Reflecting and Sharing

The last component of the activity is one that you will become involved with sooner or later as you discover the advantages of this way of providing for individual differences. It is sufficient at this point to focus on developing learning centre tasks to provide for specific needs. As you prepare learning centre tasks for a certain unit, you will acquire a sense of the great potential of learning centres for individualization of instruction and for developing in students the ability to learn independently.

◆ ◆ ◆ ◆ ◆

THE ROLE OF COMPUTERS

Another way to personalize instruction and provide for individual differences within your classroom is through the use of computers. Schools are recognizing more and more their value as educational tools and as an educational medium that has tremendous motivational value for children. Think of reasons for this as you become involved in Activity 11.7.

---

activity 11.7

THE COMPUTER: ITS ROLE IN ELEMENTARY SCIENCE

Reflect on the following statement from Abruscato's (1986) resource book for teachers, *Children, Computers, and Science Teaching: Butterflies and Bytes.*

> Now, for the first time in the history of education, science teachers have the potential to add something to the student's learning environment that is so powerful, it makes the impact of a full-color animated film on the exploration of Jupiter pale by comparison. This special resource is, of course, the computer (20).

◆ In a co-operative learning group, pool your reflections on Abruscato's statement.
◆ Think of ways in which computers can help you provide for individual differences among your students.
◆ Present your group's reaction to the class, and listen to the reactions of other groups.

☐ Reflecting and Sharing

The best way to follow up on the thoughts that evolved from your group discussion on computers and learning is to read Abruscato's book. The great potential of the computer will come through vividly as you read.

The thoughts in the remainder of this chapter and the next will also help you to crystallize your thoughts on the power of computers to provide for individual differences among *all* children.

Computers and the Personalization of Teaching/Learning

The interactive nature of computers encourages active learning, independence, and a sense of control, especially if the computers are used for a number of different purposes. The following is a discussion of the ways in which computers and computer software can enrich the science learning environment and provide for individual differences.

SIMULATIONS

A real-life problem is presented in a game-like format, with the student required to make decisions as the scenario unfolds. Environmental education issues lend themselves to this type of software. Simulations can also be models of how machines work or can teach the structure and function of the circulatory or other body systems. Another important use of simulations at the elementary level is to enable children to study science experiments that would be dangerous, expensive, complex, or simply impossible to replicate in the classroom. Simulations are available on such subjects as earthquakes, volcanoes, dinosaurs, and piloting a plane.

TUTORIALS

Tutorials provide a question-and-answer interactive format for learning new concepts or skills. They individualize learning by ascertaining the entry level of the student and by providing remediation or enrichment. Topics such as the food groups and the planets in the solar system (and their relative distances from the sun), or skills such as graphing, can be learned through tutorials.

DRILL AND PRACTICE

Using computers, learners work at their own pace and level of difficulty, with periodic tests of retention and as much repetition as necessary to achieve mastery of specific learning tasks. Abruscato (1986), while pointing out the risks of alienating children from science by drill and practice, nevertheless suggests many advantages of computer programs over traditional worksheets for this purpose. He suggests that software may be useful for review if it is entertaining and engaging, with creative animations, questions, and related diagrams in colour, and if it offers immediate feedback on whether answers are correct or incorrect, provides immediate reinforcement of correct answers, and supplies the correct answers immediately after an incorrect response.

WORD PROCESSING

The use of computers for word processing is becoming more and more important because of its value in helping children to express themselves clearly in writing.

Computers offer an excellent opportunity for students to review and practice in an exciting and entertaining way what they have learned.

Students begin by inputting their first drafts, and then check and edit their own work, "publishing" the revised version — a skill as important in science as in English. Again, the motivational quality of seeing one's observations in print as well as the ease with which descriptions can be improved are incentives to students to keep good records. Children working in a group can contribute individually to the final report as time allows, so that there is the satisfaction that comes from personal growth as well as from group goals.

DATA PROCESSING

Students are often asked to look for and classify information. Children in a Grade 3 class, for example, could work in pairs, choosing an animal they would like to find out more about. They could use graphics to draw their animals and decide beforehand on categories of information they need, such as description, habitat, food, reproduction, and so on. Information can be stored under each of these headings to form a substantial database that can be accessed and shared by all children in the class. Contrast this with older methods where a "project" was a collection of notes on an assigned topic, copied painstakingly from encyclopedias and trade books and put into a binder for presentation to the teacher for grading. With modern data processing methods, positive attitudes toward research and improved research skills develop and carry through to the higher grades.

INTERFACING

An interface is a device, composed of a circuit board, that connects a computer with other pieces of equipment so that they can be operated jointly and work as a unit. Interfacing leads to *interactive learning,* thereby increasing the potential for individualization. Examples of devices using interactive technologies are *microcomputer-based laboratory* (MBL), *interactive video* (IV), and interactive formats of *compact disc read only memory* (CD-ROM).

Microcomputer-Based Laboratory (MBL). With microcomputer-based laboratories, the computer may be connected to sensors or probes that measure temperature, light, sound, pulse rate, and so on. The data are stored, charted, graphed, and analyzed. The computer also allows students to input their own data, and to watch as their findings are displayed in new formats.

Interactive Video (IV). Among the most powerful in the new era of interactive technologies is interactive video through computer-controlled laser videodiscs. The pictures can be accessed in any order by the computer and are shown on the video monitor while sound is played by the computer's sound system. Instead of the "diagrams" of natural objects available on standard computer software, real-life photographic images are possible through interfacing a computer with a videodisc player.

Mashiter (1988) suggests that educational technology "should not aim to improve *teaching,* but to enhance *learning,*" and that the potential for learning in the use of interactive video is enormous if the design of videodiscs in the future is "education-led" rather than "commerce-led" (450).

All of the types of lessons described above — drill and practice, tutorials, data processing, and simulations — can be enhanced through the use of interactive video. The lessons can be produced by a teacher or the students. Programs are available to facilitate the process, and if done with the whole class, beginning with a flowchart for the lesson, the experience becomes an exercise in group problem solving. The amazing potential of this technology for motivation and individualization of learning is well recognized by educators (Howe 1983; Abruscato 1986; Mecklenberger 1989).

Compact Disc-Interactive (CD-I). The technology that created the audio compact disc also led to the invention of the *compact disc read only memory*

(CD-ROM) disc, on which it is possible to store immense amounts of machine-readable data. Mary Budd Rowe's (1987) *Science Helper K–8,* which is a compilation of nearly 1000 lesson plans for science experiments and activities selected from NSF-funded curriculum projects, is an example of a full-text document stored in CD-ROM. The interactive format of the compact disc (CD-I) extends the potential of CD-ROM for interactive learning by including a variety of media (multimedia). An example is Encyclopedia Britannica's *Compton's Multimedia Encyclopedia,* which includes maps, graphs, charts, and high-resolution pictures as well as sound, thus increasing the potential for interactive learning.

CD-I is described (Van Horn 1991) as an "enabling technology" (122) in that the base technology is being improved and new applications sought for use in education. An example of CD-I discs is the Interactive Production Association's program *Tell Me Why,* designed for 7- to13-year-olds. The discs are based on hundreds of questions children ask. They offer five options within a museum metaphor, allowing the student in one of these to enter one of five doorways, access museum exhibits, and select the exhibits they want to work with.

The interfacing possible through the new media enables students to have greater creative participation in the learning process and greater control of their own learning.

NETWORKING

Databases from across the continent and across the world are shared by schools participating in networks such as the National Geographic Society (NGS) Kids Network (1988). Through such networks, "environmentalists" in hundreds of elementary classes construct their own devices for collecting rain, measure its pH, record and graph the data with the computer program provided by NGS, and send the data to team members in other schools and to the NGS national network computer. Each of the participating classes is furnished with the compiled data on colour maps showing levels of acid rain recorded in various regions throughout the continent.

EVALUATION OF SOFTWARE

It is important that the software chosen for student use in tutorials, simulations, drill and practice, and so on be pedagogically appropriate. While computers have been improved and made more accessible, the quality of commercially produced software has lagged behind. Few technologists have training in education, and few teachers have the time to develop programs. The latter is the recommended route, since teachers are much more likely to match instruction to objectives. In England, groups of primary teachers have become disillusioned with much of the available software in mathematics, which merely provides repetitive drill and practice (already available at an infinitely lower cost in the back of school textbooks). These teachers have begun to collaborate on the development of their own programs.

The task of evaluating software is not an easy one, although checklists have been developed to help teachers with the process, using criteria grouped under such headings as policy issues, subject-matter standards, instructional quality, and technical quality.

Even the best software should be thought of as a teaching aid and not as a replacement for the teacher. The best software, like the best teaching, is the kind that encourages interactive learning, with children active participants in their own learning, developing skills and attitudes that will prepare them for living in the "information age."

There are many ways to use computers as a technique for individualizing learning, all of them extremely motivating to children. The data from a survey by *Computers in Education* (1991) indicated that the number of computers in Canadian schools had tripled in the three years prior to the survey, and that there was an increased emphasis on supplying computers at the elementary level. The survey revealed that provinces are recognizing the role of the computer in teaching information processing, and in allowing children to use a wide variety of thinking, problem-solving, and decision-making skills that simulate the way situations are dealt with and problems solved in real life.

◆ ◆ ◆ ◆

LOOKING BACK AND LOOKING FORWARD

This chapter has emphasized the uniqueness of every child and the need to provide for individual differences in interests, abilities, learning styles, cultural background, and gender.

Providing for a wide range of individual differences means, first of all, having a wide range of teaching strategies and specific teaching skills at your command, so that most needs are met.

To provide for differences in interests and abilities, a number of strategies have been suggested, including the use of open-ended investigations with many opportunities for choice; differentiated instruction, using programs with core, extension, and enrichment components; integrated approaches; and resource-based learning.

Individual differences in learning styles, such as learning modality preferences and differences linked to personality, have been identified. Differences in cultural background are reflected in different learning styles, as well as in differences in behaviours, value systems, and world views. The school has a role to play in teaching students to recognize cultural differences and to accept and respect these differences. Discrimination, prejudice, and stereotyping are unacceptable attitudes that the schools can help to prevent through cultivating a climate of respect for the cultural and linguistic differences of all students.

Strategies for developing positive attitudes toward others and improving the self-concept of children from minority cultures include ethnically mixed co-operative learning groups and peer tutoring. Peer tutoring is also used as a learning strategy in co-operative learning, to increase the effectiveness of the group by teaching knowledge and skills to group members who need the help.

Among other individual differences are those directly related to gender bias in the classroom — a bias that has often begun in the home before children come to school. The inequality of opportunity and the underrepresentation of girls in high-school and university science courses may be a result of sex-role stereotyping much earlier in life. Schools should avoid practices that reinforce the stereotypes and should begin interventions that increase the likelihood that girls can participate equally in science and science-related careers.

You have reviewed several techniques found to be effective in providing for individual differences — co-operative learning groups, learning centres, and the use of the computer in the classroom. Some of the same techniques can be used effectively to provide for individual differences among exceptional children who may be joining your class, and the gifted and talented children who are already there. The next chapter will focus on meeting the needs of exceptional children and helping them to reach goals developed specifically for them. It will explore the potential in elementary science for involving exceptional children in successful school experiences that will enhance their self-concept and prepare them for life.

CANADIAN ACHIEVEMENTS IN SCIENCE

DALE RUSSELL (B. 1937)

Dinosaurs and other related creatures are the stuff of which fantasy is made. They are also a focus of interest for pale-ontologists — scientists who attempt to make plausible and, where possible, testable inferences about the development of species through interpretation of the fossil record. Dale Russell, curator of fossil vertebrates at the National Museum of Natural Sciences in Ottawa, is one such person. He is also one of the leading figures in dinosaur research today.

Much of Russell's work has been con-ducted in Canada and China, which offer the best sites in the world on which to find evi-dence of dinosaur times, to reconstruct dinosaurs' way of life, and, of particular interest today, to explain why they appeared to become extinct quite suddenly about 65 million years ago.

Generally, species evolve and disappear sporadically over vast spans of time. Why, then, did the dinosaurs vanish? Speculations range from sudden global cooling, retreat of the seas, and a catastrophic loss of food, to volcanic disruptions, intense radiation from a nearby exploding star, and a devasting collision with a large asteroid or comet. In his book *An Odyssey in Time: The Dinosaurs of North America* (1990), Russell concludes, "It is highly probable that the Earth was struck by a cometary body or an asteroid about 65 million years ago and that the envi-ronmental disturbances generated by the impact were too great for the dinosaurs to endure." Given the difficulty of interpreting evidence 65 million years old, it is not surprising that different interpretations abound, but, for the time being at least, Russell's view has a great deal of support.

☐ REFERENCES

Abruscato, J. (1986). *Children, computers and science teaching: Butterflies and bytes*. Englewood Cliffs, NJ: Prentice-Hall.

Abruscato, J., and J. Hassard (1976). Fostering student involvement in science. *Learning* (August/September):32–36.

American Association for the Advancement of Science (1970). *Science: A Process Approach*. Lexington, MA: Ginn.

British Columbia (1989). *Year 2000: A Curriculum and Assessment Framework for the Future*. British Columbia Ministry of Education.

Butler, C. (1991). Special report: 1991 Computers in Education Survey of Microcomputers. *Computers in Education* (March/April):11–14.

Campbell, S., D. Herridge, S. Maitson, N. Moore, and B. Williams (1992). *Explorations in Science*. Reading, MA: Addison-Wesley.

Couchman, J., J.C. MacBean, A. Stecher, and D.F. Wentworth (1971). *Examining your environment*. Toronto: Holt, Rinehart and Winston.

Encyclopedia Britannica (1990). *Compton's multimedia encyclopedia* (CD-ROM disc). Chicago, IL: Encyclopedia Britannica.

Flick, L. (1989). Will the real scientist please stand up! *Science Scope* (November/December):6–8. Washington, DC: National Science Teachers Association.

Frize, M. (1993). Thoughts on gender biases. Personal communication.

Harlen, W. (1985). Girls and primary school education: Sexism, stereotype and remedies. *Prospects* 15(4).

Howe, S.F. (1983). Using interactive video. *Science and Children* (September):13–14. Washington, DC: National Science Teachers Association.

Johnson, D.W., R.T. Johnson, E. Holubee, and P. Roy (1984). *Circles of learning: Cooperation in the classroom*. Alexandria, VA: Association for Curriculum Development.

Johnson, R.T., and D.W. Johnson (1986). Action research: Learning in the science classroom. *Science and Children* (October):31–32.

———. (1990). A message to teachers on structuring students' interaction in the classroom. In L.W. Trowbridge and R.W. Bybee, *Becoming a better secondary science teacher,* 87. Columbus, OH: Merrill.

Kaplan, S.N., J.B. Kaplan, S.K. Madsen, and B.K. Taylor (1973). *Change for children: Ideas and activities for individualizing learning.* Santa Monica, CA: Goodyear Publishing.

Kelly, A., J. Whyte, and B. Small (1984). *Girls into Science and Technology, Final Report.* London: Project Report to the Schools Council, Shell UK Limited and the Department of Industry Education Unit.

Kenney-Wallace, G. (1988). Introduction. *Strategies: Intervention techniques to retain women in mathematics and science studies.* Toronto: York University. Women in Science, Hopefully (WISH).

Mashiter, J. (1988). Interactive video in science. *School Science Review* (March):446–50.

Mecklenberger, J.A. (1989). Technology in the 1990s: Ten secrets for success. *Principal* (November):6–8.

National Geographic Kids Network (1988). Cambridge: MA: Technical Education Resource Center (TERC).

Rowe, M.B. (1987). *The Science Helper K–8* (CD-ROM disc). Florida: University of Florida.

Russell, D. (1990). *An odyssey in time: The dinosaurs of North America.* Toronto: University of Toronto Press.

Saskatchewan (1990). *Science: A Curriculum Guide for the Elementary Level.* Saskatchewan Education.

Science Council of Canada (1982). *Who Turns the Wheel? Proceedings of a Workshop on Science Education of Women in Canada.* Ottawa: Ministry of Supply and Services.

————. (1984). *Science for Every Student: Educating Canadians for Tomorrow's World.* Ottawa: Ministry of Supply and Services.

Shepardson, D.P., and E.L. Pizzini (1991). Gender bias in the classroom — A self-evaluation. *Science and Children* (November/December):38–41.

Stief, V., and P. Williams (1991). *Innovations in Science, Level 4.* Toronto: Holt, Rinehart and Winston.

Tell Me Why (CD-I discs) (1991). Santa Monica, CA: Interactive Production Associates.

Tobin, K., and P. Garnett (1987). Gender-related differences in science activities. *Science Education* 71(1):91–103.

Van Horn, R. (1991). *Advanced technology in education.* Pacific Grove, CA: Brooks/Cole Publishing.

CHAPTER 12

Teaching Exceptional Children

PROVIDING FOR INDIVIDUAL DIFFERENCES
sets the stage for successful
MAINSTREAMING
of the

INTELLECTUALLY CHALLENGED	PHYSICALLY CHALLENGED	EMOTIONALLY CHALLENGED

by
USING EXISTING PROGRAMS
and
MAKING ADAPTATIONS
as well as
DEVELOPING INNOVATIVE APPROACHES
such as

USING MICRO- COMPUTERS	DESIGNING APPROPRIATE ACTIVITIES	ATTENDING TO SPECIFIC LEARNING MODALITIES

and
PROVIDING FOR THE GIFTED AND TALENTED
through
MODELS FOR TEACHING THE GIFTED
and
RECOGNIZING AND FOSTERING CREATIVITY

◆　◆　◆　◆　◆

Once we reach that glittering goal of individual-

ization for every child ... exceptional children

will simply meld into the school milieu, as they,

like everyone else, are instructed in ways designed

to assist them in reaching their full potential.

MARGRET WINZER (1990)

In keeping with the theme "science for life," the past two chapters have emphasized the importance of recognizing individual differences and ensuring that the goal of "science for life" means "science for life for *all* children." Implicit in this goal is a commitment to beginning science early and continuing the child-centred approaches of the beginning years through subsequent years of schooling.

As you prepare for sciencing, either as a separate curriculum emphasis, or as part of an integrated, holistic approach to learning, your classroom will reflect your concern for each child as a special person. It will be an active, dynamic classroom rich with potential for learning, with evidence that many things are going on simultaneously — in learning centres, in co-operative learning groups, at computer keyboards, sometimes with, and sometimes without, your feedback and guidance.

In this chapter, you will continue to explore ways of providing for individual differences, this time in the context of the *mainstreaming* of exceptional children into the regular classroom. Since mainstreaming (educational integration of exceptional children into regular classes) is now an accepted policy, you will include in your planning exceptional children who will be joining your class. You will encounter wide differences in intellectual ability, as you learn to provide for *intellectually challenged* children who are mainstreamed into your classroom, as well as to meet the needs of the *gifted and talented* who are already there. Among the children you teach there will doubtless be some who have *physical challenges* — the visually and orthopedically challenged, perhaps a child who is deaf. Among your students may be a boy or girl who is *emotionally challenged*.

An exciting and rewarding aspect of planning for individual differences is that, as you enlarge your repertoire of teaching strategies and your storehouse of ideas for remediation of learning on the one hand and enrichment on the other, you are learning how to provide for a still wider spectrum of differences in ability. If the learning opportunities in your classroom are ongoing and sufficiently diverse, it is possible for children with mild mental disabilities to participate with other children in activities already in progress. It is also possible for a gifted child to find challenging tasks, as well as opportunities for choice and help with self-selected projects.

Suppose two or three intellectually challenged students are joining you for science and mathematics — would the transition be an easy one for them? How would their special education teacher have prepared them for the regular classroom, and how would you prepare your regular students to accept and help the new students? Questions such as these have been asked many times during the past two decades because of new policies and new legislation on the education of challenged persons. In this chapter, you will look for some answers as you examine changes in educational policy that have heightened awareness of the need for individualization of teaching/learning and widened the spectrum of individual differences through new policies on the mainstreaming of exceptional children.

◆ ◆ ◆ ◆ ◆

EXCEPTIONAL CHILDREN IN CANADA

There has been a phenomenal growth in the provision of special education services in Canada since the early 1970s. Coupled with a movement to expand special education services in each province, there has been a significant change in public awareness and understanding of exceptional children.

In the introduction to the book *Exceptional Children in Canada* (Winzer, Rogow, and David 1987), the authors stress that all children are "special," but "exceptional children" are those who require skilled intervention and special care in order to reach their potential. This definition encompasses those who may be intellectually, physically, emotionally, or socially challenged, as well as gifted and talented children who also require specialized help to reach their fullest potential. The prevalence of challenged students in Canada is high. A 1983 estimate (Council of Ministers of Education) puts the figure at 15.5 percent of the school-age population, although the percentages vary for different provinces.

Karagianis and Nesbit (1981), reviewing the history of special education in Canada, report that up to the mid-1970s, education for exceptional children or children with special needs was provided for the most part in segregated "special education" classes, with little interaction with students in other classes or participation in nonacademic programs of the school. Changes in the provision of special educational services in Canada have come about in the aftermath of progressive legislation in the United States (the Education for All Handicapped Children Act of 1975) and the Special Education amendments in the British Education Act of 1981, which followed the publication of the comprehensive Warnock Report in 1978. In Britain, the 1981 act legislated the integration of special children into ordinary schools, a change from the traditional system of segregating most exceptional children in special schools. In both the American and British acts, the important trend has been toward normalization, reflecting the belief that the educational and life environment for all exceptional children should be as normal as possible. To accomplish this, the process of *mainstreaming* was advocated, whereby children with special needs would be placed in the "least restrictive environment" in which their special needs could be met. This meant that challenged students would be educated, to the maximum extent possible, with their peers in regular classrooms.

Mainstreaming

Mainstreaming is more commonly referred to in Canada as educational integration. Winzer (1990) suggests that mainstreaming is both philosophy and process, defining it as "the physical, intellectual, social and emotional integration of exceptional children and youth into the regular educational milieu" (84). It is an ongoing process, requiring co-operative planning between regular and special educators, and designed to prepare exceptional children for life and for work.

In Canada, education is a provincial responsibility and there is no federal equivalent to either the U.S. Education of All Handicapped Act or the 1981 British Education Act. In 1987, six provinces (Newfoundland, Nova Scotia, Quebec, Ontario, Manitoba, and Saskatchewan) had mandatory legislation for special education (Hill 1988). New Brunswick now has mandatory legislation, and the other provinces have permissive laws that are reflected in a growing trend toward integration of special-needs children into regular classrooms. This means that, as a primary or elementary teacher, you will need a general understanding of students with special needs and challenges.

Preparing for Mainstreaming

According to Winzer (1987b), students with mild mental disabilities, although showing a wide diversity in academic and behavioural performance, "learn at the rate of one-half to three-quarters the rate of normal children. They can reach the academic standard of the later elementary grades ... [and] can develop and employ adequate social, personal and communication skills" (123).

Individualized Educational Programs (IEPS), developed by a multidisciplinary team, include a statement of each child's present level of functioning, along with a list of long-term (usually annual) goals and short-term objectives. These documents become the basis for adapting and modifying instruction to accommodate the needs of each child, providing timelines for the attainment of certain objectives and suggesting ways of monitoring progress. There should be considerable dialogue between the teacher and the special education or resource teacher, and it is helpful if there is some teacher teaming in the regular classroom so that each can learn from the other.

Imagine that the initial preparation has been accomplished, and you have in your class, along with your regular students, a number of mildly challenged children who are mainstreamed for about one-half of their school day. You have had conferences with the special education teacher, who has provided data on the students' academic and social skills, the way they react to instructional techniques and materials, and their readiness for mainstreaming. Other members of the multidisciplinary team are the principal, the parents, and a school psychologist. You have told them about your program and what might be expected of the main-streamed students as they join your class. Together you have discussed each child's IEP and how short- and long-term goals can be met.

An important aspect of a smooth transition to the mainstream is the establishment of an accepting and supportive relationship between challenged and other students. Students in the class should be provided with information on specific disabilities, and should help with peer tutoring, reading directions for activities, and recording results. Continuing co-operation with the special education teacher will help you to set realistic goals for the mainstreamed student. In turn, the special education teacher will see the potential in science activities for growth in other areas.

Science has been virtually neglected in special education programs. This seems all the more regrettable when one considers children's obvious enjoyment of science, its motivating qualities, and the opportunities it provides for successful experiences with concrete materials and phenomena related to everyday life. Even today, most IEPS focus instead on the development of life skills and the remediation of basic skills in language arts and mathematics. They overlook the great potential of science activities for developing the same basic skills and enhancing learning in other areas of the elementary curriculum.

As will be seen in the next sections, the best way to proceed is to adapt your regular program to suit the "special needs" of all of the children in your classroom. As you get to know all your students, you will plan, with the help of the special education teacher, a number of modifications that will make science more accessible to all students. You will find, also, that existing curricula for primary and elementary science can be adapted and used successfully with the hearing and visually challenged, the orthopedically challenged and intellectually challenged. Other resources are available as well to facilitate the search for information and ideas on mainstreaming.

RESOURCES FOR MAINSTREAMING

Included among the sources of information and ideas on mainstreaming are:

◆ A special issue of *Science and Children* (March 1976) devoted to science for the challenged.
◆ A teacher's guide (Ball 1978), published by the Elementary Science Study, which contains suggestions for adapting 31 ESS units for use with educable mentally challenged children.

Involving all students in the integration of exceptional students into the classroom encourages accepting relationships.

◆ A program, *Me Now* (1980), specifically designed by the Biological Sciences Curriculum Study for mentally challenged students aged 10 to 13. Another unit for the primary level has been developed.

◆ Articles in teachers' journals relating to this topic. Among these journals are *Teaching Exceptional Children* and *Special Education in Canada*. See also the many articles in National Science Teachers Association (NSTA) publications such as *Science and Children* and *Science Scope*.

◆ *Teaching Handicapped Students Science*, a resource handbook for K–12 teachers (Corrick 1981), published by the National Education Association. It contains articles dealing with the prerequisite skills needed by children who are transferring to the mainstream classroom; the goals for students participating in science classes; some approaches, strategies, and curriculum materials; and ideas for evaluation. In this collection, there are articles relating to the whole spectrum of challenged students, including insightful ideas on the rationale for science for the mentally challenged and suggestions for providing science experiences for these and other mainstreamed students.

Because of the dearth of suitable curricula, and because your mainstreamed children will be following the regular science program, you may find yourself someday rewriting both commercially produced and teacher-produced activities, adapting and simplifying task cards and record sheets, and tape-recording directions for nonreaders, always mindful of the uniqueness of individuals within each group as well as within the class.

✍ From a Teacher's Journal

Mainstreaming of exceptional children can be a successful experience for everyone when the transition is planned co-operatively by the regular classroom teacher and the challenging-needs teacher, and supported as well by the school principal and the parents. The teachers can plan together so that progress toward objectives set for the mainstreamed students is ensured. Cognitive goals are met most easily when the classroom is already set up for

(continued)

✍ **From a Teacher's Journal (continued)**

individualization of instruction, with learning centres, work stations, and a variety of group and individual tasks. Affective goals are the focus as the teachers plan co-operatively how to achieve outcomes related to socialization. Groupings vary from pairs working together to larger groups of 4 to 7, where children can learn from each other as well as develop good social and communication skills.

Objectives for the intellectually challenged child should be clear and reachable. For example, if the science topic is "Seed Dispersal," the objective for the special-needs child may be to indicate three different ways seeds travel, and to select examples of each from the science table. Parents may be asked to reinforce the new knowledge by looking for seeds in the garden or a nearby field. For students who require special assistance, such as physically challenged kids, parent volunteers and teaching assistants can help. A big plus in science lessons using concrete materials is the potential for success, for all children, that is inherent in such experiences.

Kathy White

Bonavista, NF

◆ ◆ ◆ ◆ ◆

SCIENCE FOR THE INTELLECTUALLY CHALLENGED CHILD

Intellectually challenged students are likely to be encountered most often in your classroom, since they form the largest group of children with special needs. Intellectually challenged students have poorly developed reading skills. Writing may be a genuine physical difficulty because of poor muscular co-ordination.

These students may have difficulty retaining learned material and have to learn in small stages with repetition, encouragement, reinforcement, and patience. Generally, they need help with ordered routines, so it is important that tasks are uncomplicated, brief, and sequentially ordered and presented. Menhusen and Gromme (1976) suggest that these students' sense of insecurity and low self-concept can be helped if successes are built into each task. It is important, too, that what they learn makes sense to them and applies to their everyday life.

activity 12.1 WHY SCIENCE FOR THE INTELLECTUALLY CHALLENGED?

In recent years, educators are beginning to view science as a way of providing valuable educational experiences for intellectually challenged students. How would you justify the inclusion of science in the curriculum of children with learning difficulties? Make a list of the potential benefits of science for such students.

☐ Reflecting and Sharing

Science has great potential for stimulating learning for all students, and many of the techniques for individualization that have already been suggested simultaneously promote the academic and social skills of students who are mainstreamed into regular classrooms — skills such as following directions, working productively in groups, becoming involved in learning centre activities, using computer-assisted self-instruction, and sharing projects. Other reasons for including science in the education of *all* children are its high intrinsic interest and motivating qualities, and its value in providing, through concrete, meaningful experiences, opportunities for confronting perceptual errors, increasing attention span, improving logical thinking, and achieving feelings of success and an improved self-concept.

In 1975, Mary Budd Rowe reported on research that showed how challenged students can make gains in verbal fluency, content-relevant speech, reading readiness, knowledge, attitudes, and thinking skills as a result of exposure to activity-based, inquiry-oriented science. In a moving article, entitled "Help Is Denied to Those in Need," she pleaded for "direct experience with science phenomena much earlier and in larger doses" (24) as a way of reducing the deficits suffered by different types of challenged and disadvantaged children.

Educational objectives for the primary and elementary level include a number of skills that children can be expected to acquire through the school experience. Among these are skills in accurate observation, the ability to communicate, the ability to express ideas, the ability to acquire skill with numbers, and the ability to ask good questions and learn techniques for solving real-life problems. All of these are promoted through the science program, along with personal and social skills in working with other children in groups and psychomotor skills such as handling tools and equipment.

According to British educator Janet Kite (1987), children with learning difficulties can also benefit from exposure to carefully planned, developmentally appropriate science investigations. She summarizes some of the benefits of involving intellectually challenged students in science investigations:

◆ The investigations help children with learning difficulties to organize their thoughts.
◆ They provide children with opportunities to improve skills in observation.
◆ Motivation is enhanced through handling unfamiliar material.
◆ Primary science provides another medium through which literacy and numeracy skills can be improved.
◆ Usually science learning takes place in groups, where children communicate with each other as they share and make decisions.
◆ Personal pride and a sense of satisfaction and acceptance by peers come from knowing that the group has made an important contribution to the work of the class.
◆ Science can be taught as integrated units that are meaningful because of their relevance to everyday life.

Diane Keller (1981), a curriculum developer with the Biological Sciences Curriculum Study (BSCS), elaborates further on the benefits and special opportunities for intellectually challenged students that are provided by exposure to science:

◆ Intellectually challenged children, like everyone else, are faced with life problems. Science activities can be set up so that there are real-life problems to solve. This has the advantage of developing skills in problem solving, while at the same time allowing students a sense of control over their own destiny.
◆ Opportunities for manipulating scientific equipment have motivational value and bring feelings of accomplishment.
◆ Science gives children with learning difficulties the chance to work with other students on hands-on activities and to feel capable of doing so and contributing to the work.
◆ Interaction within small and large groups enhances interpersonal skills and teaches children to function as members of a team.
◆ Vocabulary skills and concepts are reinforced as children with learning difficulties converse with others during science activities.
◆ Eye–hand co-ordination as well as fine and gross motor skills are enhanced as challenged students successfully handle equipment.

- Most intellectually challenged students learn best when the science activities are tied to problems in everyday life, such as food and nutrition, gardening, cooking, and appliance maintenance.
- Outdoor activities in science give students first-hand experience with the environment and the chance to participate in predetermined individual and group projects, with follow-up in the classroom to reinforce learning. Such activities lead to feelings of success.

Adapting Materials and Pacing Instruction

It is important that mainstreamed, intellectually challenged students follow the same program as the regular class, with the activities adapted for slower-paced, repetitive practice and alternate ways of approaching the same content. It is also important to remember that there is as much diversity among such students as there is among the students in your regular class. They learn in different ways and at different rates, and have different personalities and different "frustration levels." What works for one will not work for all students, and you will be challenged to continue your efforts to provide for those individual differences. There are a number of sources of support — the individualized educational program (IEP) for each intellectually challenged child; the personnel on the team who helped to develop that profile and who can suggest strategies for remediation of deficits; and, most important, the rewards that will come as you find that a particular activity, or a certain way of teaching, has led to success for one of your special-needs children.

CURRICULUM MATERIALS: EXISTING PROGRAMS

Most elementary science activity-oriented school science programs have a definite scope and sequence, and are easily adapted for students of all levels of ability. Also, units from the National Science Foundation programs have been adapted for exceptional learners.

Elementary Science Study (ESS). The successful use of Elementary Science Study (ESS) units has been demonstrated in a number of studies involving challenged students. Davies and Ball (1978) found that using ESS with intellectually challenged students resulted in a higher level of verbal ability and the development of science skills, even in a relatively unstructured learning setting.

Science Curriculum Improvement Study (SCIS). In another study involving Science Curriculum Improvement Study (SCIS) units (Atwood and Oldham 1985), the activities were found to require little modification. Teachers had strong, positive feelings about teaching science to intellectually challenged students, which contrasted with earlier research that pointed to teacher concerns about successful mainstreaming.

Textbook Series. Some of the textbook series that offer a minimum of reading and many hands-on activities and pictorial illustrations to aid reading can be successfully adapted for use with exceptional children, as illustrated in Figure 12.1.

Whatever the program, and whether the aim is to develop process skills or concepts, the steps must be sequenced appropriately, and instructions should be clear and concise. Predictability is important. The routine for doing a science activity should be repeated, with the steps following the same sequence each time. Again, repetition and overlearning should be employed, with plenty of time allowed for the process.

Computers in Special Education

As more computers are purchased by school systems and used in special education classrooms, their great potential for facilitating and strengthening learning for intellectually challenged students is beginning to be realized. Computers can provide direct, self-paced, individualized interactive instruction to motivate the learner and raise self-esteem, while freeing the teacher from the need to arrange hours of repetitious drill and practice. The necessary skills involved in using the computer and appropriate software can be taught in the special education classroom and brought into the regular classroom.

Charles MacArthur and David Malouf (1984) of the University of Maryland are experimenting with the use of computer-assisted video instruction (CAVI) to teach functional and social skills to intellectually challenged students. The skills taught include asking for assistance, understanding feedback, and accepting criticism. Computer simulations are valuable for teaching important concepts in science. The motivational aspects of computers make them a valuable tool for learning.

Charles Norman and Grace Malicky (1987) of the University of Alberta point to the necessity for teachers to become computer literate so that articulation is maintained between the two different environments in which special education students find themselves — the special education classroom and the regular classroom. Students gain self-confidence when they have mastered the skill before entering the mainstream and can use the same software in both locations. As pointed out earlier, the choice of software is a crucial element in success. The

FIGURE *12.1*

A Large Charge

Here is a way to produce a really large electric charge.

You will need:

◆ a plastic bag
◆ two long rubber bands
◆ a thin aluminum pie pan
◆ a woollen scarf or glove
◆ a fluorescent lamp

Stretch the rubber bands across the pan. They should cross one another.

Lay the bag flat on the table. Rub it several times with the woollen scarf or glove.

With one hand, lift the pan by the rubber bands. But be sure to keep your fingers from touching the pan.

With the other hand, pick up the bag by one edge. Bring the bag and the pan together.

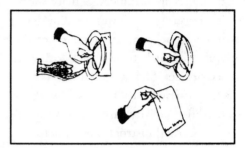

While they are together, ask someone to touch the pan. Just one quick touch will do.

Now take the pan away from the bag. Still keep your fingers from touching the pan.

Right away, bring the pan up to your nose. What do you feel? What do you hear?

Now try all these steps again. But do them in a dark room or closet.

What do your friends see when you bring the pan to your nose? What happens when you touch the pan to one end of a fluorescent lamp?

Source: V.N. Rockcastle et al. (1984). *Addison-Wesley Science, Teacher's Guide, Level 6,* 143. Menlo Park, CA: Addison-Wesley.

software must be appropriate to the needs of the learner, educationally sound, and technically accurate and easy to use. Interactive video has promise as an instructional medium that can hold students' attention and provide remedial instruction for intellectually challenged students.

Activity Sheets

Commercially produced activity sheets can be modified for exceptional learners, with larger print, lower reading level, and clear illustrations that show exactly what is to be done at each step of the activity. Janet Kite (1987) redesigned the pupil workcards from the "Moving Around" topic in the Learning through Science project. She modified them to suit the level of the children in a special class as they carried out "fair tests" with toy cars rolling down a ramp. An example of a modified activity card for this investigation is illustrated in Figure 12.2.

Recorded instructions for activities, with simple illustrations, help to alleviate reading problems and at the same time motivate students to read. Pairing a reader with a nonreader is also a good idea. Because the slow learner is over-whelmed by large amounts of factual material, charts can be supplied for recording information (as shown in Figure 12.3). These should require a minimum of writing.

Choosing Content

Content should take into consideration the limit of the intellectually challenged child's comprehension. The emphasis should be on direct involvement with concrete materials, either in small groups or individually in centres. Ideas grow because they are supported by observations and the evidence gathered during the investigation.

Questions should relate to the child's observation and manipulation of the materials. Vocabulary is derived also from what is there in 3-D as the child works with materials, and is reinforced through repetition, the use of labels, pictorial representation, data sheets, and so on. Remember that much more time is needed — indeed, essential — for the larger ideas to form, but once formed these ideas are retained and lead to further successes.

activity 12.2 CLOSING THE GAP

Imagine that you have spent some time preparing your class for the intellectually challenged children who will be joining you for part of the school day. You have enlisted the help of your regular students and have engendered a feeling of adventure and anticipation about the things they can do together.

FIGURE 12.2

Moving Around

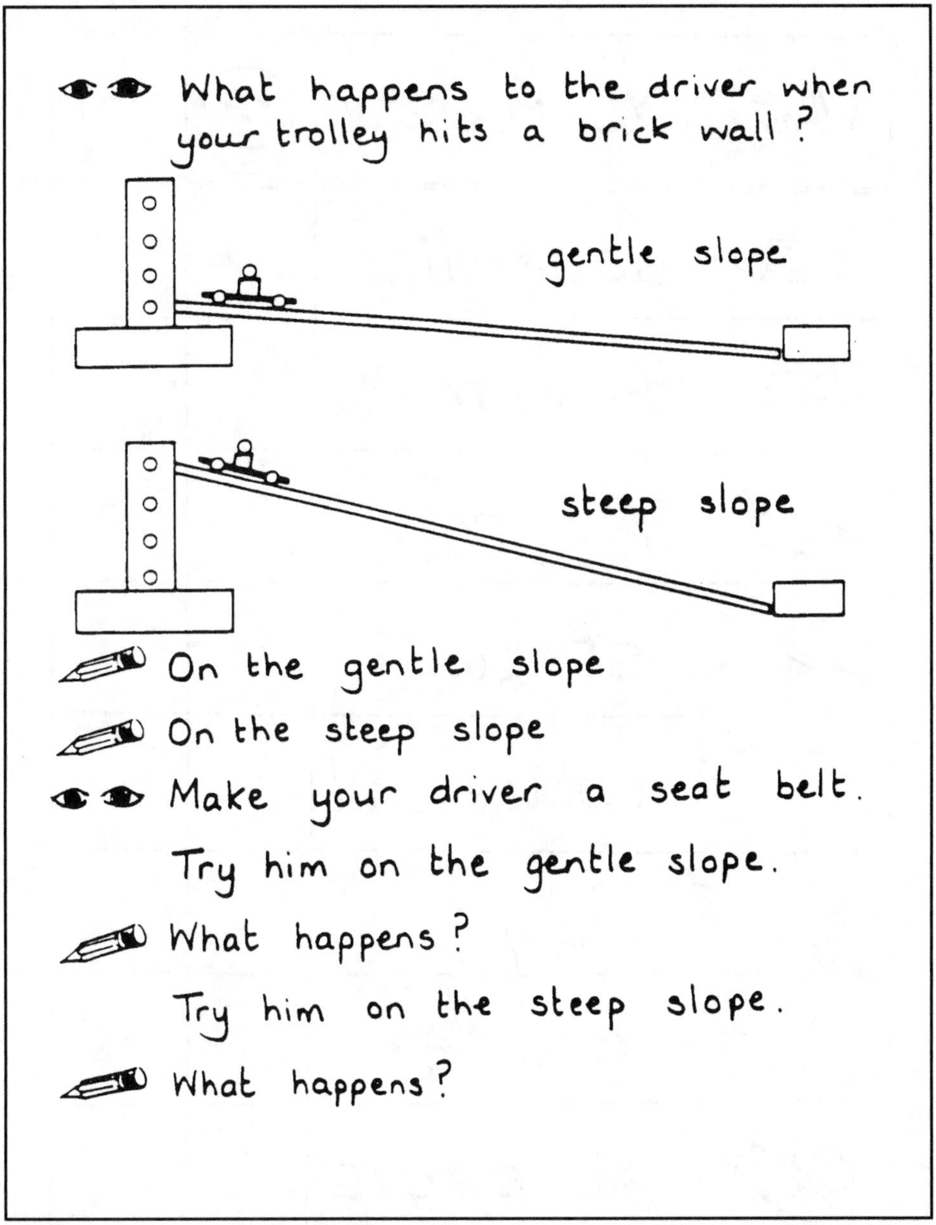

Source: J. Kite (1987). Developing a scientific approach in children with learning difficulties in the junior school. *Support for Learning* 2(1):29.

FIGURE 12.3

What Can Your Magnet Pull?

What Can Your Magnet Pull?	😊 yes	🙁 no
⬭ paperclip	✓	
♀ thumbtack		
⟁ pen cap		
╱ straw		✓
◯ cotton ball		
🔑 key		
▱ eraser		
✂ scissors		

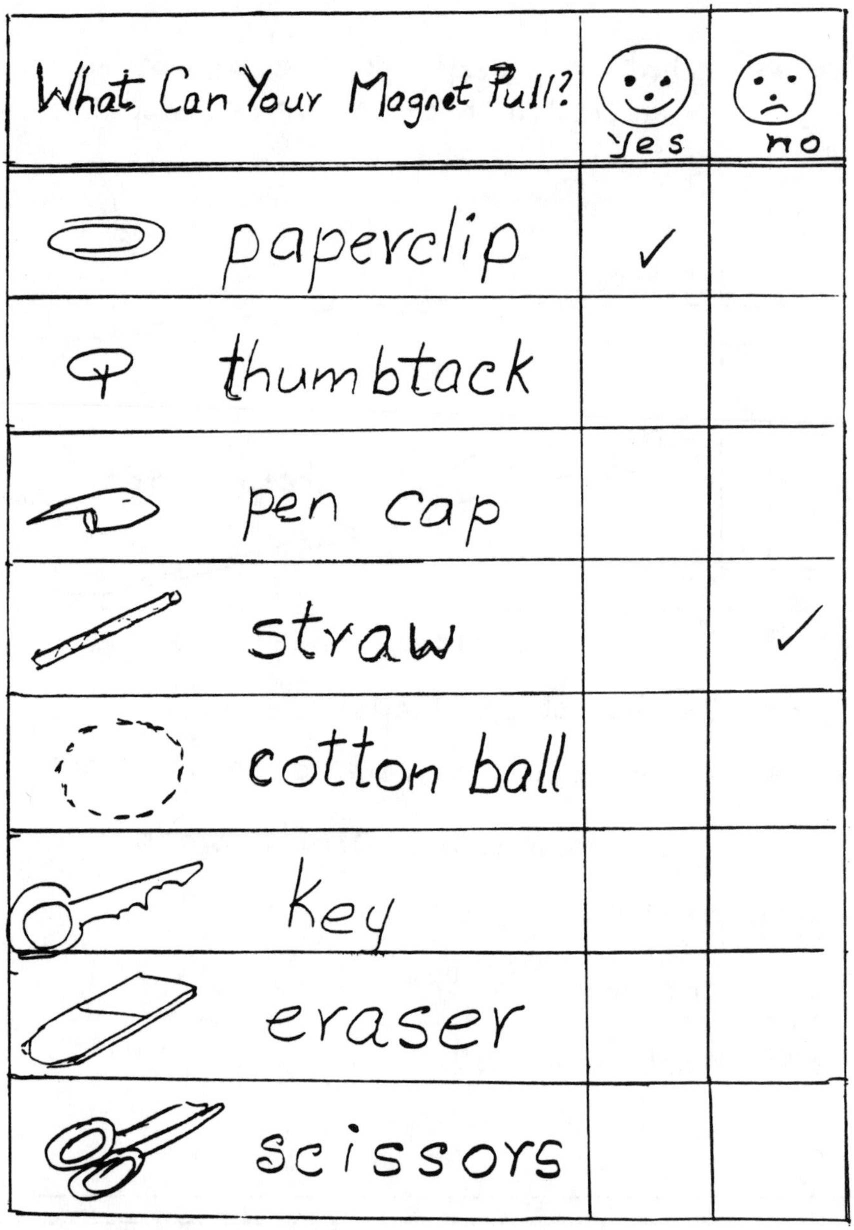

The mainstreamed children have already been prepared by their own teacher with skills that are prerequisites for learning with their peers in a much less sheltered environment.

Think about the arrangements you will make so that the transition will be smooth and the intellectually challenged students will adapt and blossom because of the positive nature of the teacher—student and student—student interactions.

❏ Reflecting and Sharing

Once your classroom is set up so that different activities are going on simultaneously, the prospect of having intellectually challenged children join the class is not a problem. There will most likely be a group that one or two of the mainstreamed students can join to work on an activity. Or there will be a task in a learning centre that the challenged child can do — either independently, if it is something being continued from another time, or with the teacher's help, if it is a new task.

One intellectually challenged child may work with a peer tutor, join a group involved in a science activity, or meet another student at a learning centre to begin an exercise on sensory observations or classification — an activity in which both can become immediately involved. Perhaps another child has been using a computer in her special class and you and the special education teacher have decided that some additional practice can be provided in this way to reinforce learning already begun. Another child may come to you to go over completed work and will be brought a small step nearer to understanding a concept or polishing a skill.

To teach children with learning difficulties, you have to be more imaginative; more enthusiastic; more willing to try new things, to take risks, to encourage active learning; more flexible with furniture arrangement and grouping and use of space; and more creative in the centres of interest that take shape in the classroom. But in the experience gained, according to Vicki Sanders (1990), director of the Special Needs Section of the Essex Education Authority in England, you too will grow as a teacher. She makes the very interesting point that teachers need children with special needs to teach them how children learn, and to show them ways of teaching that are best for all their students.

◆ ◆ ◆ ◆ ◆

SCIENCE FOR THE PHYSICALLY CHALLENGED CHILD

According to Calhoun and Hawisher (1979), the physically challenged include all students whose "physical disability impairs their mobility, coordination, stamina, communication, or learning ability to the extent that school-related goals are indeed much more difficult to accomplish, and they require special educational intervention" (5). The category "physically challenged" includes the orthopedically challenged as well as children who have visual or hearing problems.

In the aftermath of the legislation on the education of the handicapped, the National Science Foundation in the United States began funding projects designed to make science accessible to everyone, including physically challenged students who had often been barred from participation in science classes because of their disabilities. In Canada, legislation in many provinces and other educational and social policies have resulted in more and more participation of physically challenged children in regular classrooms.

The direct, hands-on experiences in inquiry-based science can contribute greatly to the general education of children with orthopedic, visual, and hearing problems. It is beyond the scope of this chapter to do more than introduce you to children with such challenges and suggest some ways in which you will modify instruction and provide a classroom environment for learning in science that will help them reach their fullest potential. There are several excellent resources, however, that can assist you both in understanding the impediments to learning for each of these challenging conditions and in planning science experiences to help overcome them.

Sourcebook: Science Education and the Physically Handicapped (Hofman and Ricker 1979) is a collection of articles and papers on mainstreaming physically challenged children at the elementary, junior high, and secondary levels that were gathered together into a sourcebook after a major national conference in the United States. Dean Brown's 1979 review of the research also examines teaching strategies, materials, equipment, and programs for physically challenged students. The literature is growing, and you will also find articles relating to individualizing instruction in science for all children in current science education and special education journals, as well as in chapters in most science methods texts.

Meeting the Needs of the Orthopedically Challenged Child

Calhoun and Hawisher (1979) offer a challenge to teachers to "learn new skills, explore new areas of knowledge and develop sensitivity and creativity to break down the barriers to the fullest possible life for persons with physical handicaps" (13).

It is not uncommon now to go into classrooms at all levels and find orthopedically challenged children sharing in science classes, working in groups with other children, being assisted where necessary, but also given the independence to do as much as possible on their own. This situation has improved since the mid-1970s when orthopedically challenged children, despite their ability to learn science and develop high levels of reasoning, were often denied the hands-on, inquiry-based experiences that could enhance their potential.

Adaptations for the physically challenged are found now in school buildings — wide doors to accommodate wheelchairs, ramps to access buildings, hand rails in corridors and restrooms. The same provision for the mobility and comfort of such students must be available in classrooms.

Social acceptance is as important as the removal of architectural barriers. Acceptance by the peer group is enhanced when the nature of a child's disability is understood. This can happen partly by the way the teacher prepares her class for the experience of helping a challenged child, and partly through frank discussion in which the orthopedically challenged child talks about what he or she can and cannot do.

The techniques emphasized earlier, such as co-operative learning in groups, involvement in learning centre tasks with a partner to assist, and participation in group and/or individual science fair projects, are all ways of ensuring that the same accepting and empowering climate will continue, leading to positive student–student interactions that benefit all students.

Your role with orthopedically challenged children will be to learn as much as you can about the medical aspects of the physical condition, to arrange the physical environment so that architectural barriers are removed to promote freedom of motion and physical activity, to emphasize multisensory experiences using everyday things, and to facilitate the child's psychological adjustment by not overprotecting but by encouraging independence.

It is important to emphasize in early childhood and elementary programs that careers in science and science-related occupations are possible despite the physical challenges, and that there are many scientists who acquired their education in a wheelchair. The American Association for the Advancement of Science (AAAS) has compiled a roster of scientists who have succeeded despite their physical challenges, and most cite as the major contributing factor enthusiastic teachers who encouraged them to participate as much as possible in what all students were doing. A similar roster of Canadian scientists would be a useful resource for your teaching.

The potential of computers for teaching physically challenged students should not be overlooked — for fun, for drill and practice, as a communication device, for access to an automated library, and for simulations of actual experiments

FIGURE 12.4

James, Grade 5

Source: James Tan, Grade 5.

that may not be possible because of restricted mobility. Instructional technology for use with students with various physical conditions is rapidly expanding. Organizations have been formed for the purpose of developing, sharing, and evaluating programs for use with the challenged. The potential in technology not only for science education but for improving daily living skills for the physically challenged will be explored in the final chapter of this book as we consider the world in which our students will work and live in the twenty-first century.

All children have the right to experiences in science that will prepare them well for that future. Berhow (1979) describes dramatic changes in behaviour of a kindergarten class of physically challenged children during one semester. Changes included gains in concept and language development, growth in self-concept, and eagerness and enthusiasm for science time each day. It is never too early to begin. Ideally, the process will have already begun in preschool and in the home and other settings for early childhood education, and what you do in kindergarten and the early years of schooling will take children another step along a continuum of increasingly positive attitudes to science and successful concept building as well as to process and skill development. Involvement with many hands-on experiences in science at this level will often give students the self-confidence to continue to succeed in laboratory sciences in junior high and secondary school, so that no doors are closed to their involvement with science throughout their future lives. This is equally important for children with vision and hearing challenges, whose problems can be ameliorated and deficits reduced through exposure to well-planned sensory experiences in science.

Meeting the Needs of the Visually Challenged Child

The term "visually challenged" is used to describe all students who require special education services because of visual problems. The degree of impairment may range from "totally blind" to "partially sighted." According to Winzer (1989), these children are more easily integrated into regular classrooms than are children with other physical conditions. Their visual impairment has caused deficits in motor ability and difficulty in understanding spatial concepts, but they are on a par with their sighted peers in intelligence and language development.

PROVIDING TACTILE EXPERIENCES

Elva Gough (1979) suggests that an important first step is to orient a visually challenged student to your classroom and to all the equipment that will be normally used. Braille labels should be applied to equipment and materials, and it is helpful, as you provide instructions, to have the student become familiar, through touch, with the equipment to be used. Your explanation should be clear and concise, naming each piece of equipment as it is included in the demonstration.

The isolation felt by blind persons is a result of the restrictive nature of their environment, which is perceived mainly by touch, and of their dependence on others because of reduced mobility. It is important to provide concrete experiences involving a large number of diverse tactile activities, to enhance dexterity, discrimination, and spatial ability. Removing the barriers to optimal learning for visually challenged children involves adapting equipment and materials and using a multisensory approach to education. Franks (1979) found that measuring equipment with raised lines, models such as pull-apart animal and plant cells, insect development kits, and simple machines are useful for sensing in the tactile mode.

A MULTISENSORY APPROACH (SCIS)

De Lucchi, Malone, and Thier (1980) of the Science Curriculum Improvement Study experimented with a multisensory approach to learning in which hearing and smelling were used to experience, for example, the reaction of vinegar and baking soda. A number of devices have been developed to allow for making nonvisual observations, for example, a buzzer to signal a completed circuit and a light-intensity sensor that uses a photoelectric cell to convert light to sound and also detect colour change.

THE SAVI PROGRAM

The Science Activities for the Visually Impaired (SAVI) program was developed as a result of comprehensive research into developing science equipment (Adapting Science Materials for the Blind, or ASMB, materials) and adapting Science Curriculum Improvement Study (SCIS) activities for blind and visually challenged students.

Activities are multisensory and interdisciplinary, with direct application to everyday life. They are designed to strengthen logical thinking and to improve manipulative skills. Both physical science and life science modules have been developed and included are outdoor activities such as a scent trail, a predator–prey game based on matching sounds, planting a garden, and visiting a petting zoo. During the trial testing of the program, it became evident that one very positive outcome was the breakdown in the social isolation normally experienced by visually challenged students. Another was the discovery of the appropriateness and value of the multisensory approach for all students, not just those for whom the program was designed.

SCIENCE AND ART EXPERIENCES

Art experiences complement experiences in science, in that both disciplines share the same procedures and study of properties — size, shape, and texture — and the same aesthetic appreciations. Hadary and Cohen (1978), who worked closely with the development of the SAVI and ASMB materials and with major earlier curricula in elementary science, developed a laboratory program in science and art experiences for blind, deaf, and emotionally challenged children in the late 1970s. The activities are adapted from SCIS, SAPA, and ESS units. The resource book for preservice and in-service teachers reflects the spirit of the program, with photographs of challenged and "ordinary" children working side by side. Sensory learning is stressed, with tactile or auditory modalities for the blind, and visual or tactile ones for the deaf. Children work in circular groups of four, so that sharing of experiences and discoveries is encouraged. Materials (which include the ASMB devices) are stored at distribution stations that remain the same all year, and are differentiated with braille labels for blind children and labels for deaf children.

Hadary (1976), along with her colleagues at the American University in Washington, reports outstanding success with the individualized science and art experiences. Many exceptional children are able to use the same craft techniques as other children, and extreme individuality and internal vision are clearly portrayed in their art. Inspiration for the activities come from study of life cycles, structure and function, sound, properties of matter, and so on. To capture the flavour of one of these experiences, use the following objectives to create a lesson plan.

activity 12.3
CREATING ROOTS: A LINEAR EXPLORATION

Science Objectives:
◆ To examine root systems developed from seeds and bulbs.

- ◆ To identify roots as both a system and a subsystem.
- ◆ To relate the structure to the function of the roots.
- ◆ To recognize similarities and differences in root systems.

Art Objectives:
- ◆ To simulate and interpret a root system in two and three dimensions.
- ◆ To express the linear quality of roots.
- ◆ To create a linear interpretation of direction: roots moving in nonstraight lines, fanning out (avoiding rocks), absorbing water and food.

Materials:
Use Plasticine, two-dimensional board and tape designs, pipe cleaners, wire, or any medium of your choice for the art experiences.

What to Do:
Teach the lesson to a small group, and discuss the potential of such activities for promoting self-confidence and love of learning.

Add your "creative expressions" to those of your classmates to make a class display.

> **Source:** D.E. Hadary et al. (1976). Interaction and creation through laboratory science and art for special children. Reprinted with permission from NSTA Publications, copyright March 1976, *Science and Children,* 32. National Science Teachers Association, 1840 Wilson Boulevard, Arlington, VA 22201–3000.

☐ Reflecting and Sharing

Your class display, like the displays resulting from such activities with children, reflects individuality of expression and gives you some idea of the potential of such integration for all children. Hadary et al. (1976) report that

> the nature of the activities and individualized approach promoted self-confidence, children expressed changes of attitudes and found learning exciting and useful, and learning with comfort replaced learning with pain (33).

Check your lesson against the sample lesson in Figure 12.5, from the laboratory science and art program.

Meeting the Needs of the Hearing Challenged Child

According to Owsley (1968), hearing challenged children are naturally curious about their physical environment and use all remaining senses to explore their world. More and more, hearing impaired children are being educated in regular

FIGURE 12.5

A Sample Science and Art Lesson

Sample Lesson
Creating the Structure of a Flower

I. *Science Objectives:*
To examine a flower and discover its structure — pistil, stamen, anthers, petals, stem.

To relate the structures of a flower to the functions.

To discover the similarities in flowers of different plants.

II. *Art Objectives:*
To reinforce clay techniques and use them in a mixed media bas relief.

To simulate a diagram of a natural object.

To create a flower that exhibits the properties of line, shape, symmetry and circularity, combining topographic and linear views.

III. *Description of Lesson*
A. Source of Design: Nature

B. Elements of Design: Bas relief of form emphasizing function as well as shape and sculpture form.

C. Techniques: Clay, utilizing ball, pinch, slab, and coil techniques.

D. Activity: Have students examine a flower to discover its structure. Have students reproduce a flower that they have examined by using clay and a variety of other materials.

IV. *Suggested Materials:*
Live flowers

Clay and clay boards

Seeds, beans, beads, and any of a wide variety of objects

Pipe cleaners

Matchsticks

Bits of cardboard

Cotton balls

Source: D.E. Hadary et al. (1976). Interaction and creation through laboratory science and art for special children. Reprinted with permission from NSTA Publications, copyright March 1976, *Science and Children,* 33. National Science Teachers Association, 1840 Wilson Boulevard, Arlington, VA 22201-3000.

classes. The enrolment in specialized schools for the hearing impaired has been decreasing, except for those who are profoundly deaf. This way, the prospects for achieving success and independence, improving social relationships, and developing language and intelligible speech are greatly enhanced.

The laboratory science and art program for blind and deaf children just described (Hadary and Cohen 1978) shows great sensitivity to the needs of these children. Through nonverbal, concrete experiences, the deaf child is encouraged to discover and internalize concepts, using language cards only during and after free exploration, and only when the child is ready for them. To prepare hearing challenged students for doing an activity, natural gestures, mime, and sign language are used.

The following suggestions are taken directly from the resource book by Hadary and Cohen:

- ◆ Have the deaf child assist with demonstrations.
- ◆ Face the class or deaf student when talking.
- ◆ Give the child freedom to explore.
- ◆ Do not stand with your back to a window or other light source.
- ◆ Use pantomime liberally.
- ◆ Demonstrate instead of giving only verbal directions.
- ◆ Use visual aids extensively.
- ◆ Use the blackboard often.
- ◆ Keep discussions to small groups.
- ◆ Seat or place participants in a circle so everyone can see everyone else's face.
- ◆ Put the question under discussion on the blackboard or on the language chart as a heading, and record the students' comments under the heading.
- ◆ Rigidly enforce "only one speaker at a time."
- ◆ Have the speaker wait a moment or two after being recognized by the leader and before starting to speak (34–35).

Teachers should not treat mainstreamed hearing challenged children any differently from other students, or force them to respond when it may be a source of embarrassment to them. However, they should be expected and encouraged to experience success.

The research on the laboratory science and art program, and other programs using experiential science with deaf children to develop cognitive skills, teach science concepts, and improve language deficits, has shown gains in achieving all of these outcomes. Previously it was thought that the language deficiency in deaf children could not be remedied because it was related to lack of stimulation in early life. However, data over the past twenty years indicate that when hearing challenged children are exposed to active learning and discovery experiences in science, language deficits are reduced.

Bybee and Hendricks (1972), using SCIS and ESS activities and objects from the children's immediate environment to foster language growth in deaf preschoolers, found gains in vocabulary and science concept development. Another study by Boyd and George (1973) showed gains in abstract categorization behaviour of deaf children aged 10 to 13, achieved through inquiry-based science instruction.

There are good indications that direct, sensory experiences in science, in which hearing challenged students are actively involved in "doing" science through hands-on, real-life experiences and direct manipulation of objects, result in gains in language performance, observing, classifying and listening skills, vocabulary enrichment, and the development of concepts and cognitive skills.

◆ ◆ ◆ ◆ ◆

SCIENCE FOR THE EMOTIONALLY CHALLENGED CHILD

Science has tremendous therapeutic value for emotionally challenged children, because it removes them from inner problems and substitutes a world of discovery and excitement that can be shared with other children. There is also an order and predictability about science that is settling to a child whose world is disordered; there is a sense of control that helps to restore self-confidence and self-esteem. A withdrawn child may suddenly come to life when something exciting happens in a group activity and the child is invited over to see. The "being wanted" is a personal and social triumph; the excitement of discovery is an affective and cognitive gain that may lead to continued interest in science.

Often a child with a behaviour problem may have a history of academic failure. The teacher's role is to build on the strengths that the student has and let the class see that these strengths are present. For example, the child can help with setting up equipment or demonstrating for the class the steps in an activity. In a mainstreamed science class, an emotionally challenged child may experience a feeling of pride if he or she is chosen to be the sighted partner for a blind child. As all children work with concrete materials in a nonthreatening environment in which the answers come from observations rather than from a book, small successes will lead to bigger ones and to feelings of self-worth.

In the six years of experience with the laboratory science and art program for blind, deaf, and emotionally disturbed children, Hadary and Cohen (1978) report that they have seen cases where the emotional disturbance disappeared with science experiences as a motivating influence. Recall that in this program art experiences parallel specific science objectives. For example, art experiences with primary and secondary colours may parallel interpretations of dissolving, colour change, miscible and immiscible substances. Their recommendation, based on the field testing of the adapted materials, is that teachers should provide for the emotionally disturbed child intellectually stimulating experiences, with a variety of sequential, orderly activities. Performance in science activities should be reinforced verbally and discussion of findings encouraged, again with the aim of developing logical, sequential thinking.

The potential for outdoor science activities, in which emotionally challenged children and their peers work in teams, has been demonstrated in the *Nature's Niche* program (Nathanson et al. 1984). The program took place in a park in Brooklyn, but it can be replicated in any nature park. Ten classes were scheduled during a twenty-week term, as well as introductory and follow-up classes related to the nature activities at the park. The experiences were multidisciplinary and projects were integrated with the regular school curriculum. Students participated in horticulture by growing their own plants and helping with a herb garden; studied animal characteristics in an animal room that housed snakes, turtles, rabbits, and guinea pigs; and were introduced to many varieties of freshwater and saltwater life in a marine science room. The students learned about local bird and sea life, reconstructing the local marshland environment and other habitats at the nature centre. Before each week's visit to the Nature's Niche Center, teachers of the emotionally challenged students were given lesson plans to prepare the students for the hands-on experiences at the park.

Evaluation of what they had learned consisted of three field trips in which the emotionally challenged students met a class of "nonchallenged" peers at the centre. They worked in teams consisting of one emotionally challenged to two nonchallenged as they practised their orientation skills and shared their knowledge. On one field trip, the emotionally challenged students acted as team leaders for the nature walk, collecting and identifying specimens and afterward introducing their teammates to habitats they had constructed themselves in class, using the library to refine their classifications and write descriptions. They enjoyed the experience of sharing their knowledge of nature with their peers, gaining academically and socially, as well as in self-esteem and self-confidence.

◆ ◆ ◆ ◆ ◆

THE GIFTED AND TALENTED: MEETING THE CHALLENGE

In the last chapter, you considered the importance of encouraging girls to continue in science so that their great potential would not be wasted and they could contribute as adults to the nation's need for people trained in science and technology. This need assumes even more importance when you consider that many of the girls who are turning away from science may also be part of another human resource that has often suffered from neglect in education — the 5 percent or more of our students who constitute the *gifted*.

Alvino and Gourley (1977) suggest that you may have gifted children in your class who are "smarter than you are," and that these pupils may absorb lessons and materials faster than the average teacher can produce them. These are the children who have the potential to be the thinkers, leaders, and creators of the future because of their high level of ability and creativity, their willingness to take risks, and their capacity for task commitment.

Recognizing and Fostering Creativity

Winchester (1985) suggests that Ontario's "shiny new legislation" on mainstreaming has placed schools in the position of being encouraged to identify, at the earliest possible moment, "those who will be our future scientists, mathematicians, sculptors, painters, composers, dancers, and so on" (70). He cites examples to show that the judgements of schools have been historically bad in the cases of some very prominent creative individuals — Newton, Einstein, Beethoven, Van Gogh, and many others whose genius schools failed to recognize. The conception of science as a discipline that ranks with art and music as a creative human endeavour indicates how difficult, and unnecessary, it is to distinguish future scientists from future artists and musicians. More important than this is for schools to recognize, stimulate, nurture, and encourage what all children have in common — their creative potential. Schools must create an environment where creativity is not stifled, but encouraged to develop.

Passow (1977) points out that if "gifted children are to become gifted adults, their creativity must be nurtured by all those who influence their development." Creativity is nurtured in an "open" environment where original ideas are encouraged, spontaneity of expression is encouraged, and the school provides students with the stimulation, motivation, and competence to behave creatively in life situations.

The importance of recognizing and nurturing creativity in gifted children is pointed out by Bybee (1980). He suggests that in fostering creativity, both the process and the product of creative thinking must be considered. Table 12.1, which indicates characteristics of creative people and ways teachers can stimulate these behaviours, is drawn from Bybee's ideas on the nurture and stimulation of creativity.

Provisions for the Gifted in Canada

Although the potential of the gifted has been recognized for some time, few provinces in the early 1980s had well-organized policies and programs to meet their needs. In a national survey by the Canadian Education Association

TABLE 12.1

Characteristics of Creative People and Ways Teachers Can Stimulate These Behaviours

Characteristics of Creative People	What Teachers Need to Do
Tolerance of ambiguity	Brainstorm for possible solutions.
Openness to new ideas and different ways of thinking	Ask questions such as "What would happen if ...?"
Fluency and flexibility	Ask divergent questions such as "How many ways could you use a plastic spoon?"
Originality — the ability to think in new, clever, or unique ways	Ask "Can you think of a new kind of alarm clock? Name your invention."
Curiosity, spontaneity, insight, fantasy	Recognize these as primary processes leading to creating. Provide a low-risk environment.
Pioneering, risk-taking spirit	Set aside a time to be used exclusively for creativity. Accept creative thinking as a purpose of education.

(Borthwick et al. 1980), in which information was gathered from departments of education, universities, and school boards, Ontario rated highest on provision of services for the gifted. Other provinces indicating active interest and support were British Columbia, Saskatchewan, Quebec, and Nova Scotia, while departments of education in the remaining provinces reported little or no direct means of support for programs for the gifted. At the university level, the range was from no courses to several courses on the topic of gifted children. The survey of school boards yielded a low rate of response and very little uniformity throughout the boards, suggesting that very few school boards had developed an integrated policy on providing for the needs of gifted and talented children.

According to Winzer (1987a), this situation is rapidly changing as society is becoming increasingly aware of the potential of Canada's gifted and talented young people. She points out the difficulties in identifying gifted students, especially those who are underachieving, and the importance of accommodating their needs within the context of the school. Early identification of gifted children is essential, followed by differentiation of curriculum and instruction to encourage exploratory behaviour, risk taking, and productive thinking, and to challenge and foster their creative potential. Differentiation of curriculum involves learning based on needs; activities that encourage higher-level thinking; more opportunities to work independently and in leadership roles; opportunities for making judgements on questions of values and morals; and time and materials for gifted children to broaden their knowledge base and pursue special interests.

Provision for the gifted may include *enrichment* (creative projects related to, but beyond, the level of the regular program); *acceleration* (reducing in various ways the time taken to complete the regular curriculum); *ability grouping* (in which gifted students interact with their true peers, usually on a part-time basis, to permit intense involvement in topics of interest); *independent study* (in which the teacher encourages and facilitates independent study beyond the classroom — in museums, libraries, and laboratories — helping students develop the skills they need to learn on their own and often learning along with them as the project expands); and *mentoring programs* (in which students study with an expert in the community a topic of interest to the student and within the mentor's area of expertise).

This section will introduce you briefly to a variety of strategies for encouraging giftedness, most of which fall into the categories mentioned above. It will review various models that have been proposed, some of which provide enrichment within the regular program, beginning with whole-class instruction and offering increasing freedom of choice as students enter an independent study or inquiry phase. In other models, gifted children are withdrawn from regular classes and grouped together for special programs. Studying these models will help you to weigh the benefits of each and prepare you to make choices when planning strategies for gifted children in your classroom.

activity 12.4   **PROVIDING FOR THE GIFTED CHILD**

As you read the remainder of this chapter and other references, compile a list of ideas to include in a plan for teaching the gifted child in the primary and elementary grades.

As you list the ideas, think about how well science-based activities and projects fit into programs designed for gifted children.

When you have compiled your list, compare it with Lenora Cohen's (1987) "13 Tips for Teaching Gifted Students" (p. 500) to see whether your ideas and hers coincide with and/or complement one another.

◆ ◆ ◆ ◆ ◆

TEACHING THE GIFTED CHILD

Whatever the strategies used for teaching the gifted, it is important that they begin as early as possible, and that the classroom environment in which they are introduced is an open one in which there is no fear of exposure or ridicule for being "different." These three beliefs set the scene for the potential of gifted children to develop and flourish rather than be hidden under a cloak of underachievement.

Early Intervention and an Open Environment

Carolyn Yewchuk (1984) of the University of Alberta points out that special programs for gifted students are usually instituted at the upper elementary or secondary level at a time when many gifted children have already become disenchanted or bored with school. It is important to begin intervention as early as possible, and, if giftedness is to flourish, to continue these special programs through the primary and elementary grades. It is crucial that teachers understand

Scheduling blocks of time for independent projects allows the creative potential of gifted students to flourish.

that gifted children, if not identified and nurtured, tend to hide their abilities and often underachieve. When there is a supportive, open environment, creativity flourishes and there is less likelihood that their potential will be missed.

This openness is evident in "learning through play," which is discussed in Chapter 7 as a valuable component of early experiences in science. Learning through play is also recognized for its potential for generating new ideas and productive thought. It is characteristic of David Hawkins's (1965) "messing about" phase of learning in science, and of the climate Romey (1980) suggests for developing "synchronicity." In both cases, the emphasis is on developing the divergent, creative, and productive thinking skills that should be fostered in gifted children.

Messing About in Science

David Hawkins (1965) suggests the need for large blocks of time if creativity is to flourish. He emphasizes the importance of play in arousing and sustaining interest in science, maintaining that the "messing about" evolves with the child, becoming the "self-disciplined probing and exploring that is the essence of creativity." As you observe children during their play, you can pinpoint areas of interest that evolve and new questions that arise which can lead to new avenues for exploration. By providing more focussed involvement in these areas, you will be encouraging giftedness in all of your students.

Fostering Synchronicity

William D. Romey (1980) has written extensively about gifted children and also about practising creative scientists. He suggests that in both cases their ways of thinking and problem solving are not always directed toward looking for cause–effect relationships. He notes that there is a high incidence of what Carl Jung called "synchronicity" in their lives. Romey cites as an example of this his own inadvertent typing of the word "R-e-a-c-h-i-n-g" when he meant to type "T-e-a-c-h-i-n-g," and suggests that it may be a "directed" mistake rather than just a slip of the finger. An environment of support, caring, and play can increase the number of such "coincidences in time and space of objects, things or ideas in which a person finds meaning" (5).

Romey suggests that to encourage giftedness in science you need to create a rich classroom environment with many opportunities for children to discover new areas of interest and to see connections in ideas and events previously thought to be separate.

From a Teacher's Journal

In a chapter pre-test or some other form of evaluation, a gifted child may already display proficiency in most of the objectives of the science program. If this happens, an alternative program can be used that parallels the program but provides enrichment and interesting things to do. Careful planning is needed to ensure that the students' needs are met by appropriate selection of alternative programming.

Sometimes ideas for extension of various science concepts are built into textbook-based programs or science modules, and the gifted child can pursue areas of interest by "going further" through additional investigations or projects. This process is most effective when mentors are available to confer with the student on specific topics, providing guidance and challenges along the way.

Diane House
St. John's, NF

◆ ◆ ◆ ◆ ◆

MODELS FOR TEACHING THE GIFTED

The Open Classroom and the SOI Model

Karnes, Schwedel, and Williams (1983) of the University of Illinois also stress the value of early identification, preferably at the preschool level, and suggest that the potential of gifted children may be actualized when the "open classroom" typical of the British Infant School is combined with a discovery approach and a framework based on Guildford's Structure of the Intellect (soi) model. The soi model recommends activities that stimulate divergent thinking, leading to fluency, flexibility, originality, and elaboration of ideas. Figure 12.6 illustrates examples of activities developed for the soi program.

FIGURE 12.6

soi-based Activities

Space Objects

Materials: five numbered pictures of "space objects"; cassette recorder and blank tape

Directions:
Pretend that you are the captain of a spaceship that is exploring outer space. You are close to a planet that you think has some sort of people on it, so you send down a scouting party to see what they can find.

When they return to the ship, the scouting crew members report that they couldn't find any people on the planet, but that they did find all kinds of strange objects. They didn't want to disturb these objects because they didn't know what they were, so they took pictures of them with their cameras and brought back the pictures to show to you. What do you think these strange objects could be? Look at each picture, and record on the tape recorder all the ideas you have of what it might be. Don't forget to say the number of the picture before you give your ideas, so everyone will know which picture you are talking about. Think of as many ideas as you can for each picture.

To Make Materials:
On a separate piece of white, heavy card-stock paper draw each of the following "space objects" as shown. Be sure to number each prominently so that the child can record the number of the object he or she is thinking about. Cover each card with clear contact paper.

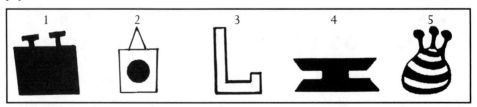

Modern Inventions

Materials: art materials; construction materials (boxes, etc.)

Directions:
An inventor is a person who makes new things that nobody has ever made before.

Figure 12.6 (continued)

Inventors make new things to solve special problems, for example, garage doors that you can open without getting out of your car.

Be an inventor and make something that no one has ever made before. Use whatever material you need to make a garbage can that a dog would especially like. Before you begin, be sure to think about what a dog would like a garbage can to be like.

Substitutions:

- a trap to catch insects alive without harming them
- a mail box that does more than hold letters and packages
- a bed that is extremely convenient for a sick person
- a television set that helps with the housework

Source: From Teaching exceptional children by M.B. Karnes, A.M. Schwedel, and M. Williams, *Teaching Exceptional Children,* Spring 1983, 133. Copyright 1983 by The Council for Exceptional Children. Reprinted with permission.

Although the work of this group focusses on the young gifted child, its methods hold promise for children through the primary and elementary grades. To begin with, the "open classroom" approach, in which risk taking is encouraged and children are given many opportunities for freedom of choice, provides a child-centred environment that stimulates and enhances learning for all children. The experiences provided have even greater potential in the early years when such an environment is combined with teaching methods, based on Guildford's SOI model, that emphasize discovery and encourage creative and productive thinking.

The Enrichment Triad/Revolving Door Model

This system for identifying and programming for gifted students has undergone extensive trial testing in both the United States and Canada. In the early 1980s, the Toronto Metropolitan Separate School Board combined the previously developed Enrichment Triad Model (Renzulli 1977) with the Revolving Door Identification Model (Renzulli, Reis, and Smith 1981). The children in junior kindergarten to Grade 4 in the program were known as the "Talent Pool." Full-time teachers of the gifted worked with one classroom teacher or librarian, designated as the "in-school enrichment teacher" for the year, who then assumed the position of teacher of the gifted, thus freeing the original full-time teachers to

FIGURE 12.7

The Enrichment Triad/Revolving Door Model

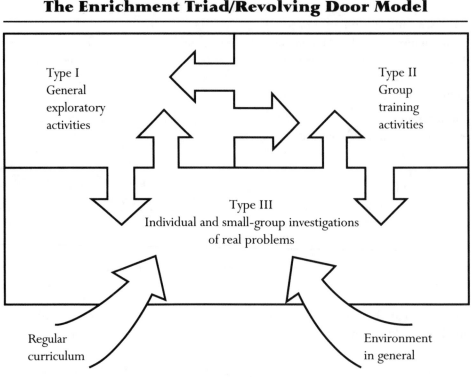

Source: S.M. Reis and A.A. O'Shea (1984). An innovative enrichment program:
The enrichment triad/revolving door model. *Special Education in Canada* 58(4):136.

work with another group of schools. It was found that the entire school (rather
than just the gifted class) benefited because of the higher student achievement
and greater interest generated by the enriched, more challenging program and
the improved quality of instruction. The regular content was covered for all
students, with the content "compacted," or covered at an accelerated pace, for
the gifted so that they would complete the same program as other students, but
would have time left over for involvement in more challenging activities. The
three types of enrichment included in the model are represented in Figure 12.7
and described below.

Type I Enrichment (General Exploratory Activities). These included novel and
interesting topics not covered in the school curriculum. Activities involved
speakers, demonstrations, field trips, and interest centres, which led to more
advanced enrichment activities for all students and a range of grade levels.

Type II Enrichment (Group Training Activities). These were arranged for an hour per week in a resource centre, with plans to extend the option to all students wishing to develop higher-level thinking processes, information gathering, and research skills. In science, students could learn science processes and then use them in experiments and problem solving.

Type III Enrichment (Individual and Small-Group Investigations of Real Problems). These involve using appropriate inquiry methods. Students are given the option of using appropriate inquiry methods to carry out an investigation of a real problem in a truly professional manner. Students work with mentors in the school or community, and produce and present to their classmates a research paper on a problem. The Action Information Message in Figure 12.8 is representative of Type III Enrichment pupil investigations, which are followed by a contract or management plan.

The Mentor-Directed Enrichment Project

Gray and Rogers in British Columbia (1982) adapted the Type III Enrichment component of the Enrichment Triad Model, in which much teacher time is spent helping gifted elementary students identify and delimit a real problem, encouraging intrinsic motivation throughout the investigation, and assisting the students in preparing an effective presentation of their findings.

A four-phase model was developed in which preservice teacher trainees, rather than teachers, served as mentors for four to five pupils. These mentors offered to share their expertise on certain topics. The experience benefited not only elementary school pupils but also the teacher trainees, who profited from coming to grips with methods of raising thought levels and guiding pupils toward independence and self-direction.

The Purdue Three-Stage Model

The Purdue Three-Stage Model is an adaptation of a three-stage model that is based on the characteristics of the gifted and on how science instruction can be organized to meet their needs. The Purdue model was designed to develop students' thinking skills, to allow interaction with other gifted children, and to develop creativity and independence in learning. Stage I encourages the development of fluency, flexibility, originality, and elaboration of ideas through divergent thinking. Stage II trains children to use creative problem-solving abilities through brainstorming, synectics, and other ways of generating unique ideas. Stage III invites children to begin an area of research of interest to them. A mentor can be available to the gifted student at this stage. The ultimate goal is for

FIGURE 12.8

Action Information Message

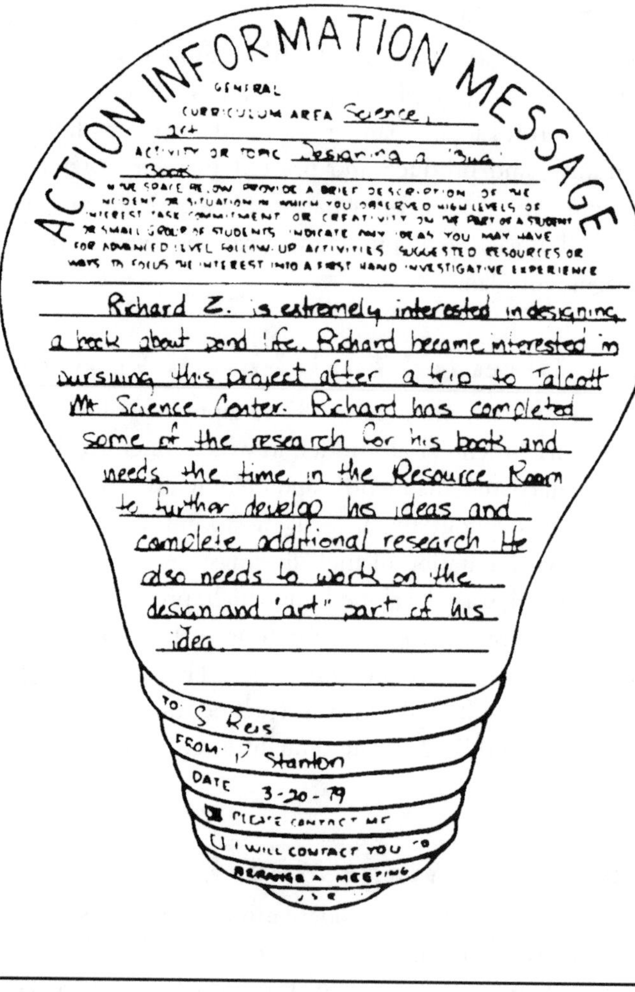

Source: S.M. Reis and A.A. O'Shea (1984). An innovative enrichment program:
The enrichment triad/revolving door model. *Special Education in Canada* 58(4):137.

the student to be able to conceptualize in science, to develop research skills, and
to become a producer of knowledge — in other words, in a very real sense, to
become a scientist. Figure 12.9 shows the kinds of thinking represented in the
model.

FIGURE 12.9

The Purdue Three-Stage Model

		CONTENT
Stage III Independent Study Project	In-depth Research / Experiment	
Stage II Problem Solving and Creative Problem-Solving Techniques	Group Investigations of Teacher-Selected Problem	
Stage I Convergent and Divergent Thinking Skills	Integrated Science Process Skills Basic Science Process Skills	

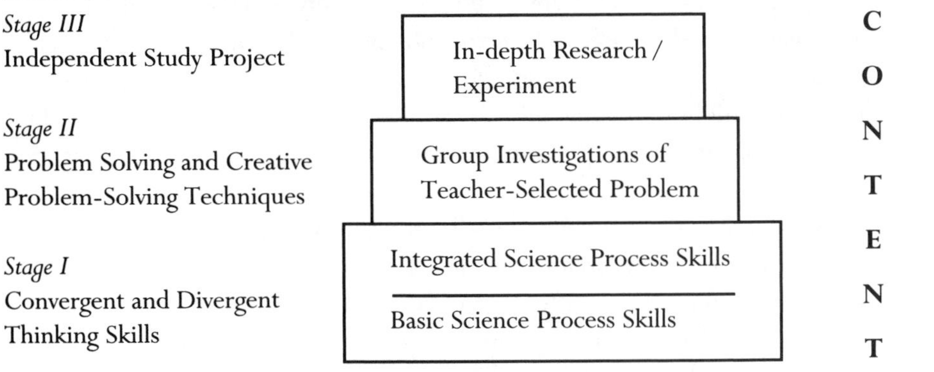

Source: S.M. Hoover (1989). The Purdue Three-Stage Model as applied to elementary science for the gifted. *School Science and Mathematics* 89(3):247.

Individual Science Packets

Blurton (1983) suggests that individual science packets can help the teacher to provide acceleration and enrichment for gifted students. The packets have an attractive cover with a synopsis of the unit, a list of objectives, a pre-test, a series of lessons with clear directions, a "learning cycle" format (exploration, elaboration, and application), a suggested deadline for completion, and a post-test. Several individualized science packets can be prepared, or one packet can be used with different students. Gifted children can also prepare science packets for other students.

◆ ◆ ◆ ◆ ◆

TEACHING THE GIFTED IN THE REGULAR CLASSROOM

Lenora Cohen (1987) offers "13 Tips for Teaching Gifted Students" that transcend programs and models and take you into the strategies you can use, the climate you will try to establish, and the organizational details that will make your efforts successful. She suggests that most provisions for the gifted must take place in the regular classroom rather than in pull-out programs. "Gifted children," she says, "are gifted *all* the time," and the following tips are designed to help with your planning from day to day as you follow through with your commitment to individualize instruction for all your students.

1. *Establish classroom setting* — noncompetitive, open, with individualization built into your regular program.
2. *Provide a safe environment* — where errors and risk taking are tolerated.
3. *Organize resources* — books, computers, community members, and guest lecturers, giving children greater control and choice of enrichment activities.
4. *Offer exposure and "Tune in"* — Provide a variety of questions and topics, and allow gifted children to "tune in" to what they want to explore. Use "webbing" as a brainstorming technique to suggest a variety of directions the investigation may take.
5. *Understand needs* — assessing skills (communication, psychomotor, social) and providing for them on an individual basis.
6. *Promote peer interaction* — with other children of like ability.
7. *Be a "child stretcher"* — maximizing students' abilities to do their best and to advance as quickly as possible in skill areas.
8. *Harness "child power"* — giving the gifted opportunities to work on world or moral issues, perhaps spearheading research for a class project.
9. *Vary content* — by acceleration, or enrichment, or moving through stages to a high level of abstraction in a subject area.
10. *Provide tools* — for further learning, such as creative-thinking and problem-solving skills, research skills, science process skills, use of technology, higher-level thinking, and communication.
11. *Vary products* — through imaginative assignments, such as newspaper articles and class surveys, with attention to accuracy and organization of findings.
12. *Investigate real problems* — questioning, experimenting, and adding information to the field.
13. *Find uniqueness* — by recognizing special gifts, such as leadership ability, gifted expression, creative thinking, and kindness, and nurturing them.

◆ ◆ ◆ ◆ ◆

THINKING BACK

Lenora Cohen's final tip for teaching gifted children, "Find uniqueness," has been the focus of this chapter, as well as of the previous chapters included in this section of the book. It takes you back to the points made about welcoming the diversity among the students in your classroom, and about placing their interests and needs at the forefront of all your decision making as you seek to maximize the potential for learning in every child. How did your list of ideas for Activity 12.4 compare with Lenora Cohen's "13 Tips"? Did you find that many of her ideas complemented yours?

What is needed for the gifted is qualitatively different instruction, which will tax your ingenuity as a teacher but open doorways for you and your students. Keep enthusiasm for learning alive through challenging problems, creative explorations, and opportunities to develop concerns and values. All of this can happen in an open environment in which uniqueness is prized and a variety of gifts and talents can develop.

◆ ◆ ◆ ◆ ◆

LOOKING BACK AND LOOKING FORWARD

This chapter has focussed on the potential of mainstreaming for meeting the needs of exceptional children. It suggests ways to meet the challenge of providing for a broad spectrum of individual differences, which includes children who are intellectually challenged, physically challenged, emotionally challenged, and those who are gifted and talented.

Although science has been often neglected in the education of intellectually challenged students, it has great potential because of its high interest, its relevance to the everyday life of students, the opportunities it provides for children to work together successfully, and the emphasis it places on learning concepts through concrete experiences. The techniques for individualization outlined earlier in the chapter are all effective ways of providing for intellectually challenged children in regular classrooms.

For the physically challenged — those with orthopedic, visual, and hearing difficulties — the challenge for you as teachers is to find ways of helping them by using programs that have been specially developed and by adapting equipment and classrooms to make it easy for them to function effectively. The potential of involving emotionally challenged children in co-operative learning and outdoor education experiences, such as the Nature's Niche parks, has been explored.

Provision for the gifted should begin early and may include enrichment, acceleration, ability grouping, independent study, and mentoring programs. A rich, supportive, open, unhurried, playful environment is important, where creativity can flourish during long periods of "messing about in science," and where the connections and coincidences that Romey cites as examples of "synchronicity" can develop.

You have been introduced to various models for teaching the gifted. These have included the SOI model (based on the open classroom and Guildford's Structure of the Intellect model); the Enrichment Triad/Revolving Door Model (where a talent pool was identified and three types of enrichment included in a program for the gifted, which led to enrichment for all students); a four-phase model (with teachers as mentors); the Purdue model (based on improving thinking skills as preparation for research); and individualized science packets (designed for independent study and project work).

The theme of *science for all children* is implicit in the broader theme of *science for life* that pervades all chapters of this book. It sets the tone for the overall goal of scientific literacy for the children who are now in school and who will live their lives in the twenty-first century. The next chapter begins the concluding section of this book, which focusses on the function of the elementary science program in preparing today's students for the world of the future and for effective participation as adults in decisions related to the interactions of science, technology, and society.

CANADIAN ACHIEVEMENTS IN SCIENCE

BIRUTÉ GALDIKAS (B. 1946)

Biruté Galdikas was born to Lithuanian parents, but was raised in Canada. Galdikas had a scientific interest in animals even as a young child. Her love of animals included an interest in humans and their early history. While studying anthropology in the United States, Galdikas met Louis Leakey, a noted anthropologist and archaeologist who had conducted explorations of Tanzania's Oduvai Gorge. She was encouraged by Leakey, and in 1971 began a long-term research project on orangutans, in which she had always had a special interest. Her work has taken her to the rain forests of Indonesia and Borneo, but she returns to Canada each year to resume her teaching and studies at Simon Fraser University in Burnaby, British Columbia.

Before Galdikas began studying orangutans, they were thought to be solitary animals that lived alone. One of Galdikas's most important discoveries is that they are, in fact, semi-solitary. She also discovered that females give birth once every eight years. This latter discovery has been a significant factor in the future survival of the orangutan: their long reproductive cycle, combined with the threat of the dying rain forests, has severely jeopardized their future.

Biruté Galdikas is responsible for establishing the Orangutan Foundation International to protect this species and to enable her to continue her studies.

REFERENCES

Alvino, J.J., and T. Gourley (1977). The challenge of our gifted children. *Teacher* (December):45–47.

Atwood, R.K., and B.R. Oldham (1985). Teachers' perceptions of mainstreaming in an inquiry-oriented elementary science program. *Science Education* 69(5):619–24.

Ball, D.W. (1978). ESS *Special education teacher's guide*. St. Louis, MO: Webster/ McGraw-Hill.

Berhow, B.F. (1979). Adapting curricula for handicapped kindergarten children. In H. Hofman and K. Ricker, *Science education for the physically handicapped,* 80–86. Washington, DC: National Science Teachers Association.

Blurton, C. (1983). Individualized science packets for gifted students. *School Science and Mathematics* 83(4) (April):326–32.

Borthwick, B., I. Dow, D. Levesque, and R. Banks (1980). *The gifted and talented students in Canada.* Toronto: Canadian Education Association.

Boyd, E., and K.D. George (1973). The effect of science categorization behavior of deaf children. *Journal of Research in Science Teaching* 10(1):91–99.

Brown, D.R. (1979). Helping handicapped youngsters learn science by doing. *What Research Says to the Science Teacher* vol. 2:80–99. Washington, DC: NSTA.

Bybee, R.W. (1980). Creativity — Nurture and stimulation. *Science and Children* (January):7–9.

Bybee, R.W., and P.W. Hendricks (1972). Teaching science concepts to pre-school deaf children to aid language development. *Science Education* 56(3):301–10.

Calhoun, M.L., and M. Hawisher (1979). *Teaching and learning strategies for physically handicapped students.* Baltimore: University Park Press.

Cohen, L.M. (1987). Thirteen tips for teaching gifted students. *Teaching Exceptional Children* (Fall):34–38.

Corrick, M.E., ed. (1981). *Teaching handicapped students science.* Washington, DC: National Education Association (NEA).

Council of Ministers of Education (1983). *Survey of special education in Canada, 1982–83.* Winnipeg: Candid Research and Council of Ministers of Education, Canada.

Davies, J.M., and D.W. Ball (1978). Utilization of the Elementary Science Study with educable mentally retarded students. *Journal of Research in Science Teaching* 15(4):281–86.

De Lucchi, L., L. Malone, and H.D. Thier (1980). Science activities for the visually impaired: Developing a model. *Exceptional Children* 46(4):287–88.

Franks, F.L. (1979). The tactile modality in adapting and developing science materials. In H. Hofman and K. Ricker, *Sourcebook: Science education and the physically handicapped,* 188–99. Washington, DC: NSTA.

Gough, E.R. (1979). Some psychological considerations in the education of blind children. In H. Hofman and K. Ricker, *Sourcebook: Science education and the physically handicapped,* 206–9. Washington, DC: NSTA.

Gray, W.A., and D. Rogers (1982). Mentor-directed enrichment projects for gifted elementary school pupils: Rationale, guidelines and benefits. *Special Education in Canada* 56(2):24–32.

Hadary, D.E., and S.H. Cohen (1978). *Laboratory science and art for blind, deaf and emotionally disturbed children: A mainstreaming approach.* Baltimore: University Park Press.

Hadary, D.E., S.H. Cohen, R. Haushalter, T.D. Hadary, and R. Levine (1976). Interaction and creation through laboratory science and art for special children. *Science and Children* (March):31–33.

Hawkins, D. (1965). Messing about in science. In *The ESS Reader.* Newton, MA: Educational Development Center, 37–44.

Hill, J.L. (1988). Integration in Canada: Implications for the certification of regular education teachers (RETs). *Canadian Journal of Special Education* 4(2):123–31.

Hofman, H.H., and K.S. Ricker (1979). *Sourcebook: Science education and the physically handicapped.* Washington, DC: NSTA.

Hoover, S.M. (1989). The Purdue Three-Stage Model as applied to elementary science for the gifted. *School Science and Mathematics* 89(3) (March):244–50.

Karagianis, L.D., and W.C. Nesbit (1981). The Warnock influence: Translation into law of Britain's preliminary answer to PL 94–142. *Canadian Journal for Exceptional Children* 1(2):62–63.

Karnes, M.B., A.M. Schwedel, and M. Williams (1983). Combining instructional models for young gifted children. *Teaching Exceptional Children* (Spring):128–35.

Keller, W.D. (1981). Science for the handicapped. *Focus on Exceptional Children* (January):1–11.

Kite, J. (1987). Developing a scientific approach in children with learning difficulties in the junior school. *Support for Learning* 2(1):26–31.

MacArthur, C., and D. Malouf (1984). Simulations in remedial and special education. *The Pointer* 28(2):36–37.

Menhusen, B.P., and R.O. Gromme (1976). Science for handicapped children, Why? *Science and Children* (13)6:35–37.

Me Now (1980). Boulder, CO: Biological Sciences Curriculum Study.

Nathanson, B., I.B. Kanis, M. Mindes, and S. Rappaport (1984). Nature's niche. *Science and Children* (April):26–27.

Norman, C., and G. Malicky (1987). Microcomputer use for special education teachers and students. *Canadian Journal for Exceptional Children* 3(3):9.

Owsley, P.J. (1968). Development of the cognitive abilities and language of deaf children through science. *Volta Review. Curriculum: Cognition and content*. Washington, DC: A.G. Bell.

Passow, E.H. (1977). Fostering creativity in the gifted child. *Exceptional Children* (March):358–64.

Reis, S.M., and A.A. O'Shea (1984). An innovative enrichment program: The Enrichment Triad/Revolving Door Model. *Special Education in Canada* 58(4):135–38.

Renzulli, J.S. (1977). *The Enrichment Triad Model*. Mansfield Center, CT: Creative Learning Press.

Renzulli, J.S., S.M. Reis, and L.H. Smith (1981). *The Revolving Door Identification Model*. Mansfield Center, CT: Creative Learning Press.

Rockcastle, V.N., B.J. McKnight, F.R. Salamon, and V.E. Schmidt (1984). *Addison-Wesley Science, Level 6*. Menlo Park, CA: Addison-Wesley.

Romey, W. (1980). Preface. *Teaching the gifted and talented in the science classroom*. Washington, DC: National Education Association.

Rowe, M.B. (1975). Help is denied to those in need. *Science and Children* (March):23–25.

Sanders, V. (1990). Mainstreaming special needs children: Meeting the special needs of classroom teachers. Address to Faculty of Education, Memorial University of Newfoundland.

Science and Children (March 1976). Washington, DC: NSTA.

Science Activities for the Visually Impaired (SAVI). Berkeley, CA: Lawrence Hall of Science.

Winchester, I. (1985). Creation and creativity in art and science. *Interchange* 16(1), 70–76.

Winzer, M. (1987a). Gifted and talented children. In M. Winzer, S. Rogow, and C. David, *Exceptional children in Canada,* 150–92. Scarborough, ON: Prentice-Hall.

————. (1987b). Mental retardation. In M. Winzer, S. Rogow, and C. David, *Exceptional children in Canada,* 105–49. Scarborough, ON: Prentice-Hall.

————. (1989). *Closing the gap: Special learners in regular classrooms.* Toronto: Copp Clark Pitman.

————. (1990). *Children with exceptionalities: A Canadian perspective.* 2d ed. Scarborough, ON: Prentice-Hall.

Winzer, M., S. Rogow, and C. David (1987). *Exceptional children in Canada.* Scarborough, ON: Prentice-Hall.

Yewchuk, C. (1984). Gifted preschoolers: Educational implications of early identification. *Special Education in Canada* 58(4):122–24.

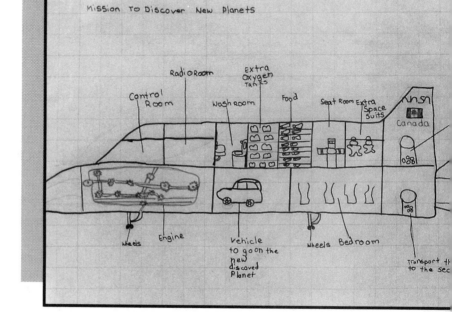

CANADA'S FIRST SPAC

Mission To Discover New Planets

Control Room

Radio Room

Washroom

Extra Oxygen Tanks

Food

Seat Room

Extra Space Suits

Canada

Wheels

Engine

Vehicle to go on the new discoved Planet

Wheels

Bedroom

Transport th to the sec

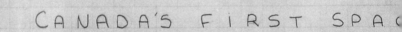

PART 4

SHUTTLE

Transport the astronaut
to the first floor

Science for Life

■ ■ ■ ■ ■ ■

CHAPTER 13 *Science, Technology, and Society*

CHAPTER 14 *Science for a Changing World*

An emphasis on science, technology, and society integrates cognitive, affective, and social goals, and focusses on the need to prepare children for scientific literacy in an increasingly technological, rapidly changing world. The final section of the book projects into the future and explores ways of preparing children for their lives in the 21st century. "Learning how to learn" techniques are needed to equip children to make responsible decisions as adults on issues related to science, technology, and society. The challenge for teachers is to prepare children to apply the concepts and skills developed in the elementary science program to a lifetime of learning — to *science for life*.

PEOPLE
are influenced by
SCIENCE AND TECHNOLOGY
which are different
but often related
and
INTERACT
in ways
that may be

HELPFUL	OR	HARMFUL

and this may be
brought out in
A VARIETY OF APPROACHES
to
CURRICULUM AND INSTRUCTION
which bear upon

CHILDREN'S UNDERSTANDING OF SCIENCE AND TECHNOLOGY	CHILDREN'S ABILITY TO PARTICIPATE IN SCIENCE AND TECHNOLOGY	CHILDREN'S ABILITY TO DEAL WITH ENVIRONMENTAL CONCERNS

◆ ◆ ◆ ◆ ◆

If Canada is to deal effectively with its future,

then a citizenry able to comprehend science issues

is a necessity. This goal will be possible only ...

if the general population understands the

important relationship between science and society.

James Page (1979)

Previous sections of this book have been concerned with aspects of the teaching, learning, and evaluation of science, particularly as these apply to children in the primary and elementary grades. The book as a whole reflects a concern that children must learn science, not just as an academic exercise but also as a force that has much potential to influence the course of their lives. This prospect comes into sharp focus in this chapter, in which the intimate links between science, technology, and society (STS) are explored, particularly as they bear collectively upon school curriculum.

◆ ◆ ◆ ◆ ◆

SCIENCE, TECHNOLOGY, AND SOCIETY IN EDUCATION

In its landmark publication *Science for Every Student: Educating Canadians for Tomorrow's World,* the Science Council of Canada (1984) has this to say:

> Science should be taught at all levels of school with an emphasis and focus on the relationship of science, technology and society in order to increase the scientific literacy of all citizens (38).

The Council further notes:

> The science that is taught to young Canadians should be set in a Canadian context (40);

and

> [s]tudents in any particular region should learn about aspects of the science-technology-society interaction that are peculiar to that region (41).

To assist children toward achieving these aims, teachers need to be aware of a range of STS issues and also possible strategies for teaching them. Developing this awareness is one purpose of this chapter. At times, the issues presented are quite sophisticated for the elementary grades; such content is provided for its illustrative value to the teacher. In other cases, activities suitable for primary and elementary children are introduced. Aikenhead (1980) provides a particularly useful primer for teachers.

◆ ◆ ◆ ◆ ◆

COMPARING SCIENCE AND TECHNOLOGY

Science and technology refer to different questions, and their practitioners have different goals and different methods. Sometimes scientific advances and everyday scientific practice depend on technological invention. Sometimes technological advance and everyday technological practice depend on scientific advances. Science and technology are best thought of as good friends, with separate identities and substantial interaction and influence on each other.

What is technology? Delegates at a 1985 UNESCO international symposium concerning the teaching of technology within general education defined technology in this way:

> Technology is the know-how and the creative process that may utilize tools, resources and systems to solve problems, to enhance control over the natural and man-made environment in an endeavour to improve the human condition (8).

Compare this definition of technology with the definition of science presented in Chapter 2 of this book:

> Science is the process and product of humankind's ongoing attempt to describe and explain the natural and manufactured world in a testable way.

These two definitions suggest that science and technology, although potentially related in their locus of interest, are different in their fundamental purpose and practice. Drawing from Fensham (1990), Table 13.1 notes four differences between science and technology. The following examples illustrate this point further.

The Genetic Code

Prior to the discovery of the genetic code by Watson and Crick in 1953, scientists had long been concerned with identifying the mechanism through which the

TABLE 13.1

Comparing Science and Technology

	Science	*Technology*
Aim	investigation and discovery	production and control
Product	explanation	application
Practice	analytical	synthetical
Knowledge	generalizable	specific

characteristics of living things are acquired. Primarily, these efforts represented a quest for knowledge for its own sake. The field of molecular biology, which arose from this work, continues in the quest for fundamental new knowledge. One result of Watson and Crick's discovery is the development of biotechnology, a new technology that is concerned with creating new genetic instructions, improving existing ones, and correcting genetic defects. Although there is incentive in the continued search for new knowledge, the prevailing interest of biotechnologists is to satisfy human need.

Plate Tectonics

A second example can be found in the field of geology. Scientists believe that the continents of the earth float on large plates. This belief, and the work leading up to it, is the product of the work of a number of scientists. The motivation to explain this aspect of nature was predominantly scientific curiosity. However, plate tectonics has implications in areas of general concern to humankind, such as the advance identification of earthquakes and the location of new oil reserves. Subsequent development of better techniques and tools to aid these quests is more in the domain of the technologist than the scientist.

Metals

In each of the above examples, scientific inquiry preceded related technological development. However, the development of relevant technology often precedes scientific advances. In fact, as a field of human endeavour technology is much older than science. Science as an experimental field of inquiry, as opposed to a philosophical field of inquiry, is recent in humankind's history. Prior to the time of Galileo (1564–1642), "scientists" tended to conduct "thought experiments" rather than laboratory experiments. On the other hand, the roots of technology can be traced back to ancient times when the first tools were fashioned and copied for widespread use in hunting and, later, primitive farming. A good example of ancient technology predating related modern scientific theory is the history of the discovery and use of metals. About 7000 years ago in Persia, it was discovered accidentally that a green stone, which we now call malachite, produced a pink substance, which we now call copper, when put into a fire. Also by chance, about 1000 years later, it was found that when another metal — tin — was added to copper it produced bronze, which is much harder and much more durable than either copper or tin alone, and therefore more useful. This discovery led to a technology that predated scientific understanding by 3000 years!

The same pattern is true of the history of many more technologies. Is this important to the education of young children? Yes! Today, more than ever, technology is a potent force in people's lives. Consider a day in the life of a modern child.

A DAY IN THE LIFE OF A CHILD

A child:

◆ awakes to the sound of an electric alarm clock or a clock radio.
◆ washes with manufactured soap.
◆ cleans teeth with a plastic, perhaps electrical, toothbrush, using a "chemical" toothpaste.
◆ gets dressed in clothes that are mostly synthetic.
◆ enjoys a breakfast of mechanically harvested and processed cereal, with pasteurized milk, toast containing dozens of artificial additives, and mechanically squeezed, chemically treated orange juice.
◆ is driven to school in the family's very technological car, perhaps after the driveway has been cleared of snow by a mechanical snowblower.

You may like to complete the child's daily activities or, better still, ask a child to do so, but the point is made clear, even though the child's day has hardly begun. We live in a society much influenced by science and technology. Understanding this fact is important to understanding life as we live it today. An understanding of the role of and interactions between science, technology, and society should not be an adjunct to the school curriculum; rather, it should be *central* to the curriculum. Today, it is more important than ever that children be equipped to deal with a technological world. This is true not only because today's citizens are empowered by the positive application of science and technology in their lives, but also because greater understanding offers them a better defence against the misuse and abuse of science and technology that also occurs.

◆ ◆ ◆ ◆ ◆

STS: **TWO FACES OF THE COIN**

It is probably true in life that for most advantages there are accompanying disadvantages. This is certainly true with respect to the impact of science and technology on our lives. Consider the following:

- Chemical fertilizers and pesticides have increased the potential to grow more food, but have increased the risk that food may be harmful sometimes.
- The splitting of the atom has led to prospects for massive energy supplies, but also to mass destruction through the use of nuclear weapons.
- Fluoridation of drinking water promotes stronger teeth in children, but has the potential to aid formation of harmful chemicals in drinking water.
- The use of factory freezer trawlers enables much more efficient fishing, which may in turn deplete fish stocks so that they become dangerously low.
- Modern tree-cutting machines enable forestry to be much more efficient, but increase the risk that it may not be possible to replenish the resource quickly enough. An extreme situation of this kind is happening in the rain forests of the Amazon, where the rapid destruction of the forests is having serious effects on the global climate.
- Canada has many communities that form as new mining, mineral, and oil exploration ventures develop. Usually, when the raw resources are sufficiently depleted, the industry dies as does the community, only more slowly.
- Medical technology has increased the potential to extend life for the terminally ill, but often at great financial cost to the community and sometimes at great psychological cost to the patient and the patient's family.
- The mining of asbestos-containing minerals yields asbestos, a very useful heat insulator. However, asbestos dust is related to fatal lung disease in miners, and even in their families.
- A blast furnace, used to extract iron from its ore for subsequent conversion to steel, provides employment for many workers, but makes the surrounding community dusty, dirty, and polluted.

There is no limit to the number of situations illustrating both the massive influence of science and technology on our lives and the fact that each field represents a double-edged sword, with potential benefits and potential losses. It is relatively easy to think of large-scale examples, but there are even more small-scale, personal examples. Consider the impact of science and technology in your community by doing Activity 13.1.

activity 13.1 SCIENCE AND TECHNOLOGY IN YOUR COMMUNITY

Canada is a strongly resource-based country. In your home community, or at least in a nearby community, there is a resource industry of some kind. It may be a fish plant, a lumber mill, an oil refinery, a power plant, a metal smelter, a mine, and so on. Suppose you are a primary or elementary teacher in that community. How will you involve your students in an sts unit, focussing on the industry concerned? Discuss your suggestions with a colleague.

❑ Reflecting and Sharing

You may wonder if it is feasible to focus directly on sts issues in the early years of school. Yet, if the introduction of these issues is delayed until they can be readily understood, it may be too late to create an effective climate for understanding and caring. The answer is to introduce sts issues naturally, as opportunities arise, beginning with a focus on issues of importance to the individual child, and gradually extending to the wider community. Consider the following issues.

In a Child's Environment. In the early years of school, it is traditional to include development of an awareness of the child's own body and how to care for it. Even with primary children, it is not difficult to extend this goal to caring for other living things, such as small animals and plants. This offers an immediate focus on a variety of environmental factors that may affect living things in general, and the child personally.

Personal Hygiene. Personal hygiene is often a focus in the primary curriculum. Again, this may lead readily to animal hygiene, and back to washing with soap and shampoo. Where do soap and shampoo come from? What is their effect on water quality? What happens to waste products passed into our water and septic systems? What effects may other waste products have on water quality and on aquatic life? What happens to water quality near, for example, the site of a sewage plant, a sawmill, a refinery, a smelter, or a power plant?

Where Does It All Go? Today's society will probably be judged by future generations as the epitome of waste. Certainly, we seem to generate huge amounts of garbage. It is possible to lead children to consider the kinds of things we throw away each week. How much could be saved and recycled? What is the cost of rejection? What is the cost of recycling? What is the effect on the environment, both in terms of production of household items and of their eventual disposal? These questions can be addressed by children in the elementary grades.

The High Cost of Energy. In today's society, the majority of Canadians live in well-lit, well-heated homes. The adult population is all too aware today of the direct cost of such comfort, but what of the indirect costs? Our electricity supplies are never entirely natural in origin. The power to drive machines to produce electricity to provide heat and light is usually obtained through burning coal or oil, through harnessing water power in huge hydroelectric installations, or through nuclear energy.

Explorations of energy sources and their uses can be initiated by inviting students to write about, or illustrate through a drawing such as the diagram of "power stations" shown in Figure 13.1, their current understanding of the generation and distribution of electrical power. The student's diagram fails to take into account energy-saving projects such as the use of solar, wind, or wave power, which may involve less potential risk to people and less damage to the environment. However, the benefits we obtain from exploiting most of our sources of electric power carry with them major environmental and societal implications. It is appropriate to consider such issues in conjunction with topics such as the science of electric circuits, heat transfer, and so on, which are typically encountered in science in the elementary grades.

Communities: The Delicate Balance. We all live in a community of some kind. It is common, in elementary science classes, to consider different kinds of nonhuman communities, for example, a woodland community, a seashore community, a pond community, or a vacant-lot community. Once the concept of community is established, it is a natural progression to examine a human community and to focus on the local human community as a starting point. Later, in middle and high-school grades, extension follows to broader communities. Issues such as the population explosion and its implications, pollution in its various forms, threats to world safety and happiness, and so on readily follow. Without wishing to pursue too far Bruner's (1960) doctrine that "anything can be taught in some intellectually honest form to children of any age" (33), there is no doubt that it is possible to examine meaningfully many STS issues with children in the elementary grades, and even to begin to introduce them in the primary grades.

Toward a Balanced Position

THE CASE AGAINST STS

You have now considered some STS issues that fit readily within the science curriculum. However, some educators have argued against the inclusion of tech-

FIGURE 13.1

Power Stations

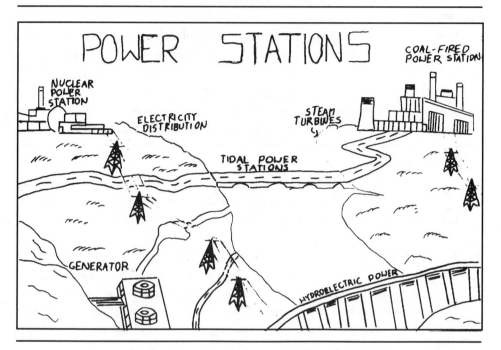

Source: Grade 4/5 student, Orde Street Public School, Toronto.

nology in science courses. Michael Scriven (1987), for example, considers technology as a field that relates to artifacts and the processes necessary to their construction; he considers science to be a field concerned with ideas and their testing. These fields, he argues, are fundamentally different and cannot be meaningfully combined in the school curriculum. In particular, Scriven claims that inclusion of technology within a science course leads to inadequate treatment of technology, because it is treated as an adjunct to the main content, science. Australian educator Peter Fensham (1990) takes the same position. Fensham concludes that science courses can successfully present technological applications, but cannot develop technological capability.

Where do primary and elementary teachers find themselves with respect to this issue? It is reasonable to suggest that the greater emphasis on interdisciplinary education found in primary and elementary schools lends itself to the development of an appropriate balance of science and technology education, to the benefit of both and the detriment of neither. Perhaps, after all, both sides of the coin can be accommodated by making appropriate combinations and appropriate distinctions as the needs of the learners and the local educational environment require.

A QUESTION OF EMPHASIS

It is possible to combine an *emphasis* on science and technology as they interact with society in today's world. The question of the balance to be maintained within that emphasis remains.

Fensham (1988) compares eight categories of science–technology–society curriculum materials. Fensham's comparison is represented in Figure 13.2.

FIGURE 13.2

✳ Categories of STS Curriculum Materials

A. Motivational Use

Descriptive accounts of technology in action are used at the beginning and throughout the learning of a science topic as a motivational aid to learning the science. There is little or no expectation that any systematic learning about the technology will occur.

B. Factual References to Randomly Chosen Examples

These materials are studded with many examples of applications that involve the concepts of the science topic. The examples are not treated or intended to be studied in detail, nor are they chosen because they are a type or category of technology. There is some expectation of rote learning of some of the factual information.

C. Factual References to Selected Examples of Related Technology

In these materials, a succession of examples, related both to the science concepts and to each other, are presented. More systematic learning about these technologies is intended that is not only descriptive but also comparative and critical in relation to the societal functions the technologies perform or to aspects of the STS issues.

D. Thematic or Topical

In these materials, a broad STS theme or technology is chosen as the object of study and it becomes the context that determines the science that will be studied. Some systematic learning about the theme or the technology is possible in parallel with the science that is to be learnt, but this is not developed as conceptually as the science is.

E. Constructional Technology

The construction of a technological model or the practice of a technological process is used as the context for learning scientific facts and principles. Learning of scientific skills and practical knowledge associated with the construction and use of the models or process is intended.

(continued)

Figure 13.2 (continued)

F. Social and Scientific Concepts Related to a Technology

A few concepts are chosen for study that are significant to the operation in society of technologies that are based on the science topic. These concepts are then studied in increasing depth as the unit progresses in a manner that parallels the sequential learning of the science concepts.

G. Scientific Aspects of Technology or of Sociotechnical Topics

These materials include some of the detailed science that is important in the construction and operation of a technology or of an STS topic, but gives more emphasis to the broader scientific principles involved, along with details of its social and economic context.

H. Science and Society

In these materials, a priority is given to systematic learning about one or more societal aspects of a major technology or a broad field of applied science. A general appreciation of the possibilities and limitations of the underlying science is intended, but not detailed learning.

Source: P.J. Fensham (1988). Approaches to the teaching of STS in science education. *International Journal of Science Education* 10(4):354. Reprinted with permission of Taylor & Francis, Washington, D.C.

activity 13.2 STS IN A SELECTED GRADE: FENSHAM'S CATEGORIES

Obtain the science text used in a primary or elementary grade in a local school. Examine its treatment of STS issues, including environmental issues. List the issues included and identify which of Fensham's curriculum material categories in Figure 13.2 fits most closely with the text.

❑ Reflecting and Sharing

The curriculum you considered may fit well with the emphasis in one or more of Fensham's categories, or perhaps you found a different emphasis. As a teacher, it is important for you to be able to examine the curriculum that you use so that you can identify the author's emphasis, and also so that you can work from an informed base to modify the STS emphasis appropriately. Different emphases are appropriate in different teaching situations, and also in societies with different value systems.

From a Teacher's Journal

To develop an understanding of science and technology, I use "challenges" that require students to design and build devices to perform specific tasks, such as climbing a ramp, hopping over a barrier, catapulting a load, and so on. Students' products are demonstrated at a "fair" or "science challenge day," and the scientific issues of the challenge are identified and related to the technology involved in the solutions to the problems.

Science features in the newspaper are an effective resource for addressing current science–technology–society (STS) developments. The science and technology connected with the issue are identified and "values" discussions held in which students consider the pros and cons regarding possible consequences of the development. Issues such as global warming, ozone depletion, and animal rights provide another arena for examining STS relationships.

Neil McAllister

Vancouver, BC

◆ ◆ ◆ ◆ ◆

INTERWEAVING STS WITH SCIENCE

Another Australian, Ian Lowe (1985), produced a typology somewhat similar to Fensham's. Lowe discusses how a variety of emphases may be used with a number of topics typically found in science curriculum materials.

Science and Health

Lowe suggests that one approach is to teach a science area with relevant STS aspects interwoven as appropriate. For example, health issues can be interwoven with biology. Consideration of cardiovascular diseases and the use of heart transplants can be included in a treatment of the circulatory system; tooth decay and sports injuries can be included in a treatment of the skeleton; and what constitutes an appropriate diet can be included in a unit on the digestive system.

From Technology to Science

A second approach suggested by Lowe is to use an application of science or a technological device to lead into the underlying science and then to a consideration of wider questions or applications relating to the same principles. Examples can include progression from discussion of a thermos flask to a discussion of heat transfer in terms of radiation, convection, and conduction, and then to aluminum foil as insulation; or progression from a wood stove to the process of combustion to society's handling of waste products from different heating devices.

From Societal Needs to Science

A third approach suggested by Lowe involves using STS as *the* organizing principle of teaching science. This approach starts with a broad problem like, "What are the needs of industrial society?" A list of responses is sought, such as food, energy, shelter, transport, water, materials, health care, and communications. Each of these is then analyzed thoroughly. For example, food is analyzed to yield the topics of nutrition, plant growth, farming and gardening, preserving and cooking. Each of these is then considered in terms of its underlying scientific principles and subsequent wider questions. A topic like nutrition, for example, can lead to a consideration of fats, proteins, carbohydrates, the body's needs, and digestion. In turn, this can lead to questions relating to a balanced diet, malnutrition, obesity, and "junk" food.

concept web

A Thematic Approach: STS Units

Finally, Lowe suggests the use of an STS question as an organizing question for a particular unit of the curriculum. As an example, the question "How can we use energy from the sun?" can lead to a consideration of the solar spectrum and to different ways of harvesting the sun's energy, such as focussing mirrors and photosynthesis. Related technical, economic, and social questions can also be considered.

activity 13.3   IDENTIFYING STS THEMES

For each of Lowe's suggested approaches, prepare an outline of a further theme that links science, technology, and society.

❏ Reflecting and Sharing

The kinds of topics generated by Lowe lend themselves to a variety of STS emphases. It is important for you as teacher to be able to understand the emphasis implied by curriculum materials and the program of study, and to be able to generate meaningful alternatives where necessary. You must be conscious of and seek out opportunities to emphasize STS, and you must also have a personal STS agenda, otherwise the treatment of STS issues in class will be artificial. An uncommitted teacher has little chance of developing commitment in the children taught. Yet, teachers often receive little or no exposure to STS issues in their training. Where can you turn for related information? Some suggestions follow. They relate more to background information for the teacher than to material for direct use in primary and elementary science, but this kind of information is important if you are to develop sufficient understanding to develop STS issues with children.

◆ ◆ ◆ ◆ ◆

SOURCES OF STS INFORMATION

Aside from the question of what constitute appropriate teaching strategies, a number of sources of STS information are useful to teachers. Common STS applications, such as energy conservation, pollution control, and the use of technological machinery are routinely illustrated in many science texts. Such information is readily available and will not be pursued here.

A different kind of information relates to issues of current concern. These may be local or more wide-ranging, and may involve problems relating to science and technology in society or to solutions for such problems. Whenever possible, it is preferable to deal with issues of local concern, especially those that can be related directly to the children or their families. The younger the child, the closer to home the content needs to be. For primary children, especially, content far removed from children's personal lives is likely to be ineffective.

Readily accessible sources of current information available to teachers include radio and television programs; newspapers and magazines; and government publications. Generally these are best considered as direct sources for the teacher, with the potential for subsequent translation to the children. Television programs such as "The Nature of Things," which has a large amount of Canadian content, as well as a variety of programs from other countries, collectively provide much useful information and raise many important issues. Radio programs such as "Quirks and Quarks," although typically intended for a more sophisticated audience, also on occasion provide relevant content. Magazines such as *Maclean's, Time, Newsweek, Omni,* and *Discovery* provide some STS coverage, in relation to agriculture or medicine, the environment, and space. Most newspapers are not noted for their coverage of science and technology issues, but a vigilant teacher can often find information that is useful, particularly when it is of local interest. Local and national government offices also produce useful STS material. Magazines intended for children, such as *Owl* and *Chickadee,* are useful Canadian sources.

Other less commonly known publications include *Canadian Research, Science Dimension, Ascent,* and *Canadian Agriculture.* All present a Canadian focus on science and technology. For example, Janigan (1988) describes work on artificial blood in Montreal; Charbonneau (1988) describes laser coronary surgery in Ottawa; Henry (1984) writes of acid rain in Canadian lakes; Winter (1985) writes of the application of biotechnology to the breeding of better trees; Martin (1988) describes the Canadian development of the world's first plane to fly on microwave power; and Atkinson (1982) describes the development of the "Canadarm," a vital tool on the U.S. Space Shuttle. If simplified by the teacher, these kinds of topics can be included at the elementary level.

Finally, the Ministry of Supply and Services Canada produces an excellent guide to STS resources, including films, videos, television and radio programs, publications, exhibits, and so on, which are available throughout Canada. The guide, called *Explorations in Science Culture,* is available from federal and provincial government publication outlets.

◆ ◆ ◆ ◆ ◆

CANADIAN SCIENCE AND TECHNOLOGY

Canada is a resources-rich country, and much of Canada's contribution to technology has been concerned with the development and utilization of its natural resources.

Canada has extensive but often remote sources of hydroelectric power. Canadian engineers have learned to deal with uncertain and different terrain featuring swamps, permafrost, high mountains, oceans, rivers, and lakes, as they struggle to bring that power to populated areas. Canadian technology is at the forefront of this field.

Canada is a world leader in nuclear-reactor technology, and the Canadian CANDU reactor is at the heart of power supplies in several countries.

Canada has a large forest-products industry, producing immense quantities of lumber and pulp, for use in the building and paper-products industries.

Canada is rich in gas, oil, and mineral reserves, and Canada's petroleum recovery and processing and petroleum-products industries are massive. In recent years, Canadian oil and gas reserves are being developed offshore as well as on land, a development that involves a large commitment to ocean engineering. In St. John's, Newfoundland, the world's largest ice tank serves as a research and development tool for scientists and engineers to study the effects of ice, wind, and waves on model ships and drilling rigs.

Canada has the ability and location to lead the world in the development of technologies such as these. This requires scientifically and technologically literate citizens who are aware of the costs as well as the benefits of technology, when prosperity and employment are followed by despair and unemployment as resources are depleted. Resource industries often bring a delicate balance between effective utilization and destruction of a natural resource. Risks to health and even life are evident. Examples include the collapse of the drilling rig *Ocean Ranger* in high seas off Newfoundland in 1982, when all 89 crew members died, and Nova Scotia's Westray coal mine disaster in 1992. Despite the risks, Canada's prosperity and well-being depend on the continuation of its technological heritage, and on the corresponding technological literacy of its citizens. Such literacy is enhanced by deliberate inclusion of technological issues in the school curriculum, beginning in the primary and elementary grades.

◆ ◆ ◆ ◆ ◆

THE FACES OF TECHNOLOGY

Technology as Problem Solving

Mills (1988) suggests a possible sequence of skills involved in technological problem solving. This sequence is represented in Figure 13.3.

Mills describes four different solutions arrived at by children, between 9 and 11 years of age, to this problem: "You are supplied with a long wooden pole … and a toy parachute. Make a device to fit to the end of the pole which will hold the parachute up high and allow you to release it when required."

In general, Mills found that these children were satisfied with any solution and were not particularly concerned with aesthetics. They required substantial

FIGURE 13.3

Steps in Solving Technological Problems

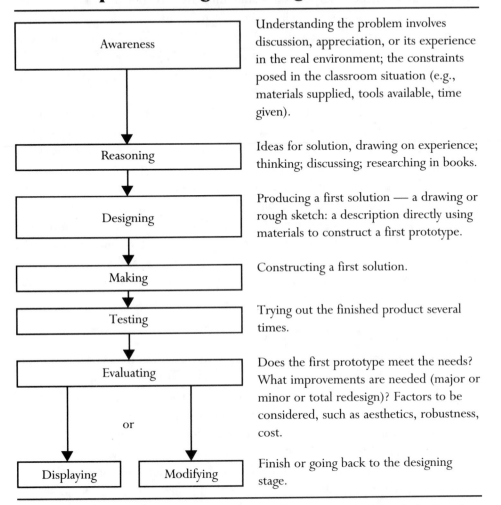

Awareness	Understanding the problem involves discussion, appreciation, or its experience in the real environment; the constraints posed in the classroom situation (e.g., materials supplied, tools available, time given).
Reasoning	Ideas for solution, drawing on experience; thinking; discussing; researching in books.
Designing	Producing a first solution — a drawing or rough sketch: a description directly using materials to construct a first prototype.
Making	Constructing a first solution.
Testing	Trying out the finished product several times.
Evaluating	Does the first prototype meet the needs? What improvements are needed (major or minor or total redesign)? Factors to be considered, such as aesthetics, robustness, cost.
Displaying or **Modifying**	Finish or going back to the designing stage.

Source: G. Mills (1988). An introduction to technology in the early years of schooling. In *Innovations in Science and Technology Education*, vol. II, 37. Paris: UNESCO. Reproduced by permission of UNESCO. © UNESCO 1988.

guidance and encouragement to move beyond their first solution. It was useful for their teachers to have ready-prepared sketches outlining a variety of alternative solutions. In a separate publication, MacLeod and Mills (1986) offer further examples and guidance.

Technology as Construction

It is not difficult for teachers to develop a variety of practical construction problems that may be incorporated readily into the class schedule. For example, children's construction sets such as Lego can be used in design projects of varying complexity; the construction of sand castles and paper airplanes provides many opportunities for design and testing; and the construction of simple model houses of varying degrees of energy efficiency can provide useful problems for solution. Constructions such as a windmill, a simple weather station, a simple wiring system for a model house, a working model of a lighthouse, and differently designed kites and periscopes all relate to technology and fit readily into primary and elementary science. Each of these examples represents technology as construction.

It is important to focus not only upon the many benefits technology offers society, but also for children to realize that there are negative aspects as well. Some examples are the potential ravages of metal ore extraction and refining, and of harmful effluents from chemical and other industrial plants; the potential pollution from coal and oil and nuclear-generating plants; and the ethical problems raised by medical research, or biotechnology, and by hydroelectric generation in the homelands of indigenous peoples. The list is large.

Technology: Ethical Issues

Ethical issues are much more difficult to pursue with children than with adolescents and adults, yet it is worth beginning to pursue them in the early grades. Children can be led to be concerned about the actions of others, and about the effects of their own actions upon others. A variety of approaches is possible, including the use of value-clarification exercises. Consider the following example.

Gennaro and Glenn (1979) illustrate the application of a value-clarification technique relating to the merits and demerits of kidney transplantation. In Gennaro and Glenn's example, students are faced with dilemmas such as, "Who should pay for a transplant? The patient or health care system?" "If the system, how much should cost determine how many such operations should be performed?" "If a choice must be made between transplant candidates, who should receive the transplant? For example, consider a doctor, a teacher, a child and a street person. Should any of these receive priority over any of the others?" "Who should have the final say about whether organs are to be taken from a body?" There are many questions.

A value-clarification activity of this kind is appropriate for Grade 5 or Grade 6 students. The point of such exercises is to gently nudge each child to think about his or her values. Topics such as sex education, drug abuse, and so on are appropriate for elementary students. For younger children, an activity such as a consideration of litter pollution in the school and community is appropriate.

Ethical considerations are related to attitudes. The next section deals with children's attitudes about science and technology in today's society.

◆ ◆ ◆ ◆ ◆

ATTITUDES ABOUT SCIENCE AND TECHNOLOGY

Chapter 8 described Krathwohl's taxonomy of objectives in the affective domain. The taxonomy is useful when considering children's attitudes about STS issues. Table 13.2 illustrates this.

TABLE 13.2

Children's Attitudes about STS Issues

Receiving	After instruction, the child describes particular ways in which science and technology affect the quality of life for the child and the local community. For example, treatment of drinking water, disposal of waste, etc.
Responding	The child participates readily in discussion relating science and technology to everyday life. For example, the creation and disposal of personal and industrial waste.
Valuing	The child initiates discussion or takes a position about issues affecting local life. For example, the siting of a new fish plant or the encroachment of a forestry operation on a local beauty spot.
Organization	The child recognizes that other value systems may affect societal issues influenced by science and technology. For example, the desirability of seal hunting or fishery conservation or the siting of a new metal smelter. *(continued)*

Table 13.2 (continued)

Characterization of a value complex	The child takes a personal position on STS issues, only after consideration of alternative positions. For example, whether widespread aerial spraying should be used to combat a forest pest, or whether roads should be heavily salted in winter.

A number of instructional strategies are available to aid attitude development. In each case, it is important to focus attention on the child's own thoughts. Teacher-oriented activities should be minimized and child-oriented activities maximized. The aim is to encourage development of the child's value system, not to transmit the teacher's value system to the child. Potential strategies include classroom discussions and debates involving value clarification, the use of critical incidents, role playing, library research, field trips, and case studies. Progress in this domain cannot be rushed, and full development has to wait beyond the end of elementary school.

◆ ◆ ◆ ◆ ◆

THE ENVIRONMENT: A SPECIAL CASE

In previous sections of this chapter, you have considered relationships between science, technology, and society. Many of the issues raised relate to questions of environmental concern. In this section, environmental education is considered further. Environmental education relates well to science education, although it also transcends it. However, the relationship is strong enough that environmental education is most often found within the science curriculum. It is considered in this context here.

In 1962, Rachel Carson published *Silent Spring,* a book that focussed much world attention on the progressive destruction of the earth's environment. *Silent Spring* provides a sharp focus for humankind. Its theme is that our environment is where we live, and that when it is harmed the quality of our lives is diminished. If the environment is harmed too much, human life, like that of the many species of animals and plants that have already disappeared, will become extinct. Realistically, futuristic speculations about space exploration aside, we have nowhere else to go. We must exist within our global environment. This is the ultimate message of environmental education, although there are other less dramatic messages that also need to be heeded. When must the foundation for these messages be laid?

From a Teacher's Journal

I think it is of utmost importance for children to develop environmental awareness at an early age. It seems natural to start this process outdoors, with observations of our local environment. Along with observation skills, children develop an appreciation of the beauty of what we have and an understanding of what we can do to help preserve it. Early in the fall I try to develop such awareness and appreciation by teaching children to respect the wildflowers, shrubs, and trees in our schoolyard. Each child in my Grade 2 class "adopts" a tree for the year, caring for it and observing and recording its changes through the changing seasons. The students are curious about the kinds of trees they are observing, and whether other trees of the type they are observing grow in the neighbourhood. They wonder why some trees remain green throughout the winter and some don't. Science is so much more meaningful for each child, and concepts seem to stay in place in each child's mind, when the new ideas that come out of their study of the environment are linked to what is already familiar.

Nikki Donlevy

Calgary, AB

At least as early as the *beginning* of school. *The necessary education should begin at primary level or earlier.* Most environmental problems are created by people, and only people can eliminate or minimize them. Where can the teacher look for help in teaching this?

Resources for Environmental Education

In Canada, environmental education, like education in general, does not have a national voice. Earlier in this chapter, it was emphasized that STS issues are best introduced through local examples, especially for younger children. A well-articulated program of environmental education in Canada could be designed to maximize the initial use of local materials by teachers. At this time, such a program does not exist.

At the provincial level, resources relating to the environment are uneven. The SEEDS (Society, Energy, Environment Development Studies) program, based in Calgary, has been influential across the country. The Western Educational Development Group on the Environment (WEDGE) has produced locally based materials for environmental education. Alberta has developed a K–12 curriculum guide for environmental education. Saskatchewan includes a major emphasis on environmental literacy in its curriculum for K–2 science. Quebec's elementary school curriculum guide for natural science has a very strong environmental emphasis. Several Ontario universities publish environmentally related materials. Institutions such as the Huntsman Laboratory in New Brunswick and the Marine Sciences Laboratory of Memorial University in Newfoundland publish useful resource materials. *Project Wild* (1991) provides a wide array of environmental activities for use in all school grades. Periodicals like *Green Teacher* and *Earthkeeper* are useful resources for teachers at all grade levels. Activist organizations like Greenpeace produce written materials. Most provincial government departments prepare for the public environmentally related materials that are useful to schools. Undoubtedly, other materials and initiatives exist. However, much depends on the commitment of the individual teacher. Activities 13.4 through 13.6 invite you to become actively involved in identifying materials that will be useful to you.

---

activity 13.4 ENVIRONMENTAL MATERIALS: GOVERNMENT SOURCES

Visit or write to the department in your provincial government offices responsible for environmental affairs, asking for any environmentally related materials that they can provide. From these materials list whatever sources of information appear to be appropriate to give to or translate for children in the primary or elementary grades.

---

activity 13.5 ENVIRONMENTAL CONCERNS IN THE SCIENCE CURRICULUM

Examine the science curriculum materials for the primary or elementary level in your province. List all topics that are environmentally related. These may include, for example, direct references to the environment, references to pollution, energy, food production, mining, resource exploration, water, pest control, population, conservation, recycling, forestation and deforestation, fuels, garbage disposal, ecosystems, and atmospheric matters such as the greenhouse effect and the ozone layer.

activity 13.6 ENVIRONMENTAL CONCERNS IN THE MEDIA

Visit your local library and examine back issues of your local newspaper. List any articles relating to environmental concerns (a) locally, (b) provincially, (c) nationally. Add to your list any other local concerns of which you are aware. Copy or make brief notes of those articles that will be useful in your teaching of environmental issues.

❏ Reflecting and Sharing

You now have a list of environmental topics. As a teacher, how will you incorporate these topics into the curriculum of your class? Think back to some of the ideas explored in previous chapters. What orientation will you adopt? Transmission, transaction, or transformation? Probably all, at different times, depending on the activity. Think about the nature of the child, and about the different approaches to teaching that you have considered in previous chapters. Look back at Activity 5.1, "Snails and Trails," Activity 6.7, "Wanted — Dead or Alive: An *Innovations in Science* Lesson," and Activity 6.9, "Earth Day, 1990" as examples that focus on cognitive and affective aspects of environmental education.

In the early school years, it is appropriate to focus on developing awareness and basic knowledge of the environment, leading to the beginning of personal concern for the well-being and sensitive treatment of plants and animals and the protection of their environment, and in the later elementary years to consideration of ethical issues. Activities 13.7 through 13.9 illustrate this development. Each activity should be conducted with children of an appropriate age.

activity 13.7 AWARENESS OF NATURE

Take a group of kindergarten or early primary children for a walk in the park or the woods or along the seashore, or anywhere else that you can get close to nature. Ask them to record what they see, hear, touch

Concern for the environment can be developed in the early school years. Planting a tree shows these children how they can become involved in protecting their environment

(carefully!), smell, and taste (with your permission). You may want to lead some children on a blindfold walk. What do they hear? What do they feel? What smells are there? The blindfold walk will undoubtedly sharpen their awareness.

activity 13.8 A SCAVENGER HUNT

Take a group of children on a scavenger hunt in the woods or the park or along the shore of a pond or the sea. How many different kinds of trees and plants can they find? How many different kinds of leaves, seeds, flowers, spiders, insects, birds, animal remains, boxes, feathers, shells, and "foot" prints can they find? What different kinds of human litter are mixed in with these?

activity 13.9 THE CONCEPT OF ENVIRONMENT

Ask a group of elementary children what makes up an "environment." Lead them to environmental factors like hot-cold, wet-dry, light-dark, sheltered-open. Ask the children to design an activity through which they could find out the preferred environment of, say, carpenters (isopods), mealworms, ants, frogs, or small fish. Perhaps they can suggest how to test for each of the environmental factors listed above for one or more of these small animals. For example, you might lead children to consider the preferred environment of isopods by making a runway of aluminum foil, arranged so that, successively, one end is warm while the other is cold; one end is wet while the other is dry. You have already encountered the concept of "optimum range" of light intensity in the SCIS unit "Environments" (1970). Have the children extend the investigation to these other aspects of the preferred environment of carpenters.

In the elementary years, it is possible to extend to larger environments, to communities, ecosystems, and the interdependence of living things, and to broaden to consider serious questions of environmental concern such as pollution, population expansion, and so on.

Environmental issues are seldom clear-cut. Gain for some people, or animals or plants, is often accompanied by loss for others. Opinions about what constitutes acceptable loss and gain vary according to the different perspectives of gainers and losers. Especially for young children, awareness of this must be developed sensitively, as these children are likely to be relatively egocentric in their thinking and will tend to see gain and loss only from one perspective, their own. It is important to keep in mind the development of a balanced perspective on environmental matters.

As with other aspects of STS, as children learn to care about the environment the teacher must remain aware of each child's developing affective profile, and attempt to encourage that development without attempting to force the attitudes of others upon the child. In the upper elementary grades, one useful approach is to confront children with ethical dilemmas. Activity 13.10 illustrates this process.

- - - - - - - - - - - - - - - -

activity 13.10 ENVIRONMENTAL DILEMMAS

Present some elementary children with each of the following dilemmas. Ask them to think about the dilemmas for a few minutes, and then to take a position on them and defend their position to a group of their classmates.

Dilemma One: You are the mayor of a declining town. The town's main industry is asbestos mining. You have recently become aware that asbestos dust causes fatal lung disease. Should you

◆ close down the mine until an efficient dust control system is set up?
◆ close down the mine permanently?
◆ wait to see if lung disease develops in the community?
◆ ignore the problem?

Dilemma Two: You are a keen gardener whose plants are being destroyed by insect infestation. Would you

◆ cease gardening for a few years and wait for the insects to go away?

◆ apply the strongest insecticide you can find, regardless of the potentially serious effects on birds and harmless insects?

◆ continue gardening as usual, but try only to spot-kill the insects as they appear, minimizing broader effects?

◆ grow the insects' favourite plants on the edge of your neighbour's property in the hope they will migrate next door?

activity 13.11 **MORE ENVIRONMENTAL DILEMMAS**
Think of some "environmental dilemmas" for elementary children to consider in the classroom. These should be as local as possible. Try them with some small groups of children. Remember, the purpose is clarification of each child's own position, not confrontation with others.

❑ Reflecting and Sharing

How did you react to the dilemmas presented in Activity 13.10? Were ready answers available? Probably not. The more often people consider such issues, the more obvious it becomes that issues like these will be resolved differently by different people, according to their level of sophistication, their existing personal belief systems, and their readiness to change their own views as others present new and compelling challenges.

How difficult was the task of handling children's ideas and reactions in Activity 13.11? Probably more difficult still. It is important for the teacher to select issues that are important and understandable to children, and that can be used effectively as children develop their individual affective awareness.

Figure 13.4 expresses poignantly one child's efforts to come to grips with the ecological implications of acid rain on Canadian lakes and rivers — the short-term and long-term effects on animal and plant life that will result if present practices continue.

Field Trips

Finally, don't forget that the environment is "out there." Field trips are an essential part of environmental education. As you plan for field trips, remember the suggestions offered in Chapter 5. Canada has such a vast and diversified environment that there can surely be no better place for this field of study. At the

FIGURE 13.4

Effects of Acid Rain

Throughout Ontario and most of eastern Canada thousand of lakes and rivers are strugling to survive the effects of acid rain and many are losing the fight. Some have already made the acidified stage and others are reaching the critical stage in the fight against acid rain. In the vast of the Canadian sheild they do not give there lakes any alkine leaving them able to die of acid rain. How quickly a lake acidifies depends on it's natural chemistry and it's geography. Each lake has it's own unique ecosystem. As the ecosystem dies out it's ability to support animals in it's ecosystem is inposable there for the animals will die. This has already happened to some lakes of ours and will happen to many more unless we do something about it soon. As the lakes start to acidify the diversity of the animals decline. As the animals die out algue, mougeotia, zygogonien and zygnema wich thrive acid to appear more often. As the animals have died out in the lakes it causes major effects on the food chain. Experaments on the algue, chysochromunila and berturrita that tiny explotions will happen under water causing noxise odurs even in not too polluted lakes. In the 1960's the lake of La Clodre Monlar in the region of Ontario lost veriaty of fish disppeared from the lake. Shinny bass and trout died out very fast as the lake acidafied. While hardier fish such as yellow pearch lake chub survived just a little longer. Fish populations vanished when reproduave falure. Acid rain is nown to erode buildings and monuments and is also suspected to be make life harder for people with diseses. Some of the things acid rain is endangering are fishery, courism, agricalture and forestry in a area of eastern Canada it measures 2.6 millon square miles.

Source: Student, Queenston Drive Public School, Toronto.

same time, don't forget that the door to the environment is no farther away than the door to your home. Take advantage of whatever features your community offers, and take advantage of opportunities provided by parks and ponds, the seashore and mountains, and salmon hatcheries, fluvaria, agricultural stations, nurseries, and local industries. But remember also the microenvironments available in your schoolyard. You can also examine the environments of small animals and plants and microscopic organisms such as brine shrimp and daphnia right in your own classroom. There are many microworlds awaiting children's consideration.

◆ ◆ ◆ ◆ ◆

LOOKING BACK AND LOOKING FORWARD

Science and technology provide vital influences on the nature and quality of life in today's society. No teacher-training program can be complete if it does not pay attention to this fact, and if it does not provide suggestions for the teaching of STS issues. This chapter addresses this fact, and includes consideration of environmental issues as a special aspect of STS education.

You have seen that science and technology are related, but also different in their purposes and methods. You have considered a number of examples of ways in which science and technology influence life today, especially as these apply in Canada, and you have considered approaches to helping children develop awareness and understanding of STS issues, including those relating to environmental concerns. These include interweaving traditional science content with technological examples; considering technology as construction and as problem solving; focussing on ethical issues through value-clarification exercises; and considering environmental dilemmas.

Finally, attitudes toward science and technology are discussed from the perspective that teachers should aim to help each child develop a personal value system. This leads naturally to the focus of the next chapter of this book, where attention is paid to the quickly changing world in which today's children live.

CANADIAN ACHIEVEMENTS IN SCIENCE

ROBERTA BONDAR (B. 1946)

For Roberta Bondar, Canada's second space pioneer, the 1992 (January 22–30) voyage of the *Discovery* fulfilled a childhood dream. While growing up in Sault Ste. Marie, Ontario, she had been enthralled with science-fiction movies and reports of the early space missions. When she entered medical school, she held an M.Sc. in experimental pathology and a Ph.D. in neurobiology. Bondar was an assistant professor of neurology at McMaster Medical Centre in Hamilton, Ontario, when she was chosen for the astronaut program in 1983. With her extensive background in science and her specialty in the body's nervous and inner-ear balancing systems, Bondar was well prepared for the responsibility she shared with Ulf Merbold, a German physicist, for 42 experiments in which an array of organisms were monitored for their responses to weightlessness and space radiation.

The flight of the *Discovery* made Canada the fourth country to put a woman into space, and an important participant in the first International Microgravity Lab (IML-1) mission. Bondar was already affiliated with a Canadian Space Agency (CSA)–funded research team at Ryerson Polytechnical Institute in Toronto, studying the cerebral physiology of space flight. Other Canadian experiments included a University of British Columbia phase-partitioning study aimed at separating bone marrow cells from other tissues for use in cancer treatment; testing of a CSA-designed anti-gravity suit; and energy-expenditure tests developed at the University of Calgary.

Bondar feels it is crucial that understanding keep pace with technology through continued research in the life sciences — biology, neurology, psychology, and their clinical applications in medicine. Currently, Bondar is continuing her space research at Ryerson, studying how blood flow to the brain is connected with the nausea and disorientation experienced by astronauts. The ultimate aim of the research is to discover how longer space missions can be made possible.

▢ REFERENCES

Aikenhead, G.S. (1980). *Science in social issues: Implications for teaching.* Ottawa: Science Council of Canada.

Atkinson, W. (1982). Canadarm: Summa cum laude. *Science Dimension* 14(1):4–10.

Bruner, J. (1960). *The process of education.* Cambridge, MA: Harvard University Press.

Caresle, X.F. (1988). Technology education in relation to science education. *Innovations in science and technology education II.* Paris: UNESCO.

Carson, R. (1962). *Silent spring.* New York: Fawcett World Library.

Charbonneau, L. (1988). Taking lasers to heart. *Canadian Research* (May):28–29.

Environments: Teacher's Guide (1970). Science Curriculum Improvement Study. Chicago: Rand McNally.

Fensham, P.J. (1988). Approaches to the teaching of STS in science education. *International Journal of Science Education* 10(4):346–56.

———. (1990). What will science education do about technology? *The Australian Science Teachers Journal* 36(3):8–21.

Gennaro, G., and A.D. Glenn (1979). Exploring value issues in science teaching. In *Science education/society: A guide to interaction and influence,* 1979 AETS Year Book. Columbus, OH: ERIC.

Henry, B. (1984). Watch on the rain: The atmosphere's acid toll. *Science Dimension* (2):7–8.

Janigan, K. (1988). Hand-made blood. *Canadian Research* (November):19.

Lowe, I. (1985). STS: The future mode of science education. *Australian Science Teachers Journal* 31(1):23–32.

MacLeod, S., and G. Mills (1986). *The teaching of science and technology in an interdisciplinary context. Approaches for the primary school.* Paris: UNESCO.

Martin, J. (1988). On a wing and microwave. *Canadian Research* (February):24–25.

Mills, G. (1988). An introduction to technology in the early years of schooling. In *Innovations in science and technology education,* vol. 2. Paris: UNESCO.

Page, J.E. (1979). *A Canadian context for science education.* Ottawa: Science Council of Canada.

Project Wild (1991). Ottawa: Canadian Wildlife Federation.

Science Council of Canada (1984). *Science for every student: Educating Canadians for tomorrow's world*. Ottawa: Science Council of Canada.

Scriven, M. (1987). *The rights of technology in education*. Education and Technology Task Force. Adelaide, South Australia: Ministry of Education and Technology.

UNESCO (1985). *Final report. International symposium on the teaching of technologies within the context of general education*. UNESCO document ED-85/Conf. 809/CDL 21). Paris: UNESCO.

Winter, P. (1985). A forest in the hand. *Science Dimension* (6):8–13.

CHAPTER 14

Science for a Changing World

SIGNS OF CHANGE

are evident in

FOCUS ON SPACE
1984 Marc Garneau
1985 Christa McAuliffe
1992 Roberta Bondar
1992 Steven MacLean

A NATIONAL VISION
Canada-Wide Science Fair
National Science and
Technology Week
Canada Scholarships Program

and a message for education

in

WHAT THE FUTURISTS ARE SAYING

about

NEEDED EMPHASES

such as

ACTIVE LIFELONG LEARNING	HIGH-LEVEL COGNITIVE SKILLS	ENGAGEMENT, EXPERIENCE, REFLECTION	HOLISTIC PERSONAL LEARNING	NURTURING THE YOUNG

which are reflected in the

PHILOSOPHY AND METHODOLOGY

of

ELEMENTARY SCIENCE

and

YOUR ROLE IN FACILITATING CHILDREN'S LEARNING

as

PREPARATION

for

SCIENCE FOR LIFE

◆ ◆ ◆ ◆

The increasing pace of change of all types means
that today's and tomorrow's citizens need to be
effective lifelong learners, capable of responding
constructively not only to conditions we cannot fore-
see, but also to those we have not yet imagined.

Ontario: *The Common Curriculum* (1993)

This chapter — the final one in the book — takes you into the future as primary and elementary teachers. It invites you to review the important aspects of teaching and learning that have been developed so that you can once more reflect upon these and use them as the basis for the choices you will make, day by day, as you begin the exciting and challenging adventure of exploring science with children.

In a sense the future is already here, and this chapter reflects the rapid pace of change that is evident in the world in which we live. It reinforces the tenets that have been presented throughout the book, and focusses once more on the continuing need in education to look carefully at the theoretical foundations on which practice is based. As the teachers of the future, you will work within the theories that have been shown to be most productive in guiding practice, becoming researchers at the classroom level as you experiment constantly with approaches, some new and some not so new, that seem to hold promise for preparing children for a changing world.

Changing views of science and its interaction with technology and society, as well as, new approaches to curriculum design and instruction, will affect the choices you will make each day and the choices children will have in their learning. These foundations, together with your daily experiences, will guide you as beginning teachers in the layout of your classrooms, the climate for learning that you will create, the teaching strategies you will use, the resources you will select, and the ways you will assess children's progress and strive to provide for their individual differences.

Your own perceptions of what life may be like in the twenty-first century will influence the way you plan your lessons. You will be constantly aware of the need to prepare children to live in and to cope successfully with a world where knowledge is expanding at a phenomenal rate, where societal values are changing, and where technological advances will bring about change at a pace unprecedented in history.

Working on the premise that the future has already begun, think about some of the following signs of change in the 1980s and 1990s, all of which impinge on the consciousness of children in primary and elementary schools.

◆ ◆ ◆ ◆ ◆
SIGNS OF CHANGE: FOCUS ON SPACE

October 1984. Quebec City – born Marc Garneau joins an American crew for the first flight of the space shuttle *Challenger* and becomes the first Canadian in space. As scientist/astronaut, he continues the tests of Canadian-built scientific equipment, especially the robotic space arm, Canadarm, and the solar photometer.

Evory and Gareffa (1985) cite Garneau's description of the eight-day shuttle mission as "an experience that will indelibly mark me for the rest of my life. ... I could have spent two months up there. I loved it."

July 1985. Plans are announced for the Space Shuttle Mission 51–l, and applications are invited from teachers in the United States to take part in that mission. Christa McAuliffe is selected from 11 000 applicants. She works with Barbara Morgan and eight other finalists, and enlists the help of many more teachers in planning lessons to teach live from the mission. The Teacher in Space Project (1985) results in the production of an abundance of new space-related, mind-stretching curriculum materials for the elementary classroom. The lessons, so eagerly anticipated by Christa McAuliffe's students, are abruptly cut off by the tragic explosion of the *Challenger* on takeoff in January 1986, when all seven crew members were killed.

January 1992. Roberta Bondar, a Canadian neurologist, is one of a crew of seven blasting off into space on the *Discovery*'s fifteenth voyage. Bondar is the second Canadian astronaut and the first Canadian woman to travel in space. Her schedule on the flight includes a series of medical tests designed by McGill University scientists to measure the effects of weightlessness on the nervous system, to assess the spread of vertebrae in the spine, and to investigate inner-ear function in space. Other tests involve cancer research and the effects of gravity on the growth of fertilized frogs' eggs.

Students and teachers at Sir James Dunn High School in her home town of Sault Ste. Marie, Ontario, follow Bondar's activities each day on television, and on January 29 her chat with the prime minister is monitored by about 700 young people at the Ontario Science Centre. On their return to Canada, she and her backup from the Canadian Space Agency, Ken Money, are greeted by 200 high-school students at the Museum of Science and Technology. Roberta Bondar describes the wonder of seeing Canada from space:

> "The view of our planet and the solitude of this planet against ... the black universe is something that I shall never forget and is something that I will endeavor for the rest of my life to try to protect" (*Evening Telegram,* St. John's, NF, 1992: 9).

October 1992. Steven MacLean, an Ottawa-born expert in laser physics, whose scheduled March 1987 flight was delayed by the loss of the *Challenger,* is the next Canadian astronaut in space. On board the space shuttle *Columbia,* one of his tasks is to test the Space Vision System component of the Canadarm. He is also in charge of experiments to determine the altitude and extent of the ozone layer. These words (Nichols 1992) express his elation: "You're very lucky if you get a chance to fly in space. I still float when I think about the fact that I'm doing what I do" (52).

The children of today share through television the same sense of exhilaration, mixed with concern, that Roberta Bondar felt as she looked through the window at the planet Earth and made a personal commitment to the preservation of its environment.

The power to share and communicate has increased exponentially and will continue to accelerate in the future, as children have access to information technology and are far more comfortable with it than most parents and teachers. They live in a world where the spectacular events marking International Space Year 1992 — such as "Mission to Planet Earth," a program involving co-ordination of Earth-observing satellites and related ground activities to monitor global environmental problems — are accepted as a matter of course. They live in a world where educational programs such as the National Geographic Kids Network allow children in Grades 4, 5, and 6 to test hypotheses, collect and analyze data, and share their results on classroom monitors with children in other parts of the continent and around the world. They live in a world where students in science museums throughout North America, by means of video signals taken by cameras mounted on the robot Jason, can explore, simultaneously with scientists in a control barge at the surface, underwater wrecks of Civil War battleships in Lake Ontario.

Figure 14.1 shows how an interdisciplinary unit on space, developed in an elementary classroom, can freely cross and enhance all areas of the curriculum, challenging students in provocative ways — through incentives for research on topics of their own choosing, through exploration of space-related literature, and through language arts and other activities that stimulate creativity and imagination.

Can you, a teacher in a primary or elementary classroom — through your own enthusiasm for science, through the opportunities given to children in your classroom to discuss projects such as these, and through the kinds of experiences provided — also help to kindle the spark that can lead to lifelong interest in science?

Fortunately, there are signs that the spark, once ignited, may now be fuelled by a growing awareness in society of the importance of science in our daily lives.

◆ ◆ ◆ ◆ ◆

SIGNS OF CHANGE: A NATIONAL VISION

In 1991, the 25th anniversary of the Science Council of Canada, Janet Halliwell, chair of the Council, announced in the newsletter *In Touch* the completion of a five-year plan for developing a national vision on science and technology, with a different theme for each year. Education was seen by the Council as an essential foundation for progress.

The Science Council of Canada no longer exists. However, there is a growing consciousness in society of the need to promote science in the schools if Canada is to have the pool of scientists and technically trained people to make the country competitive in a global context. Helping teachers in their vision for the future are events such as the Canada-Wide Science Fair, National Science and Technology Week, and programs such as Science Culture Canada, the Canada Scholarships program, and the Scientists in the Schools program.

The Canada-Wide Science Fair

The Canada-Wide Science Fair has always been a high point in the school year, inspiring young scientists to get involved in projects at the local level, to compete at that level, and to be good enough one day for national competition. A source of motivation to students in 1990 was the production of a video on the Canada-Wide Science Fair at Windsor, Ontario. The video was produced by the crew of the CBC program "Degrassi Junior High," and distributed that year by the Youth Science Foundation to 900 school boards and 100 regional contacts.

FIGURE 14.1

Space

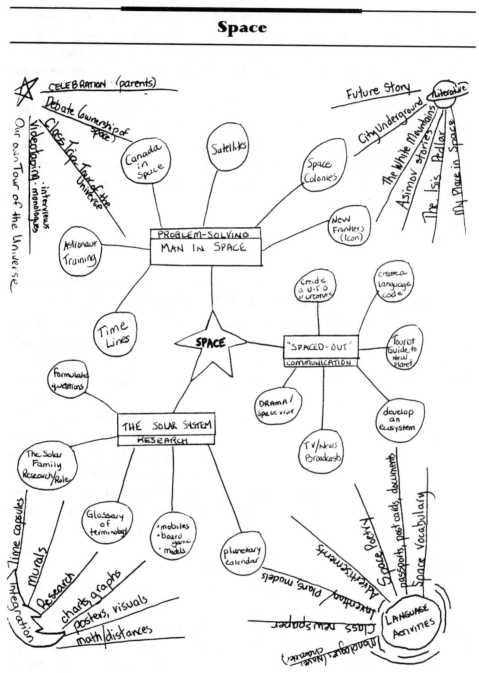

Source: Lois Roy, Queenston Drive Public School, Toronto.

National Science and Technology Week

Another high point is National Science and Technology Week, in which a variety of activities across Canada encourage involvement and raise public awareness of science in school, home, and community. The first National Science and Technology Week was celebrated in March 1989 with a number of activities aimed at younger children, inviting them to see the world as a place that is filled with special mysteries and secrets to be discovered. The 1990 National Science and Technology Week was described by a news release from the Minister for Industry, Science and Technology Canada as featuring a "range of activities from the universe to the ocean floor, to engender pride in Canada's accomplishments and science potential" (1). The Youth Science Foundation celebrated National Science and Technology Week in 1990 by having high-school students display their science projects in elementary schools across Canada. The Council of Ministers of Education (1990) endorsed National Science and Technology Week as a major annual co-operative event that would highlight national science and technology achievements, and encourage more young people to see science and technology as "exciting, rewarding, important and relevant" (1), and to consider science-related careers.

The Science Culture Canada Program

Another program developed to promote a more science-oriented culture in Canada is *Science Culture Canada*. An important objective is to "develop and sustain greater interest in, and awareness of, science and technology among Canada's young people" (Canada 1991). Each year, projects are funded that are designed to prepare Canada for a changing world by educating and preparing citizens for the challenges of tomorrow and by cultivating in young Canadians awareness of the importance of science and technology to their own futures and the future of Canada. Among projects funded by Science Culture Canada are a world-class fluvarium with an under-the-stream viewing window at the Fresh-water Resource Centre in St. John's, Newfoundland; a new film, *Messages in Stone,* on the life and death of dinosaurs, based in part on fossil research in Alberta; "Children Explore Science" participatory science exhibits in St. John, New Brunswick; and a "Live the Space Adventure" project at the Centre Aérospatial Amateur in Rosemère, Quebec.

The Canada Scholarships Program

More than 2500 top students are being encouraged each year to pursue undergraduate studies in the natural sciences and engineering through the Canada Scholarships Program. At least half of these scholarships are awarded to women.

Achievement rates are being closely followed, and two gender-related aspects of the program, discipline enrolments and general enrolments, are underway. Under the sponsorship of Women in Engineering, an interesting study is aimed at identifying gender stereotypes and systemic barriers that prevent women from entering and remaining in the engineering profession, and at finding ways to remove these barriers. Recall from Chapter 11 the thoughts on gender biases expressed by Monique Frize, chair of Women in Engineering and member of the Faculty of Engineering at the University of New Brunswick.

Another aspect of the program that bodes well for the future is the award of Junior Research Fellowships to selected Canada scholars to give them experience in research and engineering laboratories.

The Scientists in the Schools Program

The reasons advanced for the shortage of qualified scientists, engineers, and technologists in all provinces are lack of knowledge of the careers available and the failure to enrol in high-school mathematics and science programs. The *Scientists in the Schools* program takes advantage of the potential of role models for shaping attitudes toward science and informing students of diverse career opportunities in science and technology. At the upper elementary level, the program can intro-duce excitement into the classroom, excitement that can be enhanced as students are exposed to further role models, male and female, during their junior-high and high-school years. Geraldine Kenny-Wallace, president of McMaster University and past chair of the Science Council of Canada, has frequently suggested that girls can be encouraged to prepare for science-related careers by talking with women who have had successful careers in science.

Although many of the national and provincial initiatives to increase scientific literacy and public awareness in science appear to be aimed at students beyond the primary and elementary level, their proliferation is a hopeful sign. Such initiatives may help to ensure that your early efforts to stimulate and maintain interest in science, and to encourage in your students scientific ways of problem solving and looking at the world, will be nurtured further as they leave you to enter middle school and continue their journey through life.

To add to the excitement of school science it will be important for provinces to include in *Science Culture Canada* projects and future celebrations of National Science and Technology Week many activities that are geared to children in the primary and elementary grades. The importance of good beginnings cannot be overestimated.

> ### From a Teacher's Journal
>
> Technology is the application of scientific concepts and principles. It is increasingly important, as the development of technology in the modern era escalates, to create within the users of these new applications a positive technological culture. Youngsters must learn to interact positively with technologies rather than be intimidated by them. Only then can the full benefits of the new technologies be realized.
>
> Sciencing can enhance students' literacy by introducing technological and scientific language, but, more important, it can build the necessary confidence in young people to interact in a hands-on fashion with a variety of equipment and materials. Knowing one can cope in a world of rapid change is important, and school science can be the starting point.
>
> *Ernie Shaw*
> *Sarnia, ON*

Provincial Guidelines

There are signs of change all over Canada as curriculum guidelines are revised to emphasize the need for school science to prepare children for a changing world. Consider the following sampling from various provincial ministry (department) of education documents.

As we approach the 21st century, societal changes are significantly influencing our system of education ... The explosion in electronic technology and available information has outdated the significance of learning information for its own sake ... Teaching students how to learn and to express and apply knowledge is most important (New Brunswick 1992, 1).

What is certain is that all citizens will have to make more and more decisions on STS issues. Therefore, not only will our citizens and leaders have to be more scientifically and technologically literate, but they will have to be more aware of the limitations of science and technology in solving problems in our society (Alberta 1990, 2).

Only programs that are designed to be adaptable can continue to be relevant in an age of rapid change (Ontario 1993, 8).

Science is a powerful way of learning about the natural world. It is a process of asking questions and seeking answers about natural phenomena in order to make sense of the universe. One of the goals of science education is to foster in our students a lifelong appreciation of learning about science (Nova Scotia 1992, 3).

The purpose of the Primary Program is to enable the young learner to begin to develop the knowledge, skills, and attitudes that are the foundation for future school programs and for lifelong learning and participation in society (British Columbia 1989, 27).

The overall aim of the Department is to help our students become knowledgeable and independent, equipped with the skills of life-long learning (Newfoundland and Labrador 1990, 3).

Actively participating in K–12 Science will enable a student to ... develop a unique view of technology, society and the environment as a result of science education, and continue to extend this interest and attitude throughout life (Saskatchewan 1990, 1).

All of the above documents reflect a renewed emphasis on the need for scientific and technological literacy, and for preparing children for life in a world of exponential change. The sense of urgency in implementing this goal is echoed in the writings of futurists, who stress preparing children for a life not just in the future, but in a number of possible alternative futures.

◆ ◆ ◆ ◆ ◆

FUTURISTICS

Many things come to be because of powerful images that begin in the present and become the fulfilled prophecies of the future. One approach to looking at change and creating positive images of the future is to think of a number of probable, possible, and plausible futures. This approach (Lahe 1985) has been called *futuristics,* and has been used sometimes with gifted students to develop higher-level thinking skills as they reflect on their own culture in new and different ways.

A device that is frequently used is the "future wheel." A future issue or trend is drawn in the centre of a student's notebook page, with spokes drawn outward. The students, working in groups, predict and record first-order effects that might result from that trend, and then think of second-, third-, and fourth-level effects. As the future wheel expands outward, students look at the direct effects of that problem, then the implications for change resulting from these effects, and so on.

The next activity invites you to use the future wheel shown in Figure 14.2 to think through possible alternative futures.

activity 14.1

WHEEL OF THE FUTURE

1. Form a group among your classmates. Select a future issue that concerns your group, and begin to draw a future wheel, as shown in Figure 14.2.
2. Predict the results of that future issue.
3. What are the second-order effects of your issue? The third-order effects?
4. Discuss the results of the future wheel with your group.

☐ Reflecting and Sharing

What future trends did you come up with, and what did your group record as first-order effects as you expanded the future wheel? Did more than one scenario come to mind, and were you able to think of the implications for teaching and learning of each of these images of the future? As the spokes of the wheel were filled in with first-order effects, were you able to imagine what the second-order effects might be? The third?

What Futurists Are Saying

Long ago, it seems, C.P. Snow (1959) discussed the radical changes in people's lives that would result from the rapid advance in the potential for global communication, and pointed to the challenge that would face educators in preparing children for this rate of change. He drew attention both to the need for

FIGURE 14.2

Wheel of the Future

1. Select a future issue that concerns your group.
2. Predict the results of your issue.
3. What are the second effects of your issue?
4. Discuss the results of your future wheel with another group.

Example:

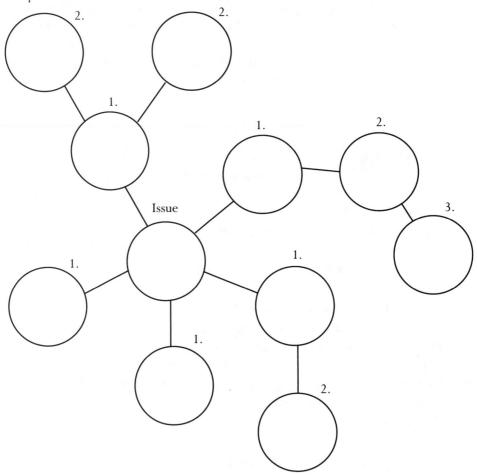

Source: From Sharing images of the future: Futuristics and gifted education by L. Lahe, *Teaching Exceptional Children*, Spring 1985, 178. Copyright 1985 by The Council for Exceptional Children. Reprinted with permission.

deep and original conceptual minds to understand the actual technique of this "cybernetic jump," and to the fact that much of our future depends upon the talent of children not yet in their teens.

Alvin Toffler's *Future Shock* (1972) was first published in 1970, but he is somewhat of an oracle in his writings about what life may hold as we enter the next century. To give some idea of the present rate of technological advancement, he cites examples of past endeavours to reach greater speeds, and compares the time lag in accomplishing this with events in the generation just past. From a modest speed of 13 km/h in a camel caravan in 6000 B.C., it took 4400 years to reach the 32 km/h speed of a horse-drawn chariot in 1600 B.C. The world waited another 3500 years for steam locomotives to reach 160 km/h, and then suddenly airplanes were travelling at a speed of 640 km/h, which increased within twenty years when rocket planes approached speeds of 6400 km/h. Soon afterward, humans were able to circle the globe in space capsules at 28 800 km/h. Toffler suggests that, if "plotted on a graph, the line representing progress in the past generation would leap vertically off the page" (26).

This phenomenal rate of progress applies equally to growth in information technology, in worldwide communication, in national and global interdependence, and in the knowledge base. All of these impinge on education and its beginnings in the primary school. In *Future Shock,* Toffler refers to knowledge as a perishable entity and advises teachers to assist children with the tasks of learning "how to learn, unlearn and relearn" (414). He writes of the necessity of preparing children to adapt to a changing society by acquiring communication and social skills, and the ability to examine and question values held by themselves, their peers, and their teachers.

Judith Dueck, writing in *Computers in Education* (1991), expresses it this way:

A crucial task of educators is to equip students with tools, procedures, skills, attitudes, and whatever else they will need to face a world which is not the same as the one of the 50s, 60s, 70s, 80s, or even the 90s ... Schools in a number of provinces are automating their libraries even at the elementary levels. They have recognized the importance of preparing students to handle information. They realize that what happens in schools today affects in a very vital way what happens in Canada tomorrow (19).

Karen Porat (1989), an assistant principal from Calgary, agrees that "it is time for reflection and a considered response to changed needs" (28). She cites a collection of views from a cross-section of society on what education for the 1990s should be like. The list includes futurists, scientists, pacifists, businesspeople, politicians, graduates, and educators. Together the futurists advocate an innovative, participative, holistic approach to education, with time for students to "engage, experience and reflect." David Suzuki agrees that children must be taught to think for themselves rather than becoming "clones of us," and that radical changes in beliefs and attitudes are needed if the world is to survive. The theme of survival is echoed by the pacifists, and the need for students to think for themselves is reiterated by Laurier LaPierre, who says that to have them do otherwise is to "remove their wings." The graduates interviewed by Porat would like students to have more time and opportunity to pursue interests and make choices, to have better access to career information from the start, to be allowed to be dreamers and doers. Educators agree that they are on the front line of change and must become "educational entrepreneurs," searching for excellence in education — for what works best.

Recommendations for Change

In the search for information about trends in society and their effects on our way of life, as well as directions that educators might take, Steve Benjamin (1989) reviewed the educational and societal futures literature. He identified the following recommendations for educational change in order of the frequency with which they appeared in the literature.

Active Learning

Active learning was understood as students' active participation — learning by doing — as well as allowing them more autonomy and freedom in their choice of learning experiences, and shifting responsibility for learning from the teacher to the student.

High-Level Cognitive Skills

Students will need the ability to think critically, creatively, and abstractly, to question and inquire, in order to succeed in a technologically advanced, complex, change-driven world.

Service Learning

Service learning, which gives students opportunities for active learning through interaction with peers and adults as volunteers in social agencies, hospitals, museums, and schools, is seen by futurists as a way of focussing on real problems and developing a service ethic.

From a Teacher's Journal

Science is not something we study, but rather something we do. Sciencing means to investigate, to make one attempt after another to find answers to questions. It is a lifelong process of seeking out solutions and finding ways to meet challenges. To this end it is imperative to challenge children at an early age to be curious, to investigate and search for answers. When investigative tasks are perceived by students as relevant to their lives, they appreciate the significance of the tasks and enjoy the challenge and the feeling of accomplishment that successful completion brings. Once you excite students with possibilities for exploration and give them opportunities for successful problem solving, they will continue to enjoy "sciencing" throughout their lives.

Ernie Shaw
Sarnia, ON

PAST/PRESENT/FUTURE FOCUS

The orientation in learning should shift from past to past/present/future, with the ability to consider alternative futures, and a sense that the future is shaped by the decisions and actions of the present.

LIFELONG LEARNING

With the explosion of knowledge and the growing complexity of society, a "learning network" will be needed to provide for the learning of new content and skills as they are needed through life.

WHOLE-PERSON LEARNING

The futurists call for a reduction in the overemphasis on the cognitive, and stress instead education of the whole range of human capacities — mental, physical, and emotional.

COPING WITH DIVERSITY

With global interdependence and ethnic and cultural diversity, students should come to expect and understand diversity, to accept and be able to cope with change.

GENERAL EDUCATION

A liberal education, including the sciences and the humanities, has the greatest potential for cultivating a flexible approach to problems and a broader vision for the future.

TRANSDISCIPLINARY EDUCATION

Because of the increasing interdependence and connectedness of the nations of the world, futurists foresee a move from fragmentation of curriculum into separate disciplines to an activity-based, thematic, integrated approach to learning.

PERSONALIZED LEARNING

To enhance uniqueness and provide adequately for individual differences, the futurists advocate the removal of arbitrary time units and grade-level types of grouping, and the creation of more flexible environments for learning.

PROCESS APPROACH

Futurists foresee a shift from passive learning to the active seeking of knowledge, from knowing to searching, from an emphasis on "what" to learn to an emphasis on "how" to learn.

EDUCATION FOR COMMUNICATION

Futurists point to the importance of interaction and communication and the development of skills in social and collaborative learning.

EARLY CHILDHOOD EDUCATION

Futurists foresee an increasingly important role for the school in nurturing the young, a role that might even involve shifting resources from the higher levels of education to provide a stronger base in the beginning years and thus prevent some of the problems that now exist.

It is significant that the last item — early childhood education — is seen in this light. It may be that childlike attitudes and ways of learning — creative, imaginative, playful, holistic — are congruent with change and can be adapted most easily to it. It may be that the higher levels of schooling can learn from the primary and elementary grades how to stimulate and sustain the "I want to know" syndrome that is so characteristic of young children and, sadly, often lost as they grow older.

Coming through clearly in Benjamin's review of the literature is the need to prepare students to cope with changes in society and their lives, to become active rather than passive learners, to acquire skills in problem solving, and to learn how to continue learning throughout their lives. The emphasis is on lifelong learning, with the notion of interdisciplinary, holistic learning, in which learning in science would reach out and encompass the humanities and the whole of life.

Pluckrose (1987) emphasizes the need for child-centred instruction to prepare the young for life in the future, suggesting that children's needs should be paramount. Only by putting children's needs first and giving children autonomy to learn on their own will schools produce the flexible people who will be equipped, emotionally and intellectually, to face the challenges and cope successfully with the changes the twenty-first century will bring.

◆ ◆ ◆ ◆ ◆

REVIEW AND REFLECTION

As you consider the kind of world that your students are living in and the world that awaits them as they grow up — the predictable pace of change in the years ahead and the increasingly important influence of science and technology — the task of preparing the children of today for *science for life* becomes an inevitable part of your planning.

The writings of the futurists have been helpful in suggesting directions and establishing guidelines for planning. Their thoughts can be added to your own reflections on science education for the primary and elementary grades, thereby providing another dimension to the kinds of experiences you provide for your students.

It is time now for your own review and reflection — for recalling ideas that remain with you and make sense to you as you look back on your explorations of developments, past and present, in science education. It is time to reflect on the experiences that have helped you to build a conceptual framework centring on expected outcomes of children's learning in science, and to think of ways that these goals may be realized some day in your classroom and other settings for teaching/learning.

You've discovered that these outcomes span the cognitive, affective, psychomotor, and social domains of learning and take into account what is known of the nature of children and their growth and development. Thinking about the potential of science as a vehicle for children's learning has brought you close to the nature of science — science as one way in which humans search for understanding of the world, science as the attitudes and interests that fuel the search, and science as the conceptual structures that result.

Process skills, concepts, and attitudes develop together, and the first step in planning for teaching is to create in your classroom a positive climate for learning — an inviting, low-risk, child-involving and child-empowering atmosphere in which children are actively involved in constructing meaning from experience. Such a setting enhances unit and lesson planning, and encourages the use of a variety of teaching methods and a wide spectrum of teaching skills and techniques. Your repertoire of teaching models will be selected from a continuum of orientations to curriculum and instruction, and as you try different approaches your students' interest will also grow. Skills in motivating and sustaining learning through co-operative learning, through playful beginnings and thoughtful questioning, and through problem solving in and beyond the classroom refine and enliven instruction and open doors to further learning. Opening doors has always been the hallmark of a good education, with students walking through these open doors on their own toward increased options and greater independence in learning.

Teaching strategies and strategies for evaluating student progress toward expected outcomes go hand in hand and take into account the highly personalized, individual nature of learning for each student. There is the constant need to try new approaches, to evaluate whether things have gone well and whether important outcomes have been realized through the experiences you have provided for children.

Guidelines for the science curriculum and ideas for fresh and novel approaches to instruction are found in the resources available to teachers for curriculum implementation. Two tasks for beginning teachers are to become familiar with curriculum materials, past and present, that can be drawn upon to help with planning units and lessons. Criteria for the selection of resources are based on the aims of elementary science and on the short- and long-term goals that you hope individual children will attain through the experiences.

Providing for uniqueness means a commitment to science for *all* children, and a recognition of the potential of learning experiences in science for preparing all children to continue to be learners throughout their lives in the twenty-first century. A commitment to science for all involves a commitment to beginning science early, and to cultivating the ways of thinking that are basically playful and childlike, yet at the same time are basically scientific. Providing for individual differences in the regular classroom ensures that children of different interests, abilities, and cultural backgrounds, and children who may be faced with a variety of intellectual, physical, and emotional challenges, are involved in learning activities. It ensures that provision is made for teaching exceptional children by meeting the needs of challenged students and by providing stimulating experiences for the gifted and talented.

A long-range goal of primary and elementary science is scientific literacy. This overriding goal incorporates cognitive and affective outcomes, and emphasizes problem solving, especially problem solving that involves weighing the merits of, and choosing from, a number of alternatives. An emphasis on exploring science–technology–society (STS) interconnections is emerging as an important trend in science education, and will surely remain an essential component of primary and elementary science in the future. Awareness of the need to preserve the environment comes early to the children of today, along with a sensitivity that is not always matched by adults. It is good to give children opportunities to discuss problems they hear about and see, to prepare them for their roles as the decision-makers of the twenty-first century. The autonomy given to children as they pursue such investigations in and beyond the classroom is valuable practice for the kind of learning that will be needed as they continue their *science for life* journey and apply these skills to the situations they will encounter in the future.

Reflect on your readings, the experiences you have had, and the ideas that have evolved from these experiences as you work through the steps in Activity 14.2. It may well be the most challenging of all the activities in the book, yet perhaps the most rewarding. It invites you to put on paper a representation of the conceptual framework you have developed about the teaching of science in Canadian elementary schools.

activity 14.2 CONCEPT MAPS TO REPRESENT CONCEPTUAL FRAMEWORKS FOR TEACHING SCIENCE

◆ Form four co-operative learning groups, one for each section of the book. The beginning task in each group is to construct a concept map for one of the following sections.

Group 1. Children and Science: Desired Learning Outcomes
Group 2. From Theory to Practice
Group 3. Science for All Children
Group 4. Science for Life

◆ Share the results and then work with the four maps to make *one* concise concept map to represent the main ideas of the entire book and the relationships between them.

◆ If your map is too cumbersome, simplify it by constructing another, using as the main concepts the key terms in the preceding "Review and Reflection" section. Then insert lines and linking words to show relationships and interrelationships.

❏ Reflecting and Sharing

Not an easy task? Concept mapping rarely is! It is, however, an excellent way to organize your thoughts and to help you define your ideas more clearly.

Because constructing meaning is a personal thing, you may not be entirely happy with the map developed by your group. You may want to modify it — to take it home, revise it, and make it your own. You may see interconnections that were not apparent in the first attempt, relationships that are apparent only to you. Keep your map and return to it in a year or so, after the experiences of your first years of teaching science and your reflections on these experiences have led to new connections and new insights.

You will continue to grow as a teacher, and one of the best ways to grow professionally is to assume the role of an active learner, trying new approaches, reflecting on the success of these approaches for certain children, and keeping notes to guide practice in the future. Part of this approach will be to involve your students in the same sort of exercise by inviting them to talk about what works for them as learners, so that they will be encouraged to do the same throughout their lifetimes. Your role is a facilitative one, as you provide the starting points, the motivating beginnings, the questions, and the challenges that will stimulate and sustain interest, as well as initiate ways of thinking and learning that will prepare your young students for *science for life*.

Always behind the planning is the hope that the strategies you use will be good choices, that the classroom environment you create, and your own commitment to lifetime learning will make school science experiences so exciting for children that they can share Roberta Bondar's feeling that "there's absolutely nothing boring. There is no boring place anywhere in this whole planet" (*Evening Telegram*, St. John's, NF, 1992: 21).

◆ ◆ ◆ ◆ ◆

LOOKING BACK AND LOOKING FORWARD

This chapter has served two purposes. The first purpose is to encourage you to reflect on the kind of world for which you are preparing your students, by looking forward to what their lives may be like in the next century. The second purpose is to encourage you to look backward to preceding chapters and reflect on the ideas you have gleaned that will help you to prepare for the challenging and exciting task of exploring science with children.

Permeating the discussion has been the concept of change — change as an inevitable, continuing process. Science, in the sense of asking questions and seeking explanations of that changing world, can help children to live useful, fruitful lives, with minds that are attuned to the world's problems and flexible enough to contribute creative and responsible solutions.

For you as teachers, the process of reflective thinking will not end with this book, but will serve you well as you try out your ideas in the classroom and beyond the classroom, wherever there are opportunities for children and science. And, in trying out these ideas and reflecting on the results of that involvement, you will be researchers at the classroom level, adding to what is known about the teaching of science and how children learn.

An overriding goal that incorporates most of the outcomes for primary and elementary science is the development of scientific literacy. Scientifically literate people are those who continue to extend their science education throughout their lives. The twenty-first century will be well along when the generation of children now entering school begin their careers. Their future has already begun. It rests with you.

◆ ◆ ◆ ◆ ◆

A FINAL WORD

You have come full circle, from expected outcomes for children's learning in science to evaluation of their progress in reaching these goals; from "what science is" to an imagined classroom where children are encouraged to question and find answers through their own investigations of the environment; from theories of how children learn to providing developmentally appropriate experiences that allow them to construct their own meaning; from an awareness of the need for science to be part of the education of all children to finding ways to provide for individual differences; from the openness that will characterize your classroom to its reflection in the flexibility and creativity your students will need for lifetime learning; and, finally, from science in Canadian primary and elementary schools to *science for life*.

CANADIAN ACHIEVEMENTS IN SCIENCE

IAN SHELTON (B. 1957)

In mid-February, 1987, a lone Canadian was responsible for operating a small telescope in the Chilean Andes. At that time Ian Shelton was an unknown research assistant, employed by the University of Toronto, whose job was to take routine photographs of the night sky. When his equipment broke down, Shelton decided to spend his time developing the photographs he had just taken. He noticed an unexpected bright spot in a photograph of a galaxy called the Large Magellanic Cloud, and went outside to look. What he saw was the bright light from a supernova (the light from an explosion representing the death of a star), something that had not been observed from Earth in almost 400 years.

Shelton's observation enabled astronomers to record the complete process of a supernova for the first time ever, and offered an unprecedented opportunity for scientists to refine their understanding of the workings of the universe.

Astronomy is still a scientific field in which the amateur or near-amateur can do significant work. At the time of his discovery, Shelton had no graduate qualification and had taken the job with the university because it allowed him to pursue his longtime interest in astronomy without a specialist qualification in the field.

Following his discovery, Shelton enrolled in the Astronomy program at the University of Toronto, obtained his Master's degree in 1990, and then began working toward a Ph.D. Whatever else happens in his future, Ian Shelton will be known to future astronomers through the supernova that bears his name, Supernova Shelton 1987A.

 R E F E R E N C E S

Alberta (1990). *STS Science Education: Unifying the Goals of Science Education.* Alberta Education: Curriculum Support Branch.

Benjamin, S. (1989). An ideascape for education: What futurists recommend. *Educational Leadership* (March):8–13.

British Columbia (1989). *Year 2000: A Curriculum and Assessment Framework for the Future*. Draft. British Columbia: Ministry of Education.

Canada (1991). *Innovaction. The Canadian strategy for science and technology*. Science Culture Canada.

Council of Science and Technology Ministers (1990). *National Science and Technology Action Plan*. Draft, for consultation only.

Dueck, J. (1991). The information centre in the information age. *Computers in Education* (January):19–20.

Evening Telegram (St. John's, NF) (1992). Mulroney chats with Bondar as Discovery sets for return. (January 29):9.

Evory, A., and P.M. Gareffa (1985). *Contemporary Newsmakers* 1:26–27. Detroit: Gale Research Company.

Lahe, L. (1985). Sharing images of the future: Futuristics and gifted education. *Teaching Exceptional Children* (Spring):177–82.

McDonald, B. (1990). Networked. *Science and Children* (May): 8–9.

National Geographic Kids Network (1988). Cambridge, MA: Technical Education Resource Center (TERC).

New Brunswick (1992). *Elementary School Science Curriculum Guide. Grades One to Three*. New Brunswick: Department of Education.

Newfoundland and Labrador (1990). *Learning How to Learn: Policy Statements on Resource-based Learning and Its Implementation in Newfoundland and Labrador Schools*. Draft. Newfoundland and Labrador: Department of Education.

Nichols, M. (1992). Touch the sky: A Canadian scientist waits to enter space. *Maclean's* (February 10):52.

Nova Scotia (1992). *Proposed Framework for the Elementary Science Program*. Nova Scotia: Department of Education.

NSTA *Reports!* (1991a). Activities are underway for International Space Year 1992. (March):5.

———. (1991b). Jason Project now scheduled for December. (April):11.

Ontario (1993). *The Common Curriculum. Grades 1–9*. Working document. February. Ontario: Ministry of Education and Training.

Pluckrose, H. (1987). *What is happening in our primary schools?* England: Basil Blackwell.

Porat, K.L. (1989). Future perspectives: Education for the nineties. *Teaching Today* (September/October):28–40.

Saskatchewan (1990). *Science: A Curriculum Guide for the Elementary Level.* Saskatchewan Education.

Science Council of Canada (1991). *In Touch* (July):1.

Snow, C.P. (1959). *The two cultures and the scientific revolution.* New York: Cambridge University Press.

Teacher in Space Project (1985). NASA *Publications,* 1–16.

Toffler, A. (1972). *Future shock.* 19th printing. New York: Bantam Books.

■ ■ ■ ■ ■ ■

APPENDIX A *Life Science Projects for the
Primary and Elementary
Grades*

APPENDIX B *Playing Different Roles*

APPENDIX A

Life Science Projects for the Primary and Elementary Grades

1. **PLANT PROPAGATION**

2. **SEED GERMINATION**

3. **HAY INFUSION**

4. **GROWING MOULDS**

5. **HYDROPONICS**

6. **LOCAL INSECTS**

7. **MEALWORMS**

8. **BRINE SHRIMP**

9. **PLANT GROWTH**

Life science projects have always been well received by primary and elementary children. The children encounter the fascination of watching plant and animal growth, and the satisfaction of being involved in the decision-making process when designing experiments. They also develop a sense of responsibility in caring for organisms. The potential for developing cognitive, affective, psychomotor, and social outcomes makes these projects very worthwhile for children.

Activities and investigations in the physical sciences can often be completed within the 40 minutes to one hour usually allotted to a science lesson. However, life science investigations usually require much longer periods of time. The units described here are introduced to the entire class during regular class periods, but from then on students work in small groups. Some projects require almost daily observations, while others are less intensive. Some may be completed in several weeks; others may last for several months.

The units suggested here can be used at a variety of grade levels, with the structure and degree of difficulty adapted to the appropriate grade level. Some of the projects readily fit into existing curricula, while others are more appropriate as supplementary units. All except the project on collecting insects are experimental in nature, and in all projects there are excellent opportunities to develop process skills.

◆ ◆ ◆ ◆ ◆

LIFE SCIENCE PROJECT 1: PLANT PROPAGATION

There are a number of benefits arising from propagating plants in the classroom. Students are exposed to a variety of techniques for starting new plants, are given opportunities to create a more aesthetically pleasing atmosphere in the classroom, and can design activities that allow for investigation of plant growth under controlled conditions. Techniques that are useful for demonstrating ways of starting new plants (but that do not necessarily lead to experimentation) include leaf cuttings, leaf sections, vein cuttings, soil layering, and air layering.

Leaf Cuttings

To grow plants from whole leaves, remove the leaf by making a diagonal cut near the bottom of the stalk. This method can be used for African violets and gloxinias, but is even better suited for those plants classified as succulents (having thick, fleshy leaves). For succulent leaves it is best to allow the cutting to dry for a day or so, so that scar tissue forms over the moist surface that is exposed, and rotting is prevented. Then place the cutting in soil just deep enough to support it firmly. Check the cutting for the appearance of roots every three or four days.

Leaf Sections

Plants such as African violets, rex begonias, and large-leaved succulents may be propagated by using leaf sections. Remove the leaf and divide it into a number of pieces, ensuring that each piece has at least one prominent vein. Again, it is best to let the sections dry for a day before pressing them about one-third of their length into the soil. As with whole-leaf cuttings, check for roots every three or four days.

Vein Cuttings

The most successful plant for vein cutting is the rex begonia. Remove a healthy leaf and make small cuts (1 or 2 cm) across the major veins. Place the leaf flat on soil or vermiculite, ensuring that it is pressed firmly against the medium by placing small stones around the leaf margins. To increase the humidity, it is advisable to cover the container with plastic wrap. However, careful monitoring of the moisture present is necessary to prevent the leaves from rotting. It is best not to check for root development; instead, simply wait for small plants to appear in the cuts on the veins.

USING A ROOTING HORMONE

The three techniques described here can be extended by using a rooting hormone and comparing the results to cuttings started without the use of a hormone. Control must be exercised in watering these cuttings. Since rot sets in easily, it is best to keep the rooting medium just slightly moist. If the cuttings show signs of drying, add just a little more water. Finally, since these techniques are relatively slow in giving results it is recommended that you run them concurrently with stem cuttings, which will be described later.

Soil and Air Layering

Methods such as soil and air layering have the tremendous advantage that the new plant already has a root system before it is severed from the original plant.

SOIL LAYERING

The soil layering technique is particularly useful for plants commonly referred to as runners or creepers, such as ivy, philodendron, and tradescantia. Also, this method works well for spider plants and strawberry geraniums that produce young plantlets on long stems. In either case, allow either a portion of the stem or the base of the plantlet to come into contact with moist soil. It may be helpful to secure the plant in place with a bent paperclip. Once roots appear, sever the stem behind the root system and you have a new plant.

Air Layering

Air layering is most successful for plants with a single, upright stem. Examples are dieffenbachia, dracaena, philodendron, and the rubber plant (ficus). Either remove two leaves or make a vertical cut in the stem and wrap this with moist soil or sphagnum moss enclosed in plastic wrap. Tie the plastic tightly to the stem above and below the cut and wait for roots to appear against the clear plastic. When this occurs, cut through the stem just below the rooted area and transplant.

Exploring Variables: Stem Cuttings

Stem cuttings offer the best possibilities for investigative activities in the classroom. Fast-rooting runners or creepers are recommended for this activity. A good experimental design is to take five cuttings from each of three different plant types. These cuttings should be 10–15 cm in length and have growing tips. Treat the cuttings as follows:

Plant Type A

A1 In water, uncovered, no hormone.

A2 In moist vermiculite, uncovered, no hormone.

A3 In soil, uncovered, no hormone.

A4 In soil, uncovered, hormone added.

A5 In water, covered with plastic bag, no hormone.

Repeat these procedures for Plant Types B and C as well. This allows for the following comparisons:

A1 vs. A2   Water vs. vermiculite

A1 vs. A3   Water vs. soil

A2 vs. A3   Vermiculite vs. soil

A3 vs. A4   No hormone vs. hormone

A1 vs. A5   Uncovered vs. covered

Similarly, compare B1 vs. B2, C1 vs. C2, and so on. You can also compare A1 vs. B1 vs. C1 and so on to see whether there are advantages to using certain plants over others.

Students should be encouraged to make careful observations of each cutting. In particular, they should record the appearance of roots, the approximate length and number of roots present, as well as the growth of the cutting.

◆ ◆ ◆ ◆ ◆

LIFE SCIENCE PROJECT 2: SEED GERMINATION

Primary and elementary students often encounter superficial activities relating to the germination of seeds. There are many missed opportunities for additional learning, particularly with respect to the development of process skills. This topic provides such a wide range of options that beginning teachers can often be overwhelmed with the choices available. A degree of structure can be imposed in this case by considering three major headings: (1) seed types, (2) methods for germination, and (3) conditions for germination.

Seed Types

When choosing seeds for classroom use, select seeds that are sufficiently large so that students can handle them easily and, perhaps more important, can observe all the changes that occur. Seeds that germinate within two to five days are best to use because younger children may become frustrated when waiting for long periods of time for signs of germination. Finally, it is best to choose seeds that have a relatively high rate of germination so that students can expect reasonable results.

Germination Methods

Planting seeds directly in soil is not a desirable method, since children will miss seeing all the changes that occur before the growing plant tip emerges. Instead, consider methods that allow the students to observe all the growth changes that occur from the time the investigation begins.

SEED-VIEW JAR

A frequently used method for observing germination is the seed-view jar. Line a clear plastic or glass jar with a cylinder of paper towelling. Wide-mouth jars allow for easier preparation. Place additional towelling in the centre to push the cylinder of paper firmly against the walls of the container. Then moisten the paper towelling and place the seeds between the walls of the jar and the paper towelling. This allows for easy viewing, enabling students to see all the changes that occur.

Flat Tray

Alternatively, a flat tray may be used to observe germination. The tray should be lined on the bottom with moist paper towelling, sawdust, or vermiculite. Place the seeds on the surface and cover the tray with plastic wrap to maintain a high level of humidity.

Inverted Jar

Unfortunately, when proper conditions for seed germination are provided, you may encounter mould growth. This is because the spores of many common moulds have virtually the same growth requirements. To prevent mould growth, soak the seeds for a few minutes in a bleach solution, or wash the seeds periodically to remove any mould growth. A more effective way of overcoming this mould problem is to use the inverted jar method. Soak the seeds in water for one day. Place a porous cloth, such as cheesecloth, over the mouth of a jar and secure it. Drain off the water in which the seeds have been soaking and then rinse the seeds with fresh water and again pour away the water. Then invert the jar and place it in another container. This allows the seeds to rest on the moist cloth and permits germination to occur. Each successive day, rinse the seeds and invert the jar once again.

Conditions for Germination

Once suitable seed types and an effective germination method have been selected, the project can be extended to include investigations of various conditions that affect the germination of seeds. These conditions include varying light, the amount of moisture present, and temperature. There is ample opportunity here for students to set up controlled experiments to investigate these variables. Emphasis should be placed on developing observation skills, making hypotheses, controlling variables, quantifying, recording data, interpreting data, and predicting.

Going Further: Additional Projects

Additional activities relating to the topic of seed germination include:

◆ classifying seeds
◆ collecting seeds from local plants
◆ germinating seeds found in a supermarket
◆ investigating seed dispersal

◆ ◆ ◆ ◆ ◆

LIFE SCIENCE PROJECT 3: HAY INFUSION

One of the most exciting science experiences for young children is the discovery of the world of microscopic organisms. With a minimum of effort, children can create the conditions necessary for protozoan growth. Within a relatively short period of time, they may encounter examples of the growth of populations and see how succession can occur in a community of micro-organisms.

To establish a boiled infusion, collect one litre of pond water, preferably from an area of a pond that is relatively still. Pour one-half litre of this water into a jar, add a handful of hay, and bring it to a boiling temperature. After fifteen minutes of boiling, remove the jar from the heat source and allow it to cool; then add the remaining half-litre of pond water. Place a cover loosely on the jar. Your students are about to discover a whole new world.

Alternatively, you may establish an unboiled infusion by simply adding a handful of hay directly to a litre of collected pond water. Again, cover the jar loosely, and you may begin observations. To increase the number of variables, collect water from two different ponds and set up a boiled and an unboiled infusion for each.

Teaching Necessary Skills

This project is particularly useful for introducing children to the microscope. Before actual observations begin, it is very important to ensure that students become proficient in using a medicine dropper, preparing slides, and working with the microscope. Initial observations may take place using low-power magnification, but ultimately students will need to use high-power magnification as well. Teach techniques such as washing slides and drying them on paper towels, and safety precautions such as washing hands afterward.

Recording Observations

Keeping detailed records of the observations is essential. Further, students should be encouraged to quantify as much as possible. It is useful to establish a system that permits students to indicate numbers of organisms present without doing an exact count. A simple coding system is:

0	no organisms present	+ +	11 to 25 organisms
+	1 to 10 organisms	+ + +	25 and over

Also, students should be encouraged to make drawings of the different organisms observed. At the elementary level, it is not expected that students will be able to name each organism. Simple drawings can be effective, and students can make up names for the various types of organisms.

To allow students to monitor the development of each type of organism over a period of time, an effective chart can be compiled as follows:

	Day 1	Day 2	Day 3	Day 4	Day 5
Organism A	+ +	+ +	+ + +	+ + +	+ +
Organism B	+	+	+ +	+ +	+
Organism C	0	+	+ +	+ + +	+ + +
Organism D	0	0	+	+	0

Often they will see a species slowly increase in numbers, peak, and then begin to disappear. Second, by looking at the entire chart, they may find examples where new species become more abundant while others dwindle in numbers. In a few small jars in the classroom, they can experience examples of the growth of a population and succession in a community, as one population competes with and replaces another.

Going Further: Exploring Other Habitats

Look at water from a variety of sources — stagnant pools, bogs, and running streams — to compare differences between samples in population and patterns of succession.

♦ ♦ ♦ ♦ ♦

LIFE SCIENCE PROJECT 4: GROWING MOULDS

The growth of moulds offers tremendous potential for learning in the elementary classroom. Children respond very well to this type of project because it is typically very successful and demonstrates quite rapid growth.

A good way to begin this project is to set up a mould garden. Place sand, vermiculite, or soil to a depth of 1 cm in the bottom of a plastic container.

Moisten the substrate, but do not saturate it, since bacteria rather than moulds tend to flourish in a very wet environment. Place several different types of food (approximately 3 cm in diameter) on the surface. Space them well apart so that as moulds develop they can grow very large before overlapping another food type.

It is very important to cover the container with clear plastic wrap. This keeps moisture levels high, prevents odours from escaping, and, perhaps most important, keeps the spores contained once the moulds reach maturity, in case one of your students may be allergic to moulds. Allergies should be identified before the mould investigation begins.

Once the mould garden is established, changes can be observed in just a day or two. First, there will be small changes in the pieces of food as they absorb moisture, and then the presence of mould will become noticeable. Students should be encouraged to note the time each mould appears, as well as the colour and size. This is an ideal opportunity to emphasize the value of quantitative observations.

As these changes occur, the children typically ask questions such as: "Where do these moulds come from?" "Why are there different types of moulds?" "How can we stop these moulds from growing?" These all serve as useful starting points for further investigation.

Conditions for Mould Growth

IDENTIFYING MOULDS

Students will certainly be curious as to the types of moulds they discover. There will be varying textures, colours, and sizes. To properly identify the various types it is necessary to look at the reproductive structures under the microscope. At first glance, most of these moulds appear similar in that, typically, they have a mass of threadlike structures — the mycelium (which students invariably refer to as "fuzz"). Once you find the reproductive structures, however, it becomes obvious that the moulds are different. Usually you will encounter *rhizopus, aspergillus,* and *penicillium*. The presence of penicillium may lead to an interesting discussion on the uses of certain moulds in the production of antibiotics, the flavouring of certain cheeses, and so on.

EFFECTS OF MOISTURE

Perhaps the most logical place to begin is to determine the effect of moisture on mould growth. Ask the students to cut a slice of bread into 3 to 4 cm squares.

Allow this bread to dry overnight to remove any moisture present. Choose five or six clear plastic bags and place a piece of bread in each. The first bag should be sealed without the addition of any water. Sufficient water should be added to another bag to completely saturate the bread. Once this amount of water is determined, choose varying amounts for the other bread pieces so that you have a range of moisture from completely dry to saturated. Within this range there will be an optimal moisture condition, that is, one that shows the greatest mould growth. The clear plastic bags allow the students to make observations without opening them. Again, encourage the students to make accurate observations.

EFFECTS OF LIGHT AND HEAT

Having determined the optimal amount of moisture, use this information to investigate the effects of light and temperature. At this time, emphasize the importance of controlling variables. For example, when varying temperature, bread samples that are placed in a refrigerator will be in total darkness and equal amounts of water will be added to each. The remaining bags should be covered to keep the light conditions constant. Similarly, when investigating the effect of light, keep temperature constant in a variety of settings from light to dark.

This project has a number of advantages. It is quite inexpensive, and because it demonstrates such rapid growth it is always fascinating for young children. Thus, it is ideally suited to the elementary classroom.

◆ ◆ ◆ ◆ ◆

LIFE SCIENCE PROJECT 5: HYDROPONICS

The notion of growing plants in the absence of soil is one that primary or elementary students have rarely encountered. This unit is most useful following activities related to seed germination and the growth of plants. At this point, the students have acquired skills in planting seeds and keeping accurate records of growth. Fast-growing plants, such as the scarlet runner or contender bean, are particularly valuable for this project. Experiment with other types of seeds and, as an alternative, try a number of houseplant cuttings.

The first step is to choose a method of hydroponic growing that is simple enough for classroom use and relatively inexpensive. Commercial practices often require pumps to provide an intermittent or continuous flow of nutrients to the roots of the plants. This setup is expensive and typically requires more space than most classrooms permit.

A simpler approach is to use two-litre plastic containers filled with a substrate such as vermiculite or sawdust. These substrates have the advantage of preventing light from reaching the plant roots, and also provide some degree of support for the seedlings. Additional support in the form of strings suspended above the containers is very useful as the plants increase in height.

Choosing a Nutrient Solution

The next step is to choose a nutrient solution that is beneficial for plant growth. Many garden centres and supermarkets can supply a premixed hydroponic fertilizer. An alternative to this is to mix your own chemicals. One effective mixture consists of:

Magnesium sulphate 0.78 g/L	Potassium nitrate	0.77 g/L
Calcium phosphate 0.40 g/L	Calcium sulfate	1.43 g/L

Note: This provides a stock solution that *should be diluted 1:20 before use* (50 mL added to 950 mL of water).

Having chosen an appropriate solution, add it to the substrate (vermiculite or sawdust) until a saturation level is reached. Insert germinated seeds in the containers, and growing without soil will begin.

When the substrate shows signs of drying, top the containers with fresh nutrient solution. Occasionally (every 3–4 weeks), it is recommended that you add water instead of nutrient solution to the drying substrate. This prevents the solution from reaching a level of concentration that might harm the plants.

Students should be encouraged to keep accurate records of the amount of solution supplied, the total height of the plants, and their general appearance.

Recording Observations

An effective class project would be to compare the rate of growth of plants using a number of different solutions. Try a commercial solution, a mixed solution, an all-purpose plant fertilizer, and water, and for the sake of comparison try some plants in soil.

A more advanced project could involve investigations into the value of each of the chemicals used in a given solution. Try a range of mixtures that eliminates one of the chemicals at a time for comparison purposes, and record the results.

Hydroponic growing provides ample opportunity for experimental activities in the classroom. It can easily lead to an increased level of interests in plants. The potential for commercial applications can be explored. The value of soilless growing in developing countries can be discussed. These ideas can be readily integrated with other areas of the curriculum.

◆ ◆ ◆ ◆ ◆

LIFE SCIENCE PROJECT 6: LOCAL INSECTS

At the primary and elementary level, there is a great deal of merit in having students develop collections. The wide assortment of local insects available makes this an obvious choice for younger students. A number of important steps such as collecting, identifying, mounting, and displaying provide ample opportunity for development of specific skills.

Normally a project of this nature would be conducted in early fall or late spring. Some consideration should be given to the range of insects to be collected. If temperatures are relatively warm it may be best to have students focus on particular types of insects because of the numbers of specimens that can be found. Alternatively, they could classify insects according to the sites where they are found, for example, those found in soil or those found near streams or ponds. Once temperatures are cool, it will be more difficult to collect insects. Students could then be given the option of including any that are available.

It is important at this stage to familiarize students with the particular characteristics of insects. Invariably they will bring in related species, but rather than reject these, use them to reinforce the specific attributes that insects possess.

Collecting Insects

Once the students are given some sense of direction as to the types of insects they might collect, they need suggestions as to how they will capture specimens. Depending on the insect, they may require collecting nets, pill bottles, forceps, and so on. Encourage them to look under rocks, find rotting logs, and search around the edges of buildings where the sod touches the walls. Another useful tip is to dig a small hole and place a bottle or can flush with the surface of the ground. Have students leave it overnight and check in the morning to see what has tumbled in!

Preserving Insects

Once the students begin to bring in their collected insects, a safe way of killing them must be considered. There are many suggested chemicals on the market, but most require special handling due to vapours released. The recommended method for the elementary level is to drop the insects into a container of rubbing alcohol. Some questions may be raised here about the ethics of killing these animals. The sheer number of insects available, however, would appear to make this less of a problem. If you feel strongly about this issue, the students could be directed to collect dead insects only.

Displaying Insects

It is a good suggestion to pin the insects immediately. Insects tend to become very brittle if left for any period of time, resulting in damaged specimens when you try to insert a pin. Large specimens are normally mounted by inserting a pin through the right side of the thorax. Moths and butterflies are exceptions, and are mounted through the centre of the thorax. Smaller insects should be glued to the tip of a small triangular piece of white cardboard and a pin placed through the broad base. Labels should be attached underneath the insect at the end of the pin. The name, date of collection, and location should be provided.

Identifying Insects

Perhaps the most challenging aspect of this project is the identification of the collected specimens. A wide range of identification guides is available, but every effort should be made to find local publications to help simplify the task. Local resource people should be consulted when difficulties arise. All insects should be included in the collection, whether identified or not. For very young students, common names should be used instead of scientific names.

Going Further: A Class Display

The final presentation or display allows for a great deal of creativity. Displays may be arranged by class, by location, or by characteristics such as flying or non-flying. An excellent suggestion for classroom use is for the teacher to develop a background scene showing different habitats and then have the children place the insects in the appropriate zone.

    This project provides students with a variety of skills in the collecting, identifying, preserving, and displaying of insects. An abundance of insects may be found, and children can acquire a greater appreciation of the variety of life in their surrounding area.

◆ ◆ ◆ ◆ ◆

LIFE SCIENCE PROJECT 7: MEALWORMS

Most primary and elementary curricula deal with animal life cycles to some degree. When concentrating on insect life cycles, the mealworm, *Tenebrio molitor,* is an extremely useful addition to any classroom. Its main attributes of having large larvae, being slow moving, and being quite easy to culture make it ideal for classroom use.

The mealworm undergoes complete metamorphosis. This involves quite radical changes as the progression through the larval, pupal, and adult stages occurs. It is highly recommended that your students initially be given just larvae. This allows them to experience the joy of discovering each new stage as it appears.

Mealworms are available through biological supply houses or pet stores, where they are sold as food for amphibians or reptiles. Since the larvae are large and slow moving, there is not a problem of having them escape and infest a classroom. Store them in smooth-walled glass or plastic containers to help prevent escapes. They are extremely easy to culture and take a relatively long time to complete their life cycle. The larval stage may last up to four to five months, the pupal stage one to three weeks, depending mostly on temperature, and the adult stage anywhere from several weeks to several months, depending mainly on availa-ble moisture.

Classroom Cultures

To familiarize the students with this insect, have them begin by making a list of observations of the larvae. They should note the segmented body, three sets of legs, the type of movement, and so on. At this time, students can pursue a range of short activities involving the larvae. Observing movement near walls, the way in which they can find food, their reaction to different colours, and their responses to stimuli such as water, low heat, light, and touch are examples that are appropriate. At this point, you might introduce students to the particular characteristics of insects that distinguish them from other arthropods such as spiders, centipedes, and crustaceans. Encourage them to make drawings and to be as detailed as possible.

Long-Term Investigations

Long-term activities include investigations of the best source of food for the development of a mealworm culture, and the effects of moisture on such a culture.

BEST FOOD SOURCE

Have the students place equal numbers of large larvae (of similar size) in four or five containers of different cereals. Encourage them to keep records indicating the number of larvae, pupae, and adults present for each observation period. At the end of this investigation, they can assess the total number of survivors, the number that reached adulthood, or the speed of progression through the stages as a means of identifying the "best" culture.

EFFECTS OF MOISTURE

To investigate the effects of moisture, set up two identical containers with the same type of cereal and same number of larvae, keeping one dry and placing a slice of apple or potato in the other as a source of moisture. This slice should be replaced each time it shows signs of drying out. Again, have the students interpret the data collected to decide which is the best condition for growth.

The important part of this unit is learning how to investigate the behaviour of an organism. With a minimum of direction, children should come up with many questions that can lead to further observations and investigations. This makes the project suitable for children at a number of grade levels.

◆ ◆ ◆ ◆ ◆

LIFE SCIENCE PROJECT 8: BRINE SHRIMP

As a classroom animal, the brine shrimp (*Artemia*) has tremendous potential for stimulating and maintaining student interest. Children may know them as "sea monkeys" from advertisements in comic books. These animals can at times be a little difficult to culture, but this very fact can lead to a wide range of experiments to find the optimal conditions for growth.

The logical way to begin is to try to find the optimal salt concentration for hatching. For younger children, the simplest method is to add varying amounts of salt by volume. Using 300 mL of water per jar, add 0, 5, 10, 15, and 20 mL of noniodized salt to each.

Try to add the same number of eggs to each salt solution. This poses a difficult problem since the eggs are so tiny. Encourage the children to work out a solution to this problem. One solution is to mark a popsicle stick 1 cm from the tip. Dip it in water to the 1 cm mark and then insert it in the container of eggs up to the same mark. The eggs that adhere should be added to the first jar and this process then repeated for the remaining jars. Ensure that all jars are exposed to the same light and temperature, and wait for hatching to take place (one to three days usually produces results).

Encourage the children to quantify the egg hatching as much as possible. A system such as: 0 (none); + (1 to 5); ++ (6 to 10); +++ (11 to 20); and ++++ (21 or more) is useful, since children can approximate rather than make a tedious, accurate count.

Once sufficient information has been collected to show which salt concentrations are most effective for egg hatching, encourage the students to vary the range of salt to a more precise amount. For example, if most eggs hatch at 5 mL and 10 mL, then repeat the original steps using 4, 6, 8, 10, and 12 mL   of salt.

Investigating Variables

To continue with investigations relating to the hatching of brine shrimp, students can begin by using the salt concentration that has provided the best results and proceed to investigate the effects of other variables. They can investigate the effects on hatching of varying temperature and light conditions. They can vary the number of eggs used or use flat dishes rather than upright jars. They can try different types of salt, such as iodized, noniodized, and marine salt. Further, they can investigate the effects of different types of water. Tap water (used directly or left standing for a day to allow the chlorine to escape), well water, pond water, or sea water may be used.

Going Further: Raising Shrimp to Adulthood

After the conditions that provide the best hatching are identified, students can then proceed to raise the young shrimp to adulthood. This often leads to problems because of the difficulty in feeding them. Powdered yeast may be used, but the slightest excess of yeast will cause the death of the shrimp. Start with extremely small amounts and increase slightly until the population shows signs of growing well. A more satisfactory approach to feeding is to encourage the growth of algae, which then becomes a source of food for the shrimp. Placing the jars near a bright light should encourage an algae bloom.

With repeated trials and varied conditions, students should have some degree of success in raising mature shrimp. It is highly recommended that the teacher have a population of mature shrimp available as students work through these activities. Students can then have some idea of what to strive for and can observe a mature population as they attempt to achieve similar results.

Encourage accurate observations of the life cycle. It is interesting to note that the first hatch after mating results in live, free-swimming shrimp. The second and subsequent matings result in "resting eggs," which float on the surface. These need to be removed and dried before they can hatch. In fact, they are exactly the type of eggs the students would use to start this project.

The supplies required are available at biological supply houses and often may be found at local pet stores. Using inexpensive equipment, this project is ideal for the primary or elementary classroom.

◆ ◆ ◆ ◆ ◆

LIFE SCIENCE PROJECT 9: PLANT GROWTH

This project helps to further students' understanding of the factors affecting plant growth. Logically, the unit should follow a series of activities on the germination of seeds. Children will be expected to germinate seeds, transplant them, and monitor the development of the seedlings over a period of time. There is ample opportunity here for developing a variety of process skills.

For classroom use it is advantageous to use fast-growing plants such as beans or peas. These show reasonably rapid changes from day to day, are easy to germinate and grow, and typically produce pods in a fairly short time. The class can be divided into groups of two or three, and each group should germinate several dozen seeds. There is an advantage in proceeding this way because seeds that are planted directly in the soil may not all germinate. This provides gaps in the collected results and leads to problems in analyzing data. A greater chance of success arises if germinated seeds are transplanted into soil and placed in the appropriate conditions.

Investigating Variables and Recording Information

EFFECTS OF WATER

Begin by determining the optimal amount of water required for plant growth. Once the seeds have germinated (reached the two-leaf stage), transfer the seedlings to five or six pots. The amounts of water to be added depend somewhat on the type of seed, soil, pot, and conditions in the room. The suggested way to proceed is to completely saturate the soil in one pot. Determine the actual amount of water used and vary this amount in the other pots. For example, when using 300 mL of soil it may take 120 mL of water to saturate the soil. The other pots should then receive 100 mL, 80 mL, 60 mL, 40 mL, and 20 mL of water respectively. It is important that the students recognize that, in order to determine the effect of water on plant growth, all other variables should remain constant. The simplest way to achieve this is to place all the plants in the same location.

Once the relative amounts of water have been determined, consideration needs to be given to the watering schedule. Suggest that the students focus on the saturated pot. When the soil shows the first signs of drying at the surface, then water using the original amount and add the appropriate amounts of water to the other pots. It is important to keep to this regimen so that the plants are subjected to the full range of moisture conditions from very wet to very dry.

Students should be encouraged to make observations two or three times each week. This rarely poses a problem because children normally are very excited about the growth of the plants. Tables should be developed that allow for recordings of changes in height, the number of leaves, and the general appearance of the plants. As the plants begin to grow, it will be necessary to provide some means of support in the form of string or sticks.

This is an ideal time to focus on the importance of defining operationally. Students need to agree on exactly how to measure the height of the plants. Variations could include from the surface of the soil to the highest point; from the surface of the soil to the very tip; from the surface of the soil to the highest set of leaves; and so on. If the teacher wishes to make class comparisons of results, then some consensus needs to be reached.

Those plants receiving adequate amounts of water should reach the stage at which flowers develop and, eventually, pods appear. At this point, the project may be terminated and the students can analyze the data. In determining the "best" moisture condition, operational definitions again need to be considered. Decisions need to be made on the basis of overall growth, general appearance, or the number of pods produced. Students need to recognize that the interpretation of the data is subject to one's definition of "best" growth.

EFFECTS OF LIGHT

Following this initial activity of determining the optimal amount of water for plant growth, the students can turn to an examination of the effects of light on plants. Once again, they should germinate seeds and begin the investigation when the seedlings have reached the two-leaf stage. In this case, students can use the results from the previous activity to decide how much water the plants should receive initially. These plants should then be subjected to different light conditions. Three possibilities are normal daylight, total darkness, and continuous light. Other variations include comparing growth when plants are grown under cellophane sheets of different colours.

Encourage the students to keep records similar to those for the experiments on moisture. A potential problem with this activity is keeping control of the amount of water added. Plants in continuous light generally require more water than the others, and those in total darkness require less. If all plants are given the same amount of water, problems may arise. Perhaps the best way of dealing with this is to suggest that the students water the plants as required, for example, when soil first feels dry to the touch. It can be argued that the plants are then receiving similar treatment.

The analysis of the results can be treated in a similar fashion to data showing the effects of water. In experimenting with light and water, students encounter some of the basic requirements for plant growth. Ample room for variation in each of these activities is created by using different types of plants. The knowledge and specific skills acquired about plants, along with the opportunity to further develop process skills, make this a valuable experience for primary or elementary school children.

APPENDIX B

Playing Different Roles

Source: Energizer: Different points of View: Playing different roles.
In SEEDS energy literacy series, SEEDS 4, (1987).
SEEDS *Newsletter* 1: 4–5.

◆ ◆ ◆ ◆ ◆

ENERGIZER: DIFFERENT POINTS OF VIEW

Playing Different Roles

SOURCE:

SEEDS Energy Literacy Series. SEEDS 4, Activity 16

OBJECTIVES

The students will:

- identify the different points of view that people in a community have with regard to extraction and development of energy sources.
- recognize that all points of view have merit.
- decide whether or not to develop an energy source in a town setting.

TEACHER BACKGROUND

By conducting a community meeting, children should be able to appreciate that each individual has a different point of view about the establishment of an energy extraction plant. Businesspeople will stand to gain through an increase of people in the community, accompanied by an increase in investment and purchasing opportunities. Others may appreciate the smallness and personal contact, the closeness to the environment, the unhurried atmosphere, and the reduction in stress that a small country community offers, and may therefore resist any change.

MATERIALS

Each child will need:

Activity Sheet 17, pencil/pen

Each group will need:

1 role card made from Activity Sheets 15 and 16

You will need:

Activity Sheets 15 and 16 to make role cards.

ACTIVITY SHEET 15

Role Cards for Activity 16

Bus Driver Because there are more workers in our town, more people will need to use the bus. We shall have to improve the service. This will mean some overtime and some extra money in my pay.	**Farmer** I am not happy because I am afraid some of my rich farmland may be taken for the coal mine. There will be less land for my cattle to graze on and my farm will not be nice to look at. They promise to make it useful for crops again, but that will take several years.
Tourist I enjoy coming here. I like the fresh air and the beautiful countryside. I am very angry because the plants and animals will be upset by this coal mine. I will no longer be able to walk along the trails through the woods and fields.	**Coal Miner** There will be more work for me and it will be much closer to home. I will be able to buy things I wanted to buy but could not afford.
Professor A lot of our wild animals will be driven away because of the noise and because their homes will be destroyed. It will be many years before the land will look like it does now. The pollution from the machinery could kill many plants.	**Bank Manager** More business will come to town and so more workers will be looking for new homes. More people will come to my bank to deposit and borrow money. Perhaps a power plant will also be built in the community. With more stores and restaurants, I will get lots of new customers.
Store Keeper More people will come to my store. I will be able to sell different kinds of articles and goods. I may even be able to take a holiday away this year.	**Service Station Owner** If the coal mine is built, more people will come to town, so there will be more cars and trucks that need gasoline and repair work. I will then be able to save enough money to open another service station to make more money.

Role Cards for Activity 16

Mail Carrier I like my job because it takes me outside in the fresh air each day. With more traffic and more people, it will take me longer to deliver all the mail. With more air pollution, my job will be less healthful than it is now.	*Carpenter* If a power plant is built here, the people who run the plant will need homes. I will be able to build homes for them. The sawmill will be kept busy.
Senior Citizen I enjoy our community as it is now. I don't want to see more people coming into town, with all their noise and changes. It will be more difficult to cross the street and all the cars will pollute the air so it will no longer be fresh as it is now.	*Homemaker* If our town is going to grow, I may be able to get a job at the restaurant. We may be able to have a special park built for the children. I hope the children will be kept away from the deep pits of the mine and the machinery or they may get hurt.
Doctor Our community is a very healthy place to live. With more people coming to town new diseases may spread around our town. With more cars, there will be more air pollution. If a power plant is built, the fresh air in our town may no longer be fresh because of the smoke from the chimneys.	*Teacher* Our town is a nice place for children to grow up in because we are so close to the woods. As the town grows larger, it will
Restaurant Owner With more workers coming to town, more people will need to eat. This will be good for business. I may even have more people help me.	

PROCEDURE

Tell children that the town council they are pretending to be part of has to make an important decision. They have to decide whether or not a large energy company will be allowed to mine for coal at a site just outside their town. Then proceed as follows:

1. Have the children choose a partner. Give each pair of children one of the role cards.
   Note: Role cards can be made from Activity Sheets 15 and 16. If you paste each square on a card, you will be able to reuse the cards for future classes.
2. Discuss the rules for holding a council meeting: each viewpoint is explained — no one interrupts; each council member votes secretly; each council member represents several other people who hold the same views; you will chair the meeting and they must abide by your decisions.
3. Hand out and explain Activity Sheet 17, telling children where to record information about their role and how to record information, as the meeting progresses, on the viewpoints of the other council members.
4. Have children read their role descriptions, then make a decision as to whether they are in favour of or against the coal mine, and determine the reasons for their choice. They will record their decisions and the reasons on Part A of Activity Sheet 17.

OBSERVATIONS AND CONCLUSIONS

Conduct the community meeting. One child from each pair presents the point of view based on the community role being played. The other partner keeps a record of the other community roles, their decisions, and the reasons for these decisions. Have them record these on Part B of Activity Sheet 17.

After all community members have explained their point of view, take a vote and decide whether the town council as a whole is for or against the coal mine. Ask children to summarize their reasons.

ACTIVITY SHEET 17

Different Points of View

Part A

My/Our Community Role _____

My/Our Decision (circle one)   FOR   AGAINST

Predict the decision the town
will make (circle one)   FOR   AGAINST

Reasons For My/Our Decision _____

Part B

As the meeting progresses, record the decisions made by each community member.

Community Roles for Town Council	FOR	AGAINST	Reason(s)

The Town Council Decided _____

◆ ◆ ◆ ◆ ◆
CREDITS AND PERMISSIONS

Photo Credits

CHAPTER 1

p.9   Paul Till
p.14   Birgitte Nielsen

CHAPTER 2

p.33   Birgitte Nielsen
p.36   Birgitte Nielsen
p.39   Birgitte Nielsen

CHAPTER 3

p.69   Paul Till
p.74   Birgitte Nielsen
p.79   Birgitte Nielsen

CHAPTER 4

p.87   Northwest Territories Education
p.104   Birgitte Nielsen

CHAPTER 5

p.141   Cathie Archbould
p.155   Birgitte Nielsen
p.162   Birgitte Nielsen
p.166   Paul Till
p.173   Birgitte Nielsen

CHAPTER 6

p.189   Birgitte Nielsen
p.201   Birgitte Nielsen
p.206   Birgitte Nielsen
p.213   Birgitte Nielsen

CHAPTER 7

p.237   Jen Ling Chang-Wells
p.246   Birgitte Nielsen
p.251   Birgitte Nielsen
p.260   Birgitte Nielsen
p.276   Birgitte Nielsen

CHAPTER 8

p.299   Birgitte Nielsen
p.316   Birgitte Nielsen

CHAPTER 9

p.351   Birgitte Nielsen
p.362   ©Harcourt Brace Jovanovich, 1991
p.366   Birgitte Nielsen

CHAPTER 10

p.386   Paul Till
p.396   Paul Till
p.401   Paul Till
p.415   Paul Till

CHAPTER 11

p.432   Jen Ling Chang-Wells
p.442   Birgitte Nielsen
p.445   Birgitte Nielsen
p.453   Birgitte Nielsen

CHAPTER 12

p.466   Cathie Archbould
p.491   Birgitte Nielsen

CHAPTER 13

p.534   Jen Ling Chang-Wells

PART OPENERS

Part 1   Birgitte Nielsen
Part 2   Birgitte Nielsen
Part 3   Birgitte Nielsen, Northwest Territories Education, Paul Till
Part 4   Jen Ling Chang-Wells, Birgitte Nielsen, Paul Till

CANADIAN ACHIEVEMENTS IN SCIENCE

p.24 (Bell)   The Bettman Archive
p.56 (Rutherford)   McGill University Archives
p.81 (Brooks)   McCord Museum of Canadian History; Notman Photographic Archives
p.128 (Banting)   The Bettman Archive
p.179 (Herzberg)   National Research Council of Canada
p.230 (Franklin)   Canapress Photographic Services
p.289 (Polanyi)   Richard Palmer, Calgary
p.322 (Taylor)   ©1980, Yousuf Karsh
p.369 (Bartlett)   Photograph courtesy of the University of British Columbia Archives
p.419 (Suzuki)   Fred Phipps — CBC Television
p.458 (Russell)   Andrew Newton
p.503 (Galdikas)   Orangutan Foundation International
p.539 (Bondar)   National Research Council of Canada
p.565 (Shelton)   ©Ian Shelton, 1990

Abruscato, J., 145, 312, 430, 451, 452, 454

Ahearn, S.K., 225–26

Aikenhead, G.S., 332, 513

Alfke, D., 283

Alvino, J.J., 488

Arends, R.I., 234

Atkinson, W., 525

Atwood, R.K., 471

Ausubel, D.P., 108, 115–16, 199–200, 240

Ball, D.W., 466, 471

Banks, R., 489

Banting, F., 128

Barba, R.H., 247

Barnes, D., 4, 78, 145, 240

Bartlett, N., 369

Beatty, R., 411

Bell, A.G., 24

Benjamin, S., 556–59

Benmore, B., 205, 255

Bergen, D., 144

Berhow, B.F., 480

Berkheimer, G., 284

Biddulp, F., 283

Birnie, H.H., 250

Black, P., 4

Bloom, B.S., 11, 281–82, 294, 297–301

Blurton, C., 499

Bodner, G.M., 204

Bondar, R., 163, 429, 545–46

Bonisteel, R., 294

Bonnstetter, R.J., 143

Borthwick, B., 489

Bosak, D.A., 347, 356, 357

Bosak, S.V., 356, 357

Bourgeois, P., 364

Boyd, E., 485

Brooks, H., 81

Brown, D.R., 478

Bruner, J.S., 37–39, 53, 102, 105, 256, 388, 402, 518

Butler, C., 456

Bybee, R.W., 331, 361, 481, 488

Calhoun, M.L., 477–78

Calinger, B.J., 21

Campbell, S., 103, 105, 429

Carson, R., 530

Case, R., 45–48, 63, 246–47

Case-Cadigan, J., 196–97

Champagne, A.B., 20, 21

Charbonneau, L, 525

Clarke, C., 15, 277

Cobb, V., 253

Cohen, S.H., 482–86

Cohen, L.M., 490, 499–500

Cohen, S.H., 482–86

Collins, A., 20–21, 326

Collins, D., 50, 407–408

Comenius, J.A., 386

Cooke, S., 41, 100

Cooper, B., 436–37

Corrick, M.E., 467

Cosgrove, M.M., 118–19

Couchman, J.H., 355, 429

Crim, J., 390

Crockover, G.H., 16

Curwin, R.L., 174, 175

Darling, K., 253

David, C., 463, 489–90

Davies, J.M., 471

Dawson, C.J., 121

De Lucchi, L., 481

De Vito, A., 16

DeBruin, J., 245

Dewey, J., 388

Donlevy, N., 531

Doran, R.L., 294

Doughty, W., 411
Dow, I., 489
Driver, R., 52, 117, 245–46
Duckworth, E., 388
Dueck, J., 556
Dunsmore, B., 210–211

Eisner, E.W., 297
Evory, A., 545

Fantini, M., 218
Farmer, W.A., 158
Farrell, M.A., 158
Fensham, P.J., 513, 519–22
Feynman, R., 28, 79
Fillinger, P., 411
Flick, L., 439
Franklin, U., 230
Franks, F.L., 481
Fraser, B.J., 142, 148, 150–53, 156–57
Freedman, A.M., 218
Freyberg, R., 103, 117–18
Frize, M. 440–41, 550
Froebel, F., 385–87, 388
Fuhrmann, B.S., 174

Gabel, L.L., 332
Gagné, R.M., 41–46, 63, 114–15
Galdikas, B., 503
Gareffa, P.M., 545
Garneau, M., 545
Garnett, P., 440
Gennaro, G., 528
George, K.D., 485
Gertzog, W.A., 121, 130
Glaserfeld, E.V., 52
Glenn, A.D., 528
Goldberg, L., 144, 185, 186, 404
Goodrum, D., 161
Gough, E.R., 481
Gough, R.L., 94, 330
Gourley, T., 488
Gowin, D.B., 108–11, 240
Graika, T., 257–59
Gray, W.A., 497

Griffin, M., 364
Griffiths, A.K., 309
Gromme, R.O., 469
Gronlund, N., 294
Guesne, E., 117

Hadary, D.E., 482–86
Hadary, T.D., 482–84
Halliwell, J., 547
Hanesan, H., 115
Harcourt, L., 363
Harlen, W., 97, 99, 125, 239–42, 382, 438
Harms, N., 330, 364
Hart, E.P., 332, 341
Hassard, J., 145, 312, 430
Hastings, J.T., 294, 297–300
Haushalter, R., 482–84
Hawisher, M., 477–78
Hawkins, D., 136, 144, 265, 492
Hehner, B., 356
Hein, G., 262
Hendricks, P.W., 485, 488
Henniger, M.L., 403
Henry, B., 525
Herridge, D., 429
Herzberg, G., 179
Hewson, P.W., 121, 130
Hildebrand, R., 411
Hill, J.L., 464
Hofman, H.H., 478
Holford, D., 94
Holubee, E., 444–47
Hoover, S.M., 499
Horak, W.J., 253
House, D., 493
Howe, S.F., 454
Hughes, J.L., 385–87
Hurd, P.D., 102

Inhelder, B., 39
Isaacs, N., 94, 382
Ivany, J.W.G., 267–71

Janigan, K., 525
Jelly, S., 97, 239–40

Johnson, D.W., 141–43, 257, 444–47
Johnson, R.T., 141–43, 149, 257, 444–47
Johnson-Laird, P.N., 51
Joyce, B., 237–38, 261

Kahl, S., 332, 364
Kanis, I.B., 487
Kaplan, H.T., 218
Kaplan, N., 247
Kaplan, J.B., 424
Kaplan, S.N., 424
Karagianis, L.D., 463–64
Karnes, M.B., 493–95
Keller, W.D., 470–71
Kelly, A., 441
Kenney-Wallace, G., 441, 550
Keough, K., 160–61
Kirkham, J., 60
Kite, J., 470, 474–75
Krathwohl, D.R., 300–301, 529–30
Krockover, G.H., 16
Kuehn, C., 117

La Pierre, L., 556
Labinowich, E., 278–81
Lahe, L., 553
Leithwood, K.A., 199
Levesque, D., 489
Levine, R., 482–84
Liem, T.K., 16, 252–53
Loucks-Horsley, S., 84, 102
Lovitts, B.E., 20, 21
Lowe, I., 522–24
Lundgren, R., 94

MacArthur, C., 472
MacBean, J.C., 355
MacLean, S., 546
MacLeod, S., 527
Madaus, G.F., 294, 297–300
Madsen, S.K., 424
Mager, R.F., 297
Mahoney, M.J., 53
Mahung, S., 327–28
Maitson, S., 429

Malcolm, C., 411
Malicky, G., 472
Malone, L., 481
Malouf, D., 472
Marek, E.A., 108
Martin, J., 525
Mashiter, J., 454
Masia, B.B., 300–301
Maxwell, D.E., 284
McAllister, N., 117, 522
McCauliffe, C., 545
McConnell, V., 365
McKnight, B.J., 91, 202–203, 330, 507
Mecklenberger, J.A., 454
Medawar, P., 51
Mendler, A., 174, 175
Menhusen, B.P., 469
Miller, J.P., 22, 187–94
Mills, G., 526–27
Mindes, M., 487
Money, K., 546
Montessori, M., 387
Moore, N., 429
Mowat, F., 10
Mutton, R., 263

Nadeau, L., 7
Nathanson, B., 487
Nesbit, W.C., 463–64
Nesbitt, A., 147–48
Newman, J.M., 265–68
Nichols, M., 546
Norman, C., 472
Novak, J.D., 110–111, 115, 240
Novick, S., 121–24, 240
Nussbaum, J., 109, 121–24, 240

O'Shea, A.A., 496–98
Oldham, B.R., 471
Olford, D., 94
Onody, J., 305–306, 314
Orem, R.C., 387
Orpwood, G., 331–34, 338
Osborne, R., 103, 118–19, 240–42,
    283

Owsley, P.J., 483–84

Padilla, M.J., 284, 286
Page, J.E., 332, 365, 512
Pascual-Leone, J., 45
Passow, E.H., 488
Penick, J.E., 135, 142–43, 147, 149
Penny, W., 359
Peturson, R., 362
Piaget, J., 30–39, 40, 45, 46, 53, 63, 105–
    106, 388, 391–92, 402, 427
Pines, A.L., 86
Pizzini, E.L., 263–64, 438
Pluckrose, H., 559
Polanyi, J., 289
Pollishuke, M., 154
Popper, K.R., 52
Porat, K.L., 556
Posner, G.J., 4–8, 121, 130
Potter, T.G., 253
Puppa, B.A., 356–57

Rappaport, S., 487
Regan, E., 154
Reis, S.M., 495–97
Renner, J.W., 108
Renzulli, J.S., 495–97
Richards, C., 94
Ricker, K.S., 478
Roberts, D.A., 332
Rockcastle, V.N., 91, 200–201, 206, 243,
    330, 473
Rogers, C., 113, 219, 235
Rogers, D., 497
Rogow, S., 463, 489–90
Romey, W., 492
Ross, C., 364
Rousseau, J.J., 386
Rowe, M.B., 123, 155, 272–74, 350, 455,
    469
Rowell, J., 121
Roy, P., 444–47
Russell, D., 458
Rutherford, E.J., 56
Rutherford, F.J., 359–60

Ryan, A., 250

Sadock, B.J., 218
Salamon, F.R., 91, 202–203, 330, 506
Sanders, V., 472
Schmidt, V.E., 91, 202–203, 330, 506
Schon, D.A., 4
Schwab, J.J., 102, 327
Schwartz, S., 154
Schwebel, A., 8
Scriven, M., 519
Seed, D., 364
Seller, W., 22, 187–94
Selnes, M., 253
Severeide, R.C., 263–64
Shaw, E., 284, 286
Shaw, E., 551
Shelton, I., 565
Shepardson, D.P., 438
Shepherd, S., 68, 75–76
Shrigley, R.L., 256
Shulman, L., 37
Shwedel, A.M., 493–95
Shymansky, J.A., 349–50
Simpson, E., 302, 323
Small, B., 441
Smith, L.H., 495–97
Snow, C.P., 555
Squires, A., 95–96
Stecher, A., 355, 429
Stepans, J., 117–20
Stief, V., 429
Strike, K.A., 121, 130
Suchman, J.R., 251, 256
Sutton, C.R., 79
Suzuki, D., 60, 331, 356, 419
Symons, T.H., 331, 365

Taba, H., 238, 282
Tanir, P., 37
Taylor, B.K., 424
Taylor, R., 185, 322
Thier, H.D., 481
Tiberghein, A., 117
Tischer, R.P., 283

Tobin, K., 142, 143–44, 148, 150–53, 156–57, 274–75, 440
Toffler. A., 555
Travers, R.M., 37

Van Horn, R., 455
Vargaz–Gomez, R.G., 151
Vygotsky, L., 39–41, 46, 53, 105

Wallace, S., 364
Wasserman, S., 267–71
Wastnedge, E.R., 112–13
Weil, M., 237–38, 261
Weininger, O., 154
Weinstein, G., 218
Welch, W.W., 142
Wentworth, D.F., 355, 429
Wheeler, A.A., 155
Whiles, L., 365

White, K., 467–68
White, R.T., 283
Whyte, J., 441
Williams, M., 493–95
Williams, P., 429
Wilson, J.D., 334
Winchester, I., 488
Winter, P., 525
Winzer, M., 462–65, 481, 489–90
Wiseman, M., 414–416
Woods, P.E., 5
Wortham, S.C., 294
Wortzman, R., 363
Wright, E.L., 253

Yager, R.E., 143, 151
Yewchuk, C., 491–92

Zaccharias, J.R., 184

SUBJECT INDEX

American Association for the Advancement of Science (AAAS), 102, *see also* Project 2061

Bloom's taxonomy, 297–300, *see also* Domains of learning
levels of questioning, 281–82

Canada, achievements in science
Banting, Frederick, 128
Bartlett, Neil, 369
Bell, Alexander Graham, 24
Bondar, Roberta, 539
Brooks, Harriet, 81
Franklin, Ursula, 230
Galdikas, Birute, 503
Herzberg, Gerard, 179
Polanyi, John, 289
Russell, Dale, 458
Rutherford, Ernest, 56
Shelton, Ian, 565
Suzuki, David, 43
Taylor, Richard, 322
Change
pace of, 544, 555
preparing children for, 544, 551–53
signs of, 544–50
Canada Scholarships, 549–50
Canada-Wide Science Fair, 547–48
National Science and Technology Week, 549
Science Culture Canada, 549
Scientists-in-the-Schools, 550
provincial guidelines, 551–53
recommendations for education, 551–53, 556–59
what futurists are saying, 555–56
Child
as learner, 28
as pre-school scientist, 383–84
as scientist, 185–86

attitudes towards science, 151–53, 382
exceptional, 463–64, *see also* Exceptional child, Mainstreaming
talking science, 78, 79, 145
Child-centred environments, 153–56, 391–93, 406, 414–16, *see also* Primary school years characteristics of, 154–56, 414–16
NAEYC guidelines around, 153, 391–92, 406
implications for practice, 391–93, 414–48
Classroom climate, *see* Learning environments, Learning, motivation of
Classroom management, *see* Learning environments
Commission on Canadian Studies, 331–32
Computers in education,
data processing, 453
drill and practice, 452
interfacing, 454–55
Jason project, 546
Mission to Planet Earth, 546
National Geographic Kids Network, 360, 455, 546
networking, 455
role in elementary science, 451
simulations, 452
software evaluation, 455–56
tutorials, 452
use in special education, 472, 474
word processing, 452–53
Concept(s)
as "stepping stones" to scientific understandings, 95–96
construction of, 84–86, 94–96
interdependence with processes, 84
meaning of, 85–86
types of, 86–92
classificational, 86–87, 89
relational, 87–88, 89

theoretical, 88, 89
Concept development
  conceptual themes approach, 102
  constructivist approaches, 103–106,
      206–209, *see also* Constructivism
    inquiry-discovery, 104-105, 206–209
    developmental, 105–108
    concept mapping, 108–12
    personal directions approach, 112–13
  learning hierarchy approach, 114–15
  meaningful learning approach, 115–16
  role of concrete experiences, 85
  selection of concept areas, 99–101
  selection of content, 96–99
  teaching of
    classificational concepts, 90
    relational concepts, 90–91
    theoretical concepts, 92
Concept maps, 108–112
Concept teaching models
  concept attainment, 237–38
  conceptual change, 123, 125–26,
      240–43
    generative learning, 240–42
    learning cycle, 242
  concept formation, 238–39
Conceptual change, *see* Concept teaching
    models
Conceptual themes, 101–103, *see also*
    Learning theories, Bruner
  as "big ideas" of science, 102–103
  scope and sequence, 101
Constructivism
  a constructivist classroom, 143
  constructivist emphasis in new curricula,
      361
  constructivist view of science, 51–52
  constructivist view of concept develop-
      ment, 93–96
  transactional methods as construction of
      knowledge, 204
Creativity
  as convergent thinking, 15
  as divergent thinking, 14–15
  as insight, 15

characteristics of creative people, 489
  encouraging creativity, 257–72, 488–92
    brainstorming, 259–60, 489
    low-risk environments, 488
    open-ended problems, 257–59
    play, 262–72, 492
Curriculum guides
  aims expressed, 332–46
    Alberta, 343
    British Columbia, 343
    Manitoba, 341
    New Brunswick, 337
    Newfoundland and Labrador, 335–36
    Northwest Territories, 344
    Nova Scotia, 336
    Ontario, 338, 339
    Prince Edward Island, 337
    Quebec, 338, 339
    Saskatchewan, 341, 342
    Yukon, 345
  resources recommended, 346–48
  trends reflected, 329–34
    influence, Science Council of Canada
      study, 331–34
    national and regional trends, 330–31
    worldwide trends, 329–30
Curriculum materials, American
  Elementary Science Study (ESS), 64–67,
      265–66, 348–49
  Full Option Science System, 361
  Insights, 219–24
  National Geographic Kids Network, 360, 546
  Science: A Process Approach (SAPA), 43, 60,
      63, 348–49
  Science Curriculum Improvement Study
      (SCIS), 36, 46, 106–107, 121, 42,
      348–49, 359, 535
  Science for Life and Living, 360
Curriculum materials, British
  Learning Through Science, 354
  National Curriculum, 355
  Nuffield Junior Science, 75, 112–13, 354,
      407, 409–11
  Science 5/13, 75, 206–209, 213, 354,
      407, 411

Science Horizons, 355

Curriculum materials, Canadian,

Examining Your Environment (EYE), 355, 429

Explorations in Science, 103, 105, 363, 429

Innovations in Science, 213–27, 359, 428–29

Know Your World, 363

Let's Find Out, 363

Looking At..., 356

Project Wild, 356, 532

Science Is..., 356

Society, Environment and Energy Development (SEEDS), 355–56, 530, 590–94

Western Educational Development Group (WEDGE), 355, 532

Other Canadian materials, 363–67

Curriculum materials, historical overview

NSF programs of the 1960s, 348–50

programs of the 1970s and 1980s, 353–56

programs of the 1990s, 356–64

Canada, 361–64

United States, 359–61

Curriculum materials, other sources

government publications, 365–26

non-print resources, 367

science activity books, 364

science magazines, 367

science trade books, 366

teacher-produced materials, 364–65

Curriculum materials, selecting

evaluating materials, 328–29

Mahung's criteria, 327–28

recommended resources, 346–48, *see also* Curriculum materials

criteria for selecting textbook programs, 352

Curriculum materials, textbook-based programs, 350–51

criteria for comparing textbook programs, 352

Curriculum orientations

as a continuum, 194, 195

transaction, 22, 93, 187, 191–92, 234

teaching strategies, 204–18

transformation, 22, 93, 187, 192–94, 234

teaching strategies, 218–28

transmission, 22, 93, 187, 189–91, 234

teaching strategies, 199–204

Curriculum resources, *see* Curriculum materials

Difference, individual

child-centred approaches, 390–93

computer education, 451–89

co-operative learning groups, 443–46

cross-cultural education, 433

differentiation of instruction, 427–30

early beginnings, *see* Kindergarten, Primary School Years

in development, 427

in gender, 382, 438–43

in home environment, 426

in interests and abilities, 426–27

in learning styles, 429–30

in racial and ethnic origins, 430–32

language development approaches, 432, 434–35

learning centres, 448–50

multisensory approaches, 439

resource-based learning, 435–37

Discovery learning, 39, 40–41, 206–209, 243–46, 256, *see also* Inquiry, Learning theories, Bruner

Domains of learning, *see also* Bloom's taxonomy

affective, 10–11, 13, 136, 300–301

levels of affective awareness 300–301

cognitive, 11, 13, 297–301

taxonomy of cognitive objectives, 297–300

psychomotor, 12, 13, 301–302

levels in psychomotor domain, 301–302

Education, environmental

concept of environment, 534–35

developing awareness and concern, 533–34

environmental dilemmas, 261–62,
535–37, 591–94
dilemma analysis cards, 261, 536
role playing, 261
nature-related activities, 533–34
A Tree for All Seasons, 214–18
Snails and Trails, 138–41, 533
Earth Day 1990, 225–28, 533
field trips, 175–76, 536–37
resources for, 524–25, 536–37
Elementary Science Study (ESS), *see* Curriculum
materials, American
Evaluation
criterion-referenced, 297
diagnostic-prescriptive, 295, 295–97
formative, 295, 296–97
norm-referenced, 296
planning for, 303–305
summative, 295–96, 297
techniques, 306–313
anecdotal records, 311–12
checklists, 308, 309, 310
free-response, 315
major reports, 315–16
objective questions, 316–19
portfolios, 313
rating scales, 308–311
validity and reliability, 319–21
within affective domain, 300–301
within cognitive domain, 297–300
within psychomotor domain, 301–302
Exceptional child, 462–501, *see also*
Mainstreaming
emotionally challenged, 462, 486–87
gifted and talented, 462, 487–88
acceleration and enrichment, 490,
495–99
fostering creativity, 488–89, 491–95
identification and early intervention,
488–91
providing rich, open environments,
491
models for teaching the gifted,
493–501
individual study, 499

mentoring programs, 490, 497
tips for teaching, 499–501
intellectually challenged, 462, 468–71
and science, 469–71
adapting curriculum materials, 471,
475–76
computer-assisted learning, 472, 474
pacing instruction, 471
physically challenged, 462, 477–78
and science, 477–78
hearing challenged, 483–86
orthopedically challenged, 478–79
visually challenged, 480–81
science in special education, 465–71
concrete, meaningful experiences,
469
enhancement of learning, 465, 469–71
motivational value, 469
basic skill development, 469–70
potential for success, 471
Experiences
as content for concept development,
97–99
role in concept development, 85, 94
Explorations in Science, see Curriculum
materials, Canadian

Fair test, 72, 247
Full Option Science System (FOSS), 361, *see
also* Triad projects
Futuristics, 555–59, *see* Change

Gender, 49, 438–43, *see also* Difference,
individual
gender biases in teaching, 440
girls and school science, 438
masculine image of science, 439
overcoming gender biases, 438–43
fostering positive attitudes, 442
gender equity: practical suggestions,
443, 549–50
in the Canada Scholarships
program, 549–50
by Women in Engineering, 550
Gifted child, *see* Exceptional child

Higher order thinking skills, *see also*
Problem solving, Creativity
developing inquiry skills, 250–55
learning through discovery, 37–39,
206–209, 243–47
problem-solving using science processes,
246–50
problem-solving on STS issues, 526–28
problem-solving through science projects,
283–86
Canada-wide science fair, 547
poster sessions, 294
science challenges, 284–85
science Olympics, 285–86

Individualized Educational Programs (IEPs),
465, *see* Mainstreaming
Inquiry
as problem solving, 250
defined, 250
developing inquiry skills, 250–55
inquiry training, 251–52
learning through inquiry-discovery,
104–105, 204–206
open inquiry, 254–55
phenomena for inquiry, 253
Innovations in Science, see Curriculum
materials,
Canadian
Insights, 219–24
Instruction, *see* Teaching
Integration
conceptual themes, 102, 406–414
developing integrated units, 78, 138–40,
446
science across the curriculum, 209–210
science and language development, 78–
79, 211–13
special education, science and art,
themes, unit planning, 195–98

Kindergarten
history of, 385–388
Froebel, 385–387
Montessori, 387–388

nature of, 388–402
as a special experience, 389–400
as basic skill development, 393–402
as child-centred, 390–393, 414–416
as integrative learning, 406–14
as learning through play, 402
as learning through the senses, 394–99
programs, 393–411
SCIS: *Beginnings,* 393
provincial arrangements, 384–85
Knowledge construction model, 106–107,
121, *see also* Learning cycle

Language development
English as a Second Language (ESL), 433
minimizing technical language of science,
79, 211
science and language development ,
211–213, 433–34
talking science, 78–79, 145
Learning, assessment of, *see* Evaluation
Learning centres
designing a centre, 449–50
developing learning centre tasks, 450
goals and guidelines, 448–49
preparing and organizing, 171–72
Learning, co-operative
co-operative learning groups, 443–46
group characteristics, 445–46
motivational aspects of, 257
role of teacher, 447–48
Learning cycle, 106–108, *see also* Science
Curriculum Improvement Study
(SCIS)
and equilibration, 106
as knowledge construction, 106–107,
121
three phases of, 106, 242
Learning environments, *see also* Teaching,
excellence in
characteristics of effective, 136–46,
154–56, 235–36
active involvement, 143–44
co-operative learning, 142–43
nurturing, safe environment, 145

playfulness, 144
positive interactions, 141
teacher/student respect, 144
classroom management, 158–71
the early years, 153–56
orderliness, 158–159
physical set-up, 161–164
equipment and materials, 164–166
ordering supplies, 164–165
procedures and routines, 170–71
safety, 168–70
storage and accessibility of supplies, 177
organization and preparation for science, 171–175
discipline, 174–75
field trips, 175–76
group activities, 172–73
learning centres, 171–72
project work, 176
Learning hierarchies, *see* Learning theories, Gagné
Learning, motivation of
motivational techniques, 256–72
brainstorming, 259–260
buzz groups, 260
co-operative learning, 257
dilemma analysis, 261
discrepant events, 256
open-ended problems, 257–259
play, 262– 64
role playing, 261
intrinsic motivation, 191, 193, 250, 256, *see also* Learning theories, Bruner
Learning outcomes
and science for life, 556–59
and scientific literacy, 19–21, 330, 512, 561
expressed in provincial policy statements, 333, 334–46
in Report 36, Science Council of Canada, 16–17, 142–43
in Project Synthesis report, 147–48
potential learning outcomes, 9–11
affective: attitudes, interests, values, 13

cognitive: facts, concepts, processes, 13
psychomotor: manipulative skills, 13
other potential learning outomes, 11–17
social, 13
interdisciplinary, 14
Learning problems, 28–29
Learning, theories of
Ausubel, D., 115–16, 199–200
advance organizers, 115–16, 199
linking new to existing knowledge, 116, 199–200
meaningful reception learning, 108, 116, 199
Bruner, J., 37–39,
conceptual themes approach, 102
guided discovery, 37, 38–39, 206–209
intrinsic motivation, 256
structure in learning, 37–38, 102, 518
Case, R., 45–47, 63,
M-power of learner, 45–46
M-demand of learning situation, 46–47
maximizing intellectual development, 63, 247
Gagné, R., 41–45, 114–15
conditions of learning, 43–44
domains of learning, 43–45
hierarchies of learning, 41–44
Piaget, J., 30–39, 43, 88, 92–93, 105–107, 116, 341, 444
accommodation, 35
assimilation, 35
concrete experience, 105
developmental stages, 30–35
equilibration, 35, 106
personal activity, 35
self regulation, 35,
social interaction, 105–106
Vygotsky, L., 39–41
egocentric thought, 39–40
inner speech, 40
role in reflective thinking, 105
role of language, 39

zone of proximal development, 40–41
Learning through play, 402–406, *see also*
  Play
Learning hierarchies, *see* Learning theories,
  Gagné
Lesson planning, 198–199

M-Power, *see also* Learning theories, Case
Mainstreaming, 464–66, 488–90, *see also*
  Exceptional child
  Special education in Canada, 463–64,
    488–90
  preparing for mainstreaming, 464–66
  Individual Educational Programs (IEPs),
    465
  resources for, 466
Meaningful reception learning, *see* Learning
  theories, Ausubel
Multiculturism in Canada, 392, 426, 432,
  See also Difference, individual

National Association for the Education of
  Young Children (NAEYC), 153–56,
  391
National Association for Research in Science
  Teaching (NARST), 330
National Council on Science and
  Technology Education, 330
National Geographic Kids' Network project, *see*
  Triad projects
National Science Board (NSB): *Educating
  Americans for the Twenty-first Century* 330,
  359
National Science Resource Center (NSRC),
  360, 361
National Science Foundation (NSF)
  programs, *see* ESS, SAPA, SCIS, Triad
  projects
National Science Teachers Association
  (NSTA), 330, 359, 367, *see also*
  Project Synthesis
  NSTA professional journals
    Science and Children, 367
    Science Scope, 367

*Science-Technology-Society: Science education
  for the 1980s,* 359
Nature of Science,
  relationship to technology, 513–515
  scientific attitude, 53–54
  scientific knowledge, 49–50, 51–53
  scientific method, 50–51, 185–87
  stereotypical images of science, 49, 439
    Picture a Scientist, 49
    Draw a Scientist, 439
Nuffield Junior Science, see Curriculum
  materials, British

Orientations to curriculum and instruction,
  see Curriculum orientations

Parents and school science
  recycling materials, 166, 175
  science-related projects, 177, 284
  science with everyday things, 165
Piagetian tasks, 33–35
Play
  as initiating phase of instruction, 265–72
    play as "messing about" in science,
      265–66
    play-debrief-replay sequence, 267–68
  as motivational technique, 262–65
  in education of the gifted, 492
  learning through, 144, 402–406
    sand, 404–405
    structures, 405–406
    water, 405
  role in science, 262–264
Plowden report, 330
Primary school years, *see also* Kindergarten
  child-centred instruction, 390–92,
    414–416
  children's play, 402–404
  developmentally appropriate practice,
    391
  from guidelines to practice, 392–406
  importance of early beginnings, 17,
    382–83
  integrative themes, 406–14
    Growing, Growing, 411–14

Rainy Day Things, 408–11

pre-school science, 383–84

primary school years, 382–83, 385, 406–414

Problem-solving, 246–250, 283–86, *see also* Higher order thinking skills

in science projects, 283–86

using science processes, 246–50

Processes

and concept of "fair test", 72, 247

and variables

controlled, 72

dependent or responding, 72

independent or manipulated, 72

evaluation of, 308–309

Science A Process Approach (SAPA) list of processes, 60–63

classifying, 63, 69–70

communicating, 62, 65, 70

controlling variables, 62, 64, 72

defining operationally, 61, 65, 71

experimenting, 62, 66, 73

formulating models, 63, 66–67, 73–74

hypothesizing, 62, 66, 71

inferring, 62, 65–66, 67–68

interpreting data, 62, 66, 73

observing, 41, 64, 67

predicting, 62, 66, 70–71

quantifying, 61, 66, 70

Project 2061: *Science for All Americans* (AAAS), 102, 344, 359

Project Synthesis (NSTA)

goals for school science, 147–48

Search for Excellence, 147–48, 330

Questioning

convergent vs. divergent, 276–81

levels of, 281–82, *see also* Bloom's taxonomy

lifting thought levels (Taba), 282

operational questions, 283

refining pupils' questions, 283

teachers' questions, 275–76

wait-time, 272–75

Resource-based learning, 436, *see also* Integration, Unit planning

Safety, 168–70

Science 5/13, see Curriculum materials, British

Science: A Process Approach (SAPA), *see* Curriculum materials, American

Science Council of Canada

aims of, 16–17, 140–43

Report 36, *Science for Every Student: Educating Canadians for Tomorrow's World,* 16, 330–31

Science Curriculum Improvement Study (SCIS), *see* Curriculum materials, American

Science for all Children, 382, 424, 462, *see also* Individual differences

Science Technology and Society (STS)

in education, 513–14

science and technology, 513–17

advantages & disadvantages, 516

attitudes about, 528–529

compared, 513–515

defined, 513

in the life of a child, 515

in the local community, 517

choosing STS curriculum materials, 518–25

approaches to instruction, 522–24

categories of materials, 520–21

sources of information, 524–25

towards a balanced position, 518

Canadian science and technology, 525–26

aspects of technology, 526–29

as construction, 528

as ethical issues, 528–29

as problem solving, 526

STS and the environment, 520–27, *see also* Environmental education

resources for, 531–32

activities for, 533–37

Scientific attitude, 53–54, *see also* Nature of science

arguments against, 53–54

traditional views, 53

Scientific knowledge, 49–53, *see also* Nature of Science

    constructive nature of, 49–50, 51–53

    tentativeness of, 93, 191

Scientific literacy, 20, 326

    as learning outcome, 19–21, 326, 512, 561

    as guide to practice, 326

    defined, 20

    human component, 20

    procedural component, 20

    structural component, 20

Scientific method, 50–51, *see also* Nature of science

    scientists as children, 185, 187

    science as play, 186

Search for Excellence in Science Education, 146–48, *see also* Exemplary science teaching

Self-Help Elementary Level Science Project (SHELLS) project, 350

Structure of discipline, 37, *see also* Bruner

Teachers' Journals

    Benmore, Bob, 205, 255

    Case-Cadigan, Janet, 196

    Clarke, Cynthia, 15, 277

    Collins, Doreen, 50, 407–408

    Cooke, Sharro, 41, 100

    Cooper, Betty, 436–37

    Crim, Joyce, 390

    Donlevy, Nikki, 531

    Dunsmore, Brenda, 210–211

    House, Diane, 493

    Keough, Karen, 160–61

    McAllister, Neil, 117, 522

    Mutton, Ronald, 263

    Nadeau, Linda, 7

    Nesbitt, Alan, 147–48

    Onody, Judy, 305–306, 314

    Penny, Wallace, 358

    Shepherd, Sandra, 68, 75–76

    Shaw, Ernie, 551

Teaching

    becoming a teacher, 5–7

    reflective, 4–5

    teachers' concerns, 8

    teachers' frames, 5

    expository methods, 199–204

    inquiry/discovery, 206–209

Teaching, excellence in, *see also* Learning environments

    child-centered instruction, 154–57, *see also* Child-centred environment

    Exemplary practice in Science and Mathematics Education, 148–53

        assessing the psychosocial environment, 150–51

        My Class Inventory (MCI) Questionnaire, 150–53

    Search for Excellence in Science Education, 146–48

        characteristics of exemplary programs, 149

Teaching models, 237–43, *see also* Concept teaching models

Teaching models, gifted and talented

    Enrichment Triad/Revolving Door, 495–497

    Mentor-Directed Enrichment, 497

    Purdue Three-Stage, 497–99

    Structure of the Intellect (SOI), 493–95

Teaching skills

    lesson planning, 198–99

    unit planning, 195–98

    motivational techniques, 256–72

    questioning techniques, 272–81

Textbook-based programs, 350–51, *see also* Curriculum materials, textbook-based

    Addison-Wesley Science, 202–204, 265–66

    Innovations in Science, 103, 213–18, 428–29

    Explorations in Science, 103, 105, 363, 429

Themes, *see also* Conceptual themes,

Integration, Unit planning
A Tree for All Seasons, 214–18
Bouncing Balls, 209–210
Triad projects
Full Option Science System, 361
National Geographic Kids Network, 360
Science for Life and Living (BSCS), 360

Unit and lesson planning, 195–198

Values, clarification of, 221–224, 225–228
Variables, 72, *see also* Processes of science
controlled, 72
dependent or responding, 72
independent or manipulated, 72

◆ ◆ ◆ ◆ ◆

READER REPLY CARD

We are interested in your reaction to *Science for Life: The Teaching of Science in Canadian Primary and Elementary Schools* by Ruby L. Gough and Alan K. Griffiths. You can help us to improve this book in future editions by completing this questionaire.

1. What was your reason for using this book?

    ☐ university course ☐ college course   continuing education course
    ☐ professional   ☐ personal   other (please specify) _____
        development   interest   _____

2. If you are a student, please identify your school and the course. If you used this book for a program, what was the name of the program?

3. Which chapters or parts of this book did you use?

4. If you omitted any chapters or parts, which ones?

5. What did you like best about this book? What did you like the least? Please identify any topics you think should be added to future editions.

6. Were the boxed articles in each chapter of interest to you?

7. Was the information in this textbook presented in an interesting manner?

8. Add any comments or suggestions.

(fold here and tape shut)

- -

MAIL ⇒ **POSTE**

Canada Post Corporation / Société canadienne des postes

Postage paid
If mailed in Canada

Port payé
si posté au Canada

**Business
Reply**

**Réponse
d'affaires**

0116870399   01

0116870399-M8Z4X6-BR01

Heather McWhinney
Publisher, College Division
HARCOURT BRACE & COMPANY, CANADA
55 HORNER AVENUE
TORONTO, ONTARIO
M8Z 9Z9